INTERMEDIATE *Algebra*
ENLARGED EDITION
With an Introduction to Advanced Algebra

WILLIAM G. SHUTE
WILLIAM E. KLINE
WILLIAM W. SHIRK
LEROY M. WILLSON

AMERICAN BOOK COMPANY

New York   Cincinnati   Atlanta   Dallas   Millbrae

Intermediate Algebra, Enlarged Edition by WILLIAM G. SHUTE, WILLIAM W. SHIRK
Instructors in Mathematics, The Choate School, Wallingford, Connecticut
WILLIAM E. KLINE
Supervisor of Testing, Board of Education of Baltimore County, Towson, Maryland
and LEROY M. WILLSON
Associate Professor of Mathematics, Georgia State College of Business Administration,
Atlanta, Georgia

Copyright © 1964 by American Book Company

EP   15   14   13   12   11   10   9   8   7   6   5   4   3   2   1

Preface

Intermediate Algebra, Enlarged Edition, follows sound principles of organization. From the outset students are encouraged to take the initiative, not only in learning algebraic principles but also in the daily application of operations so they can attain an efficiency of which they will be proud. The foreword "To the Student" contains helpful directions on how to study, supplemented by advice on handwriting for algebra. The student is led almost without his being aware of it in the direction of economical mathematical thinking. Important algebraic principles are framed so that the student's eye will be carried to the thought to be mastered. In the chapter on Logarithms, for instance, the interpolation process is boxed off in heavy black type. This process, which could be made intricate, will not be disturbing to the student in this text because of the skillful use of arrows which serve not only to bracket the chief operation but also to show its direction.

An abundance of well-selected material is efficiently arranged. Complete explanatory material and Illustrative Examples precede each exercise. The combination of explanatory material, illustrative examples, and written exercises is repeated as each new topic is introduced. The approach to the individual topics is gradual, with only one step introduced at a time, and with fundamental processes and skills carefully graduated so that the student can build a solid foundation. The frequent Oral Exercises were devised to encourage student participation in the recitation period. In general they are simpler than the written problems and quite suitable for the spoken word. They need not be assigned to all students, but they are excellent for drill purposes and can be used effectively as written exercises for students having difficulty.

Many students have difficulty with word problems. This text offers the student aid in translating words into algebraic symbols. Practice is given in organizing the data of a problem by placing the algebraic expressions in "box" or "table" form. Finally, there are exercises in writing equations based upon the data thus organized. When this material was tried in experimental form, the authors found that their students gained unusual confidence in solving word problems.

This material is presented in the same form as that of *Elementary Algebra, Enlarged Edition;* however, the tempo has been increased. Full explanations are still given, but repetitious detail is avoided. The opening chapters offer a comprehensive review of first year algebra. For the more advanced students the review of elementary algebra can be covered rapidly by using these Review Exercises as a battery of tests. Chapter Review Exercises and Cumulative Review Exercises are placed at the end of each chapter. The cumulative testing program is comprehensive for every chapter and for the entire book.

Historical notes in the form of attractive "flashbacks" are used to stimulate an increased interest in mathematics. Dimbo, the happy-go-lucky boy familiar to students of *Elementary Algebra,* continues to point out common pitfalls and errors. The meaningful use of color and attractive cartoons help to sustain the student's interest throughout the course.

Chapter 20 is made up of three review exercises and two pretested, objective type, comprehensive examinations. Any one of these five exercises may be used as a final examination. All the exercises in this chapter are of the multiple-choice type used in state or national testing programs; in particular, they contain questions similar to those on tests offered by the College Entrance Examination Board and by the United States Armed Services.

To prepare the student more effectively for college mathematics and to challenge the student to attempt more than the usual syllabus requirements, this text offers a chapter on Permutations, Combinations, and Probability and a chapter giving an Introduction to Analytic Geometry and Statistics.

An "Introduction to Advanced Algebra" is provided as optional material. In this section various applications of the theory of sets are presented. The section begins with a review of the basic ideas of sets. Among the more advanced topics which are discussed are the union and intersection of sets; ordered pairs of numbers; the Cartesian set; equations and inequalities in two variables; relations and functions and their graphs; and selected aspects of the structure of algebra.

Contents

CHAPTER		PAGE
	To the Student	vi
1.	Fundamental Operations	1
2.	First-Degree Equations	23
3.	Special Products and Factoring	43
4.	Fractions	74
5.	Equations Containing Fractions	95
6.	Simultaneous Linear Equations	110
7.	Ratio, Proportion, and Variation	157
8.	Exponents	174
9.	Radicals	190
10.	Quadratic Equations in One Unknown	214
11.	Theory of Quadratic Equations; Inequalities	242
12.	Graphs of Quadratic Equations in Two Variables	260
13.	Systems of Quadratic Equations	279
14.	Arithmetic and Geometric Progressions	297
15.	Logarithms	323
16.	Trigonometry of the Right Triangle	358
17.	Binomial Theorem	383
18.	Permutations, Combinations, and Probability	397
19.	Introduction to Analytic Geometry and Statistics	419
20.	Review Exercises and Examinations	445
	Introduction to Advanced Algebra: Set Theory	467
	Tables	
	Approximate Square Roots	482
	Powers and Roots of Numbers	486
	Mantissas of Logarithms of Numbers	487
	Values of Trigonometric Functions	489
	Logarithms of Trigonometric Functions	492
	Index	495

To the Student

Why should I study Intermediate Algebra? In answer to this question let us consider the following: Never before in the history of America has the demand for engineers, trained scientists, and technicians been so great, with the rewards high to those who meet the required standards. For a student to qualify for these professions and occupations it is important that he continue his study of mathematics throughout his high school course.

Many colleges, universities, and technical schools will not accept students who have completed only one year's study of algebra. A course in intermediate algebra is always required before a student is admitted to an advanced course in mathematics. In order to understand the work of elementary college courses in physics, chemistry, psychology, economics, engineering drawing, and many other subjects, it is essential that the student have a good working knowledge of the principles of intermediate algebra. To proceed to advanced work in any science, in engineering, in business, in architecture, in the study of education, and in many other fields, a familiarity with the material that you will find in this text is necessary.

Even if you are planning not to attend college, there is much of value in algebra that you may be able to put to good practical use in later work, whether you become an artist or musician, a bricklayer, carpenter, or plumber, a mechanic, an office worker, a tradesman, a nurse, or a housekeeper. Once you have thoroughly mastered the topics of algebra you will be able to find many uses for them, not only in your chosen work but often in other ways.

Will I find Intermediate Algebra difficult? You can readily test yourself to find the answer to this question. There is evidence that success in solving the usual exercises in intermediate algebra depends largely upon three factors:

1. skill in manipulating elementary algebraic expressions;
2. reasoning of a deductive nature; and
3. verbal ability, i.e., a facility for understanding and using words.

From your course in elementary algebra, you doubtless developed ability to manipulate algebraic expressions; that is, to factor, to operate with fractions, and to solve equations. Second, in your study of arithmetic and plane geometry, you have applied deductive reasoning in solving problems and in demonstrating geometric proofs. Third, in many of your daily experiences and especially in your English classes, you have increased your verbal skills in reading and in writing.

Besides the three abilities listed above, skill in performing the fundamental operations in arithmetic (addition, subtraction, multiplication, and division) is, of course, necessary in algebra. The student who makes frequent errors will find that, although he fully understands the new algebraic principle under discussion, he has trouble solving the assigned problem correctly. It is hoped that, in gaining an understanding of the rules of algebra, you will find how simple and obvious the rules of arithmetic are. Although it is possible to study algebra in a routine way that will shed little light on arithmetic, this text attempts to avoid mere routine and to concentrate on the development of ideas. These ideas are developed not only to give meaning to algebra but to related subjects as well.

As you have progressed in school, you have become increasingly aware of the use of reasoning. In the elementary grades more emphasis was placed on method and less emphasis on the reasons behind the method. In the higher grades, increasing emphasis is placed on *why* as well as on *how*. One of the principle objectives of this text is to explain to you the reasons for working through the steps of a new operation. Behind each rule there is a *why*.

If you develop clear ideas as the course progresses, you will be able to retain your algebraic ability much longer. Unless you have gained an understanding of the reason behind the method, merely memorizing an algebraic method will have little value after you have ceased your study of algebra. Do not be satisfied with only learning *how*, but strive also to learn *why*.

IMPORTANCE OF HANDWRITING IN ALGEBRA

Writing rapidly, copy the following letters, numbers, and symbols in the same order as they appear:

a 7   9 b 6 c r s $+$ t f x $\times$ n u 3 z

y x z 2   1 l n 17 s 5   4 y 7 h k

m 177

Do not read beyond here until you have copied the above lines. After you have written these lines, without checking against the book, look at your paper to see if you have written any two figures in succession that look alike. Then check your list with the list above.

The motions of the hand in writing are motions of habit. We can write words, numbers, and symbols without giving a thought to each movement of the pencil. Often the same or a similar movement is used by the writer for different letters; for example, many persons start the letters x and y with similar strokes, as $\diagdown$; for an x the writer adds a stroke, thus, $\mathbf{X}$; for a y he also adds a stroke, thus, $\mathbf{Y}$. Because the motions are similar, the writer often makes the initial stroke of the x too short, or he makes the initial stroke of the y too long, with the result that both look alike.

$$x = \mathbf{X} \qquad y = \mathbf{X}$$

Even before you begin the study of algebra, you can easily see how wrong answers may occur if one misreads the letter y for x, or vice versa. To avoid this difficulty you should adopt a new style of x or y to use in your algebra work. You may wish to write a y in this manner: y.

The following list shows some pairs of letters, numbers, or symbols that have been misread by algebra students in the past. The third column shows the changes that were recommended so that the students would not have the same difficulty in the future.

This list does not contain all the possible confusions. Each person who uses a pencil develops his own writing habits, and no two persons will have the same habits.

CONFUSED PAIR		RECOMMENDED CHANGE
$z = Z$	$2 = 2$	Change z to $\boldsymbol{z}$.
$5 = S$	$s = S$	Write the horizontal top on the 5 after writing the rest of the number; or write s as $\boldsymbol{\varsigma}$.
$x = \times$	$y = y$	Change y to $\boldsymbol{y}$.
$y = y$	$z = y$	Change y to $\boldsymbol{z}$.
$4 = 4$	$y = 4$	Change 4 to $\boldsymbol{y}$.
$t = +$	$+ = +$	Change t to $\boldsymbol{t}$.
$z = 3$	$3 = 3$	Change 3 to $\boldsymbol{z}$.
$7 = 7$	$y = 7$	Change 7 to $\boldsymbol{y}$.
$b = b$	$6 = 6$	Change b to $\boldsymbol{b}$.
$h = h$	$k = k$	Change k to k.
$n = u$	$u = u$	Change u to $\boldsymbol{n}$.
$f = f$	$t = t$	Change f to $\boldsymbol{f}$ and t to $\boldsymbol{t}$.
$c = c$	$r = r$	Change c to c.
$n = n$	$17 = 17$	Change n to $\boldsymbol{n}$.
$m = m$	$177 = 177$	Change m to $\boldsymbol{m}$.
$l = l$	$1 = 1$	Change l to $\boldsymbol{\ell}$.

SUGGESTIONS FOR STUDY

Ideas, in order to be useful and to be retained, must be combined with practice. Theory alone, without practice, is not worth much. No one would ever become an outstanding athlete or a concert musician by studying theory alone; he must practice long and hard. This text contains plenty of exercises for you to use as practice.

To use this text most effectively and to your best advantage, it is recommended that you follow these suggestions.

1. When you are asked to study a topic in the text, read through carefully the verbal explanation of this topic.

2. Read the problem given in the Illustrative Example.

3. Try to solve the problem yourself. You learn much faster and better by doing a problem alone than by watching someone else do it.

4. When you complete the problem, compare your method with that given in the text.

5. If you cannot do the problem as stated in the Illustrative Example, start to read the given *Solution*.

6. After you have read enough of the *Solution* to obtain an idea as to how to solve the problem, attempt to complete the solution yourself. Avoid the habit of asking too many questions; you will learn more if you dig out the solution yourself.

7. After you have gained an understanding of the problem in the Illustrative Example, proceed with the exercises to develop your skill and to give yourself the practice that is needed to establish firmly in your mind the new principles which you have learned.

CHAPTER 1   *Fundamental Operations*

Numbers used in algebra.   A quantity is something that can be counted or measured. Its magnitude is always indicated by a number. For example, the length of a line may be expressed as a certain number of inches; the area of a surface, as a certain number of square yards; the volume of a solid, as a certain number of cubic feet; the weight of an object, as a certain number of pounds; the temperature of the air, as a certain number of degrees.

These numbers that indicate quantities may be *arithmetic numbers*, that is, numbers made up entirely of the digits 0, 1, 2, 3, 4, 5, 6, **7**, 8, 9. For example, when we say that a line is 15 in. long, the number 15 is an arithmetic number. On the other hand, the numbers we use may be *literal numbers*, that is, numbers that are represented by letters. For example, when we say that the volume of a solid is v cubic feet, the number v is a literal number.

The numbers we use may also be *signed numbers*, that is, numbers

1

that measure direction as well as size. For example, when we say that the temperature of the air is $+ 6°$ (6° above zero) or $- 10°$ (10° below zero), the numbers $+ 6$ and $- 10$ are signed numbers. In algebra we use arithmetic numbers, literal numbers, and signed numbers.

Fundamental operations.   The four fundamental operations of arithmetic are addition, subtraction, multiplication, and division. In your elementary algebra course you learned to apply these four operations to the numbers of algebra. You will remember that the symbol $+$ indicates addition; the symbol $-$ indicates subtraction; a raised dot indicates multiplication (in the case of literal numbers, the raised dot is usually omitted); and the symbol $\div$ indicates division. A review of the four fundamental operations as they apply to signed numbers is given on the following pages.

"*x* plus *y*"
"*x* increased by *y*" $\Big\}$ $x + y$
"the sum of *x* and *y*"

"*x* minus *y*"
"*x* decreased by *y*" $\Big\}$ $x - y$
"*y* subtracted from *x*"

"5 times *a*"
"5 multiplied by *a*" $\Big\}$ $5 \cdot a$ or $5a$
"the product of 5 and *a*"

"*a* divided by *b*" $\rightarrow a \div b$ or a/b or $\dfrac{a}{b}$

Signed numbers.   Positive and negative numbers are called signed numbers and indicate direction as well as size. A positive number is written with a plus sign in front of the number, or the plus sign may be omitted. A negative number is written always with a minus sign in front of the number. In the figure below, a line is shown in a horizontal position, and a point on the line is labeled zero. Units are laid off to the right and left of this point. The distance (number of units) from the zero point to a point on the right is

$$-5 \quad -4 \quad -3 \quad -2 \quad -1 \quad 0 \quad 1 \quad 2 \quad 3 \quad 4 \quad 5$$

positive $(+)$, while the distance from the zero point to a point on the left is negative $(-)$. On this line, a number is greater than any number to its left and smaller than any number to its right.

The *absolute value* of a signed number is the size of the number regardless of its sign. Thus on the above scale, the absolute value of a number is its distance (number of units) from the zero point, regardless of its direction (right or left) from the zero point. Thus the absolute value of $- 9$ is 9, just as the absolute value of $+9$ is 9; the absolute value of -11 is 11; the absolute value of $+11$ is 11, etc.

Rules for the addition of signed numbers. From your work in elementary algebra you will remember the following rules:

To add two or more numbers with like signs: add the absolute values of the numbers and prefix their common sign.

To add two numbers of unlike signs: find the difference of their absolute values and prefix the sign of the number whose absolute value is the larger.

ILLUSTRATIVE EXAMPLES: Applying the rules for addition of signed numbers

1. Find the sum of 32 and -41.

Solution. Since the numbers have unlike signs, we take the difference of their absolute values and prefix the sign of the number whose absolute value is larger. Notice the use of parentheses in the horizontal arrangement.

VERTICAL ARRANGEMENT
$$\begin{array}{r} 32 \\ -\,41 \\ \hline -\,9 \end{array}$$

HORIZONTAL ARRANGEMENT
$$32 + (-41) = -9$$

2. Find the sum of -20 and -17.

Solution. Since the numbers have like signs, we add their absolute values and prefix their common sign. Again notice the use of parentheses in the horizontal arrangement.

VERTICAL ARRANGEMENT
$$\begin{array}{r} -\,20 \\ -\,17 \\ \hline -\,37 \end{array}$$

HORIZONTAL ARRANGEMENT
$$(-20) + (-17) = -37$$

EXERCISES: Adding signed numbers

Find the sum of each of the following:

1.	21	**3.**	-45	**5.**	28	**7.**	90
	14		24		-28		-30
2.	38	**4.**	-31	**6.**	-15	**8.**	-36
	-17		-50		19		-36

9. 　　44
　 　− 35

10. − 38
　 　− 62

11. 　 96
　 　− 97

12. 　　74
　 　− 80

13. $16 + 69$
14. $(- 12) + 8$
15. $15 + (- 9)$
16. $(-28) + (- 20)$
17. $(- 18) + 18$

18. $47 + (- 17)$
19. $(- 29) + (- 2)$
20. $73 + (- 72)$
21. $(- 54) + (- 16) + 50$
22. $33 + (- 33) + 1$
23. $(- 45) + (- 24) + 60$
24. $(- 30) + 31 + (- 9)$

The frog in the well. A frog fell into a well 20 ft. deep. In trying to get out, the frog jumped upward. Each jump he made was 2 ft. upward, but after each jump he slipped downward 1 ft. In how many jumps did the frog get out of the well?

Rule for the subtraction of signed numbers. From your work in elementary algebra you will remember the following rule:

> To subtract one signed number from another, change the sign of the subtrahend and then proceed as in addition.

I L L U S T R A T I V E E X A M P L E S : Applying the rule for subtraction of signed numbers

1. Subtract 14 from 33.

Solution. We write this statement algebraically
$$(33) - (14)$$
Changing the sign of the subtrahend, and changing to addition
$$(33) + (- 14) = 19$$
Or we may write:

$$
\begin{array}{r}
33 \\
\text{Subtract } \underline{14} \\
19
\end{array}
$$

where we *mentally* change the sign of the 14 to minus and then add.

2. Subtract − 24 from 13.

Solution. We write this statement algebraically:
$$(13) - (- 24)$$

Changing the sign of the subtrahend, and changing to addition

$$(13) + (+ 24) = 37$$

Or we may write:

$$\begin{array}{r} 13 \\ \text{Subtract} \quad -24 \\ \hline 37 \end{array}$$

where we *mentally* change the sign of the -24 to plus and then add.

E X E R C I S E S : Subtracting signed numbers

Perform each of the following subtractions:

1. 27 16	**4.** -26 24	**7.** 8 -21	**10.** 62 62
2. 42 -15	**5.** 27 -30	**8.** -49 -38	**11.** -53 23
3. -31 21	**6.** 16 20	**9.** 17 -17	**12.** -18 -28

13. $18 - (28)$

14. $(-18) - (4)$

15. $29 - (-24)$

16. $(-29) - (-20)$

17. $-34 - 34$

18. $(-25) - (25)$

19. $72 - (-46)$

20. $(-51) - (-11)$

21. $47 - (-3)$

22. $18 - (-18)$

23. $(62) - (-18)$

24. $(-83) - (-88)$

Rules for the multiplication of signed numbers. From your work in elementary algebra you will remember the following rules:

> The sign of the product of two numbers with like signs (both positive or both negative) is positive.
> The sign of the product of two numbers with unlike signs (one positive and the other negative) is negative.

I L L U S T R A T I V E E X A M P L E S : Applying the rules for the multiplication of signed numbers

1. Multiply -5 by 7.

Solution. The numbers have unlike signs; hence the sign of their product will be negative. We write:

$$(-5)(7) = -35 \quad \text{or} \quad \begin{array}{r} -5 \\ 7 \\ \hline -35 \end{array}$$

2. Find the product $(-9)(-4)$.

Solution. The numbers have like signs; hence the sign of their product will be positive. We write:

$$(-9)(-4) = 36 \quad \text{or} \quad \begin{array}{r} -9 \\ -4 \\ \hline 36 \end{array}$$

EXERCISES: Multiplying signed numbers

Find the product of each of the following:

1. $\begin{array}{r} -20 \\ 4 \\ \hline \end{array}$	**4.** $\begin{array}{r} -12 \\ -10 \\ \hline \end{array}$	**7.** $\begin{array}{r} -15 \\ 6 \\ \hline \end{array}$	**10.** $\begin{array}{r} -40 \\ -11 \\ \hline \end{array}$
2. $\begin{array}{r} -9 \\ -6 \\ \hline \end{array}$	**5.** $\begin{array}{r} 30 \\ -5 \\ \hline \end{array}$	**8.** $\begin{array}{r} 41 \\ -3 \\ \hline \end{array}$	**11.** $\begin{array}{r} -40 \\ -30 \\ \hline \end{array}$
3. $\begin{array}{r} -6 \\ 7 \\ \hline \end{array}$	**6.** $\begin{array}{r} -60 \\ 4 \\ \hline \end{array}$	**9.** $\begin{array}{r} 38 \\ -2 \\ \hline \end{array}$	**12.** $\begin{array}{r} -15 \\ 15 \\ \hline \end{array}$

13. $8(-4)$

14. $(-6)(-5)$

15. $(-8)(7)$

16. $3(-9)$

17. $(-1)(-1)$

18. $20(-\frac{1}{4})$

19. $(-10)(25)$

20. $12(-11)$

21. $(-2)(-26)$

22. $(-39)(0)$

23. $(-\frac{1}{2})(-\frac{1}{4})$

24. $(60)(-\frac{1}{4})$

Rules for the division of signed numbers. From your work in elementary algebra you will remember the following rules:

> The sign of the quotient of two numbers with like signs (both positive or both negative) is positive. The sign of the quotient of two numbers with unlike signs (one positive and the other negative) is negative.

ILLUSTRATIVE EXAMPLES: Dividing signed numbers

1. Find the quotient $\dfrac{-56}{7}$.

Solution. The numbers have unlike signs; hence their quotient is negative. We write:

$$(- 56) \div 7 = - 8 \text{ or } \frac{- 56}{7} = - 8$$

2. Divide $- 36$ by $- \frac{1}{2}$.

Solution. The numbers have like signs; hence their quotient is positive. To divide a number by a fraction, we invert the fraction and proceed as in multiplication:

$$(- 36) \div (- \tfrac{1}{2}) \qquad \frac{- 36}{- \frac{1}{2}}$$
$$(- 36)(- 2) = 72 \quad \text{or} \quad (- 36)(- 2) = 72$$

E X E R C I S E S : Dividing signed numbers

Find each of the following indicated quotients:

1. $\dfrac{- 28}{7}$	**4.** $\dfrac{- 63}{- 7}$	**7.** $\dfrac{- 99}{11}$	**10.** $\dfrac{- 20}{- \frac{1}{2}}$
2. $\dfrac{24}{- 12}$	**5.** $\dfrac{- 80}{- 20}$	**8.** $\dfrac{- 48}{8}$	**11.** $\dfrac{91}{- 13}$
3. $\dfrac{- 72}{- 9}$	**6.** $\dfrac{60}{- 15}$	**9.** $\dfrac{- 92}{- 92}$	**12.** $\dfrac{- 1}{- \frac{1}{4}}$

13. $- 85 \div 17$

14. $- 144 \div (- 6)$

15. $84 \div (- 21)$

16. $- 54 \div (- 18)$

17. $24 \div (- \tfrac{2}{3})$

18. $- 18 \div (- \tfrac{1}{2})$

19. $52 \div (- 13)$

20. $- 85 \div 17$

21. $- 57 \div (- 3)$

22. $34 \div (- 34)$

23. $0 \div (- 1)$

24. $- 18 \div (- 1\tfrac{1}{2})$

Algebraic expressions and terms. Whenever numbers, either arithmetic or literal, are combined with the symbols that indicate addition, subtraction, multiplication, or division, an algebraic expression is formed. The following are algebraic expressions:

$$3\,xy \qquad a - b \qquad 2a + b \qquad xy - 5x + 7$$

If an algebraic expression is not separated into parts by a plus or a minus sign, the expression is a *term*. If an algebraic expression is separated into parts by plus or minus signs, each of these parts is a term of the expression. The first algebraic expression given above, $3\,xy$, contains one term; an algebraic expression containing only one term is called a *monomial*. The next two algebraic expressions, $a - b$ and $2a + b$, each contain two terms;

an algebraic expression containing two terms is called a *binomial*. The last algebraic expression, $xy - 5x + 7$, contains three terms; an algebraic expression containing three terms is called a *trinomial*. An algebraic expression consisting of more than one term is called a *polynomial;* binomials and trinomials are examples of polynomials.

ORAL EXERCISES

State whether each of the following is a monomial, binomial, or trinomial:

1. $3x - 5y$ **5.** $27 \div 9 + 5$ **9.** $8 \div 4 - 2 + 1$

2. $6xy$ **6.** $2 \times 3 + 4 - 5$ **10.** $1 - 6xyz$

3. $x - y + z$ **7.** $3xy - 2$ **11.** $\dfrac{2ab}{3xy}$

4. $\dfrac{2a}{b}$ **8.** $a \div b + c \div d$ **12.** $10 \div 2 + 6 - 3 \times 4$

Order of operations.   When several numbers are connected by the signs $+$, $-$, $\times$, and $\div$, such as

$$12 \div 3 - 2 \times 5$$

the indicated multiplications and divisions are to be performed before additions and subtractions. Since a plus or a minus sign separates an expression into terms

$$\underbrace{12 \div 3}_{\text{term}} - \underbrace{2 \times 5}_{\text{term}}$$

we can state our order of operations as:

> Simplify terms before adding them or subtracting them from other terms.

To find the value of $12 \div 3 - 2 \times 5$, we recognize that this is a binomial. First we perform the indicated division in the first term and the indicated multiplication in the second term. Then we subtract the second term from the first. Thus: $12 \div 3$ is 4; 2×5 is 10; and finally, 10 subtracted from 4 is -6.

ILLUSTRATIVE EXAMPLES: Order of operations; evaluating polynomials

1. Find the value of $5 + 5 \div 5$.

Solution. Given binomial $\qquad\qquad\qquad 5 + \underbrace{5 \div 5}$

Simplifying the second term $\qquad\qquad 5 + 1$

Adding the two terms $\qquad\qquad\qquad\quad 6 \quad$ Answer

2. If $a = 2$ and $b = -4$, find the value of $2b - 3a$.

Solution. Given binomial $\qquad\qquad\quad 2b - 3a$

Substituting 2 for a and -4 for b $\qquad 2(-4) - 3(2)$

Performing the indicated multiplications $\quad (-8) - (6)$

Subtracting 6 from -8 $\qquad\qquad\qquad\quad -14 \quad$ Answer

E X E R C I S E S : Order of operations; evaluating polynomials

Find the numerical value of each of the following:

1. $3 \times 5 + 6$ **4.** $9 + 18 \div 9$ **7.** $4 \times 3 - 8 \div 2 - 10$

2. $13 - 5 \times 4$ **5.** $2 \times 5 - 6 \div 3$ **8.** $4 \div 4 - 4 \times 4 - 4$

3. $20 \div 4 - 5$ **6.** $45 \div 15 - 6 \times 7$ **9.** $3 \times 6 - 6 \div 2 - 2$

In exercises 10–18, find the value of each expression if $a = -2$, $b = 3$, $x = -4$, and $y = 5$.

10. $a + 2b$ **13.** $ay - bx$ **16.** $10ab - 3xy$

11. $2x + y$ **14.** $xy - ab$ **17.** $3xy + 5ab$

12. $ax + by$ **15.** $x - ab - y$ **18.** $ab - bx + xy$

Factors, coefficients, and exponents. When two or more numbers are multiplied together to form a product, each of the numbers is a *factor* of that product. Since the product of 5 and 11 is 55, each of the numbers 5 and 11 is a factor of 55. In the algebraic expression $5ax$, each of the numbers 5, a, and x is a factor of the expression.

> **In the expression**
> **$5\,ax$**
> **5, a, and x are**
> **factors**

If an expression is in factored form, each factor is the coefficient of the remaining factors. In the expression $6by$, the coefficient of by is 6, the coefficient of b is $6y$, and the coefficient of y is $6b$. If an expression con-

> **In the expression**
> **$6by$**
> **6 is the numerical**
> **coefficient**

tains a single numerical factor, that number is said to be the numerical coefficient; if no number appears in the expression, a numerical coefficient of 1 is understood.

An exponent is a small number written to the right of, and above, a second number called the base. When the exponent is a positive

whole number, it indicates how many times
the base is used as a factor. If the exponent
of a number or a letter is 1, it is not generally
indicated.

$$4^3 \quad \overset{\text{exponent}}{\underset{\text{base}}{}}$$

4^3 means $4 \cdot 4 \cdot 4$

ORAL EXERCISES

1. In the expression $3xy$, what is the numerical coefficient? What is
the coefficient of y?

2. In the expression x^2y, what is the numerical coefficient? What is
the exponent of x? What is the exponent of y?

ILLUSTRATIVE EXAMPLES: Evaluating algebraic expressions
containing exponents

1. Find the value of $(-2)^3$.

> *Solution.* The expression $(-2)^3$ means $(-2)(-2)(-2)$, hence
> $$(-2)^3 = -8 \quad \text{Answer}$$

2. If $x = -3$, find the value of $2x^2 + 3x - 10$.

> *Solution.* Given expression $\qquad 2x^2 + 3x - 10$
> Substituting -3 for x $\qquad 2(-3)^2 + 3(-3) - 10$
> Simplifying each term $\qquad\qquad 18 \qquad -9 \quad -10$
> Collecting $\qquad\qquad\qquad\qquad -1 \quad$ Answer

EXERCISES: Evaluating algebraic expressions

1. If $a = 2$ and $b = 3$, find the value of $a^2 + b^2$.
2. If $a = 3$ and $b = 4$, find the value of $a^2 - b^2$.
3. If $x = -2$, find the value of $x^2 + x + 1$.
4. If $a = -1$ and $b = 2$, find the value of $a^3 - b^3$.
5. If $x = 2$, find the value of $x^3 - 5x^2 + x - 1$.
6. If $y = -2$, find the value of $6y^3 + 7y^2 - 19y - 18$.

Like terms.   Like terms, or similar terms, are
terms that have identical literal factors. The
terms $4a$ and $9a$ are like terms since their
literal factors are identical; likewise, $-2y^2$
and $14y^2$ are like terms. The terms $3b$ and
$-6c$ are *not* like terms since their literal factors
are *not* identical; likewise, $-5a^2b$ and $8ab^2$ are
not like terms.

Like terms may be added or subtracted (collected); unlike terms may not be added or subtracted. You will remember from your earlier work in algebra:

> To add or subtract like terms, add or subtract the numerical coefficients of the like terms and multiply this number by the literal part of the terms.

ILLUSTRATIVE EXAMPLES: Adding and subtracting like terms

1. Simplify by collecting like terms: $5x + 2x - 10x$.

Solution. Given expression $5x + 2x - 10x$
From our work in signed numbers, we know that instead of subtracting $10x$, we can add $-10x$. Therefore we consider the example to be

$$5x + 2x + (-10x)$$

Adding, in order, we have: $7x + (-10x)$

$5x$ plus $2x$ is $7x$; $7x$ plus $-10x$ is $-3x$
$$-3x \quad \text{Answer}$$

2. Simplify by collecting like terms: $2x^2 - 5x + 8x^2 - x^2 + 3x$.

Solution. Placing like terms together
$$2x^2 + 8x^2 - x^2 - 5x + 3x$$
Collecting like terms
$$9x^2 \quad - \quad 2x \quad \text{Answer}$$

ORAL EXERCISES: Adding and subtracting like terms

Collect like terms in each of the following:

1. $2a - 6a + 3a$
2. $7x + 9x - 8x$
3. $7b - 3b - 5b$
4. $-5y + y - 4y$
5. $4a + 6a - 12a$

6. $7x - 6x - 5x + 8x - 3x$
7. $9x^2 - 5x^2 + 3x^2 - 11x^2$
8. $2x^2 - 5x - 7x - 6x^2 + 12x$
9. $5b - b^2 - 8b - 3b^2 + 6b^2$
10. $x^2y - xy^2 + 5x^2y - 4xy^2 - 6x^2y$

Addition of polynomials. The addition of polynomials consists merely of doing several additions of like terms. To add polynomials, we arrange the polynomials vertically with like terms in the same column. Each column is then added, and the sums are connected with their proper signs.

I L L U S T R A T I V E   E X A M P L E : Adding polynomials

Find the sum of $3a - 5b + c,\ -2a - 3b - 4c,$ and $8b + 6a - 7c.$

Solution. Arranging the polynomials
vertically and with like terms in the same
column

$$
\begin{array}{r}
3a - 5b + c \\
-2a - 3b - 4c \\
6a + 8b - 7c \\
\hline
\end{array}
$$

Adding

$$7a + 0\ \ - 10c$$

or $\qquad 7a - 10c \quad$ Answer

E X E R C I S E S : Adding polynomials

In exercises 1–5, find the sum of the polynomials.

1. $5a - 6b + 7c$
$\underline{3a + 4b - 9c}$

2. $4x + 5y + 6z$
$\underline{x - 8y - 2z}$

3. $10x^2 - 9x + 8$
$\underline{9x^2 + 9x - 4}$

4. $2a^3 - 5a^2b + 4ab^2 + 7b^3$
$3a^3 + 7a^2b + 9ab^2$
$\underline{a^3 \qquad\qquad - 8ab^2 - 9b^3}$

5. $12x^3 - 10x^2 + 8x - 6$
$5x^3 \qquad\qquad - 3x - 1$
$\underline{x^3 + 4x^2 \qquad\quad + 7}$

In exercises 6–10, arrange the polynomials vertically and then find their sum.

6. $5a + b - 8c$ and $4a - 2b + 12c$

7. $5x^2 - 9 + 4x,\ 8 - 6x^2 + 13x,$ and $4 - 11x - 2x^2$

8. $4x^3 - 7x + 12,\ 15x^2 - 3x - 8,$ and $9x^2 - 17x^3 + 15x$

9. $3a^2 - a^3 + 4a - 8,\ 7 - 6a + 4a^3 - a^2,$ and $7a^2 + 3$

10. $x^3 + x^2y - y^3,\ 3xy^2 - 3y^3,$ and $4x^3 - 3x^2y + xy^2 + 2y^3$

Subtraction of polynomials.   To subtract one polynomial from another, we write the polynomials vertically with the terms of the subtrahend below the like terms of the minuend. We then subtract the terms of the subtrahend from the like terms of the minuend and connect these differences with their proper signs.

I L L U S T R A T I V E   E X A M P L E : Subtracting polynomials

Subtract $4x^3 - 7x + 12$ from $6x^3 - 4x - 5x^2 + 10.$

Solution. Arranging the polynomials vertically with the terms of the subtrahend below the like terms of the minuend

$$6x^3 - 5x^2 - 4x + 10$$
$$4x^3 \qquad - 7x + 12$$

Subtracting

$$2x^3 - 5x^2 + 3x - \ 2 \qquad \text{Answer}$$

EXERCISES: Subtracting polynomials

In exercises 1–6, subtract the lower polynomial (the subtrahend) from the one above it (the minuend).

1. $8a - 7b - 6c$
   $3a - 5b + 9c$

2. $9x + 6y - 4z$
   $7x + 8y - 5z$

3. $8x^2 - x + 10$
   $9x^2 - 3x - 2$

4. $5x^3 + 7x^2 - 2x - 1$
   $3x^3 \qquad - 9x + 7$

5. $a^4 \qquad - 3a^2 + \quad a + 16$
   $\quad 6a^3 - 4a^2 + 10a - \ 3$

6. $\quad 5a^3 - \ 4a^2b - \ 6ab^2 + \ 5b^3$
   $- 10a^3 + 16a^2b + 19ab^2 + 20b^3$

7. From $8a^3 - a^2b + 4ab^2 - 12b^3$ subtract $6a^2b - ab^2 + 8b^3$.
8. Subtract the sum of $4x^2 + 2x - 6$ and $3x^2 - 12$ from $5x^2 + 4x + 6$.
9. How much larger is $3y^2 + 4y + 5$ than $5y^2 - 3y + 5$?
10. From the sum of $18 + 2x - 5y$ and $1 - 3x$ subtract the sum of $5x - 4$ and $3y + 7$.

Doings of Dimbo.   Dimbo ran into too many negatives in trying to solve the following problem. What is the correct answer?

Find the value of $x^3 - 3x^2 + x - 3$ if $x = -3$.

Dimbo's solution

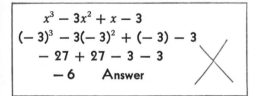

$$x^3 - 3x^2 + x - 3$$
$$(-3)^3 - 3(-3)^2 + (-3) - 3$$
$$-27 + 27 - 3 - 3$$
$$-6 \qquad \text{Answer}$$

Multiplication of monomials. As you learned in arithmetic and in your previous work in algebra, if three or more numbers are to be multiplied together, it does not matter in what order the multiplication is performed. Thus, in the indicated product $2 \times 3 \times 4$, we may first multiply the first two numbers:

$$2 \times 3 \times 4 = 6 \times 4$$
$$= 24$$

or we may first multiply the last two numbers:

$$2 \times 3 \times 4 = 2 \times 12$$
$$= 24$$

or we may first multiply the first and last numbers:

$$2 \times 3 \times 4 = 8 \times 3$$
$$= 24$$

When some of the numbers are positive and some are negative, we may follow the same procedure. Since the sign of the product of two negative numbers is positive:

> Whenever there are an even number of negative factors in a product, the sign of the product is positive; whenever there are an odd number of negative factors in a product, the sign of the product is negative.

We have learned that x^2 means $x \cdot x$ and x^3 means $x \cdot x \cdot x$. Thus the product $(x^2)(x^3)$ means $(x \cdot x)(x \cdot x \cdot x)$ or $x \cdot x \cdot x \cdot x \cdot x$ which we may write as x^5. We notice that the product $x^2 \cdot x^3$ can be simplified to x^5 by *adding* the exponents 2 and 3 to obtain the exponent 5.

$$x^2 \cdot x^3$$
$$x^{2+3}$$
$$x^5$$

> To find the product of expressions having the same base, we write that base and use as its exponent the result obtained by adding the original exponents.

ILLUSTRATIVE EXAMPLES: Multiplying monomials

1. Find the product: $(-5a)(3b)(-2c)$.

> *Solution.* Given example $(-5a)(3b)(-2c)$
> This means $(-5)(a)(3)(b)(-2)(c)$

Since there are an even number of negative factors the sign of the product will be positive; multiplying the numerical factors and indicating the product of 30 and the literal factors a, b, and c, we have

$30\,abc$ Answer

2. Find the product: $(-8x^2)(4x^3y)$.

Solution. Given example $(-8x^2)(4x^3y)$
The product of -8 and 4 is -32; the product of x^2 and x^3 is x^5. Indicating the product of -32, x^5, and y we have $-32x^5y$ Answer

ORAL EXERCISES: Multiplying monomials

Find each of the following products:

1. $(-6a)(8b)$ 4. $(3x^2y)(-7xy^2)$ 7. $-3a^2b(2a)(-3b)$
2. $(-5a)(2a)(-3a)$ 5. $(-8a^3)(-\frac{1}{2}a^2)$ 8. $(-9m^3)(3m^2)(-m)$
3. $(4x)(-2x^2)(2x)$ 6. $(-3a)(-2b)(5ab)$ 9. $\frac{1}{2}x^2(-\frac{1}{4}x)(8x)$

Division of monomials. To simplify the fraction $\frac{26}{39}$ we first factor the numerator and the denominator. This gives $\frac{2\cdot13}{3\cdot13}$. Then we divide numerator and denominator by 13, obtaining the equivalent fraction $\frac{2}{3}$. Similarly, we can simplify the fraction $\frac{x^2}{x}$. We first factor the numerator to obtain $\frac{x\cdot x}{x}$. Then we divide numerator and denominator by x, obtaining $\frac{x}{1}$, or x. In like manner, we can show that the fraction $\frac{a^5}{a^3}$ can be simplified to a^2. Thus:

$$\frac{a^5}{a^3}$$
$$a^{5-3}$$
$$a^2$$

To find the quotient of two expressions having the same base, we write that base and use as its exponent the result obtained by subtracting the exponent of the divisor from the exponent of the dividend.

ILLUSTRATIVE EXAMPLE: Dividing monomials

Simplify: $\dfrac{-24x^5y^8}{-6x^2y^4}$

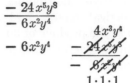

> *Solution.* Given example
> Dividing numerator and de-
> nominator by

$$\dfrac{-24x^5y^8}{-6x^2y^4}$$

$$-6x^2y^4$$

$$\dfrac{-\overset{4x^3y^4}{\cancel{24x^5y^8}}}{-\underset{1\cdot1\cdot1}{\cancel{6x^2y^4}}}$$

$4x^3y^4$ Answer

ORAL EXERCISES: Dividing monomials

Find the quotient of each of the following:

1. x^7 divided by x^5

2. $12a^3$ divided by $-6a$

3. $-20y^4$ divided by $5y^3$

4. $-14x^8$ divided by $-7x^2$

5. $-9x^5y^6$ divided by $9xy^3$

6. $18a^{10}b^{20}$ divided by $-6a^5b^{10}$

7. $\dfrac{15a^3b^3}{-5ab^3}$

8. $\dfrac{-9x^2y}{3xy}$

9. $\dfrac{-12a^5x^6}{-\frac{1}{2}a^3x^6}$

10. $\dfrac{81r^3t^2}{-8.1rt}$

Symbols of grouping. You will remember from your study of elementary algebra that parentheses, brackets, and other symbols of grouping are  used to indicate that the expression within them is to be considered as a single quantity. If a pair of parentheses is preceded by a plus sign, we may remove the parentheses without changing the sign of any term that was within the parentheses. If a pair of parentheses

$(a - b) - (x - y)$
$a - b - x + y$

is preceded by a minus sign, we may remove the parentheses provided we change the sign of every term that was within the parentheses. Conversely, terms of an algebraic expression may be placed within parentheses preceded by a plus sign if the sign before each term is left unchanged.

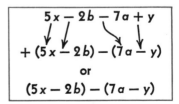

Terms of an algebraic expression may be placed within parentheses preceded by a minus sign if the sign before each term is changed.

In simplifying algebraic expressions where symbols of grouping appear within other symbols of grouping, we remove the symbols of grouping one at a time beginning with the innermost set.

I L L U S T R A T I V E   E X A M P L E :   Removing symbols of grouping

Simplify the expression $3x - [6x - (x - 2a)]$.

Solution. Given	$3x - [6x - (x - 2a)]$
Since the parentheses are contained within the brackets, we first remove the parentheses	$3x - [6x - x + 2a]$
Collecting like terms within the brackets	$3x - [5x + 2a]$
Removing the brackets	$3x - 5x - 2a$
Collecting like terms	$-2x - 2a$ Answer

E X E R C I S E S :   Symbols of grouping

In ex. 1–10, simplify each expression by removing the symbols of grouping and then collecting like terms:

1. $15a + (4a - b) - (3a - 2b) + b$
2. $10m - (3m + 4) - (2m + 2)$
3. $5x - (x + 1) + (2x - 1)$
4. $9x - \{7x - (12a + 2b) + (a - 2b)\}$
5. $[6m + (3n - m)] - [-(4n - m) - 2m]$
6. $4p - [p - (2p - 3q) + 3p] + (5q - 4)$
7. $3r - [3r - (4r - 3s)] + (4s - 3r)$
8. $2a - 2b - [\{2c + 8a - (b - 5c) + 7a\} - c]$
9. $7m - [3m - 5n - \{10m - 12n\} - m] + 5n$
10. $-a - [-a - \{-a - (a)\}]$
11. In the expression $3x - y + a - 2b$, enclose the middle two terms within parentheses preceded by a minus sign.
12. In the expression $x^2 - 3x + 2$, enclose the last two terms within parentheses preceded by a plus sign.
13. In the expression $a^5 - a^4 + a^3 - a^2 + a - 1$, enclose the first three terms within parentheses preceded by a plus sign and the last three terms within parentheses preceded by a minus sign.
14. In the expression $a^2 - b^2 + 2bc - c^2$, enclose the last three terms within parentheses preceded by a minus sign.
15. In the expression $ax + ay - bx - by$, enclose the first two terms within parentheses preceded by a plus sign and the last two terms within parentheses preceded by a minus sign.

Multiplying a polynomial by a monomial.   To multiply a polynomial by a monomial, we multiply each term of the polynomial by the monomial. Thus the product of $5x - 2y + 3$ and $3x$ is $15x^2 - 6xy + 9x$.

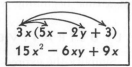

$$3x(5x - 2y + 3)$$
$$15x^2 - 6xy + 9x$$

E X E R C I S E S : **Multiplying a polynomial by a monomial**

In ex. 1–12, find each of the indicated products:

1. $5(a - b + c)$ **5.** $- 2b(a - b - b^2)$ **9.** $- y(3 - 4y + y^2)$

2. $- x(2x^2 - x + 1)$ **6.** $- xy(x + xy - y)$ **10.** $xy(3x - xy + 5y)$

3. $2a(a^2 - a - 1)$ **7.** $- 4(2a - b + 3c)$ **11.** $- 2(3a^2 + 2ab - b^2)$

4. $5x(x^2 - 4x + 2)$ **8.** $- 5a^2(4a - b^2)$ **12.** $a^2b(a^2 - 2ab + b^2)$

In ex. 13–15, simplify by removing parentheses and collecting like terms.

    13. $2(x - 3) - 3(2x + 1)$

    14. $5(a - b) + 2(3b - a) - (a + b)$

    15. $x(x - 2) - 3(x^2 - x + 1) + 2(x^2 + 3x - 1)$

Multiplying one polynomial by another polynomial.   To multiply one polynomial by another polynomial, multiply each term of the first by each term of the second and collect the partial products. In performing this multiplication, it is helpful to arrange each polynomial in ascending or descending powers of the same letter.

I L L U S T R A T I V E   E X A M P L E : **Multiplying polynomials**

Multiply as indicated: $(3x - 2)(2x^2 + 5 + 4x)$.

Solution. Arranging each polynomial in descending powers of x

$$2x^2 + 4x + 5$$
$$3x - 2$$

Multiplying by $3x$ $\overline{6x^3 + 12x^2 + 15x}$

Multiplying by $- 2$ $- 4x^2 - 8x - 10$

Adding the partial products $\overline{6x^3 + 8x^2 + 7x - 10}$ Answer

Check. We let x equal a positive number other than 1 and substitute this value for x in each polynomial and in the product. In this case, let $x = 2$:

$$(2x^2 + 4x + 5)(3x - 2) \stackrel{?}{=} 6x^3 + 8x^2 + 7x - 10$$
$$(8 + 8 + 5)(6 - 2) \stackrel{?}{=} 48 + 32 + 14 - 10$$
$$(21)(4) \stackrel{?}{=} 84$$
$$84 = 84 \text{ Check}$$

E X E R C I S E S : Multiplying polynomials

In ex. 1–6 multiply the upper polynomial (the multiplicand) by the lower polynomial (the multiplier).

1. $2x - 5$
$3x + 2$

3. $x^2 - 2x + 5$
$x - 3$

5. $x^3 - x^2 + x - 1$
$x + 2$

2. $4a + 3b$
$5a - 2b$

4. $3y^3 - 2y^2 + 1$
$y - 4$

6. $3x^2 + 4x - 8$
$x^2 - 2x + 1$

In ex. 7–12 perform the indicated multiplication and check the result.

7. $(4x - 7)(x - 4)$
8. $(a + 1)(a^2 - 2a + 3)$
9. $(2x - 3 + x^2)(x^2 - 6 + x)$

10. $(y^2 + 4y - 2)(1 - y^2 + 2y)$
11. $(a^2 + ab + b^2)(a - b)$
12. $(x + y + z)(x + y - z)$

Dividing a polynomial by a monomial. To divide a polynomial by a monomial, we divide each term of the polynomial by the monomial. Thus the quotient obtained by dividing $10x^2 - 15x$ by $5x$ is $2x - 3$.

$$\frac{10x^2 - 15x}{5x}$$
$$2x - 3$$

O R A L   E X E R C I S E S : Dividing a polynomial by a monomial

Divide as indicated:

1. $\dfrac{14x + 7y}{7}$

4. $\dfrac{24a - 15b + 21c}{-3}$

7. $\dfrac{36y^5 + 44y^4 - 8y^3}{-4y}$

2. $\dfrac{20x^2 - 12}{4}$

5. $\dfrac{55x^5 - 22x^2}{11x^2}$

8. $\dfrac{-6x^3y^3 + 54x^2y^2}{-6x^2y}$

3. $\dfrac{8a^5 + a^3}{a^2}$

6. $\dfrac{-18a^4 + 30a^3}{-6a^2}$

9. $\dfrac{24m^3 - 72m^2 + 88m}{-8m}$

10. $(-8b^3 + 28b^2 - 12b) \div (-4b)$
11. $(9x^3y^2 - 3x^2y^2 + 15x^4y^3) \div (-3x^2y^2)$
12. $(36x^7 - 48x^6 + 12x^5 - 12x^3) \div (-12x^3)$

Dividing one polynomial by another polynomial. This type of division is similar to long division in arithmetic. We arrange the terms of both polynomials in descending (or ascending) powers of the same letter. We divide the first term of the dividend by the first term of the divisor to obtain the first term of the quotient. Each term of the divisor is multiplied by the first term of the quotient and this product is subtracted from the dividend. The pattern is then repeated until the division is complete.

ILLUSTRATIVE EXAMPLES: Dividing a polynomial by another polynomial

1. Divide $2x^3 - 11x^2 + 11x - 3$ by $2x - 1$.

Solution.

$$
\begin{array}{r}
x^2 - 5x + 3 \qquad \text{Quotient} \\
2x - 1 \,\overline{)\,2x^3 - 11x^2 + 11x - 3} \\
\underline{2x^3 - x^2} \\
-10x^2 + 11x \\
\underline{-10x^2 + 5x} \\
6x - 3 \\
\underline{6x - 3} \\
0
\end{array}
$$

Check. As a numerical check, we substitute a value for x other than 1, such that the divisor does not equal zero. In this case, let $x = 2$:

$$\frac{2x^3 - 11x^2 + 11x - 3}{2x - 1} \overset{?}{=} x^2 - 5x + 3$$

$$\frac{16 - 44 + 22 - 3}{3} \overset{?}{=} 4 - 10 + 3$$

$$\frac{-9}{3} = -3 \quad \text{Check}$$

2. Divide $9x^5 - x^2 + 6 - 16x^3$ by $3x - 2$.

Solution. When we arrange the terms of the dividend in decreasing powers of x, in the sequence of exponents the terms containing x^4 and x are missing. We write zero as the coefficients of these terms in arranging our work:

$$
\begin{array}{r}
3x^4 + 2x^3 - 4x^2 - 3x - 2 \quad \text{Partial quotient} \\
3x - 2 \,\overline{)\,9x^5 + 0x^4 - 16x^3 - x^2 + 0x + 6} \\
\underline{9x^5 - 6x^4} \\
6x^4 - 16x^3 \\
\underline{6x^4 - 4x^3} \\
-12x^3 - x^2 \\
\underline{-12x^3 + 8x^2} \\
-9x^2 + 0x \\
\underline{-9x^2 + 6x} \\
-6x + 6 \\
\underline{-6x + 4} \\
2 \quad \text{Remainder}
\end{array}
$$

The preceding division may be expressed in the form:

$$\frac{9x^5 - 16x^3 - x^2 + 6}{3x - 2} = 3x^4 + 2x^3 - 4x^2 - 3x - 2 + \frac{2}{3x - 2}$$

EXERCISES: Division of polynomials

Perform each of the following indicated divisions:

1. $(3x^2 - 8x + 4) \div (x - 2)$
2. $(6x^2 + 5x - 6) \div (3x - 2)$
3. $(y^3 + 2y^2 + 2y + 1) \div (y + 1)$
4. $(4a^4 - 11a^2 + a + 3) \div (2a - 3)$
5. $(3x^3 + 7x^2y + xy^2 - 2y^3) \div (x + 2y)$
6. $(2x^4 - x^3 - 4x^2 + 4x - 1) \div (x^2 + x - 1)$
7. $(a^3 + ab^2 - 3b^3) \div (a - b)$

8. $\dfrac{125a^3 - 8}{5a - 2}$

9. $\dfrac{8x^3 + y^3}{2x + y}$

10. $\dfrac{3a^3 - 12b^3 + 5ab^2 - 6a^2b}{a - 2b}$

11. $(ax + bx + ay + by) \div (a + b)$
12. $(b^2 + bc + bd + cd) \div (b + d)$
13. $(k^3 + 2k^2 + k) \div (k + 1)$
14. $(x^2 + xy + 2xz + yz + z^2) \div (x + z)$
15. $(yz - z^2 + 2zw - yw - w^2) \div (z - w)$
16. $(a^2 + 2ab + ac + b^2 + bc) \div (a + b)$
17. $(8m^2 + 22mn + 15n^2) \div (4m + 5n)$
18. $(6mn - 8n^2 + 34nq - 18mq - 30q^2) \div (n - 3q)$
19. $(a^4 + 3a^3 - 7a^2 - 15a + 18) \div (a^2 + a - 6)$
20. $(a^4 - 9a^2b^2 - 6ab^3 - b^4) \div (a^2 - 3ab - b^2)$

CHAPTER REVIEW EXERCISES

1. What is the sum of x^2 and x^2?
2. What is the product of x^3 and x^3?
3. In the expression $2xy^3$, what is the numerical coefficient? What is the exponent of x? What is the exponent of y?
4. Which is larger: 2 or -8?
5. Find the numerical value of $2 \times 3 + 8 \div 2 - 12$.
6. Subtract $5x$ from $3 + x$.

7. If $x = 2$, $y = -3$, and $z = 0$, find the value of $2x - 3y + 4z$.

8. If $x = -2$, find the value of $3 + 5x + 2x^2$.

9. Multiply $-5x^2$ by $3x$.

10. Divide $20x^2y^3$ by $-5xy$.

11. Simplify each of the following by performing the indicated operation:

$$a)\ 2x^2(3x - 5) \qquad\qquad b)\ \frac{15x^3 - 10x^2}{-5x}$$

12. From the sum of $2a + 3b - 4c$ and $a - 2b - 3c$ subtract $4a - b + 2c$.

13. Simplify by removing parentheses and brackets and collect like terms:

$$4a + [a - (b + 2a)] - [2a - (b - 2a)]$$

14. Multiply $x^2 - x + 1$ by $3x + 5$.

15. Divide $x^3 - 19x + 30$ by $x + 5$.

16. Divide $(3a^3 - 5a^2b + ab^2 + b^3)$ by $(a - b)$.

17. Divide $(x^6 - x^4y^4 + 2x^3y^3 + y^6)$ by $(x^3 - x^2y^2 + y^3)$.

18. Divide $(12c^3 + 8c^2d + 9cd^2 - 20d^3)$ by $(6c - 5d)$.

CHAPTER 2 *First-Degree Equations*

Reviewing some definitions. You may recall from your elementary algebra that an equation is an algebraic statement that one quantity is equal to another quantity. In every equation the equal sign separates the equation into two parts, the *left member* and the *right member*. In the equation $x - 10 = 24$, the left member is $x - 10$ and the right member is 24.

An equation such as $x - 10 = 24$ may be expressed verbally as "There is some number, x, which, when decreased by 10, equals 24." The equation may also be expressed verbally as the question "What number, x, when decreased by 10 is equal to 24?" To solve the equation is to find the number which answers the question. The value of the unknown letter which satisfies the equation is called the *root* of the equation. The root of the equation $x - 10 = 24$ is 34.

If an equation, such as $x - 10 = 24$, is true for only a certain value or values of the unknown, it is an *equation of condition* or simply, an equation. If an equation is true for all values of the unknown, as in the equation $2(x + 6) = 2x + 12$, it is called an *identity*.

First-degree equations. A first-degree equation is one which, when reduced to its simplest form, contains the unknown letter or letters raised to the first power only. The equations $5x + 6 = 26$ and $4y = y - 18$ are first-degree equations. In elementary algebra you solved first-degree equations by adding, subtracting, multiplying, or dividing both members of the equation by the same number; in doing this, you applied the following axioms:

---

1. The same number may be added to both members of an equation (addition axiom).

2. The same number may be subtracted from both members of an equation (subtraction axiom).

3. Both members of an equation may be multiplied by the same number (multiplication axiom).

4. Both members of an equation may be divided by the same number, provided that the number by which they are divided is not zero (division axiom).

You will remember that the name *transposing* is often given to the process of moving, with a change of sign, terms from one member of an equation to the other member. It is simply an application of the addition or the subtraction axiom. For example, in the equation $x - 10 = 24$, we may transpose the term $- 10$ from the left member, writing it in the right member as $+ 10$, thus: $x = 24 + 10$. Notice that in this case we have added 10 to both members of the equation.

ILLUSTRATIVE EXAMPLES: Solving first-degree equations by applying axioms

1. Solve for x and check: $5x - 4 = 2x + 8$.

Solution. Given equation $\qquad\qquad 5x - 4 = 2x + 8$

Writing the equation with the terms containing x in the left member and the other terms in the right member (addition and subtraction axioms) $\qquad 5x - 2x = 8 + 4$

Collecting like terms $\qquad\qquad\qquad\qquad 3x = 12$

Dividing both members by 3 $\qquad\qquad\qquad x = 4$ Answer

Check. Given equation $\qquad\qquad 5x - 4 = 2x + 8$

Substituting 4 for x

$$5(4) - 4 \overset{?}{=} 2(4) + 8$$
$$20 - 4 \overset{?}{=} 8 + 8$$
$$16 = 16 \quad \text{Check}$$

2. Solve for y: $3(4y + 6) = 5(y - 4) + 24.$

Solution. Given equation $\qquad 3(4y + 6) = 5(y - 4) + 24$

Removing parentheses $\qquad\qquad 12y + 18 = 5y - 20 + 24$

Collecting terms in the right member $\qquad\qquad 12y + 18 = 5y + 4$

Transposing (subtraction axiom) $\quad 12y - 5y = 4 - 18$

Collecting like terms $\qquad\qquad\qquad\quad 7y = -14$

Dividing both members by 7 $\qquad\qquad y = -2 \quad$ Answer

Summary. The following methods are applied in solving first-degree equations:

1. Write the equation.

2. Remove parentheses or other symbols of grouping and collect like terms in each member.

3. Transpose terms so that every term containing the unknown is in one member and every other term is in the other member.

4. Collect like terms.

5. Divide both members by the coefficient of the unknown.

E X E R C I S E S : Solving first-degree equations

Solve each of the following equations.

1. $2x + 5 = x - 4$

2. $12x + 16 + 3x = 11$

3. $7y - 17 + 9y = 4y + 7$

4. $25x + 32 - 5x = -68 - 5x$

5. $3(x + 1) = 5x + 1$

6. $5 - 2(x - 3) = 15 + 4x$

7. $6x + 4(2x - 6) + 17 = 0$

8. $18 - 9(5x - 2) = x - 10$

9. $25y - 10(2y - 11) = 14 - 3y$

10. $3(5x - 8) - 2(4x - 9) = 16$

11. $8(x - 3) - 7(2x + 1) = 2$

12. $2(-5 + 4x) = 6(x + 4) - (4 + 2x)$

Decimal equations. In solving equations in which there are terms with decimal coefficients, it is helpful to remove the decimals by multiplying both members by a power of 10.

ILLUSTRATIVE EXAMPLE: Solving a first-degree equation with decimal coefficients

Solve for x: $.03x + 1.4 = .02x + 1$.

$$
\begin{aligned}
\textit{Solution.} \text{ Given equation} &\quad .03x + 1.4 = .02x + 1 \\
\text{Multiplying both members by } \mathbf{100} &\quad 3x + 140 = 2x + 100 \\
\text{Solving for } x &\quad 3x - 2x = 100 - 140 \\
&\quad x = -40 \quad \text{Answer}
\end{aligned}
$$

EXERCISES: Solving first-degree equations with decimal coefficients

Solve each of the following equations:

1. $.5x = 1$
2. $2.4x = 14.4$
3. $-2.7x = 24.3$
4. $-3.2x - 1.6 = 4.8$
5. $x - 1 = 6.5 - .5x$

6. $.125x = 1$
7. $.0625y = 4$
8. $1.9 - 4.7x + 3.1 - .3x = 0$
9. $2.1y + 1.8 - .1y = 7.8$
10. $.09x = 63 + .02x$

First-degree literal equations. The equations $5x + 8 = 23$ and $ax + b = c$ are in the same "form"; the second equation contains the literal numbers a, b, and c, while the first equation contains the arithmetic numbers 5, 8, and 23. When some of the numerical values in an equation are represented by letters, the equation is called a *literal equation.* These literal numbers, or constants, are usually represented by letters at the beginning of the alphabet. The letters toward the end of the alphabet are usually used to represent the unknown. Literal equations are solved by the same methods as those applied in solving numerical equations.

ILLUSTRATIVE EXAMPLE: Solving a literal equation

Solve for x in terms of the other letters: $ax + b = c$.

$$
\begin{aligned}
\textit{Solution.} \text{ Given equation} &\quad ax + b = c \\
\text{Transposing (subtraction axiom)} &\quad ax = c - b
\end{aligned}
$$

Dividing both numbers by the coefficient of x $\quad x = \dfrac{c - b}{a} \quad$ Answer

EXERCISES: Solving literal equations

Solve each of the following equations for x in terms of the other letters.

1. $mx - b = 0$
2. $2x - a + b = 4$

3. $3 - b = px - c$
4. $3x + m - 2n = 0$

5. $2bx - 3c = a + c$
6. $3ax - 4 = a(x - 1)$
7. $7 + 5bx = b(3 - x)$

8. $m(2x - 4) = 3(m + 2)$
9. $2b(x - 3) + 3b(x + 6) = 0$
10. $-2m(x + 5) + 5m(x - 4) = 6m$

Formulas. The first literal equations you studied were simple formulas in arithmetic problems. Formulas are important, too, in advanced mathematics, physics, chemistry, aeronautics, engineering, psychology, and many other fields. To master the study of any of these fields, it is necessary to be able to solve formulas for one letter in terms of the other letters and to evaluate the formulas.

ILLUSTRATIVE EXAMPLE: Solving a formula

The formula for the perimeter of a rectangle is $p = 2l + 2w$, where p is the perimeter, l is the length, and w is the width.
  a) Solve for w in terms of p and l.
  b) Find w if $p = 60$ in. and $l = 9$ in.

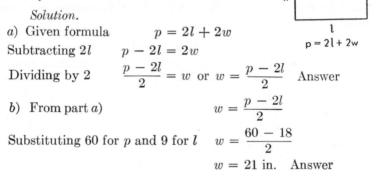

$p = 2l + 2w$

  Solution.
  a) Given formula $\qquad p = 2l + 2w$
  Subtracting $2l \qquad\quad p - 2l = 2w$
  Dividing by 2 $\qquad \dfrac{p - 2l}{2} = w$ or $w = \dfrac{p - 2l}{2}$ Answer

  b) From part *a)* $\qquad\qquad\qquad w = \dfrac{p - 2l}{2}$

  Substituting 60 for p and 9 for $l \qquad w = \dfrac{60 - 18}{2}$

  $\qquad\qquad\qquad\qquad\qquad\qquad\quad w = 21$ in.   Answer

EXERCISES: Formulas

In each formula solve for the indicated letter in terms of the remaining letters.

1. The formula for the area, A, of a rectangle is $A = lw$.
a) Solve for l.   *b)* Solve for w.   *c)* Find l if $A = 62$ and $w = 2$.
2. The formula for the area of a triangle is $A = \frac{1}{2}bh$.
a) Solve for b.   *b)* Solve for h.   *c)* Find h if $A = 28$ and $b = 14$.
3. The formula for the sum of the interior angles of a polygon of n sides is $S = (n - 2)180$.
a) Solve for n.   *b)* Find n if $S = 720$.

4. The formula for the area of a trapezoid is $A = \dfrac{h}{2}(b + b')$.

a) Solve for h.   *b)* Find h if $A = 112$, $b = 16$, $b' = 12$.

5. In the formula $C = \dfrac{5}{9}(F - 32)$,

a) solve for F;   *b*) find F if $C = 20$.

6. In the formula $S = \frac{1}{2}gt^2$,

a) solve for g;   *b*) find g if $S = 400$ and $t = 5$.

7. In the formula $E = \dfrac{Wv^2}{2g}$,

a) solve for W;   *b*) solve for g;   *c*) find the value of E if $W = \frac{1}{2}$, $v = 40$, $g = 32$.

8. In the formula $P = \dfrac{rd^2l}{w}$,

a) solve for r;   *b*) solve for w;   *c*) find l if $P = 37{,}500$, $r = 50$, $d = 30$, and $w = 60$.

ILLUSTRATIVE EXAMPLES: Representing one number in terms of another

1. Jane's mother is four times as old as Jane. If x represents Jane's age, how would you represent her mother's age?

Solution. Jane's age is **x**. Her mother's age is **four times Jane's age**. Four times **x** is **4 x** which represents Jane's mother's age.

2. A boy has a total of 35 cents in his two pockets. If he has x cents in one pocket, how much has he in the other pocket?

Solution. In one pocket he has **x** cents. His total amount is **35** cents. We must **subtract the amount in the first pocket, x, from 35** to represent the amount in the second pocket, **35 − x.**

ORAL EXERCISES: Representing two numbers in terms of a single letter

Complete orally the following statements.

1. A number twice as large as x is represented by ——.
2. A number five greater than x is represented by ——.
3. A number b less than x is represented by ——.
4. A number five times as great as x is represented by ——.
5. The sum of two numbers is 50. If the larger number is represented by l, the smaller is represented by ——.

6. The sum of two numbers is 25. If the smaller number is represented by s, the larger is represented by ———.

7. The difference between two numbers is 100. If the larger number is represented by l, the smaller is represented by ———.

8. The difference between two numbers is 5. If the smaller number is represented by s, the larger is represented by ———.

9. A man invests $20,000 in stocks and bonds. If x represents the money invested in stocks, the money invested in bonds is represented by ———.

10. A boy has 16 coins consisting of dimes and nickels. If d represents the number of dimes, the number of nickels is represented by ———.

11. The number which is x greater than b is represented by ———.

12. If the number x is reduced by b, the result is represented by ———.

Writing equations.   An important step in solving problems in algebra is expressing the verbal statement of each problem in the form of an algebraic equation. By practicing first with simple statements, the student will soon learn that he can form equations from more complex statements.

ILLUSTRATIVE EXAMPLE: Expressing a verbal statement as an equation

Write the following statement as an algebraic equation: Twice a certain number when diminished by 5 is equal to 29.

Solution. We let x represent the number. Then we translate as follows:

Twice a certain number   when diminished by 5   is equal to   29.

$$2x \qquad - \qquad 5 \qquad = \qquad 29$$

Therefore the equation is $2x - 5 = 29$.

EXERCISES: Expressing verbal statements as algebraic equations

Write each of the following statements as an algebraic equation.

1. $6x$ is equal to $3x$ plus 2.

2. $11x$ plus 7 is equal to $4x$ plus 65.

3. Four added to twice a certain number is equal to 17.

4. If 7 is added to sixteen times a number, the result is equal to 31.

5. $32x$ diminished by 17 is equal to 12 increased by $15x$.

6. 64 is 18 greater than twice a certain number.

7. 72 is 3 less than four times a number.

8. If 17 is added to twice a number, the result is 3 less than three times the number.

9. If a number is subtracted from 50, the result is 2 less than twice the number.

10. Two times a number is 12 greater than 50.

11. If 7 is added to four times a number, the sum is 31.

12. If 21 is subtracted from eight times a number, the difference is 51.

13. If three times a number is diminished by 10, the difference is equal to 78.

14. Four times a number is 5 more than 8 diminished by the number.

15. Twice a number is 12 less than the number increased by 28.

16. Three times a number is 44 more than the sum of the number and 8.

IMPORTANT STEPS IN SOLVING PROBLEMS

1. Read the problem **carefully.** In reading, ask yourself, "What does this problem tell me, and what am I asked to find?"

2. As a partial answer to the question, let the **unknown** number be represented by a letter. We usually use the letter x.

3. Express the statement of the problem as an algebraic **equation.**

4. Solve the equation.

5. Check your results. Determine whether the result satisfactorily answers the question in the stated problem.

ILLUSTRATIVE EXAMPLE : Solving a problem about numbers

The sum of two numbers is 43. Twice the larger number exceeds three times the smaller number by 16. Find the numbers.

Solution. We represent the smaller number by x. Since the sum of the two numbers is 43, we can represent the larger number by $43 - x$. If we restate the second sentence, we can translate it directly into an algebraic equation. "Twice the larger number is 16 greater than three times the smaller number."

Twice the larger number	is 16	greater than	three times the smaller number
$2(43 - x)$	$= 16$	$+$	$3x$

Restating the equation	$2(43 - x) = 16 + 3x$
Removing parentheses	$86 - 2x = 16 + 3x$
Transposing (subtraction axiom)	$-2x - 3x = 16 - 86$
Collecting like terms	$-5x = -70$
Dividing by -5	$x = 14$

Answering the question, we find the smaller number is 14 and the larger number, $43 - x$, is $43 - 14$, or 29.

Check. From the problem, the sum of the numbers is $14 + 29$ or 43. Check. Twice the larger number (58) exceeds three times the smaller number (42) by 16.

$$58 - 42 = 16 \quad \text{Check}$$

E X E R C I S E S : Problems about numbers

1. The sum of two numbers is 96. The larger number exceeds the smaller number by 4. Find the numbers.
2. The sum of two numbers is 144. Twice the smaller number exceeds the larger number by 36. Find the numbers.
3. If the smaller of two numbers is 12 less than the larger, and if their sum is 92, find the numbers.
4. The difference between two numbers is 27, and their sum is 75. Find the numbers.
5. Separate 88 into two parts such that one part may be 22 less than the other.
6. Five times the difference of 19 subtracted from a number is the same as the number increased by 5. Find the number.
7. The difference between two numbers is 6, and their sum is three times the smaller number decreased by 9. Find the numbers.
8. The sum of two numbers is 27. The larger number subtracted from 25 is equal to 50 subtracted from five times the smaller number.

Consecutive integers.   An integer is a "whole" number. Examples are $1, 2, 7, -25, -99, 106$. *Consecutive integers* are integers which follow each other in order, such as $1, 2, 3$, or $-17, -16, -15$. To find each successive integer we add 1 to the integer which precedes it. If x represents an integer, then the consecutive integer which follows x is $x + 1$.

Consecutive even integers are even integers which follow in order, such as $2, 4, 6$. To find each successive even integer we add 2 to the even integer which precedes it. If x represents an even integer, the next consecutive even integer is $x + 2$.

Consecutive odd integers are odd integers which follow in order, such as $13, 15, 17$. To find each successive odd integer we add 2 to the odd integer which precedes it. If x represents an odd integer, the next consecutive odd integer is $x + 2$.

I L L U S T R A T I V E   E X A M P L E : Consecutive integers

Find three consecutive odd integers such that twice the largest integer increased by 13 is equal to three times the smallest integer.

Solution. We represent the three consecutive odd integers as x, $x + 2$, and $x + 4$.

$$\underbrace{\text{Twice the largest integer}}_{2(x + 4)} \quad \underbrace{\text{increased by}}_{+} \quad \underbrace{13}_{13} \quad \underbrace{\text{is equal to}}_{=}$$

$$\underbrace{\text{three times the smallest integer}}_{3x}$$

$$2(x + 4) + 13 = 3x$$

Removing parentheses $\qquad\qquad 2x + 8 + 13 = 3x$

Transposing (subtraction axiom) $\qquad 2x - 3x = -8 - 13$

Collecting like terms $\qquad\qquad\qquad -x = -21$

Multiplying by -1 $\qquad\qquad\qquad\quad x = 21$

Hence $x + 2 = 23$; $x + 4 = 25$.

The three consecutive odd integers are 21, 23, 25.   Answer

Check.   From the statement of the problem:

$$2(25) + 13 \overset{?}{=} 3(21)$$
$$50 + 13 \overset{?}{=} 63$$
$$63 = 63 \quad \text{Check}$$

E X E R C I S E S :   Consecutive integer problems

1. Find three consecutive integers whose sum is 300.

2. Find three consecutive even integers whose sum is 114.

3. Find three consecutive odd integers whose sum is 189.

4. Find three consecutive integers if the sum of the smallest and largest is 56.

5. Find three consecutive even integers such that three times the smallest integer exceeds twice the largest integer by 16.

6. If the largest of three consecutive even integers is multiplied by four, the result is 2 greater than five times the smallest integer. Find the integers.

7. If the smallest of three consecutive odd integers is tripled, the result is 21 more than twice the largest integer.   Find the integers.

8. Find five consecutive integers such that twice the sum of the last two exceeds the sum of the first three by 19.

Introduction to age problems.   To find the age of any person five years ago, we can subtract 5 from his present age. Similarly, to find his age five years from now we can add 5 to his present age. If a man is x years old now, then four years ago he was $x - 4$ years old. Similarly, four years from now he will be $x + 4$ years old.

E X E R C I S E S : Arranging work in age problems

Copy the following boxes and fill in the blank spaces with the correct data. Please do not write in this book.

1.

	Age 10 Years Ago	Present Age	Age in 4 Years
Helen		$x + 5$	
Betty		x	

2.

	Age 6 Years Ago	Present Age	Age in 5 Years
Roy	$6x$		
Sandy	x		

3.

	Age 5 Years Ago	Present Age	Age in 10 Years
Peter			x
Gordon			$3x$

4.

	Age 2 Years Ago	Present Age	Age in 6 Years
Mary		x	
Jane		$24 - x$	

5.

	Age 4 Years Ago	Present Age	Age in 3 Years
Father	$3x - 5$		
Son	x		

I L L U S T R A T I V E   E X A M P L E : Age problem

Five years ago Betty was twice as old as Jay. In 6 years the sum of their ages will be 40 years. What is the present age of each?

Solution. In solving age problems it is helpful to arrange the data of the problem in box form. Let x represent **Jay's age 5 years ago.**

	Age 5 Years Ago	Present Age	Age in 6 Years
Betty	$2x$	$2x + 5$	$2x + 11$
Jay	x	$x + 5$	$x + 11$

From the statement of the problem, **"in 6 years the sum of their ages will be 40."**

$$(2x + 11) + (x + 11) = 40$$
$$3x = 40 - 22$$
$$3x = 18$$
$$x = 6$$

Hence Jay's present age, $x + 5$, is $6 + 5$ or **11 years**

Betty's present age, $2x + 5$, is $12 + 5$ or **17 years**   Answer

E X E R C I S E S : Age problems

1. A father is now 30 years older than his son. In 5 years he will be three times as old as his son. What is the present age of each?

2. Ruth is 6 years older than Harriet. In 10 years the sum of their ages will be 30 years. Find the age of each.

3. A mother's age now is 2 years more than seven times the age of her daughter. In 2 years the mother will be five times as old as her daughter. How old is each?

4. A father is twice as old as his daughter. Twenty years ago the father was twelve times as old as his daughter. Find the present age of each.

5. Five years ago Howard was four times as old as Amy, and in 5 years he will be twice as old as Amy. Find the present age of each.

6. John's age is 10 years less than four times the age of George. In 8 years John's age will exceed George's age by 26 years. Find the age of each.

7. Olin is now 6 years less than twice the age of Stephen. Nine years ago Olin was three times the age of Stephen. Find the age of each.

8. Kate's age exceeds twice Martha's age by 6 years. Eight years ago four times Martha's age exceeded Kate's age by 6 years. Find the age of each.

Introduction to coin problems.   Because a nickel is worth **5 cents,** the value in cents of x **nickels** is x times 5, or **5x** cents. Similarly, the value in cents of y dimes is $10y$ cents; and the value in cents of z quarters is $25z$ cents.

Because a nickel is worth **.05 dollars,** we can express the value in dollars of x **nickels** as **.05x.** Similarly, the value in dollars of y quarters is $.25y$.

E X E R C I S E S : Arranging work in coin problems

Copy the following boxes and fill in blank spaces with the correct data. Please do not write in this book.

1.

	Number of Coins	Value in Cents
Nickels	x	
Dimes	$15 - x$	

2.

	Number of Coins	Value in Dollars
Quarters	$18 - x$	
Half Dollars	x	

3.

	Number of Coins	Value in Cents
Nickels	$16 - 7x$	
Dimes	$6x$	
Quarters	x	

4.

	Number of Coins	Value in Dollars
Dimes	x	
Quarters	$2x + 3$	
Half Dollars	$3x - 4$	

ILLUSTRATIVE EXAMPLE: Coin problem

Monty has $2.00 consisting of nickels, dimes, and half dollars. He has twice as many dimes as nickels, and one half as many half dollars as nickels. How many of each coin does he have?

Solution. In solving coin problems it is helpful to arrange the data of the problem in box form. Let **x** represent the **number of half dollars.**

	Number of Coins	Value in Cents
Nickels	$2x$	$10x$
Dimes	$4x$	$40x$
Half Dollars	x	$50x$

Since the **total value of all the coins is 200 cents,**

$$10x + 40x + 50x = 200$$
$$100x = 200$$
$$x = 2; \ 2x = 4; \ 4x = 8$$

Monty has 2 half dollars, 4 nickels, and 8 dimes.   Answer

Check. $100 + 20 + 80 \overset{?}{=} 200$
$$200 = 200 \quad \text{Check}$$

EXERCISES: Coin problems

1. Harry has twice as many quarters as dimes and the same number of nickels as he has of dimes. The total value of his coins is $1.95. How many coins of each kind has he?

2. A boy has $1.70 in nickels, dimes, and quarters. The number of dimes is 2 less than three times the number of quarters, and the number of nickels is 2 greater than the number of quarters. How many coins of each kind has he?

3. A boy has $1.30 in half dollars, dimes, and nickels. He has four times as many nickels as half dollars, and the number of dimes is 2 greater than the number of nickels. How many coins of each kind has he?

4. A man has $3.10 in half dollars, quarters, and dimes. The number of dimes exceeds twice the number of quarters by 2; and the number of half dollars exceeds the number of quarters by 2. How many coins of each kind has he?

5. A man has $10.70 in half dollars, dimes, and nickels. The number of half dollars is 2 less than the number of nickels and the number of dimes exceeds the sum of the half dollars and nickels by 14. How many coins of each kind has he?

6. A boy has 8 more nickels than dimes. If he had twice as many nickels the total value of the boy's coins would be $4.00. How many coins of each kind has he?

7. A boy has 16 coins consisting of nickels, dimes, and quarters. The number of nickels is 3 less than the number of dimes and the value of the quarters is 55 cents greater than the value of the dimes. How many coins of each kind has he?

Introduction to investment problems.   A formula frequently used in investment problems is

$$I = prt$$

where I represents the number of dollars in interest; p represents the number of dollars in the principal; r represents the annual rate of interest; and t represents the number of years the principal is invested.

Therefore the annual income for a principal of x **dollars,** invested at an annual rate of **4% interest,** is $.04x$ $\left(\text{or } \dfrac{4x}{100}\right)$. In this case $t = 1$ year. Similarly, if $1000 is invested at x per cent, the annual return is $1000\left(\dfrac{x}{100}\right)$, or $10x$ dollars.

ORAL   EXERCISES: Investment problems

Complete the following statements orally.

1. If a man invests x dollars at 6%, then the number of dollars in annual interest is represented by ——.

2. A lady invests $(5000 - x)$ dollars in stocks that pay 4% annually. The number of dollars received each year as income is represented by ——.

3. An investment trust invests $2x$ dollars in bonds that pay $2\frac{1}{2}$% annually. The number of dollars in interest received each year is represented by ——. Hint: $2\frac{1}{2}$% = .025.

4. A man invests $3x$ dollars in real estate that yields him an annual income of $6\frac{1}{2}$% on the money invested. This annual income is represented by ——.

5. If $50,000 were invested in utilities paying x% annually on the invested capital, the annual interest in dollars is represented by ——.

6. A man owned a paid-up insurance policy valued at x dollars which paid $3\frac{1}{4}$% annually. His yearly income in dollars from the policy is represented by ——.

7. A man owned a farm whose value was $40,000. His annual income was x% of his invested capital. His annual income from the farm expressed in dollars is represented by ——.

8. If x dollars of a trust fund of $25,000 is invested in stocks paying 7% annually and the remainder in bonds paying $3\frac{1}{4}$% annually, the annual income from the stocks is represented by —— and the annual income from the bonds is represented by ——.

EXERCISES: Arranging work in investment problems

Copy the following boxes and fill in the blank spaces with the correct data. Please do not write in this book.

1.

Principal	× Rate	=	Annual **Interest**
x	.03		

2.

Principal	× Rate	=	Annual **Income**
$5000 - x$	.04		

3.

	Principal	Rate	Annual Interest
Stocks	x	08	
Bonds	$50,000 - x$	.03	

4.

	Principal	Rate	Annual Interest
Savings	x	.035	
Endowment	$2x + 5000$	.055	

ILLUSTRATIVE EXAMPLE: Investment problem

A man invested $50,000, part in a small business at 12% and the remainder in real estate at 8%. His annual income from these investments is $5400. How much has he invested in business and how much in real estate?

Solution. In solving investment problems it is helpful to arrange the data of the problem in box form. Let *x* represent the "part" of the principal invested in business.

	Principal	Rate	Annual Income
Business	x	.12	$.12x$
Real Estate	$50,000 - x$	.08	$.08(50,000 - x)$

The total annual income from business and real estate is $5400. There-
fore, the equation is $\quad .12x + .08(50,000 - x) = 5400$
Multiplying by 100 $\quad 12x + 8(50,000 - x) = 540,000$
Removing parentheses $\quad 12x + 400,000 \quad - 8x = 540,000$
Transposing (subtraction axiom) $\quad 12x - 8x = 540,000 - 400,000$
Collecting terms $\quad 4x = 140,000$
Dividing by 4 $\quad x = 35,000$

Answering the question : The amount invested in business was **$35,000;**
the amount invested in real estate was $50,000 − $35,000 or **$15,000.**

EXERCISES: Investment problems

1. A man invested a certain amount of money at 3% and twice as much at 9%, giving him an annual income of $315. How much did he invest at each rate?

2. A man invests a certain amount of money at 3% and $1000 less than this amount at 5%. If his annual income is $270, how much has he invested at each rate?

3. A man invests a part of $20,000 in a local industry yielding 7% annually on his investment and the rest in real estate, yielding 10% annually. If his yearly income is $1646, how much has the man invested in the local industry? in real estate?

4. From a fund of $50,000, a trust company invested a certain amount at 4%, twice as much at 3%, and the remainder at 5%. If the annual income from these investments was $2000, how much money was invested at each rate?

5. A banker invested $80,000 for a client in two different accounts, one account yielding $5\frac{1}{2}\%$ and the other yielding $3\frac{1}{2}\%$. If the total annual income was $2900, how much money was invested in each account?

6. An estate of $4700 consisted of stocks and bonds, the stocks paying 7.25% and the bonds paying 4.5%. If the annual income from the stocks equaled the annual income from the bonds, how much money was invested in each?

7. A broker invested for his client a certain amount of money in industrial stocks yielding 5.5% annually; a second amount, $3200 more than the first, in real estate yielding 6% annually; and a third amount, $6800 more than the second, in a commercial enterprise, yielding 6.25% annually. If the annual income from the three investments was $2947, how much money was invested in each?

8. A man's savings were invested in common stocks paying 8% annually; in preferred stock paying 6%; and in bonds, paying 4%. The money invested in bonds exceeded the money invested in preferred stocks by $500, and the money invested in preferred stocks was $2000 less than the money invested in common stock. The annual income from the common stocks was twice the income of the preferred stocks and bonds combined. How much was invested in each category?

Introduction to lever problems. One of the simplest mechanical instruments, used by man for thousands of years, is the lever. The seesaw, familiar to all of us from early childhood, operates on

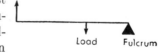

the principle of the lever. Among the many other everyday uses of the lever principle are the crowbar, wheelbarrow, can opener, and scissors.

The formula $w_1 d_1 = w_2 d_2$ expresses the physical law of the lever. For example, the seesaw is in balance when the product of one weight (w_1) and its distance (d_1) from the fulcrum is equal to the product of the second weight (w_2) and its distance (d_2) from the fulcrum.

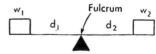

ILLUSTRATIVE EXAMPLE: Lever problem

A boy, wishing to raise a rock, used a 10 ft. plank as a lever with the fulcrum 2 ft. from the rock. How great a force must he exert downward to lift a rock weighing 300 lb.?

Solution. Apply the formula $w_1d_1 = w_2d_2$. Since the rock is 2 ft. from the fulcrum, and since the plank is 10 ft. long, the boy exerts the force w_1 8 ft. from the fulcrum, hence $d_1 = 8$, $d_2 = 2$ and $w_2 = 300$.

$$\text{Substituting in the formula} \quad 8w_1 = 2(300)$$
$$8w_1 = 600$$
$$w_1 = 75$$

The boy exerts a force of 75 lb.

$$\textit{Check.} \quad 8 \cdot (75) \stackrel{?}{=} 2(300)$$
$$600 = 600$$

EXERCISES: Lever problems

1. A seesaw is balanced by two boys, one weighing 108 lb. and the second 90 lb. If the first sits 10 ft. from the fulcrum, how far is the other seated from the fulcrum?

2. A girl, sitting 5 ft. from the fulcrum of a seesaw, balances a second girl weighing 60 lb. and sitting 6 ft. from the fulcrum. What is the weight of the first girl?

3. Cary and Dan together weigh 280 lb. and are at balance on a seesaw with Cary 6 ft. and Dan 10 ft. from the fulcrum. What is Cary's weight?

4. A scout using a 10-ft. pole with a log as a fulcrum, throws his weight of 110 lb. on one end of the pole to lift a rock on the other end $1\frac{1}{2}$ ft. from the fulcrum. What is the weight of the rock?

5. Two youngsters weighing 60 lb. and 40 lb. respectively, balance each other on a seesaw 10 ft. long. If each boy sits at an end of the seesaw, how far from the fulcrum should each sit?

6. A stone weighing 320 lb. was raised by a boy exerting a force of 80 lb. on one end of a lever which is 60 in. long. How far from the fulcrum was the stone?

7. If the handles of a wheelbarrow are 4 ft. 6 in. from the axle (fulcrum) and the load of 240 lb. is centered 18 in. from the axle, what force must be exerted on the handles to lift the load?

Hint: $4\frac{1}{2}w = (1\frac{1}{2})(240)$

CHAPTER REVIEW EXERCISES

In ex. 1–4, solve each equation for x and check your answer.

1. $3x + 4 - 6x = 28 - 12x + 3$

2. $.7x + 3.2 - .4x + .5x = 6.7 - 2.7x$

3. $.18x - .534 - .42x + .654 = 0$

4. $3(4x + 8) - 12(2x - 3) = 72$

5. Solve for x in terms of p and q:
$$4x(p + q) - p - 4q = 4(px - q)$$

6. Write an equation for the statement, "The number x is 15 greater than the difference obtained by subtracting x from 12."

7. Write an equation for the statement, "If 81 is added to a certain number, the sum is equal to 12 diminished by the number."

8. When twice a number is subtracted from 35, the result is equal to 3 more than twice the number. Find the number.

9. The sum of two numbers is 48. Twice the first number increased by three times the second, is equal to 36 subtracted from three times the first number. Find the numbers.

10. Four years ago a mother was six times as old as her daughter, and 2 years from now she will be three times as old as her daughter. How old is each at the present time?

11. What force in pounds must a man use to lift a weight of 400 lb. by means of a lever, if the weight is 12 in. from the fulcrum and the lever is 72 in. long?

12. A boy has twice as many nickels as quarters and twice as many dimes as nickels. If the value of his coins is $2.25, how many coins of each kind has he?

13. A man invested a part of his savings in stocks paying $6\frac{1}{2}\%$ and a part in bonds paying $3\frac{1}{2}\%$. If his savings totaled $20,000 and his yearly income from these investments was $1060, how much did he invest in stocks? in bonds?

14. If the largest of three consecutive odd integers is multiplied by four, the product exceeds three times the smallest odd integer by 61. Find the integers.

CUMULATIVE REVIEW EXERCISES

1. From the sum of the polynomials $4x^2 + 3x + 2$ and $5x - 5 + x^2$ subtract the polynomial $8 + 3x^2 - 6x$.

2. If $a = 2$, $b = -3$, and $c = -\frac{1}{2}$, find the value of $4a^2 - 6b^2 + 12bc + 5ab - 6abc$.

3. Perform the indicated multiplication:
$$3ab^2(a^3 - 6a^2b + 2ab^2 - 4b^3).$$

4. Divide $x^3 + x^2y - 3xy^2 + y^3$ by $x^2 + 2xy - y^2$.

5. Simplify: $2a - [6a - (3b + 2a) + 4b]$.

6. Solve for x: $2(3x - 4) - 7(8 - 2x) = -74$.

7. Solve for x in terms of the other letters: $6x + 9bc = 4(2bc - x)$.

8. Solve for x: $.6x - .5 - 3.2x = 7.6 - 1.2x + 1.7$.

9. Express as an equation, "The sum of a number x and 25 is equal to the result obtained when twice the number is subtracted from 44."

10. If a girl's present age in years is represented by $3x - 6$, how would you represent her age 5 years ago?

11. A boy had 15 coins whose value was $1.20, consisting of dimes, nickels, and quarters. He had 4 more dimes than quarters. How many coins of each kind did he have?

12. A man invested twice as much money in a savings bank, paying 3% annually, as he invested in bonds paying 4% annually. If his annual income from these two investments was $750, how much did he have invested in the bank?

CHAPTER 3

Special Products and Factoring

Some short cuts.   We are constantly seeking more efficient ways of doing our work.   In arithmetic the memorization of the multiplication tables enabled us to do our number combinations with speed and accuracy.   In algebra we may effectively employ many short cuts in doing our algebraic manipulations.   When two expressions are multiplied by short-cut methods, the products are called *special products*.   In this chapter we shall review the special products studied in elementary algebra.   We shall study, also, methods of factoring algebraic expressions.

Powers and roots of monomials.   Raising a monomial to a power is a special case of the multiplication of monomials.   The square of a monomial is the

$$(4x^3y)^2 = 16x^6y^2$$
$$(3x^2)^3 = 27x^6$$

product obtained when the monomial is multiplied by itself. The square of $4x^3y$, written $(4x^3y)^2$, means $(4x^3y)(4x^3y)$ and equals $16x^6y^2$. The cube of a monomial is the product formed by using the monomial three times as a factor. The cube of $3x^2$, written $(3x^2)^3$, means $(3x^2)(3x^2)(3x^2)$ and equals $27x^6$. Observe that:

To square a monomial: Square its numerical coefficient, and multiply this number by each literal factor with each exponent doubled.

To cube a monomial: Cube its numerical coefficient, and multiply this number by each literal factor with each exponent tripled.

The square root of a monomial is one of the two equal factors of the monomial. Since $(3a^4)(3a^4)$ equals $9a^8$, then $3a^4$ is a square root of

---

The square roots of $9a^8$
are $\pm\,3a^4$

$9a^8$. Also, since $(-3a^4)(-3a^4)$ equals $9a^8$, then $-3a^4$ is a square root of $9a^8$. Every positive monomial has two square roots, one positive and one negative. The expression $\pm\,3a^4$ is read "plus or minus $3a^4$," and means $+3a^4$ and $-3a^4$. Since the positive square root is used more often, it is called the *principal square root*.

The radical symbol, $\sqrt{}$, indicates that the square root is to be taken. Thus $\sqrt{25x^2y^4}$ indicates the square root of $25x^2y^4$ is to be found. When no sign precedes the radical, the sign is understood to be plus and the principal square root is to be found. If the negative square root is desired, the minus sign must precede the radical.

$$\sqrt{25\,x^2y^4} = 5xy^2$$
$$-\sqrt{25\,x^2y^4} = -5xy^2$$

The cube root of a monomial is one of the three equal factors of the monomial. Since $(2a^2b)^3$ equals $8a^6b^3$, then $2a^2b$ is the cube root of $8a^6b^3$. To indicate the cube root of a number, we use the radical symbol with an index of 3, as $\sqrt[3]{}$. Thus $\sqrt[3]{8a^6b^3}$ is equal to $2a^2b$; similarly, the cube root of $-64x^{12}$, written $\sqrt[3]{-64x^{12}}$, is equal to $-4x^4$.

$$\sqrt[3]{8\,a^6b^3} = 2a^2b$$
$$\sqrt[3]{-64x^{12}} = -4x^4$$

To take the square root of a monomial: Take the square root of its numerical coefficient, and multiply this number by each literal factor with each exponent divided by two.

To take the cube root of a monomial: Take the cube root of its numerical coefficient, and multiply this number by each literal factor with each exponent divided by three.

ORAL EXERCISES: Finding powers and roots of monomials

In ex. 1–8, raise each of the following to the indicated power.

1. $(4x)^2$ **5.** $(-2x^2y)^3$
2. $(3b^2)^2$ **6.** $(-2x^3)^5$
3. $(-6a)^2$ **7.** $(-2ab^2)^4$
4. $(-2y)^3$ **8.** $(-2c^2d)^5$

In ex. 9–14, find each indicated root.

9. $\pm\sqrt{100x^2}$ **12.** $-\sqrt[3]{-27m^3n^9}$
10. $-\sqrt[3]{8b^3}$ **13.** $\sqrt{(a-b)^2}$
11. $\sqrt{81r^4s^6}$ **14.** $\sqrt[3]{-125x^{12}y^{15}}$

The product of two binomials.   In Chapter 1 we reviewed the multiplication of one polynomial by another polynomial.   In your work in elementary algebra you learned to find the special product of two binomials by the F O I L method.   Let us compare the multiplication of the binomials $3x+2y$ and $5x-4y$ by the method used in Chapter 1 (shown at the right) and by the F O I L method outlined below.

$$\begin{array}{r} 3x+2y \\ 5x-4y \\ \hline 15x^2 + 10xy \\ -12xy - 8y^2 \\ \hline 15x^2 - 2xy - 8y^2 \end{array}$$

F indicates the product of the
   First terms of the binomials: $(3x+2y)(5x-4y)$ $15x^2$

O indicates the product of the
   Outside terms of the binomials: $(3x+2y)(5x-4y)$ $-12xy$

I indicates the product of the
   Inside terms of the binomials: $(3x+2y)(5x-4y)$ $10xy$ $\Big\}$ $-2xy$

L indicates the product of the
   Last terms of the binomials: $(3x+2y)(5x-4y)$ $-8y^2$

After some practice you will be able to multiply two binomials mentally and to write the answer directly. If the two binomials have like terms, the outside and inside products are like terms and can be collected. If the two binomials do not have like terms, the product will contain four terms, since the outside and inside products will not be like terms and cannot be collected.

Multiplying the sum of two terms by the difference between the same two terms is a special case of the FOIL method. The product of the sum of two terms and the difference between the same two terms is the difference between the squares of these two terms in the same order. Thus

$$(a + b)(a - b) = a^2 - b^2$$

Finding the square of a binomial is another special case of the FOIL method. We observe the following rule:

> To square a binomial: Square the first term; double the product of the two terms; square the last term. Express the three results as a sum.
> Thus, $(a - 3b)^2 = a^2 - 6ab + 9b^2$

ORAL EXERCISES: Finding the product of the sum of two terms and the difference between the same two terms

Find each of the following indicated products.

1. $(3a + 2b)(3a - 2b)$
2. $(x + 3y)(x - 3y)$
3. $(p + q)(p - q)$
4. $(4r - s)(4r + s)$
5. $(x - y)(x + y)$
6. $(x + 4)(x - 4)$
7. $(2cd - 3)(2cd + 3)$
8. $(3\pi - 1)(3\pi + 1)$
9. $(a^2 + b)(a^2 - b)$
10. $(3a^2b - 7)(3a^2b + 7)$
11. $(\frac{1}{2}rs^2 - \frac{1}{3})(\frac{1}{2}rs^2 + \frac{1}{3})$
12. $(.5c^2d^3 + 1)(.5c^2d^3 - 1)$

ORAL EXERCISES: Squaring binomials

Find each of the following indicated squares.

1. $(m + n)^2$
2. $(a - b)^2$
3. $(p + q)^2$
4. $(r + s)^2$
5. $(c - d)^2$
6. $(2a + 1)^2$
7. $(1 - 3b)^2$
8. $(3x + y)^2$
9. $(2x - y)^2$
10. $(a - 2b)^2$
11. $(2m - 3n)^2$
12. $(3p + 2q)^2$

I L L U S T R A T I V E   E X A M P L E S : Multiplying binomials by the FOIL method

1. Multiply $y + 7$ by $y - 5$.

Solution. Given example $(y + 7)(y - 5)$

In this example, the outside and inside products are like terms and can be collected; usually this is done mentally and the final answer is written directly.

$y^2 - \mathbf{5y} + \mathbf{7y} - 35$

$y^2 + \mathbf{2y} - 35$ Answer

2. Multiply as indicated: $(2x - a)(x + 3b)$.

Solution. Given example $(2x - a)(x + 3b)$

In this example, the outside and inside products are not like terms and cannot be collected; there are four terms in the answer.

$2x^2 + 6bx - ax - 3ab$ Answer

E X E R C I S E S : Multiplying binomials

Multiply each of the following:

1. $(x + 2)(x + 3)$
2. $(y - 6)(y - 1)$
3. $(a + 3)(a - 4)$
4. $(2x + 1)(2x - 11)$
5. $(x + 5)(2x - 5)$
6. $(x + y)(a - b)$

7. $(7 - y)(5 + y)$
8. $(2x - 3)(x + 4)$
9. $(2a + x)(3b - 2y)$
10. $(3x - y)(x + 2y)$
11. $(6x - 5y)(2x + 5y)$
12. $(5x + 2y)(5x - 3y)$

13. $(9 - 4x)(7 + 2x)$
14. $(a^2 + 6b)(a^2 - 3c)$
15. $(ab^2 + 1)(ab^2 - 2)$
16. $(x^2 - 2)(x + 3)$
17. $2(3x - 5)(2x + 3)$
18. $10(3x - 7y)(2x + 5y)$

Factoring. Factoring a quantity means finding two or more expressions whose product equals that quantity. For example, since the product of 5 and 11 is 55, we know that 5 and 11 are factors of 55. Similarly, 7 and 2 are factors of 14.

$5 \times 11 = 55$ | $55 = 5 \times 11$
Multiplying | Factoring

You will notice that **multiplying** and **factoring** are **inverse operations.**

Common monomial factor. The product of 8 and $a - b$ is $8a - 8b$. Since factoring is the inverse operation of multiplication, the factors of $8a - 8b$

are 8 and $a - b$. Thus:

$$8(a - b) = 8a - 8b \qquad\qquad 8a - 8b = 8(a - b)$$
$$\text{\small Multiplying} \qquad\qquad\qquad\qquad \text{\small Factoring}$$

Although $8a - 8b$ is also equal to $4(2a - 2b)$, the factoring in this case is not complete since $2a - 2b$ contains the common factor **2**. To factor completely a polynomial which contains a common monomial factor, the *largest* common monomial factor must be selected as one of the factors. Thus:

To factor a polynomial containing a monomial factor:
1. Determine the largest monomial by which each term of the polynomial can be divided. This is the monomial factor.
2. To obtain the other factor divide the given polynomial by the largest common monomial factor.

ILLUSTRATIVE EXAMPLE: Common monomial factor

Factor: $8x^4 - 6x^3y + 4x^2y^2$.

> *Solution.* The largest monomial factor common to the three terms of the polynomial is $2x^2$. Dividing $8x^4 - 6x^3y + 4x^2y^2$ by $2x^2$ gives the quotient $4x^2 - 3xy + 2y^2$, which is the other factor. We write the solution as follows:

Given example $8x^4 - 6x^3y + 4x^2y^2$

Factoring $2x^2(4x^2 - 3xy + 2y^2)$ Answer

To check, we multiply mentally the factors obtained; their product should be the original polynomial.

ORAL EXERCISES: Common monomial factor

Factor each of the following:

1. $ax + ay$	**5.** $2a + 2b$	**9.** $4 + 8a + 12b$
2. $ax - bx$	**6.** $3x + 3y - 3z$	**10.** $25x - 10y + 5$
3. $mn + mp$	**7.** $ax - bx + cx$	**11.** $9c + 6d - 3e$
4. $rs - rt$	**8.** $2am + 2an + 2ap$	**12.** $10 - 20r + 30s$

EXERCISES: Common monomial factor

Factor each of the following:

1. $6x - 12y$	**3.** $\pi R^2 + \pi r^2$	**5.** $x + xy$
2. $ab + ac$	**4.** $10a - 25b + 5c$	**6.** $b - ab^2$

7. $7 - 14x + 7x^3$

8. $2\pi rh + 2\pi r^2$

9. $8c^2d^3 + 20c^3d^2$

10. $39y^4 - 65y^3 - 13y^2$

11. $-x^3y^2 + x^2y - xy^3$

12. $2ac + 4a^2c - 6ac^2$

13. $14c^3 - 42c^2 + 56c$

14. $-6xyz - 15yz^2 - 12xz^2$

15. $6x^2y^2 - 12xy^3 - 4x^3y^2$

16. $a^5x^4y^4 + a^2x^7y^2 + a^3x^5y^6$

17. $20a^2b^2 - 10a^3b^2 + 15a^5b^4$

18. $3a^2 - 9ab + 18ac - 6a$

Solving literal equations by factoring. Some literal equations of the first degree can be solved by factoring a common monomial factor. In Chapter 2 you solved literal equations of the first degree which did not involve factoring. In the following examples we follow the same procedure except that we also apply factoring.

ILLUSTRATIVE EXAMPLE: Solving a literal equation

Solve for x in terms of the other letters: $a(2x - 3) - x(a + b) = a$

Solution. Given example $\qquad a(2x - 3) - x(a + b) = a$

Removing parentheses $\qquad 2ax - 3a - ax - bx = a$

Placing all terms containing x in the left member and all other terms in the right member $\qquad 2ax - ax - bx = a + 3a$

Collecting like terms $\qquad ax - bx = 4a$

Factoring the left member $\qquad \boldsymbol{x(a - b) = 4a}$

Dividing both members by the coefficient of x, which is $a - b$ $\qquad x = \dfrac{4a}{a - b}$ Answer

EXERCISES: Solving literal equations of the first degree

In ex. 1–9, solve each equation for x in terms of the other letters.

1. $3x = 7a - b$

2. $ax = 5a - bx$

3. $ax - a^2 = bx$

4. $a(2x - 1) = bx$

5. $bx - a = ax + b$

6. $x = ax + a$

7. $a(x + b) = b(x - a)$

8. $a(x - 3) = b(x - b)$

9. $cx - c^2 = x - a$

10. Solve for s in the formula: $s = a - r(s - l)$.

11. Solve for d in the formula: $d = a - l + nd$.

12. Solve for s in the formula: $as - ar^n = rs - a$.

Common binomial factor. You will remember that parentheses, or other symbols of grouping, indicate that the expression within the parentheses is to be considered as a single quantity. Thus the expression

$$5x(a - b) + 3y(a - b)$$ is in the same form as the
expression $$5xz + 3yz.$$ In the first expression we
have a common binomial, $(a - b)$ in the place of a common monomial,
z, in the second expression. We consider the common binomial $(a - b)$
to be a single quantity and factor the first expression in exactly the same
manner as we factor the second expression.

Given expressions $$5x(a - b) + 3y(a - b); \ 5xz + 3yz$$

One factor of the first expression is
the common binomial $(a - b)$; we
obtain the other factor of the first
expression by dividing each of the
two terms by $(a - b)$ $$(a - b)(5x + 3y); \qquad z(5x + 3y)$$

This type of factoring is exactly the same as factoring a common monomial
factor except that, in this case, the common factor is a binomial.

ILLUSTRATIVE EXAMPLES: Common binomial factor

1. Factor: $2a(x + y) - (x + y)$.

Solution. Given example $$2a(x + y) - (x + y)$$
The common binomial factor
is $(x + y)$; dividing $(x + y)$
into the first term we get $2a$;
dividing $(x + y)$ into the
second term we get $- 1$.
Thus we obtain $(2a - 1)$ as
the other factor $$(x + y)(2a - 1) \quad \text{Answer}$$

2. Factor: $a(x - y) + b(y - x)$.

Solution. Given example $$a(x - y) + b(y - x)$$
As the example is written, the
binomials are not the same.
However, if we change the
sign of the second term to
minus and change the sign of
each term within the paren-
theses, we have $$a(x - y) - b(- y + x)$$
This is the same as $$a(x - y) - b(x - y)$$
Factoring $$(x - y)(a - b) \quad \text{Answer}$$

E X E R C I S E S : Common binomial factor

Factor each of the following:

1. $2(x + y) - a(x + y)$
2. $2x(a + 2b) - y(a + 2b)$
3. $a(x^2 + y) + (x^2 + y)$
4. $(y^2 + 3) - x(y^2 + 3)$
5. $2a(5x + 6) - 3b(5x + 6)$
6. $x(a - b) + y(b - a)$
7. $2a(y - 1) - b(1 - y)$

8. $a(x + 1) + (b + 1)(x + 1)$
9. $3(2a - 1) - (2a - 1)(x + y)$
10. $a(x + 2) + b(x + 2) + c(x + 2)$
11. $a(2x^3 - 3) + 2(3 - 2x^3)(b - 1)$
12. $(x + y)(x - y) - (x - y)$
13. $2a(x + 1) + (1 + x)$
14. $ab(c + d) - (d + c)$

Grouping terms of a polynomial to obtain a common binomial factor. It is sometimes possible to group the terms of a polynomial in pairs to obtain a
common binomial factor. From our previous work we know that the
expression $a(x - y) + b(x - y)$ can be factored. If we multiply each
binomial by the monomial in front of the parentheses, we have the equivalent expression $ax - ay + bx - by$. By reversing our steps, we can factor
this four-term polynomial. The following examples demonstrate this
method of factoring.

I L L U S T R A T I V E   E X A M P L E S : Factoring by grouping

1. Factor: $2a - 4b + ax - 2bx$.

   Solution. Given example $2a - 4b + ax - 2bx$

   Grouping the first two terms
   together and the last two
   terms together $(2a - 4b) + (ax - 2bx)$

   Factoring 2 from the first group
   and x from the second group $2(a - 2b) + x(a - 2b)$

   The common binomial is
   $(a - 2b)$. Factoring $(a - 2b)(2 + x)$ Answer

2. Factor: $x^2 - xy - 4x + 4y$.

   Solution. Given example $x^2 - xy - 4x + 4y$

   Grouping the first two terms
   together and the last two terms
   together $(x^2 - xy) + (- 4x + 4y)$

   Factoring x from the first
   group and $- 4$ from the second
   group $x(x - y) - 4(x - y)$

   Factoring $(x - y)(x - 4)$ Answer

EXERCISES: Factoring by grouping

Factor each of the following:

1. $ay + by + ax + bx$
2. $ay - by + ax - bx$
3. $ax - bx - ay + by$
4. $2ax - 2ay - 3x + 3y$
5. $4ax - 3bx + 3by - 4ay$
6. $9x^2 - 15xy - 3x + 5y$
7. $a^2 - ab - a + b$
8. $8ax + 15by - 6bx - 20ay$
9. $6ar - 9br + 4as - 6bs$
10. $15ax - 6bx - 35ay + 14by$
11. $6bxy + 3ab - 2xy - a$
12. $15x^2y^2 - 1 - 5x^2 + 3y^2$

Factoring trinomials of the form $ax^2 + bx + c$.   We observed on page 45 that the product of two binomials will often be a trinomial in the form $ax^2 + bx + c$, where a, b, and c can be positive or negative.   For example,

$$(2x + 3)(x - 4) = 2x^2 - 5x - 12$$

Thus we know that the factors of the trinomial $2x^2 - 5x - 12$ are $2x + 3$ and $x - 4$.   These factors may be determined by the process illustrated in the following examples.   Keep in mind that not all trinomials can be factored.

ILLUSTRATIVE EXAMPLES: Factoring trinomials of the form $ax^2 + bx + c$

1. Factor: $y^2 - 9y + 8$.

   Solution.   In the expression $y^2 - 9y + 8$, there is no common monomial factor.   Therefore, if $y^2 - 9y + 8$ can be factored, its factors will be two binomials such that:

   a) The **first** terms of the binomials will be factors of y^2:
   $$y^2 - 9y + 8 = (y \qquad)(y \qquad)$$

   b) The **last** terms of the binomials will be factors of 8:
   $$y^2 - 9y + 8 = (\ +1)(\ +8) \quad \text{or} \quad (\ +2)(\ +4)$$
   $$\text{or} \quad (\ -1)(\ -8) \quad \text{or} \quad (\ -2)(\ -4)$$

   c) Since the sum of the **outside** product and the **inside** product must be minus, the last terms of the binomials must both be minus.   Thus we have the possibilities $(y - 1)(y - 8)$ and $(y - 2)(y - 4)$.

   d) We now check these two possibilities to see if either will give the correct middle term, $-9y$.

Possible Factors	Middle Term
$(y - 2)(y - 4)$	$-6y$ incorrect
$(y - 1)(y - 8)$	$-9y$ correct

We write the solution as follows:

| Given example | $y^2 - 9y + 8$ |
| Factoring | $(y - 1)(y - 8)$ Answer |

2. Factor: $6x^2 - 11x - 10$.

Solution. The given trinomial does not contain a common monomial factor. Therefore, if $6x^2 - 11x - 10$ can be factored, its factors must be two binomials. Since the constant term of the trinomial is -10, the last two terms of the binomials must have **unlike signs.** The possible factors of $6x^2$ are $6x$ and x, or $3x$ and $2x$. The possible factors of 10 are 10 and 1, or 5 and 2. We try these in various combinations until we find that $(3x + 2)(2x - 5)$ equals a product whose middle term is $-11x$. Thus:

| Given example | $6x^2 - 11x - 10$ |
| Factoring | $(3x + 2)(2x - 5)$ Answer |

3. Factor: $30x^3 + 2x^2 - 4x$.

Solution. Given example	$30x^3 + 2x^2 - 4x$
Removing the common monomial factor, $2x$, we have	$2x(15x^2 + x - 2)$
Factoring the trinomial	$2x(3x - 1)(5x + 2)$ Answer

ORAL EXERCISES: Factoring trinomials of the form $ax^2 + bx + c$

Factor each of the following:

1. $x^2 + 3x + 2$	**7.** $6 - 5y + y^2$	**13.** $x^2 - 4x - 5$
2. $x^2 - 4x + 3$	**8.** $15 - 8s + s^2$	**14.** $y^2 - 5y - 36$
3. $m^2 + 9m + 8$	**9.** $40 - 13t + t^2$	**15.** $m^2 - 6m - 27$
4. $p^2 - 7p + 12$	**10.** $30 + 11y + y^2$	**16.** $x^2 + 8xy - 20y^2$
5. $r^2 + 9r + 14$	**11.** $18 - 11y + y^2$	**17.** $40y^2 + 6xy - x^2$
6. $x^2 - 3xy + 2y^2$	**12.** $m^2 - 7mn + 6n^2$	**18.** $28p^3 - 3pq - q^2$

EXERCISES: Factoring trinomials of the form $ax^2 + bx + c$

Factor each of the following. **Be sure to remove first the largest common monomial factor, if one exists.**

1. $x^2 + 5x + 6$	**7.** $6m^2 - 5m + 1$
2. $x^2 - 8x + 7$	**8.** $10p^2 + 3p - 1$
3. $y^2 - 7y + 10$	**9.** $2x^2 + 5x + 2$
4. $a^2 - 9ab + 20b^2$	**10.** $4a^2 - 11a + 6$
5. $y^2 - y - 6$	**11.** $3y^2 + y - 14$
6. $a^2 - 5a - 24$	**12.** $3z^2 + 2z - 8$

13. $2y^3 + 5y^2 - 3y$	**22.** $4s^2 - 52s + 144$
14. $4y^2 - 2y - 12$	**23.** $36a^2 - a - 2$
15. $1 - 2y + y^2$	**24.** $2x^2y + 15xyz + 27yz^2$
16. $5b^2 + 13b - 6$	**25.** $5 - 27a^2 + 42a$
17. $24x^2 - 7x - 5$	**26.** $15a^2 - 12b^2 - 8ab$
18. $10a^2 + 7a - 12$	**27.** $(x + y)^2 - 2(x + y) - 15$
19. $20x^2 - 11x - 3$	**28.** $3(a + b)^2 - 7(a + b) + 2$
20. $-y^2 + 3y + 18$	**29.** $y^{2a} - 9y^a + 20$
21. $15x^2y + 42xy - 9y$	**30.** $3x^{2n} + 13x^n + 4$

Factoring a trinomial square.   Since $(3x + 5)^2 = 9x^2 + 30x + 25$, we know that we can factor the trinomial $9x^2 + 30x + 25$ as $(3x + 5)(3x + 5)$ or $(3x + 5)^2$. This trinomial is a square since it is the product of the two equal factors $3x + 5$. Factoring trinomial squares is a special case of factoring trinomials by "trial."   In the trinomial $9x^2 + 30x + 25$, observe that :

1. The first term, $9x^2$, is a square ; its square root is $3x$.
2. The last term, $+ 25$, is a square ; its square root is 5.
3. The middle term, $+ 30x$, equals twice the product of the square roots of the other two terms : $30x = 2(3x)(5)$.

These characteristics are true of all trinomial squares. While trinomial squares can be factored by the method shown on page 51, we should be able to recognize those trinomials that are squares.

I L L U S T R A T I V E   E X A M P L E : Factoring a trinomial square

Factor : $4x^2 + 12x + 9$.

> *Solution.*   Two of the terms, $4x^2$ and $+ 9$, are squares whose square roots are $2x$ and 3, respectively. The middle term, $+ 12x$, equals twice the product of $2x$ and 3. Therefore, the trinomial is a square and can be expressed as the square of a binomial :
>
> Given example $4x^2 + 12x + 9$
> Factoring $(2x + 3)^2$ Answer

O R A L   E X E R C I S E S : Factoring trinomial squares

Factor each of the following :

1. $a^2 + 2ab + b^2$	**5.** $a^2 + 2a + 1$	**9.** $y^2 - 4y + 4$
2. $x^2 - 2xy + y^2$	**6.** $b^2 - 2b + 1$	**10.** $y^2 - 6y + 9$
3. $d^2 + 2cd + c^2$	**7.** $x^2 + 4x + 4$	**11.** $a^2 + 8a + 16$
4. $m^2 - 2mn + n^2$	**8.** $m^2 + 6m + 9$	**12.** $b^2 - 8b + 16$

EXERCISES: Factoring trinomial squares

Factor each of the following, expressing your answer as the square of a binomial:

1. $9x^2 + 24x + 16$ **5.** $25a^2 - 20ab + 4b^2$ **9.** $16x^2 + 24xy + 9y^2$
2. $4y^2 - 4y + 1$ **6.** $4b^2 - 28bc + 49c^2$ **10.** $49x^4 - 56x^2y + 16y^2$
3. $9a^2 - 30ab + 25b^2$ **7.** $64x^2 + 144xy + 81y^2$ **11.** $36r^2 + 25t^2 - 60rt$
4. $36m^2 + 36mn + 9n^2$ **8.** $1 + 100t^3 - 20t$ **12.** $x^2 + .4x + .04$

Factoring the difference between two squares. The binomial, $x^2 - y^2$, consists of two squares, x^2 and y^2, which are connected with a minus sign. We describe such a binomial as the difference between two squares. Since we know from our preceding work that $(x + y)(x - y) = x^2 - y^2$, the factors of $x^2 - y^2$ are $x + y$ and $x - y$. Thus,

> One of the factors of the difference between two squares is the difference between their square roots taken in the same order; the other factor is the sum of their square roots.

ILLUSTRATIVE EXAMPLES: Factoring the difference between two squares

1. Factor: $4a^2 - b^2$.

Solution. Given example $4a^2 - b^2$
Factoring, we obtain $(2a - b)(2a + b)$ Answer

2. Factor: $2x^2 - 18y^4$.

Solution. This expression is not the difference between two squares. However, we observe that there is a common monomial factor of 2. When this factor is removed, we have a binomial factor which is the difference between two squares. We factor as follows:

Given example $2x^2 - 18y^4$
Removing the common monomial factor $2(x^2 - 9y^4)$
Factoring the binomial $2(x + 3y^2)(x - 3y^2)$ Answer

3. Factor: $x^4 - 16$.

Solution. Given example $x^4 - 16$
Factoring the difference between two squares $(x^2 - 4)(x^2 + 4)$

The binomial $x^2 - 4$ is the difference between two squares; hence $(x^2 + 4)(x - 2)(x + 2)$ Answer

ORAL EXERCISES: Factoring the difference between two squares when the squares are monomials

Factor each of the following:

1. $m^2 - n^2$
2. $x^2 - y^2$
3. $p^2 - q^2$
4. $x^2 - 25$

5. $m^2 - 9$
6. $9r^2 - 16s^2$
7. $4a^2 - 9b^2$
8. $16x^2 - 25y^2$

9. $49a^2 - 36b^2$
10. $81x^2 - 64y^2$

EXERCISES: Factoring the difference between two squares when the squares are monomials

Factor each of the following. **Be sure to remove first the largest common monomial factor, if one exists.**

1. $a^2 - 9b^2c^2$
2. $36x^2 - 100y^2z^2$
3. $4 - a^2b^2c^2$
4. $100a^2 - x^4$
5. $32a^2 - 50b^2$

6. $a^{14} - 81$
7. $81b^8 - 49c^8$
8. $3x^2 - 48$
9. $4a^4 - b^6$
10. $5x^4 - 80$

11. $8x^4y - 2x^2y^3$
12. $27a^3b^2 - 12ab^4$
13. $.49 - .04x^2$
14. $x^{2a} - 64$
15. $1.21x^6 - 1.69y^{4a}$

ILLUSTRATIVE EXAMPLES: Factoring the difference between two squares

1. Factor: $a^2 - (2x + y)^2$.

Solution. Here we have the difference between two squares, where the second term is the square of a binomial. The square root of the binomial $(2x + y)^2$ is $2x + y$. Thus:

    Given example $a^2 - (2x + y)^2$

    Factoring $[a + (2x + y)][a - (2x + y)]$

    Removing parentheses $[a + 2x + y][a - 2x - y]$ Answer

2. Factor: $(x + y)^2 - 4(a - b)^2$.

Solution. Given example $(x + y)^2 - 4(a - b)^2$

Factoring the difference between two squares $[(x + y) + 2(a - b)][(x + y) - 2(a - b)]$

Removing parentheses $[x + y + 2a - 2b][x + y - 2a + 2b]$ Answer

ORAL EXERCISES: Factoring the difference between two squares

Factor each of the following:

1. $(a + b)^2 - 4$
2. $(x - y)^2 - 9$
3. $(2a - b)^2 - 25$
4. $(a + 7)^2 - 49b^2$

5. $(m + n)^2 - 4a^2$
6. $(p + q)^2 - 64r^2$
7. $(r - s)^2 - 81$
8. $(x + y)^2 - 100$

9. $(2a - b)^2 - 121$
10. $(a + 2b)^2 - 144$
11. $25 - (a + b)^2$
12. $16 - (x - y)^2$

EXERCISES: Factoring the difference between two squares

Factor each of the following:

1. $9 - (x + y)^2$
2. $(a - b)^2 - x^2$
3. $4a^2 - (x - y)^2$
4. $(2a - b)^2 - c^2$
5. $1 - (a + b)^2$
6. $a^2 - (b - c)^2$

7. $(m - n)^2 - r^2$
8. $4x^2 - (3a + 2b)^2$
9. $(3a - 2b)^2 - (x + y)^2$
10. $(2x - y)^2 - (a - 2b)^2$
11. $(x + 5)^2 - 4(a - b)^2$
12. $9(5a + b)^2 - 25(3x - 2y)^2$

Grouping terms of a polynomial to obtain the difference between two squares. It is sometimes possible to group the terms of a polynomial in such a way as to obtain the difference between two squares. From our previous work we know that we can factor the expression $(a - b)^2 - x^2$. If we square the binomial, we have the equivalent expression $a^2 - 2ab + b^2 - x^2$. By reversing our steps, we can factor this four-term polynomial. The following examples demonstrate this method.

ILLUSTRATIVE EXAMPLES: Factoring after grouping terms to obtain the difference between two squares

1. Factor: $x^2 + 2xy + y^2 - 4$.

   Solution. Given example
   $$x^2 + 2xy + y^2 - 4$$

   The first three terms form a trinomial square; grouping these together
   $$(x^2 + 2xy + y^2) - 4$$

   Writing the trinomial as the square of a binomial
   $$(x + y)^2 - 4$$

   Factoring the difference between two squares
   $$[(x + y) + 2][(x + y) - 2]$$

   Removing parentheses
   $$[x + y + 2][x + y - 2] \quad \text{Answer}$$

2. Factor: $4b + a^2 - 1 - 4b^2$.

   Solution. Given example $4b + a^2 - 1 - 4b^2$

   The three terms -1, $4b$,
   and $-4b^2$, *with their signs
   changed*, form a trinomial
   square; we group them
   together. $a^2 - (1 - 4b + 4b^2)$

   Writing the trinomial as the
   square of a binomial $a^2 - (1 - 2b)^2$

   Factoring $[a + (1 - 2b)][a - (1 - 2b)]$

   Removing parentheses $[a + 1 - 2b][a - 1 + 2b]$ Answer

E X E R C I S E S : Factoring after grouping terms to obtain the difference between
two squares

   Factor each of the following:

1. $x^2 + 6x + 9 - y^2$ 6. $a^2 - b^2 + 2bc - c^2$
2. $a^2 - 4a + 4 - b^2$ 7. $10ab - a^2 - 25b^2 + 25c^2$
3. $4x^2 - 4xy - 1 + y^2$ 8. $6y - 9 + x^2 - y^2$
4. $9a^2 - 4x^2 - 4x - 1$ 9. $1 - 6xy - 9y^2 - x^2$
5. $4y + 4x^2 - y^2 - 4$ 10. $1 - x^2 - 2y^2 + y^4$

Solving quadratic equations by factoring.   The equations which appeared in
Chapter 2 were first-degree equations.   In a first-degree equation no exponent of the unknown is greater than 1.   In this chapter we shall solve
some equations in which the exponent of the unknown letter is 2.   Such
equations are called second-degree equations, or *quadratic* equations.   A
quadratic equation contains the second power (square) of the unknown
letter, but no higher power.   It may or may not contain the first power
of the unknown, and it may or may not contain a constant term.   The
following are examples of quadratic equations:

$$x^2 - 3x - 28 = 0 \qquad 2y^2 = 13y \qquad 16x^2 - 9 = 0$$

   The solution of quadratic equations by factoring is based upon the
following principle:

> If the product of two or more factors is zero, then at
> least one of these factors is zero.

For example, if $5 \cdot x = 0$, then x must equal zero.   Also, if $a \cdot b = 0$, then

$a = 0$ or $b = 0$ or both a and b equal zero. Likewise, if $(x + 4)(x - 3)$ $= 0$, then $x + 4 = 0$ or $x - 3 = 0$ or both $x + 4$ and $x - 3$ equal 0.

Not all quadratic equations can be solved by factoring. Other methods of solving quadratic equations will be explained in Chapter 10. You will notice in the following examples that *all quadratic equations have two roots.* To solve a quadratic equation by factoring:

---

1. Transpose all terms to one member of the equation, making the other member zero.
2. Factor.
3. Set each factor containing the unknown equal to zero, and solve the resulting first-degree equations.

ILLUSTRATIVE EXAMPLES: Solving quadratic equations by factoring

1. Solve for x and check: $2x^2 + 2 = 5x$.

Solution. Given equation $\qquad\qquad 2x^2 + 2 = 5x$

Transposing $5x$ to the left member $\qquad 2x^2 - 5x + 2 = 0$

Factoring $\qquad\qquad\qquad (2x - 1)(x - 2) = 0$

Setting each factor equal to zero $\quad 2x - 1 = 0$ and $x - 2 = 0$

Solving each first-degree equation $\qquad\qquad x = \tfrac{1}{2}$ and $x = 2$ Answers

Check. Given equation $\qquad\qquad 2x^2 + 2 = 5x$

Substituting $\tfrac{1}{2}$ for x $\qquad\qquad 2(\tfrac{1}{4}) + 2 \overset{?}{=} 5(\tfrac{1}{2})$

$\qquad\qquad\qquad\qquad\qquad\qquad 2\tfrac{1}{2} = 2\tfrac{1}{2}$ Check

Substituting 2 for x $\qquad\qquad 2(4) + 2 \overset{?}{=} 5(2)$

$\qquad\qquad\qquad\qquad\qquad\qquad 10 = 10$ Check

2. Solve for x: $x(x - 1) + 2(x + 2)^2 = 14$.

Solution. Given example $\qquad x(x - 1) + 2(x + 2)^2 = 14$

Squaring the binomial in the second term $\qquad x(x - 1) + 2(x^2 + 4x + 4) = 14$

Removing parentheses $\qquad\qquad x^2 - x + 2x^2 + 8x + 8 = 14$

Transposing the 14 to the left member and collecting like terms $\qquad\qquad 3x^2 + 7x - 6 = 0$

Factoring $\qquad\qquad\qquad (3x - 2)(x + 3) = 0$

Setting each factor equal to
zero $3x - 2 = 0$ and $x + 3 = 0$
Solving each first-degree
equation $x = \frac{2}{3}$ and $x = -3$ Answers

E X E R C I S E S : Solving quadratic equations by factoring

Solve each of the following equations and check your answers.

1. $x^2 - 6x + 5 = 0$
2. $x^2 - 3x - 18 = 0$
3. $x^2 + 2x = 8$
4. $x^2 + 16 = 10x$
5. $42 - x = x^2$
6. $3x^2 = 11x - 10$
7. $3x^2 - 2 = 5x$
8. $14y^2 - 9y - 8 = 0$

9. $4x^2 - 25 = 0$
10. $6x^2 - 7x = 0$
11. $2x^2 + 20 = 13x$
12. $4(10 - x^2) = 27x$
13. $x(2x - 9) = 18$
14. $14 = x(3x - 1)$
15. $3y^2 - 4y = y(1 - y)$
16. $(z - 2)^2 = 2(3z - 10)$

17. $(2x + 1)^2 - (x - 2)^2 = 0$
18. $(x - 3)(2x - 1) = (x + 3)^2 - 18$
19. $11x + (6x - 5)(x + 1) = (2x + 3)^2 + 4$
20. $(x - 7)(2x - 3) = (x - 6)(3x - 4) - (3 - x)$

Doings of Dimbo.   Dimbo made a poor selection only to get everything he didn't want. What mistake did he make?

Factor:

$$x^2 - x - y^2 - y$$

Dimbo's solution.

$$x(x - 1) - y(y + 1)$$
$$(x - y)(x - 1)(y + 1)$$

Factoring the sum of two cubes and the difference between two cubes.   If we divide $a^3 + b^3$ by $a + b$, we obtain $a^2 - ab + b^2$ as the quotient.   If we divide $a^3 - b^3$ by $a - b$, we obtain $a^2 + ab + b^2$ as the quotient.   Thus the factors of $a^3 + b^3$ and $a^3 - b^3$ are:

$$a^3 + b^3 = (a + b)(a^2 - ab + b^2)$$
$$a^3 - b^3 = (a - b)(a^2 + ab + b^2).$$

Notice that one factor of the *sum* of two cubes is the *sum* of their cube roots.   Notice, too, that one factor of the *difference* between two cubes is the *difference* between their cube roots:

$$a^3 + b^3 = (a + b)(\qquad) ; \qquad a^3 - b^3 = (a - b)(\qquad)$$

The trinomial factor in each case was obtained by division, but we can obtain this factor by inspection.   The first term of the trinomial factor can be obtained by squaring the first term of the binomial factor:

$$a^3 + b^3 = (\boldsymbol{a} + b)(\boldsymbol{a^2} \qquad) ; \qquad a^3 - b^3 = (\boldsymbol{a} - b)(\boldsymbol{a^2} \qquad)$$

The second term of the trinomial factor can be obtained by multiplying together the terms of the binomial factor, and taking the opposite sign from that in the binomial:

$$a^3 + b^3 = (a + b)(a^2 \boldsymbol{- ab} \quad) : \qquad a^3 - b^3 = (a - b)(a^2 \boldsymbol{+ ab} \quad)$$

The third term of the trinomial factor can be obtained by squaring the last term of the binomial factor:

$$a^3 + b^3 = (a + \boldsymbol{b})(a^2 - ab + \boldsymbol{b^2}) ; \quad a^3 - b^3 = (a - \boldsymbol{b})(a^2 + ab + \boldsymbol{b^2})$$

ILLUSTRATIVE EXAMPLES: Factoring the sum of two cubes and the difference between two cubes

1. Factor: $27\,x^3 - y^3$.

Solution.   This binomial is the difference between two cubes.   One of its factors is the difference between the cube roots, that is, $3x - y$.   The trinomial factor is obtained by inspection as explained above:

Given example	$27\,x^3 - y^3$
Factoring the difference between cubes	$(3x - y)(9x^2 + 3xy + y^2)$ Answer

2. Factor: $2a^4 + 16\,ab^6$.

Solution. Given example	$2a^4 + 16\,ab^6$
Removing the common monomial factor, $2a$	$\boldsymbol{2a}(a^3 + 8b^6)$
Factoring the sum of two cubes	$2a(a + 2b^2)(a^2 - 2ab^2 + 4b^4)$ Answer

E X E R C I S E S : Factoring the sum of two cubes and the difference between two cubes

Factor each of the following. Be sure to remove first the largest common monomial factor, if one exists.

1. $x^3 - y^3$

2. $x^3 + y^3$

3. $8b^3 - 1$

4. $x^2 + 27c^3x^2$

5. $64m^3 + 125n^3$

6. $27c^3 - 8d^3$

7. $16a^3 - 250b^3$

8. $a^4x^3 - ay^3$

9. $8b^6 + m^6$

10. $.001y^3 - z^3$

11. $\dfrac{8}{y^3} - n^3$

12. $(a + b)^3 - c^3$

Factoring binomials in the form $a^n \pm b^n$ when n is odd. When n is an odd integer, one factor of $a^n - b^n$ is $a - b$. For example, when n is 3, we know that one factor of $a^3 - b^3$ is $a - b$. If n is 5, we have the binomial $a^5 - b^5$. If we divide $a^5 - b^5$ by $a - b$, we obtain a quotient of $a^4 + a^3b + a^2b^2 + ab^3 + b^4$. Therefore we can factor $a^5 - b^5$ as:

$$a^5 - b^5 = (a - b)(a^4 + a^3b + a^2b^2 + ab^3 + b^4)$$

Observe that **when the binomial factor is $a - b$, all signs in the polynomial factor are positive;** the polynomial factor is in descending powers of a and in ascending powers of b. We can write this polynomial factor by inspection.

When n is an odd integer, one factor of $a^n + b^n$ is $a + b$. For example, when n is 3, we know that one factor of $a^3 + b^3$ is $a + b$. If n is 5, we have the binomial $a^5 + b^5$. If we divide $a^5 + b^5$ by $a + b$, we obtain as a quotient $a^4 - a^3b + a^2b^2 - ab^3 + b^4$. Therefore we can factor $a^5 + b^5$ as:

$$a^5 + b^5 = (a + b)(a^4 - a^3b + a^2b^2 - ab^3 + b^4)$$

When the binomial factor is $a + b$, the signs in the polynomial factor alternate; the polynomial factor is in descending powers of a and in ascending powers of b. We can write this polynomial factor by inspection.

I L L U S T R A T I V E E X A M P L E : Factoring binomials in the form $a^n \pm b^n$ when n is odd

Factor: $32x^5 - 243y^5$.

Solution. This binomial may be expressed as $(2x)^5 - (3y)^5$. This is the difference between two fifth powers. One of its factors is $2x - 3y$. The other factor is obtained by inspection, as explained above.

Given example $(2x)^5 - (3y)^5$

Factoring $[2x-3y][(2x)^4+(2x)^3(3y)+(2x)^2(3y)^2+(2x)(3y)^3+(3y)^4]$

Simplifying $[2x-3y][16x^4+24x^3y+36x^2y^2+54xy^3+81y^4]$ Answer

E X E R C I S E S : Factoring binomials in the form $a^n \pm b^n$ when n is odd

Factor each of the following. Be sure to remove first the largest common monomial factor, if one exists.

1. $x^5 + y^5$
2. $x^5 - y^5$
3. $a^5 - 1$
4. $1 - y^5$

5. $x^5 + 1$
6. $x^7 - y^7$
7. $m^7 + n^7$
8. $a^7 - 1$

9. $a^5 + 32$
10. $243x^5 - 1$
11. $64x^6 - 2x$
12. $486xy^6 - 2xy$

Complete factoring. A prime number is one which has no integral factor except itself and 1. In algebra, also, a prime factor is an expression which has no factor except itself and 1. **To factor an expression completely means to factor it to make all of the polynomial factors prime.** It is not necessary in complete factoring to factor the common monomial factor.

The following suggestions should help you to recognize the standard types of factoring which we have studied thus far. To factor a polynomial completely:

1. Always remove the largest common monomial factor first.

2. When factoring a *binomial,* determine whether the binomial is:

   a) the difference between two squares
   b) the difference between two cubes
   c) the sum of two cubes
   d) the sum of two odd powers of the same degree
   e) the difference between two odd powers of the same degree

3. When factoring a *trinomial,* determine whether the trinomial is:

   a) a trinomial square
   b) a general trinomial of the form $ax^2 + bx + c$

4. When factoring *polynomials of four terms,* consider the following possibilities:

   a) group "2 and 2" to obtain a common binomial factor
   b) group "3 and 1" to obtain the difference between two squares

5. Check each polynomial factor in your answer to be sure each is prime.

ILLUSTRATIVE EXAMPLES: Complete factoring

1. Factor completely: $3x^5 - 15x^3 + 12x$.

Solution. Given example $\qquad 3x^5 - 15x^3 + 12x$

Removing the common monomial factor, $3x$, we obtain $\qquad \mathbf{3x(x^4 - 5x^2 + 4)}$

Factoring the trinomial $\qquad 3x(\mathbf{x^2 - 1})(\mathbf{x^2 - 4})$

Factoring each binomial as the difference between two squares
$$3x(x + 1)(x - 1)(x + 2)(x - 2) \quad \text{Answer}$$

2. Factor completely: $x(a + b)(4x - 5) - 6(a + b)$.

Solution. Given example $\qquad x(a + b)(4x - 5) - 6(a + b)$

Removing the common binomial factor, $a + b$, we obtain $\qquad [\mathbf{a + b}][x(4x - 5) - 6]$

Removing parentheses $\qquad [a + b][\mathbf{4x^2 - 5x - 6}]$

Factoring the trinomial $\qquad (a + b)(\mathbf{4x + 3})(\mathbf{x - 2}) \quad$ Answer

REVIEW EXERCISES: Miscellaneous types of factoring

Factor each of the following completely.

1. $a^2 - 4b^2$

2. $5a^4 - 45a^2$

3. $2x^2 + 7x + 3$

4. $y^2 + 2y - 35$

5. $4m^2 + 12m + 9$

6. $7p^2 - 112q^2$

7. $9b^3 - 39b^2 - 30b$

8. $(x + y)^2 - 9$

9. $x(a + b) - y(a + b)$

10. $ax + bx - cx$

11. $x^2 - 12xy + 36y^2$

12. $m^3 - 8n^3$

13. $9m^3 + 9n^3$

14. $25r^2 - (p + 2q)^2$

15. $18x^2y - 60xy + 50y$

16. $27a^3 + 1$

17. $ax + bx - ay - by$

18. $x^2 + 2x + 1 - y^2$

19. $196b^2c^2 - 49d^6e^4$

20. $a^2x - x$

21. $xy^2 - xy - 12x$

22. $m(x - y) - n(x - y)$

23. $ax + 3bx - 2ay - 6by$

24. $13a^2 + 26ab + 13b^2 - 52c^2$

25. $a^3 - b^3 - a + b$

26. $c^2 - (a - b)^2$

27. $\pi r^3 - \pi s^3$

28. $27x^3y - 75xy^3$

29. $2x^2 + 16x + 32$

30. $6a^2 + 42a + 60$

31. $s^3t - s^2t - 2st$

32. $9x^2 - 4 - 6xy + y^2$

33. $36(r + s)^2 - 9$

34. $8x^2 + 21xy + 10y^2$

35. $a(x^2 - y^2) + b(x^2 - y^2)$

36. $72 - y - y^2$

37. $6p^2 - 3p - 18$

38. $x^5 - 16x$

39. $8a - 450ax^2$

40. $a^4 - 32a^2 + 256$

41. $ax^3 + ab^3y^3$

42. $2x^4 - 18x^2 + 40$

43. $12a^2 - 13a - 14$

44. $a^2b - abx + a^2x - ax^2$

45. $3y^6 - 78y^4 + 75y^2$

46. $rs + pq - pr - qs$

47. $15mn - 45rn + 30ms - 90rs$

48. $x^4 + x^3y - xy^3 - y^4$

49. $x^3 - 2x^2 - x + 2$

50. $72a - 19ax - 3ax^2$

51. $(a + b)^2 - (b - c)^2$

52. $x^3 + x^2 - 4x - 4$

53. $(x + y) - (x + y)^3$

54. $x^4 - (x - 2)^2$

55. $.4ax - 2.4ax^2 + 2ax^3$

56. $50b + 140by + 98by^2$

57. $144y^2 + 12y + .25$

58. $x^5 + y^5$

59. $10x^5 - 320$

60. $25(a + b)^2 - 20(a + b) + 4$

61. $(a^2 + 2a + 1)^2 - (a + 1)^2$

62. $x^2 - x - y^2 - y$

63. $x^2 - (y - 2a)x - 2ay$

64. $128a^2 + 162b^2 - 288ab$

65. $8x^4 - 74x^2 + 18$

66. $a^3 - a^2 + b^3 + b^2$

67. $a^{2n+1} - a$

68. $4y^{2b} - 43y^b - 60$

69. $27nx^2y^2 - 81nxy + 4mxy - 12m$

70. $x^{2n} + 2x^ny^n + y^{2n}$

71. $x^2(x - 2) - (x - 2)(x + 6)$

72. $(x^2 - 1)^2 - (x - 1)^2$

73. $2(a^3 - 1) - 7(1 - a^2)$

74. $81x^2 - 198xy + 121y^2 - (r + s)^2$

75. $4a^2 + 20ab + 25b^2 + 2a + 5b$

76. $a^{x+2} + 3a^{x+1} - 4a^x$

Synthetic division is the name of a special method that reduces the amount of work involved in dividing a polynomial in x by a binomial of the form $x + a$ or $x - a$. To demonstrate the reasons for the method of synthetic division we shall divide $3x^3 - 2x^2 + 5x - 4$ by $x - 2$.

$$
\begin{array}{r}
3x^2 + 4x + 13 \\
x - 2 \overline{\smash{\big)}\, 3x^3 - 2x^2 + 5x - 4} \\
\underline{3x^3 - 6x^2} \\
4x^2 + 5x \\
\underline{4x^2 - 8x} \\
13x - 4 \\
\underline{13x - 26} \\
22
\end{array}
$$

If we eliminate the x's and use only the numerical coefficients, the result of the divisions on the preceding page would be

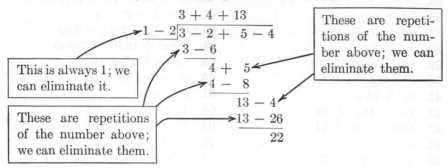

$$
\begin{array}{r}
3 + 4 + 13 \\
\overline{1 - 2\,|\,3 - 2 + \;5 - 4} \\
3 - 6 \\
\overline{4 + \;5} \\
4 - \;8 \\
\overline{13 - 4} \\
13 - 26 \\
\overline{22}
\end{array}
$$

This is always 1; we can eliminate it.

These are repetitions of the number above; we can eliminate them.

These are repetitions of the number above; we can eliminate them.

After the eliminations, indicated in the above diagram, have been performed, the result is

$$
\begin{array}{r}
3 + 4 + 13 \\
\overline{- 2\,|\,3 - 2 + \;5 - \;4} \\
- 6 \\
\overline{4} \\
- \;8 \\
\overline{13} \\
- 26 \\
\overline{22}
\end{array}
$$

If change this sign, we must add the partial products instead of subtracting.

This gives

$$
\begin{array}{r}
3 + 4 + 13 \\
2\,|\,3 - 2 + \;5 - \;4 \\
+ 6 \\
\overline{4} \\
+ \;8 \\
\overline{13} \\
+ 26 \\
\overline{22}
\end{array}
$$

If we eliminate the quotient on the top and raise the partial products to the same horizontal line, the result is:

$$
\begin{array}{r}
3 - 2 + \;5 - \;4\,\lfloor 2 \\
+ 6 + \;8 + 26 \\
\overline{3 + 4 + 13 + 22}
\end{array}
$$

$3x^2 + 4x + 13 + \dfrac{22}{x - 2}$ is the quotient.

Notice that the 3 below the line is the coefficient of the first term in the quotient. The 3 is multiplied by the 2 of the divisor, and the product 6 is then placed beneath the second term, -2, of the dividend. Adding 6 and -2, we get 4 as the coefficient of the second term in the quotient. This 4 is multiplied by the 2 of the divisor, and the product 8 is written under the next term of the dividend, 5. The process is repeated until the division is completed.

ILLUSTRATIVE EXAMPLE: Synthetic division

Using synthetic division, divide $x^3 + 3x^2 - 4$ by $x + 2$.

Solution. Since there is no x term in the dividend, we write 0 as the coefficient of the x term.

$$1 + 3 + 0 - 4 \,\lfloor -\, 2$$

Because the divisor is $x + 2$, we use -2 in the divisor position.

$$\begin{array}{r} 1 + 3 + 0 - 4 \,\lfloor -\, 2 \\ -2 - 2 + 4 \\ \hline 1 + 1 - 2 + 0 \end{array}$$ The remainder is zero.

The quotient is $x^2 + x - 2$ Answer

EXERCISES: Synthetic division

Using synthetic division, divide as indicated.

1. $(x^3 - 8x^2 + 17x - 10) \div (x - 5)$
2. $(x^3 - 7x^2 + 16x - 12) \div (x - 2)$
3. $(x^3 + 6x^2 + 11x + 6) \div (x + 1)$
4. $(x^4 + 2x^3 + 3x - 18) \div (x + 3)$
5. $(x^3 - 2x + 6) \div (x - 1)$
6. $(x^3 + 3x^2 + 3x - 7) \div (x - 2)$
7. $(x + 3x^4 - 2x^3 + 5) \div (x - 2)$
8. $(-3x^3 + 6x - 7x^2 + 1) \div (3 + x)$

A function of x. The expression $2x^2 + 5x - 3$ is a function of x. As x changes in value, the function $2x^2 + 5x - 3$ takes on corresponding values. For example, if $x = 2$, then the function $2x^2 + 5x - 3$ has the value $2(2)^2 + 5(2) - 3$, or when simplified, 15. Similarly, $2x^3 - 5x^2 + 4x - 1$ is a function of x; $x^4 - 7x + 6$ is a function of x, etc. Any expression whose value depends upon the value of x is a function of x.

We often abbreviate the words "function of x" by the symbol $f(x)$.

Here $f(x)$ is read "f of x;" it does *not* mean f times x. Similarly $g(x)$, $p(x)$, $F(x)$, or $Q(x)$ have the same meaning.

If we are concerned with a particular function of x, for example $3x^3 - 2x^2 + 5x - 4$, we write: $f(x) = 3x^3 - 2x^2 + 5x - 4$. When we evaluate this function for a certain value of x, say $x = 2$, we **replace x by 2**; that is, if

$$f(x) = 3x^3 - 2x^2 + 5x - 4$$

Then, $f(2) = 3(2)^3 - 2(2)^2 + 5(2) - 4$, or $f(2) = 22$.

Similarly, the notation $f(a)$ means that we **replace x by a** in the function:

$$f(a) = 3a^3 - 2a^2 + 5a - 4.$$

Using synthetic division to find the value of a function.   If we divide the function $f(x) = 3x^3 - 2x^2 + 5x - 4$ by $x - 2$, we can show that the remainder is equal to $f(2)$.

Factoring x from the first three terms

$$f(x) = x\{3x^2 - 2x + 5\} - 4$$

Factoring x from the first two terms within the braces

$$f(x) = x\{x[3x - 2] + 5\} - 4$$

Factoring x from the first term within the brackets

$$f(x) = x\{x[x(3) - 2] + 5\} - 4$$

If we evaluate this expression for $x = 2$, the steps are identical with the steps used in synthetic division.

$$
\begin{array}{r}
3 - 2 \quad 5 - 4 \underline{2} \\
6 \quad 8 \quad 26 \\
\hline
3 \quad 4 \quad 13 \quad 22
\end{array}
$$

These identical steps are:
1. multiply: $2 \times 3 = 6$
2. add: $6 - 2 = 4$
3. multiply: $2 \times 4 = 8$
4. add: $8 + 5 = 13$
5. multiply: $2 \times 13 = 26$
6. add: $26 - 4 = 22$

This value 22 is the remainder obtained when $3x^3 - 2x^2 + 5x - 4$ is divided by $x - 2$. This value 22 is also the value of $f(2)$.

ILLUSTRATIVE EXAMPLE: Finding the value of a function

If $f(x) = x^3 + 4x^2 + x - 6$, find the value of $f(-3)$ by two methods.

Solution. By substituting -3 for x:

$$f(-3) = (-3)^3 + 4(-3)^2 + (-3) - 6$$
$$f(-3) = -27 + 36 - 3 - 6$$
$$f(-3) = 0 \quad \text{Answer}$$

By synthetic division:

$$
\begin{array}{rrrr|r}
1 & 4 & 1 & -6 & \underline{-3} \\
  & -3 & -3 & 6 & \\
\hline
1 & 1 & -2 & 0 &
\end{array}
$$

$$f(-3) = 0 \quad \text{Answer}$$

EXERCISES: Finding the value of a function

1. If $f(x) = 5x - 2$, find the value of $f(3)$ by substituting 3 for x.
2. If $f(x) = x^3 - 2x + 5$, find the value of $f(-1)$ by synthetic division.
3. If $F(x) = 2x^2 + x - 4$, find the value of $F(2)$ by two methods.
4. If $Q(x) = x^3 - 3x^2 + 3x - 1$, find the value of $Q(1)$ by two methods.
5. If $f(y) = y^3 - 6y^2 + 3y$, find the value of $f(0)$.
6. If $f(x) = 3x^2 + 1$, and $g(x) = 7x + 3$, find the value of $f(2) - g(2)$.
7. If $f(x) = x^2 - 3x + 5$, find the value of $f(2) + f(-2)$.
8. If $f(x) = x^3 - 7x + 2$, find the value of $f(3) - f(2)$.

The remainder theorem. On p. 68 we demonstrated that by dividing $f(x)$ by $x - 2$, where $f(x) = 3x^3 - 2x^2 + 5x - 4$ we obtained a remainder that was equal to $f(2)$. If we generalize this fact, we have the remainder theorem:

> If a polynomial $f(x)$ is divided by a binomial in the form $x - a$, the remainder obtained is equal to $f(a)$.

Proof of the remainder theorem. Let $f(x)$ represent a polynomial in x. When this polynomial is divided by $x - a$, let the partial quotient obtained be represented by $Q(x)$, and the remainder be represented by R, which does not contain x. Since in any division:

$$\text{dividend} = (\text{partial quotient})(\text{divisor}) + \text{remainder}$$

we have, $f(x) = [Q(x)][x - a] + R$

To find $f(a)$, we replace x by a:

$$f(a) = [Q(a)][a - a] + R$$
$$f(a) = [Q(a)][\,0\,] + R$$
$$f(a) = R$$

The factor theorem.   The factor theorem is a special case of the remainder theorem.   If, for a given function of x, we can find a number a such that $f(a)$ is zero, then if $f(x)$ is divided by $x - a$, the remainder will be zero; that is, $f(x)$ can be divided exactly by $x - a$. This means that $x - a$ is a factor of $f(x)$. The factor theorem states that:

The binomial $x - a$ is a factor of a polynomial $f(x)$ if $f(a)$ equals zero.

ILLUSTRATIVE EXAMPLES: Applying the factor theorem

1. Factor: $x^3 - 5x^2 + 8x - 4$

Solution.   If in this polynomial there is a binomial factor, in the form $x - a$, then a must be an exact divisor of 4, the constant term.   The possible values for a are ± 1, ± 2, and ± 4.   Thus the possible binomial factors of the polynomial are $x - 1, x + 1, x - 2, x + 2, x - 4$, and $x + 4$. Let us first test the factor $x - 1$.   If $f(1) = 0$, then $x - 1$ will be a factor:

$$
\begin{array}{rrrr|l}
1 & -5 & 8 & -4 & \underline{1} \\
  & 1 & -4 & 4 & \\
\hline
1 & -4 & 4 & 0 & \text{Therefore } f(1) = 0
\end{array}
$$

By the factor theorem, $x - 1$ is a factor of the given polynomial.   The other factor, $x^2 - 4x + 4$, is the quotient that we obtained by dividing $x^3 - 5x^2 + 8x - 4$ by $x - 1$.   Thus:

Given example $\qquad\qquad x^3 - 5x^2 + 8x - 4$

By the factor theorem $\quad (x - 1)(x^2 - 4x + 4)$

Factoring the trinomial $\quad (x - 1)(x - 2)(x - 2)$ Answer

2. Factor: $x^4 - 2x^3 - x^2 - 4x - 6$

Solution.   Factors of 6, the constant term, are ± 1, ± 2, ± 3, and ± 6. Let us first try $f(+ 1)$:

$$
\begin{array}{rrrrr|l}
1 & -2 & -1 & -4 & -6 & \underline{1} \\
  & 1 & -1 & -2 & -6 & \\
\hline
1 & -1 & -2 & -6 & -12 & f(1) = -12; \text{ hence,} \\
 & & & & & x - 1 \text{ is not a factor.}
\end{array}
$$

Let us next try $f(- 1)$:

$$
\begin{array}{rrrrr|l}
1 & -2 & -1 & -4 & -6 & \underline{-1} \\
  & -1 & 3 & -2 & 6 & \\
\hline
1 & -3 & 2 & -6 & 0 & f(-1) = 0; \text{ hence,} \\
 & & & & & x + 1 \text{ is a factor.}
\end{array}
$$

The other factor, $x^3 - 3x^2 + 2x - 6$, is the quotient that we obtained by dividing $x^4 - 2x^3 - x^2 - 4x - 6$ by $x + 1$.

Given example	$x^4 - 2x^3 - x^2 - 4x - 6$
By the factor theorem	$(x + 1)(x^3 - 3x^2 + 2x - 6)$

The **four-term** polynomial can be factored, in this case, by grouping 2 and 2; $(x + 1)[(x^3 - 3x^2) + (2x - 6)]$
otherwise we would continue to apply $(x + 1)[x^2(x - 3) + 2(x - 3)]$
the factor theorem $(x + 1)(x - 3)(x^2 + 2)$ Answer

EXERCISES: Applying the factor theorem

Factor each of the following:

1. $x^3 - 3x^2 + 3x - 1$

2. $x^3 + x^2 - 3x + 1$

3. $x^3 - 4x^2 + 2x + 4$

4. $x^3 - x^2 - 4$

5. $x^3 + x^2 - 4x - 4$

6. $x^4 + x^3 - x^2 + x - 2$

7. $x^4 + 5x^3 + 7x^2 + 5x + 6$

8. $2x^3 + 5x^2 + 3x + 2$

9. $x^3 + 3x^2 + 4x + 2$

10. $x^3 + x^2 - x + 2$

11. $x^3 - x^2 - x + 1$

12. $3x^3 - x^2 - 8x - 4$

ILLUSTRATIVE EXAMPLE: Solving equations by using the factor theorem

Solve for x: $x^3 + 2x^2 - 5x - 6 = 0$.

Solution. Given example $x^3 + 2x^2 - 5x - 6 = 0$

Factoring by the use of the factor theorem $(x - 2)(x + 1)(x + 3) = 0$

Setting each factor equal to zero $x - 2 = 0; x + 1 = 0; x + 3 = 0$

Solving each equation for x $x = 2, x = -1,$ and $x = -3$ Answers

EXERCISES: Solving equations by using the factor theorem

Solve each of the following equations by using the factor theorem.

1. $x^3 - 6x^2 + 11x - 6 = 0$

2. $x^3 - 5x^2 + 2x + 8 = 0$

3. $x^3 + 3x^2 - 4 = 0$

4. $x^3 - 11x^2 + 34x - 24 = 0$

5. $x^3 - 6x^2 + 12x - 8 = 0$

6. $x^4 - 5x^3 + 5x^2 + 5x - 6 = 0$

7. $x^4 - 4x^3 - x^2 + 16x - 12 = 0$

8. $x^3 + 6x^2 + 11x + 6 = 0$

9. $x^3 - 6x^2 + 5x + 12 = 0$

10. $x^4 - 9x^3 + 23x^2 - 15x = 0$

CHAPTER REVIEW EXERCISES

In ex. 1–10, find each indicated product.

1. $-2a(2a - 3b + c)$
2. $(3x - 5)(3x + 5)$
3. $(2y - 3)^2$
4. $(3a - b)(2a + 5b)$
5. $(3x - 4y)(2x - 3y)$

6. $(2a - 1)(3b + 7)$
7. $3x(x - 4)(5x - 1)$
8. $3(2a + 3b)^2$
9. $xy(3x - y)(3x + y)$
10. $ab(a + 2)(3 - b)$

In ex. 11–13, simplify by removing parentheses and collecting like terms.

11. $3(x + 3y)(2x - y) - 2(x + 2y)^2$
12. $(3x - 7y)(3x + 7y) - (3x + 7y)^2 + 7y(7y + 6)$
13. $(a - b)^2 - (a + b)^2 - a(a - b) + b(a + b) + (a + b)(a - b)$

In ex. 14–29, factor completely.

14. $3x^2 - 12$
15. $a(x - y) - bx + by$
16. $y^2 - 10y + 24$
17. $(a - b)^2 - 1$
18. $5a^4 - 40ab^3$
19. $54x^3 + 2$
20. $ax^2 - x^2 + y^2 - ay^2$
21. $b^2 - c^2 + a^2 + 2ab$

22. $3y^4 - 27y^2 + 60$
23. $-2x^2 - x + 15$
24. $36x - 25x^3 + 4x^5$
25. $2(a + b)^2 - 3(a + b) - 2$
26. $x(x + 2)(a - b) + (a - b)$
27. $a^3x - y - x + a^3y$
28. $3x^5 - 3$
29. $x^3 - 13x + 12$

In ex. 30–35, solve each equation for x.

30. $ax - a = bx + b$
31. $mx = n(2m - x)$
32. $4x^2 - 25x - 21 = 0$
33. $4(x + 2)(x + 3) = 5 + (2x - 1)(2x + 1)$
34. $x(3x - 4) - (2x - 3)^2 = 3$
35. $x^3 - 4x^2 + x + 6 = 0$

36. Using two different methods, find the value of the following polynomial when x has the value 7 :

$$x^4 + 3x^3 - 68x^2 - 16x + 15$$

37. If $f(x) = x^3 + 3x - 2$, find the remainder when $f(x)$ is divided by $x + 2$.

38. Without substituting, find the value of $2x^3 - 3x^2 + 5$ when $x = 2$.

CUMULATIVE REVIEW EXERCISES

1. Express algebraically, "a squared diminished by twice the square of b."
2. If $x = -2$ and $y = 3$, find the value of $(x + y)(2x - y)$.
3. How much less than $4x^2 + 1 - 3x$ is $1 - x^3 - x$?

4. What is the quotient when $x^3 - y^3$ is divided by $x - y$?

5. Solve for y: $5(y - 12) - 8(y - 2) + 50 = 0$.

6. Simplify by removing symbols of grouping and collecting like terms:
$$- (6x - y) + [2y - 3(y - 4x) + x]$$

7. Simplify: $\dfrac{5x^5 - 30x^3}{-5x^2}$.

8. Solve for y in terms of a and b: $a(y - 2b) - ab = b(a - y)$.

9. If $x = -2$, find the value of y when $y = \dfrac{3x + 16}{5}$.

10. Factor: $10x^3 + 11x^2 - 6x$.

11. Solve for y: $(y + 2)(y - 1) = 70$.

12. A boy has $5.70 in nickels, dimes, and quarters. The number of dimes he has is 5 more than the number of nickels, and the number of quarters he has is twice the number of nickels. How many of each kind of coin has he?

CHAPTER 4   *Fractions*

Algebraic fractions.   In arithmetic we added, subtracted, multiplied, and divided fractions.   In algebra we must be able to perform these same operations when the fractions involved are algebraic.   To handle algebraic fractions in a satisfactory manner requires a thorough understanding of factoring methods and of short methods of multiplication.

The algebraic expression, $\frac{n}{d}$, is a fraction; n is the numerator of the fraction, and d is the denominator of the fraction.   A fraction is an indicated division.   Thus, $\frac{n}{d}$ means n divided by d.

Fundamental principle of fractions.

> Both numerator and denominator of a fraction may be multiplied or divided by the same quantity (zero excepted) without changing the value of the fraction.

74

For example, in the fraction $\frac{12}{20}$, both 12 and 20 may be divided by the same number, 4, to produce the equivalent fraction $\frac{3}{5}$:

$$\frac{12 \div 4}{20 \div 4} = \frac{3}{5}$$

Reversing the procedure, we can multiply both members of the fraction $\frac{3}{5}$ by the number, 4, to produce the equivalent fraction $\frac{12}{20}$:

$$\frac{3 \cdot 4}{5 \cdot 4} = \frac{12}{20}$$

Signs of a fraction. Every fraction has three basic signs: (1) the sign of the numerator; (2) the sign of the denominator; (3) the sign of the fraction itself. You remember from your study of elementary algebra that:

> Any two of the three basic signs of a fraction may be changed without changing the value of the fraction.

This means: $\dfrac{a}{b} = -\dfrac{a}{-b} = +\dfrac{-a}{-b} = -\dfrac{-a}{+b}.$

To change the sign of the denominator of a fraction when that denominator is a polynomial, we change the sign of every term of the polynomial. In order not to change the value of the fraction, then, we must change, also, either the sign of the fraction or the sign of the numerator. For example,

$$+\frac{x}{-x+y} = -\frac{x}{x-y}$$

Similarly, to change the sign of the numerator of a fraction when that numerator is a polynomial, we change the sign of every term of the polynomial. In order not to change the value of the fraction, we must change, also, either the sign of the fraction or the sign of the denominator. For example,

$$\frac{a^2 - b^2 - c^2}{a+b} = -\frac{b^2 + c^2 - a^2}{a+b}$$

If the numerator or denominator of a fraction is expressed in factored form, it is necessary that we remember the rule from elementary algebra:

> A change in sign of an even number of factors of an expression will not change the sign of the expression. A change in sign of an odd number of factors of an expression will change the sign of the expression.

For example, $\qquad (a - b)(c - d) = (b - a)(d - c)$

and $\qquad\qquad (r + s)(x - y) = -(r + s)(y - x)$

ORAL EXERCISES: Changing the signs of fractions

In ex. 1–8 state the terms or factors necessary to replace the question marks.

1. $\dfrac{-5}{9} = -\dfrac{?}{9}$

2. $\dfrac{m}{-2n} = \dfrac{?}{2n}$

3. $-\dfrac{7r}{-6t} = \dfrac{7r}{?}$

4. $\dfrac{c}{b - a} = \dfrac{?}{a - b}$

5. $\dfrac{m}{-c - d} = -\dfrac{m}{?}$

6. $\dfrac{5}{(a - b)(b - a)} = -\dfrac{5}{(a - b)(\,?\,)}$

7. $\dfrac{a + b + c}{b + c - 3a} = -\dfrac{a + b + c}{(\,?\,)}$

8. $\dfrac{(5)(-6)(-a)(-b)}{b^2 - a^2} = \dfrac{(5)(\,?\,)(\,?\,)(\,?\,)}{a^2 - b^2}$

In ex. 9–17 state an equivalent fraction that has both positive numerator and denominator.

9. $+\dfrac{-2}{a}$

10. $+\dfrac{-3}{-7}$

11. $-\dfrac{+8}{-c}$

12. $\dfrac{-x}{-y}$

13. $\dfrac{4}{-a - b}$

14. $-\dfrac{c}{(-a)(+b)}$

15. $\dfrac{-x}{-3 - y}$

16. $\dfrac{-1}{(-x - 2)^2}$

17. $\dfrac{(a)(-b)(-c)(-d)}{-x - y}$

In ex. 18–25 express the fractions of each example with the same denominator:

18. $\dfrac{7}{a - b} - \dfrac{c}{b - a}$

19. $\dfrac{3m}{b^2 - c^2} + \dfrac{m - n}{c^2 - b^2}$

20. $\dfrac{r}{y-x} + \dfrac{r+t}{x-y} - \dfrac{r-t}{y-x}$

21. $\dfrac{8}{r-s-t} - \dfrac{2x}{s-r+t} - \dfrac{3y}{r-t-s}$

22. $\dfrac{2a}{x-a} + \dfrac{3x}{a-x}$

23. $\dfrac{2}{a-b+c} + \dfrac{3}{b-a-c} - \dfrac{4}{b-c-a}$

24. $\dfrac{5}{(a-b)(b+a)} + \dfrac{8}{(a-b)(a+b)} - \dfrac{2}{(a+b)(b-a)}$

25. $\dfrac{4}{(a-x)(x-a)} - \dfrac{6}{(a-x)(a-x)} + \dfrac{3}{(x-a)^2}$

Reducing fractions to lowest terms. A fraction is in lowest terms when its numerator and denominator have no common factor except 1.

> To reduce a fraction to lowest terms: Factor both numerator and denominator of the fraction; divide the numerator and the denominator by all factors common to both.

Dividing the numerator and the denominator of a fraction by a common factor is sometimes called "canceling" the common factors. It is permissible to use this word "canceling" provided we fully recognize the algebraic operation we are performing — that is, we are reducing a fraction by dividing numerator and denominator by like factors.

I L L U S T R A T I V E   E X A M P L E S : Reducing fractions to lowest terms

1. Reduce to lowest terms: $\dfrac{46x^2y^2}{69x^3y}$

    Solution. Given fraction $\dfrac{46x^2y^2}{69x^3y}$

    Factoring $\dfrac{2 \cdot \cancel{23} \cdot \cancel{x} \cdot \cancel{x} \cdot y \cdot \cancel{y}}{3 \cdot \cancel{23} \cdot \cancel{x} \cdot \cancel{x} \cdot x \cdot \cancel{y}}$

    Dividing numerator and
    denominator by $23 \cdot x \cdot x \cdot y$ $\dfrac{2y}{3x}$ Answer

2. Reduce to lowest terms: $\dfrac{a^2 - 8a + 15}{15a + 7a^2 - 2a^3}$

Solution. We see that the numerator is written in descending powers of a while the denominator is written in ascending powers of a. First, we rewrite the denominator in descending powers of a. To make the factoring easier, we change the sign of each term in the denominator. In order that the value of the fraction may not be changed, we also change the sign of the fraction itself. We show our work as follows:

Given fraction $\qquad\qquad\qquad\qquad\qquad \dfrac{a^2 - 8a + 15}{15a + 7a^2 - 2a^3}$

Changing the sign of each term of the
denominator and changing the sign of $\qquad -\dfrac{a^2 - 8a + 15}{2a^3 - 7a^2 - 15a}$
the fraction

Factoring and dividing $\qquad\qquad\qquad -\dfrac{(a - 5)(a - 3)}{a(2a + 3)(a - 5)}$

We obtain $\qquad\qquad\qquad\qquad\qquad -\dfrac{(a - 3)}{a(2a + 3)}$

We may also write the fraction as $\qquad \dfrac{3 - a}{a(2a + 3)}$ Answer

The fraction $-\dfrac{(a - 3)}{a(2a + 3)}$ is not an incorrect answer. It is customary, however, to express, when possible, the answer as a positive fraction rather than a negative fraction. Thus the sign of each term in the numerator was changed when the minus sign preceding the fraction was changed.

E X E R C I S E S : Reducing fractions to lowest terms

Reduce to lowest terms:

1. $\dfrac{105}{45}$

2. $\dfrac{18c^3d^5}{9c^7d^4}$

3. $\dfrac{7x^5y^8z^{10}}{21x^5y^7z^2}$

4. $\dfrac{ma^2 + 3m}{a^2 + 3}$

5. $\dfrac{4r - 8t}{2t - r}$

6. $\dfrac{4b^2 - 1}{4b + 2}$

7. $\dfrac{y - x}{-(x - y)}$

8. $\dfrac{75 - 27b^2}{3b^2 - 8b + 5}$

9. $\dfrac{ay^2 - 4a}{y^3 + 8}$

10. $\dfrac{14y^2 - 31y - 10}{7y^2 - 33y - 10}$

11. $\dfrac{x^4y - y^5}{y^2 - x^2}$

12. $\dfrac{ac + ad + bc + bd}{c^2 + cd}$

13. $\dfrac{(y - 1)^3}{(1 - y)^2}$

14. $\dfrac{9y^2 - x^2}{x^2 - 6xy + 9y^2}$

15. $-\dfrac{9c^2 - 71cd - 8d^2}{72c^2 - cd - d^2}$

16. $\dfrac{3 + 9a + 27a^2}{27a^3 - 1}$

17. $\dfrac{-2(a^3b^3y - a^2b^3y^2)}{3ab^4y^2 - 3a^2b^4y}$

18. $\dfrac{(4 - 9b^2)x - (4 - 9b^2)y}{(2 + 3b)(y - x)}$

19. $\dfrac{a^{2t} + a^t b^r}{a^{2t} - b^{2r}}$

20. $-\dfrac{x^2 + 2xy + y^2 - z^2}{z - x - y}$

21. $\dfrac{x^2 - y^2}{x^5 + y^5}$

22. $\dfrac{4 - (c - 3d)^2}{(2 - c)^2 - 9d^2}$

23. $\dfrac{c^3 - c^2d - cd^2 + d^3}{d^4 - c^4}$

24. $\dfrac{8(a + 2b)^2 - 2a - 4b - 1}{1 - 4(a + 2b)^2}$

Multiplying fractions. In multiplying and dividing algebraic fractions, we follow the same procedures that we used in arithmetic.

> To multiply fractions: Multiply their numerators to obtain the numerator of the product; multiply their denominators to obtain the denominator of the product.

For example,

$$\frac{a^2}{x^2} \cdot \frac{x}{a^3} = \frac{a^2x}{a^3x^2} \quad \text{or} \quad \frac{1}{ax}$$

The product should always be expressed in lowest terms. This can be more easily accomplished by dividing by like factors before doing the multiplication. Thus,

$$\frac{\overset{1}{\cancel{a^2}}}{\underset{x}{\cancel{x^2}}} \cdot \frac{\overset{1}{\cancel{x}}}{\underset{a}{\cancel{a^3}}} = \frac{1}{ax}$$

The reciprocal of a number. The reciprocal of a number is unity divided by the number. Thus, the reciprocal of 2 is $\frac{1}{2}$; the reciprocal of n is $\dfrac{1}{n}$.

The reciprocal of $\dfrac{2}{x}$ is $\dfrac{1}{\dfrac{2}{x}}$ or $\dfrac{x}{2}$. We observe that to obtain the reciprocal of

a fraction, we merely "invert" the fraction. For example, the reciprocal of

$\dfrac{x-y}{x+y}$ is $\dfrac{x+y}{x-y}$.

Dividing fractions. To divide a fraction by a second fraction, we multiply the first fraction by the reciprocal of the second fraction. Thus,

$$\frac{x}{y} \div \frac{z}{w} = \frac{x}{y} \cdot \frac{w}{z} = \frac{xw}{yz}.$$

The rule for dividing one fraction by another fraction can be stated in this manner:

To divide one fraction by another: Invert the fraction by which you are dividing and proceed as in multiplication.

I L L U S T R A T I V E   E X A M P L E S : Multiplying and dividing fractions

1. Multiply : $\dfrac{m^2 - mn}{2\,n^2} \cdot \dfrac{mn + n^2}{m^2 - n^2}$

$\quad$ *Solution.* Given example $\qquad \dfrac{m^2 - mn}{2\,n^2} \cdot \dfrac{mn + n^2}{m^2 - n^2}$

$\quad\quad$ Factoring and dividing $\qquad \dfrac{m(m-n)}{\underset{n}{2n^2}} \cdot \dfrac{n(m+n)}{(m+n)(m-n)}$

$\quad\quad$ Multiplying $\qquad\qquad\qquad\qquad\qquad \dfrac{m}{2\,n}$ Answer

2. Divide : $\dfrac{a^2 + 7\,ab + 12\,b^2}{3\,a^2 - 3\,ab} \div \dfrac{a^2 + ab - 6\,b^2}{4\,b^2 - 3\,ab - a^2}$

$\quad$ *Solution.* We write the denominator of the second fraction in descending powers of a. In order to factor with greater ease, we change the sign of each term in the denominator. We, therefore, also change the sign of the fraction.

Given example $\qquad\qquad\qquad \dfrac{a^2 + 7\,ab + 12\,b^2}{3\,a^2 - 3\,ab} \div \dfrac{a^2 + ab - 6\,b^2}{4\,b^2 - 3\,ab - a^2}$

Changing signs in the second $\qquad \dfrac{a^2 + 7\,ab + 12\,b^2}{3\,a^2 - 3\,ab} \div \left[-\dfrac{a^2 + ab - 6\,b^2}{a^2 + 3\,ab - 4\,b^2} \right]$
fraction

Inverting second fraction, factoring and dividing

$$\frac{(a+3b)(a+4b)}{3a(a-b)}\cdot\left[-\frac{(a+4b)(a-b)}{(a+3b)(a-2b)}\right]$$

Multiplying

$$-\frac{(a+4b)^2}{3a(a-2b)}\quad\text{or}\quad\frac{(a+4b)^2}{3a(2b-a)}\quad\text{Answer}$$

3. Perform the indicated operations:

$$\frac{3+x-2x^2}{x^3+x^2+x}\cdot\frac{1-x^3}{3x-2x^2}\div\frac{x^4-1}{x^4+x^2}$$

Solution. Changing signs in the first and second fractions,

we have $\quad-\dfrac{2x^2-x-3}{x^3+x^2+x}\cdot\dfrac{x^3-1}{2x^2-3x}\div\dfrac{x^4-1}{x^4+x^2}$

Inverting the fraction after ÷ sign; factoring; dividing

$$-\frac{\cancel{(2x-3)}\cancel{(x+1)}\cdot\cancel{(x-1)}\cancel{(x^2+x+1)}}{\cancel{x}\cancel{(x^2+x+1)}}\cdot\frac{1}{\cancel{x}\cancel{(2x-3)}}\cdot\frac{\cancel{x^2}\cancel{(x^2+1)}}{\cancel{(x^2+1)}\cancel{(x+1)}\cancel{(x-1)}}$$

Rewriting each fraction $\qquad -\tfrac{1}{1}\cdot\tfrac{1}{1}\cdot\tfrac{1}{1}$

Multiplying $\qquad\qquad -1\quad$ Answer

EXERCISES: Multiplying and dividing fractions

Perform the indicated operations:

1. $\dfrac{18b^3}{25c^6}\cdot\dfrac{5c^4}{3b^2}$

2. $\dfrac{r^2t^3w^5}{x^4y}\cdot\dfrac{xy}{r^3t^2w}$

3. $\dfrac{10\,ab}{c^3d}\div\dfrac{15\,ab^3}{7\,c^3d^4}$

4. $\dfrac{9\,x^2y}{4}\div 18\,x^3$

5. $\dfrac{m^3+m^2n}{5\,m}\cdot\dfrac{25}{3n+3m}$

6. $\dfrac{7x-2y}{x+2y}\cdot\dfrac{x^2-4y^2}{49\,x^2-4y^2}$

7. $\dfrac{ab^2}{a-3b}\div\dfrac{a^3b+a^2b^2}{(a-3b)^2}$

8. $\dfrac{4\,a^2b^2-a^2}{6b-4}\div\dfrac{10\,ab-5\,a}{3b-2}$

9. $\dfrac{4x+8}{9x+9}\div\dfrac{2(x+2)^2}{1-x^2}$

10. $\dfrac{(a-b)^3}{2a+b}\cdot\dfrac{ab}{(b-a)^2}$

11. $\dfrac{x^2+xy}{x-5y}\div\dfrac{y^2-x^2}{5y-x}$

12. $\dfrac{3x^2-13x+4}{9x^2-6x+1}\cdot\dfrac{28+7x}{x^2-16}$

13. $\dfrac{r}{r^2-rt-12t^2}\cdot\dfrac{r^2+3rt}{r-4t}$

14. $\dfrac{4\,m^2-n^2}{8\,m^2+10\,mn+3n^2}\cdot\dfrac{4\,m^2-9\,mn-9n^2}{2\,m^2-5\,mn-3n^2}$

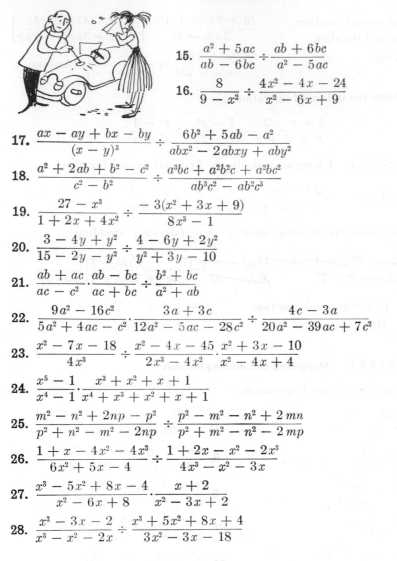

15. $\dfrac{a^2 + 5ac}{ab - 6bc} \div \dfrac{ab + 6bc}{a^2 - 5ac}$

16. $\dfrac{8}{9 - x^2} \div \dfrac{4x^2 - 4x - 24}{x^2 - 6x + 9}$

17. $\dfrac{ax - ay + bx - by}{(x - y)^3} \div \dfrac{6b^2 + 5ab - a^2}{abx^2 - 2abxy + aby^2}$

18. $\dfrac{a^2 + 2ab + b^2 - c^2}{c^2 - b^2} \div \dfrac{a^3bc + a^2b^2c + a^2bc^2}{ab^3c^2 - ab^2c^3}$

19. $\dfrac{27 - x^3}{1 + 2x + 4x^2} \div \dfrac{-3(x^2 + 3x + 9)}{8x^3 - 1}$

20. $\dfrac{3 - 4y + y^2}{15 - 2y - y^2} \div \dfrac{4 - 6y + 2y^2}{y^2 + 3y - 10}$

21. $\dfrac{ab + ac}{ac - c^2} \cdot \dfrac{ab - bc}{ac + bc} \div \dfrac{b^2 + bc}{a^2 + ab}$

22. $\dfrac{9a^2 - 16c^2}{5a^2 + 4ac - c^2} \cdot \dfrac{3a + 3c}{12a^2 - 5ac - 28c^2} \div \dfrac{4c - 3a}{20a^2 - 39ac + 7c^2}$

23. $\dfrac{x^2 - 7x - 18}{4x^3} \div \dfrac{x^2 - 4x - 45}{2x^3 - 4x^2} \cdot \dfrac{x^2 + 3x - 10}{x^2 - 4x + 4}$

24. $\dfrac{x^5 - 1}{x^4 - 1} \cdot \dfrac{x^3 + x^2 + x + 1}{x^4 + x^3 + x^2 + x + 1}$

25. $\dfrac{m^2 - n^2 + 2np - p^2}{p^2 + n^2 - m^2 - 2np} \div \dfrac{p^2 - m^2 - n^2 + 2mn}{p^2 + m^2 - n^2 - 2mp}$

26. $\dfrac{1 + x - 4x^2 - 4x^3}{6x^2 + 5x - 4} \div \dfrac{1 + 2x - x^2 - 2x^3}{4x^3 - x^2 - 3x}$

27. $\dfrac{x^3 - 5x^2 + 8x - 4}{x^2 - 6x + 8} \cdot \dfrac{x + 2}{x^2 - 3x + 2}$

28. $\dfrac{x^3 - 3x - 2}{x^3 - x^2 - 2x} \div \dfrac{x^3 + 5x^2 + 8x + 4}{3x^2 - 3x - 18}$

Adding and subtracting fractions. To add or subtract fractions with the same denominators, we combine their numerators to form the numerator of a fraction whose denominator is the denominator common to the fractions. For example,

$$\frac{3}{x} + \frac{2}{x} - \frac{1}{x} \text{ is equal to } \frac{4}{x}$$

To add or subtract fractions with different denominators, we first change the fractions to equivalent fractions whose denominators are the same. We then combine the fractions as above. Thus, to add

$$\frac{3}{2x} + \frac{5}{3x}$$

We change to

$$\frac{9}{6x} + \frac{10}{6x}$$

We add to get

$$\frac{19}{6x}$$

A multiple of a number.   A multiple of a number is a second number into which the given number is exactly divisible. For example, 12 is a multiple of the number 3. Since 12 is also a multiple of the number 4, we say that 12 is a common multiple of the numbers 3 and 4. There are other common multiples of the numbers 3 and 4. Can you name two of them?

In the addition example, $\frac{3}{2x} + \frac{5}{3x}$, the smallest number into which the

denominators, $2x$ and $3x$, are divisible is $6x$, and this is called the lowest common multiple of the denominators or the **Lowest Common Denominator (L.C.D.).** We use the lowest common denominator in the addition and subtraction of fractions to keep our computations as simple as possible.

ILLUSTRATIVE EXAMPLE: Finding the lowest common denominator

Find the L.C.D. of the fractions:

$$\frac{x}{14\,a^3b}, \ \frac{y}{4\,ab^2c^2}, \ \frac{z}{3\,c^4}$$

Solution.   Finding the prime factors of the denominators, we have

$$\frac{x}{2\cdot7\cdot a\cdot a\cdot a\cdot b}, \ \frac{y}{2\cdot2\cdot a\cdot b\cdot b\cdot c\cdot c}, \ \frac{z}{3\cdot c\cdot c\cdot c\cdot c}$$

The different factors are: 2, 7, 3, a, b, c.

2 will occur in the L.C.D. **twice** as a factor. (Notice that the greatest number of times that 2 appears as a factor in any one denominator is twice.)

7 will occur in the L.C.D. **once** as a factor. (Why?)

3 will occur in the L.C.D. **once** as a factor.

a will occur in the L.C.D. **three times** as a factor. (Why?)

b will occur in the L.C.D. **twice** as a factor.

c will occur in the L.C.D. **four times** as a factor.

Therefore, the L.C.D. is $2\cdot2\cdot7\cdot3\cdot a^3\cdot b^2\cdot c^4$ or $84\,a^3b^2c^4$ Answer

E X E R C I S E S : Finding the lowest common denominator

In each of the following examples, find the L.C.D. of the fractions.

1. $\dfrac{a}{9}, \dfrac{b}{6}, \dfrac{c}{2}$

2. $\dfrac{a}{12}, \dfrac{b}{54}$

3. $\dfrac{a}{26}, \dfrac{b}{169}, \dfrac{c}{4}$

4. $\dfrac{a}{rs}, \dfrac{b}{st}, \dfrac{c}{rt}$

5. $\dfrac{a}{4\,x^3yz^2}, \dfrac{b}{6\,xy^5z^3}, \dfrac{c}{3\,x^2y^4z^3}$

6. $\dfrac{a}{3\,y - 9}, \dfrac{b}{y^2 - 9}$

7. $\dfrac{a}{x^2 + xy}, \dfrac{b}{xy^2 + y^3}$

8. $\dfrac{a}{x^2 - y^2}, \dfrac{b}{x^2 - 2\,xy + y^2}$

9. $\dfrac{a}{3\,m + 3n}, \dfrac{b}{m - n}, \dfrac{c}{m^2 - n^2}$

10. $\dfrac{a}{x - 6}, \dfrac{b}{x + 4}, \dfrac{c}{x^2 - 2\,x - 24}$

11. $\dfrac{a}{x^2 - x - 12}, \dfrac{b}{x^2 + x - 20}$

12. $\dfrac{a}{x^2 - 2\,x + 1}, \dfrac{b}{x^2 + 2\,x + 1}, \dfrac{c}{x^2 - 1}$

13. $\dfrac{a}{(c - d)^4}, \dfrac{b}{(c - d)^3}, \dfrac{c}{c - d}$

14. $\dfrac{a}{m^2 + 5\,m + 6}, \dfrac{b}{m^2 - 5\,m - 6}$

15. $\dfrac{a}{x^2 - 4}, \dfrac{b}{x^2 - x - 6}, \dfrac{c}{x^2 - 5x + 6}$

I L L U S T R A T I V E   E X A M P L E : Changing fractions to equivalent fractions each having the same denominator

Change to equivalent fractions having the L.C.D. as denominators:

$$\frac{a^2 + 4\,b^2}{2(a^2 - b^2)}, \quad \frac{a - 2b}{3(a + b)}, \quad \frac{ab}{6(a - b)}$$

Solution. Writing the fractions with their denominators in factored form, we have

$$\frac{a^2 + 4\,b^2}{2(a + b)(a - b)}, \quad \frac{a - 2b}{3(a + b)}, \quad \frac{ab}{6(a - b)}$$

The L.C.D. is $6(a + b)(a - b)$. Each of the new fractions must have as its denominator this L.C.D. If we divide the L.C.D., $6(a + b)(a - b)$, by the denominator of the first fraction, $2(a + b)(a - b)$, we obtain a quotient of **3**. By multiplying both the numerator and the denominator of the first fraction by 3, in accordance with the Fundamental Principle of Fractions, we find that

$$\frac{3}{3} \cdot \frac{a^2 + 4b^2}{2(a + b)(a - b)} = \frac{3(a^2 + 4b^2)}{6(a + b)(a - b)}$$

Similarly, in the second fraction, dividing the L.C.D. by the denominator, $3(a + b)$, gives a quotient of **2(a − b)**. Multiplying both numerator and denominator of the second fraction by $2(a - b)$, we find that

$$\frac{2(a - b)}{2(a - b)} \cdot \frac{a - 2b}{3(a + b)} = \frac{2(a - b)(a - 2b)}{6(a - b)(a + b)}$$

Similarly, in the third fraction, dividing the L.C.D. by the denominator, $6(a - b)$, gives a quotient of **(a + b)**. Multiplying both numerator and denominator of the third fraction by $(a + b)$, we find that

$$\frac{(a + b)}{(a + b)} \cdot \frac{ab}{6(a - b)} = \frac{ab(a + b)}{6(a - b)(a + b)}$$

E X E R C I S E S : Changing fractions to equivalent fractions each having the L.C.D. as the denominator

In each of the following change to equivalent fractions with the L.C.D. as the denominator:

1. $\dfrac{x}{4}, \dfrac{y}{18}, \dfrac{z}{9}$

2. $\dfrac{2}{7a}, \dfrac{5}{3b}, \dfrac{11}{21ab}$

3. $\dfrac{4}{x^2y}, \dfrac{5}{xyz}, \dfrac{2}{y^2z^2}$

4. $\dfrac{a}{a - 2b}, \dfrac{b}{a + 4b}$

5. $\dfrac{5cd}{6c - 2d}, \dfrac{2cd}{3c - d}$

6. $\dfrac{5}{6x - 18}, \dfrac{4}{3x + 9}$

7. $\dfrac{3x}{(x - 1)^2}, \dfrac{2x^2}{x - 1}, \dfrac{5x^3}{(x - 1)^3}$

8. $\dfrac{a - 1}{4a^2 - 1}, \dfrac{6}{2a + 1}$

9. $\dfrac{7}{a^2 + 4a + 4}, \dfrac{5}{4 - a^2}$

10. $\dfrac{x - 1}{x^2 + 7x + 12}, \dfrac{x + 1}{x^2 - 2x - 15}, \dfrac{x + 2}{x^2 - x - 20}$

11. $\dfrac{5cd}{16d^2 - 12cd - 4c^2}, \dfrac{cd}{2c^2 - 2d^2}$

12. $\dfrac{2x^2 - 1}{x^3 - 8}, \dfrac{1}{x - 2}, \dfrac{2x}{5x^2 + 10x + 20}$

Adding and subtracting fractions with different denominators.   After finding the L.C.D. for two or more fractions, and after changing these fractions to equivalent fractions with the L.C.D. as denominator, we are ready to perform the indicated addition or subtraction. We combine the numerators and express the result as a numerator of a fraction whose denominator is the L.C.D.

ILLUSTRATIVE EXAMPLE: Adding and subtracting fractions

Add or subtract as indicated: $\dfrac{2b-1}{2b-6} + \dfrac{5b-4}{9-b^2} - \dfrac{b-1}{b+3}$

Solution. To put the denominators in similar form, we change the sign of the denominator in the second fraction; therefore, we must change the sign preceding that fraction.

$$\frac{2b-1}{2b-6} - \frac{5b-4}{b^2-9} - \frac{b-1}{b+3}$$

Writing the denominators in factored form

$$\frac{2b-1}{2(b-3)} - \frac{5b-4}{(b+3)(b-3)} - \frac{b-1}{b+3}$$

The L.C.D. is $2(b-3)(b+3)$.
Changing to equivalent fractions with L.C.D. as denominator

$$\frac{(b+3)(2b-1)}{2(b-3)(b+3)} - \frac{2(5b-4)}{2(b-3)(b+3)} - \frac{2(b-3)(b-1)}{2(b-3)(b+3)}$$

Instead of writing three fractions as shown above, we can proceed directly to the step below. We should clearly understand that the single denominator (the L.C.D.) represents the denominator of three distinct fractions.

Writing the three fractions as a single fraction with L.C.D. as denominator

$$\frac{(b+3)(2b-1) - 2(5b-4) - 2(b-3)(b-1)}{2(b-3)(b+3)}$$

Removing parentheses

$$\frac{2b^2 + 5b - 3 - 10b + 8 - 2b^2 + 8b - 6}{2(b-3)(b+3)}$$

Collecting terms in the numerator $\dfrac{3b-1}{2(b^2-9)}$ Answer

EXERCISES: Adding and subtracting fractions

Combine each of the following into a single fraction. **Express the result in lowest terms.**

1. $\dfrac{7}{12} + \dfrac{5}{6} - \dfrac{8}{9}$

2. $\dfrac{9c}{8} - \dfrac{11c}{28} - \dfrac{c}{4}$

3. $\dfrac{5a}{12} - \dfrac{3b}{8} + \dfrac{c}{48}$

4. $2 + \dfrac{x}{5} + \dfrac{3y}{2}$

5. $\dfrac{3}{a} + \dfrac{2}{ab} + \dfrac{1}{abc}$

6. $\dfrac{2b}{a^2} - \dfrac{4}{ab} + \dfrac{a}{b^2}$

7. $\dfrac{2x - 1}{6} + \dfrac{x + 3}{12}$

8. $\dfrac{3x - 4}{20} - \dfrac{x - 1}{8}$

9. $\dfrac{x + y}{xy} - \dfrac{x + z}{xz} - \dfrac{y + z}{yz}$

10. $\dfrac{x - 4}{5x} - \dfrac{2x - 3}{4x}$

11. $\dfrac{8 - y}{9y} + \dfrac{y + 2}{3y} - 2$

12. $\dfrac{2}{a - b} + \dfrac{3}{a + b}$

13. $\dfrac{d}{c^2 + cd} - \dfrac{2c}{cd + d^2}$

14. $\dfrac{3x}{x - y} + \dfrac{3y}{y - x}$

15. $\dfrac{m}{1 - m} + \dfrac{1}{m - 1} - 1$

16. $\dfrac{6}{x + y} - \dfrac{2y - 3x}{y^2 - x^2}$

17. $\dfrac{3}{4x - 4y} - \dfrac{4}{3y - 3x}$

18. $\dfrac{1}{a^2 - 4b^2} + \dfrac{1}{(a - 2b)^2}$

19. $3 + \dfrac{2b}{a - b}$

20. $\dfrac{c - d}{c + d} - \dfrac{c + d}{c - d}$

21. $\dfrac{1}{a + 1} - \dfrac{a}{a - 2} + \dfrac{a^2 + 2}{a^2 - a - 2}$

22. $\dfrac{3}{a + b} + \dfrac{2}{b - a} - \dfrac{7a + b}{a^2 - b^2}$

23. $\dfrac{3x - y}{x + 3y} - \dfrac{x + 2y}{y - 2x}$

24. $x - 2 - \dfrac{x^2 - x + 1}{2x + 3}$

25. $\dfrac{3xy(x + y)}{x^3 + y^3} + 1$

26. $\dfrac{2a + b}{a + b} - \dfrac{2a - b}{a - b} - \dfrac{3a^2 - b^2}{a^2 - b^2}$

27. $\dfrac{2n - m}{n^2 - m^2} - \dfrac{3}{m - n} + \dfrac{2}{m}$

28. $\dfrac{x}{x^2 - x - 20} + \dfrac{2}{x + 4}$

29. $\dfrac{2y - 1}{y^2 - 5y + 6} + \dfrac{2y + 3}{4 - y^2}$

30. $\dfrac{a - 4}{a^2 + 5a + 6} - \dfrac{a - 1}{a^2 + 4a + 3}$

31. $\dfrac{2b + 3c}{6b^2 + 7bc - 3c^2} + \dfrac{b - c}{3b^2 + 2bc - c^2}$

Suggestion: Reduce the first fraction to lowest terms before finding the L.C.D.

32. $\dfrac{x^2 - 1}{x^3 - 1} - \dfrac{x}{2x^2 + 2x + 2}$

33. $\dfrac{1}{b^2 + a^2} + \dfrac{2b^2}{a^4 - b^4} + \dfrac{1}{b^2 - a^2}$

34. $\dfrac{4x - 10y}{6x^2 + 3xy - 45y^2} - \dfrac{2x + y}{3y^2 + 4xy - 4x^2}$

35. $\dfrac{1}{(x - y)(y - z)} + \dfrac{2}{(z - x)(z - y)} + \dfrac{3}{(x - y)(z - x)}$

The lowest common denominator.   Although occasionally in the fifteenth and sixteenth centuries the arithmeticians used the lowest common denominator in adding and subtracting fractions, it was not until the seventeenth century that it became more generally used.   The early mathematicians usually used for the new denominator the product of the given denominators, reducing the final result to lowest terms.   Because the denominators were often very large, as a result of this method, the early *Rechenmeister* (teachers of arithmetic) in Germany ordinarily added only two fractions at a time.

Mixed expressions.   An algebraic mixed expression is a polynomial in which both fractional and integral terms appear.   For example, $a + \dfrac{x}{y}$ and $3 - \dfrac{5}{a+b} + c$ are mixed expressions.   When mixed expressions appear in an indicated multiplication or division, we change them to the fractional form before performing the multiplication or division.

$$a + \frac{x}{y} \qquad \textbf{mixed expression}$$

$$\frac{a}{1} + \frac{x}{y}$$

$$\downarrow$$

$$\frac{ay + x}{y} \qquad \textbf{equivalent fraction}$$

ILLUSTRATIVE EXAMPLE: Multiplying mixed expressions

Perform the indicated operation:

$$\left(x - \frac{10}{x-3}\right)\left(1 - \frac{x^2 - 5x - 2}{x^2 - 4x - 5}\right)$$

Solution.   Given example

$$\left(x - \frac{10}{x-3}\right)\left(1 - \frac{x^2 - 5x - 2}{x^2 - 4x - 5}\right)$$

Changing each mixed expression to a fraction

$$\frac{x^2 - 3x - 10}{x - 3} \cdot \frac{x^2 - 4x - 5 - x^2 + 5x + 2}{x^2 - 4x - 5}$$

Completing the operation

$$\frac{(x-5)(x+2)}{x-3} \cdot \frac{x-3}{(x-5)(x+1)}$$

$$\frac{x+2}{x+1} \qquad \textbf{Answer}$$

E X E R C I S E S : Multiplying and dividing mixed expressions

Perform the indicated operations:

1. $\left(\dfrac{x}{y} - 1\right) \div \left(\dfrac{x}{y} + 1\right)$

2. $\left(1 + \dfrac{b}{a}\right)\left(1 + \dfrac{b^2}{a^2 - b^2}\right)$

3. $\left(\dfrac{1}{m^2} - 2\right) \div \left(2m - \dfrac{1}{m}\right)$

4. $\left(\dfrac{b}{c} - 3\right) \div \left(2b + 3c - \dfrac{b^2}{c}\right)$

5. $\left(a - \dfrac{4}{a}\right) \div \left(\dfrac{6}{a} + a + 5\right)$

6. $\left(2x + 5y - \dfrac{15y^2}{x - y}\right) \div \left(2x - \dfrac{9xy - 15y^2}{x - y}\right)$

7. $\left(\dfrac{1}{a} - 1 + a\right) \div \left(a + \dfrac{1}{a^2}\right)$

8. $\left(2x + \dfrac{1}{4x^2}\right) \div \left(2x + \dfrac{1}{2x} - 1\right)$

9. $\left(a + 1 - \dfrac{a^2}{a - 1}\right)\left(a - \dfrac{3a - 1}{a + 1}\right)$

10. $\left(1 + \dfrac{xy}{x^2 - xy + y^2}\right) \div \left(\dfrac{x^3 - x^2 y}{x^3 + y^3} - 1\right)$

11. $\left(1 - \dfrac{3y^2}{x^2 - y^2}\right)\left(2 - \dfrac{x^2 + 10xy + 7y^2}{x^2 + 4xy + 4y^2}\right)$

12. $\left(\dfrac{2b + 8}{b^2 + b - 6} + 1\right)\left(b + 1 - \dfrac{4}{b + 1}\right) \div \left(b - \dfrac{3b - 2}{2 - b}\right)$

Complex fractions. A complex fraction is a fraction whose numerator or denominator or both contain fractions or mixed expressions. Examples of complex fractions are:

$$\frac{a - \dfrac{c}{b}}{a + \dfrac{c}{b}} \quad \text{and} \quad \frac{ab}{\dfrac{c}{d}}$$

Since a complex fraction is an indicated division, it can be simplified by dividing its numerator by its denominator. First the entire numerator must be changed to a single fraction. Then the entire denominator must be changed to a single fraction. The final simplification follows after the fraction in the numerator is divided by the fraction in the denominator and the result is reduced to lowest terms.

ILLUSTRATIVE EXAMPLE: Simplifying a complex fraction

Simplify: $\dfrac{2 - \dfrac{b}{a}}{\dfrac{b}{a} + 2}$

Solution. Writing the given example as a division problem $\left(2 - \dfrac{b}{a}\right) \div \left(\dfrac{b}{a} + 2\right)$

Changing each mixed expression to a fraction $\dfrac{2a - b}{a} \div \dfrac{b + 2a}{a}$

Completing the solution $\dfrac{2a - b}{\not{a}} \cdot \dfrac{\not{a}}{b + 2a}$

$\dfrac{2a - b}{2a + b}$ Answer

EXERCISES: Simplifying complex fractions

Simplify each of the following:

1. $\dfrac{\dfrac{x^2y}{w}}{\dfrac{xy^2}{w^2}}$

2. $\dfrac{\dfrac{2}{x+y}}{\dfrac{2}{x-y}}$

3. $\dfrac{\dfrac{x}{y} - w}{m + \dfrac{n}{y}}$

4. $\dfrac{\dfrac{2}{5c} + \dfrac{4}{3c}}{\dfrac{3}{2c} - \dfrac{1}{5c}}$

5. $\dfrac{\dfrac{2}{x} - \dfrac{3}{y}}{\dfrac{4}{x^2} - \dfrac{9}{y^2}}$

6. $\dfrac{\dfrac{5a}{2b} + 1}{5 + \dfrac{2b}{a}}$

7. $\dfrac{\dfrac{a-b}{1}}{\dfrac{b}{a} - 1}$

8. $\dfrac{\dfrac{6y^2 - 11y - 35}{9y^2 - 25}}{\dfrac{2y^2 + 3y - 35}{3y^2 - 5y}}$

9. $\dfrac{x - \dfrac{5x - 6}{x}}{\dfrac{1}{x} - \dfrac{3}{x^2}}$

10. $\dfrac{2 - ax + \dfrac{ax}{3}}{\dfrac{ax}{3} - 1}$

11. $\dfrac{\dfrac{b}{4} - \dfrac{2}{b^2}}{\dfrac{b}{2} + 1 + \dfrac{2}{b}}$

12. $\dfrac{2 + \dfrac{8}{x} - x}{x + 6 + \dfrac{8}{x}}$

13. $\dfrac{2 - \dfrac{2 - 3x}{x^2}}{x - \dfrac{5}{2} + \dfrac{1}{x}}$

14. $\dfrac{x - \dfrac{4}{x}}{\dfrac{16}{x^3} - x}$

15. $\dfrac{a - \dfrac{b^2}{a}}{\dfrac{1}{2} + \dfrac{a}{2a - 4b}}$

16. $\dfrac{3 - \dfrac{16\,y^2}{3\,x^2}}{\dfrac{4\,y^2}{x} - 6y + \dfrac{9\,x}{4}}$

17. $\dfrac{\dfrac{1}{3x} - 1}{1 - 2x^2 - \dfrac{7\,x}{3}}$

18. $\dfrac{2a + 9b - \dfrac{2ab - 25b^2}{3\,a}}{\dfrac{a - 5b}{3} - a}$

19. $\dfrac{\left(5 - \dfrac{5}{c + 2}\right)\left(1 + \dfrac{2}{c + 1}\right)}{4 + \dfrac{4}{c + 2}}$

20. $\dfrac{\dfrac{2}{a + b} - \dfrac{1}{a - b}}{\dfrac{1}{a} + \dfrac{b^2}{a^3} + \dfrac{b^4 - 3\,a^3 b}{a^3(a^2 - b^2)}}$

21. Find the value of $\dfrac{x + 3}{x - 2}$ in terms of a and b, if $x = \dfrac{a - b}{b}$.

22. Find the value of $\dfrac{1 + x}{2x - 1}$ in terms of b, if $x = \dfrac{b}{2b - 3}$.

23. Using the formula $S = \dfrac{a}{1 - r}$, find S when $a = \frac{3}{4}$ and $r = \frac{1}{3}$.

24. Using the formula $h = \dfrac{2A}{b - c}$, find h when $A = \frac{43}{9}$, $b = \frac{7}{3}$, and $c = \frac{5}{4}$.

25. Using the formula $I = \dfrac{E}{r + \dfrac{r'}{n}}$, find I when $n = 4$, $r = \frac{1}{2}$, $r' = \frac{1}{3}$, and $E = \frac{9}{4}$.

EXERCISES : True-false test

On a sheet of paper, write in a column the numbers 1 through 22 and study each of the following fractions. If the equation is true for all values of the letters included in the equation, write "true" next to the corresponding number. If the equation is not always true, write "false" next to the corresponding number.

1. $\dfrac{ab}{a} = b$

2. $\dfrac{x - 2y}{x} = 1 - 2y$

3. $\dfrac{x - 2b}{x - b} = 2$

4. $\dfrac{x + z}{y + z} = \dfrac{x}{y}$

5. $\dfrac{3x}{c} - \dfrac{2y}{c} = \dfrac{3x - 2y}{c}$

6. $\dfrac{cd + d}{c} = 2d$

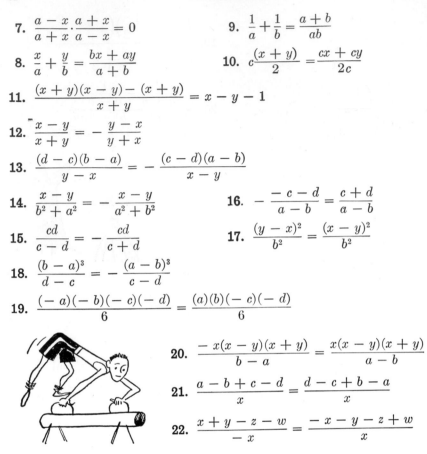

7. $\dfrac{a-x}{a+x}\cdot\dfrac{a+x}{a-x}=0$

9. $\dfrac{1}{a}+\dfrac{1}{b}=\dfrac{a+b}{ab}$

8. $\dfrac{x}{a}+\dfrac{y}{b}=\dfrac{bx+ay}{a+b}$

10. $c\dfrac{(x+y)}{2}=\dfrac{cx+cy}{2c}$

11. $\dfrac{(x+y)(x-y)-(x+y)}{x+y}=x-y-1$

12. $\dfrac{x-y}{x+y}=-\dfrac{y-x}{y+x}$

13. $\dfrac{(d-c)(b-a)}{y-x}=-\dfrac{(c-d)(a-b)}{x-y}$

14. $\dfrac{x-y}{b^2+a^2}=-\dfrac{x-y}{a^2+b^2}$

16. $-\dfrac{-c-d}{a-b}=\dfrac{c+d}{a-b}$

15. $\dfrac{cd}{c-d}=-\dfrac{cd}{c+d}$

17. $\dfrac{(y-x)^2}{b^2}=\dfrac{(x-y)^2}{b^2}$

18. $\dfrac{(b-a)^3}{d-c}=-\dfrac{(a-b)^3}{c-d}$

19. $\dfrac{(-a)(-b)(-c)(-d)}{6}=\dfrac{(a)(b)(-c)(-d)}{6}$

20. $\dfrac{-x(x-y)(x+y)}{b-a}=\dfrac{x(x-y)(x+y)}{a-b}$

21. $\dfrac{a-b+c-d}{x}=\dfrac{d-c+b-a}{x}$

22. $\dfrac{x+y-z-w}{-x}=\dfrac{-x-y-z+w}{x}$

CHAPTER REVIEW EXERCISES

1. Rewrite each of the following as an equivalent fraction with all signs in the denominator positive:

a) $-\dfrac{-a}{-b}$

c) $\dfrac{a}{(-x)(-y)(-z)}$

e) $\dfrac{4}{-a-b}$

b) $\dfrac{2}{-3}$

d) $\dfrac{-x}{(-a)(-b)(c)(d)(-e)}$

f) $\dfrac{-4}{-a-b-c}$

2. Reduce to lowest terms:

a) $\dfrac{16x^2y^5z^3w^4}{28x^2y^4z^3w^5}$

c) $\dfrac{(c-d)^3}{c^3-d^3}$

e) $\dfrac{x^3-2+x-2x^2}{x^4-1}$

b) $\dfrac{78a(a-b)^2}{13a^2b^2-13a^4}$

d) $\dfrac{35a^2+6a-9}{14a^2+22a-12}$

3. Multiply as indicated:

a) $\dfrac{ac - ad}{d} \cdot \dfrac{ad - bd}{bd - bc}$

c) $\dfrac{a^3 - a^2}{a^2 - 1} \cdot \dfrac{a^2 - 2a + 1}{3 - 3a}$

b) $\dfrac{20x^2 - 13x + 2}{2 + 5x - 3x^2} \cdot \dfrac{15x^2 + 2x - 1}{1 - 9x + 20x^2}$

d) $\dfrac{1 - 8x^3}{2x - 4x^2} \cdot \dfrac{x^4}{x^2 + 2x^4}$

4. Divide as indicated:

a) $\dfrac{b^3}{b - 1} \div \dfrac{b^2}{a - ab}$

c) $\dfrac{2m^2 - 5m - 7}{3m^2 - 4m + 1} \div \dfrac{7 - 9m + 2m^2}{3m^2 + 2m - 1}$

b) $\dfrac{m^2n - m^3}{n} \div \dfrac{m^4 - m^2n^2}{n^2 + mn}$

d) $\dfrac{a^4 - 4}{14a^3} \div \dfrac{a^3 - 2a + 4}{7a^2}$

5. Combine each of the following into a single fraction:

a) $\dfrac{3x}{5} - \dfrac{5x}{12} - \dfrac{x}{3}$

e) $\dfrac{x^2 + y^2}{x^2 - y^2} - \dfrac{x + y}{x - y}$

b) $\dfrac{1}{ab} + \dfrac{2}{ac} + \dfrac{3}{bc}$

f) $\dfrac{3}{x^2 - 2x - 8} - \dfrac{2}{x^2 + 3x + 2}$

c) $\dfrac{2y - 3}{24} - \dfrac{3y - 4}{36}$

g) $\dfrac{2x - 1}{(x - 2)^2} - \dfrac{2x + 1}{4 - x^2}$

d) $\dfrac{r - 1}{r^2 - rs} + \dfrac{s - 1}{s^2 - rs}$

h) $\dfrac{2x - 1}{2x - 3} - \dfrac{3x - 2}{4x - 5} - \dfrac{2x^2 - 5x + 4}{8x^2 - 22x + 15}$

6. Perform the operation indicated:

a) $\left(7 + \dfrac{2}{a - 1}\right)\left(\dfrac{6a - 4}{7a - 5} - 1\right)$

b) $\left(5 - \dfrac{1}{b} - \dfrac{4}{b^2}\right) \div \left(2b - \dfrac{9b - 5}{2b}\right)$

7. Simplify:

a) $\dfrac{\dfrac{1}{c + d} - \dfrac{1}{c - d}}{\dfrac{d}{d - c}}$

c) $\dfrac{x + 1 - \dfrac{6}{x}}{x - 1 - \dfrac{2}{x}}$

b) $\dfrac{\dfrac{c^2}{4} - \dfrac{1}{d^2}}{\dfrac{1}{d} + \dfrac{c}{2}}$

d) $2 + \dfrac{1}{2 - \frac{1}{2}}$

CUMULATIVE REVIEW EXERCISES

1. If $a = 3$, $b = -2$, $c = 1$, what is the value of $3a - 2b + c$?

2. If $x = -2$, what is the value of $2x^2 + 4x - 5$?

3. Multiply $3x^2 - 2x - 1$ by $6x + 2$.

4. Divide $8a^3 + 38a^2 - 13a - 15$ by $2a + 1$.

5. Solve for x: $0.3x - 2.5 = 0.1x - 0.1$

6. Solve for x: $3(x + 5) - 5(2x + 8) + 4 = 0$

7. Find each product:

    a) $(2x + 3)(3x - 4)$

    b) $(ax - b)(ax + b)$

    c) $2m(m - n)^2$

    d) $-3xy(x - y)(2x - y)$

8. Factor completely:

    a) $4x^2 - 49y^2$

    b) $6a^2 - 17a + 12$

    c) $x^4 - 5x^2 + 4$

    d) $2ax^2 - 4a^2x + 2a^3$

    e) $mx + ny - nx - my$

    f) $4x^2 - 4y^2 + 4x + 1$

9. Solve for x: $mx - n = n(2m - x)$

10. Solve for x: $2x^2 - 5x + 2 = 0$

11. Mary's age 6 years from now will be one half her mother's age at that time. If her mother now is 10 years less than three times Mary's age, what is Mary's age now?

12. A man had invested \$8000, part at 5% annual interest and the remainder at $6\frac{1}{2}\%$. If his annual income was \$475, how much did he have invested at 5%?

13. Combine into a single fraction: $\dfrac{3y + 2x}{(x - y)^2} - \dfrac{2}{y - x}$

14. Perform the operation indicated:

$$(a + b)\left(\frac{1}{a - b} - \frac{1}{a + b}\right) + \frac{a^2b + ab^2}{a^2 - b^2}$$

15. Simplify: $\dfrac{\dfrac{m + 2}{m - 1} + 2}{1 + \dfrac{1 - 2m}{m - 1}}$

CHAPTER 5

Equations Containing Fractions

Fractional equations.   Equations that contain fractions are, in general, solved most easily by first eliminating the fractions from the equation. From your elementary algebra you remember that the root of an equation is not changed if both members of the equation are multiplied by the same number (zero excepted).   If we multiply both members of the equation by the lowest common denominator of all the fractions in the equation, the equation in its new form will have no fractions, but its roots will be the roots of the original equation.

I L L U S T R A T I V E   E X A M P L E S : Solving equations which contain fractions

1. Solve : $\dfrac{5}{2x} = \dfrac{3}{4x} + \dfrac{9}{8}$

Solution: Given example $\dfrac{5}{2x} = \dfrac{3}{4x} + \dfrac{9}{8}$

Indicating the multiplication of each term of both members by $8x$. the L.C.D.

$$\overset{4}{\cancel{8x}}\left(\frac{5}{\cancel{2x}}\right) = \overset{2}{\cancel{8x}}\left(\frac{3}{\cancel{4x}}\right) + \overset{x}{\cancel{8}}x\left(\frac{9}{\cancel{8}}\right)$$

Multiplying

$$8x\left(\frac{5}{2x}\right) = 8x\left(\frac{3}{4x}\right) + 8x\left(\frac{9}{8}\right)$$

$$20 = 6 + 9x$$

Completing the solution

$$14 = 9x$$

$$x = \frac{14}{9} \quad \text{Answer}$$

Check.   Substituting $\frac{14}{9}$ for x in the given example

$$\frac{5}{2(\frac{14}{9})} \overset{?}{=} \frac{3}{4(\frac{14}{9})} + \frac{9}{8}$$

$$\frac{5}{\frac{28}{9}} \overset{?}{=} \frac{3}{\frac{56}{9}} + \frac{9}{8}$$

$$\frac{90}{56} \overset{?}{=} \frac{27}{56} + \frac{63}{56}$$

$$\frac{90}{56} = \frac{90}{56} \quad \text{Check}$$

2. Solve : $\dfrac{x^2 + 9}{x^2 - 9} + \dfrac{x}{3 - x} = \dfrac{3}{x + 3}$

Solution.   We factor the denominator of the first fraction ; we change the signs in the denominator of the second fraction and, at the same time, change the sign preceding that fraction.

Thus

$$\frac{x^2 + 9}{(x + 3)(x - 3)} - \frac{x}{x - 3} = \frac{3}{x + 3}$$

Clearing the equation of fractions by multiplying each term of both members by $(x + 3)(x - 3)$, the L.C.D.

$$x^2 + 9 - x(x + 3) = 3(x - 3)$$

Removing parentheses

$$x^2 + 9 - x^2 - 3x = 3x - 9$$

Completing the solution

$$9 - 3x = 3x - 9$$

$$18 = 6x$$

$$x = 3 \quad \text{Answer}$$

Check.   Substituting 3 for x in the given example

$$\frac{9 + 9}{9 - 9} + \frac{3}{3 - 3} \overset{?}{=} \frac{3}{3 + 3}$$

$$\frac{18}{0} + \frac{3}{0} \overset{?}{=} \frac{3}{6}$$

Because division by zero is not possible, 3 does not check as a root of the equation. **The equation has no solution.**

Note. In checking this example a quick glance at the denominators of the fractions in the given equation would indicate immediately that 3 is extraneous. This example points out the need to:

> Check all the roots that are found if in the course of solution both members of the equation are multiplied by a factor that contains the unknown.

E X E R C I S E S : Solving equations which contain fractions

Solve each of the following:

1. $\dfrac{x}{3} + \dfrac{3x}{4} = \dfrac{13}{3}$

2. $\dfrac{4y}{3} + \dfrac{y}{6} + \dfrac{3}{4} = 0$

3. $\dfrac{x-1}{2} = \dfrac{x+2}{3}$

Note: When there are only two fractions in the equation, the equation may be cleared of fractions by "cross multiplication." Thus,

$$\frac{x-1}{2} \diagdown \frac{x+2}{3}$$

$$3(x-1) = 2(x+2)$$

Complete the solution.

4. $\dfrac{2x+5}{5} = \dfrac{3x+11}{4}$

5. $\dfrac{w-4}{4} + \dfrac{3w+5}{2} = 12$

6. $\dfrac{2y-1}{7} - \dfrac{3y+5}{3} = \dfrac{1}{3}$

7. $\dfrac{y+5}{2} - \dfrac{5}{3} = \dfrac{3y}{4} - \dfrac{2y-1}{6}$

8. $\dfrac{7}{2y} = \dfrac{3}{4}$

9. $\dfrac{5}{y} - \dfrac{3}{2y} = \dfrac{7}{6}$

10. $\dfrac{2x-3}{3x} = \dfrac{5}{6}$

11. $\dfrac{4w+1}{4w} - \dfrac{w-2}{6w} = 2$

12. $\dfrac{w-5}{3} = \dfrac{4-w}{4w} + \dfrac{4w+3}{12}$

13. $\dfrac{17+2y}{3y} = \dfrac{y+5}{y} - \dfrac{2y-5}{2y}$

14. $\dfrac{2x^2+7}{10x} - \dfrac{x-1}{2x} = \dfrac{x-2}{5}$

15. $\dfrac{3x^2+10}{6x} = \dfrac{x+4}{2x} + \dfrac{x-2}{3}$

Note: Clearing the equation of fractions gives a quadratic equation. Complete the solution by the "factor" method. See page 58.

16. $\dfrac{y+6}{5y} + \dfrac{y-2}{2y} = \dfrac{y+1}{3}$

17. $\dfrac{3}{w-3} = \dfrac{5}{2w-7}$

18. $\dfrac{6}{3w+11} - \dfrac{4}{6w+1} = 0$

19. $\dfrac{w+2}{w-1} + \dfrac{3}{w} = 1$

20. $\dfrac{3y}{2y+3} - \dfrac{y}{3-2y} = \dfrac{8y^2+12}{4y^2-9}$

21. $\dfrac{1}{x+2} - \dfrac{2}{x-2} = \dfrac{5}{3}$

24. $\dfrac{y-4}{y-2} + 2 = \dfrac{3y-1}{y+5}$

22. $\dfrac{4}{3+x} + \dfrac{3}{x-3} = \dfrac{18}{x^2-9}$

25. $\dfrac{10x-3}{4x^2-1} = \dfrac{2x}{2x-1}$

23. $\dfrac{3w-1}{9w-5} = \dfrac{w+1}{3w+1}$

26. $\dfrac{5x}{x-1} + \dfrac{4x^2+5}{x-x^2} = \dfrac{x+4}{x}$

27. $\dfrac{4}{3x-5} + \dfrac{2x^2+35x+36}{25x-9x^3} = \dfrac{3}{3x+5}$

28. $\dfrac{y^2+1}{y^3+1} - \dfrac{5}{y^2-y+1} = \dfrac{1}{y+1}$

29. $\dfrac{w-1}{w+4} + \dfrac{5-6w+2w^2}{20+w-w^2} + \dfrac{w-2}{w-5} = 0$

30. $\dfrac{y+2}{2y^2+y} = \dfrac{3y}{2y^2-y-1} - \dfrac{1}{y-1}$

31. $\dfrac{2}{x+3} - \dfrac{x^2+3x-10}{x^3+5x^2+6x} = \dfrac{x-4}{x^2+3x}$

32. $\dfrac{y^2+y}{y^2-y-2} = \dfrac{y-9}{y-5} + \dfrac{3}{y-2}$

Hint: Reduce the first fraction to lowest terms before clearing the equation of fractions.

33. $1 + \dfrac{x^2+6x-7}{1-x^2} + \dfrac{x+6}{x+2} = 0$

ILLUSTRATIVE EXAMPLE: Solving literal equations containing fractions

Solve for x in terms of the other letters: $\dfrac{x-a}{x-b} = \dfrac{b}{a}$

Solution. Given example $\dfrac{x-a}{x-b} = \dfrac{b}{a}$

Clearing the equation of fractions $a(x-a) = b(x-b)$

Removing parentheses $ax - a^2 = bx - b^2$

Transposing to place all terms containing the unknown x in the left member $ax - bx = a^2 - b^2$

Factoring $(a-b)x = (a+b)(a-b)$

Dividing each side by $a - b$ $x = \dfrac{(a+b)\cancel{(a-b)}}{\cancel{a-b}}$

$x = a + b$ Answer

EXERCISES: Solving literal equations

In ex. 1–16, solve for x, y, z, or w in terms of the remaining letters:

1. $mx + n = p$

3. $\dfrac{w}{b} = a$

5. $\dfrac{x - t}{t} = 4$

2. $aby = a^2$

4. $\dfrac{m}{bx} = t$

6. $\dfrac{bw - c}{c} = \dfrac{3}{2}$

7. $\dfrac{a}{b} = \dfrac{z}{d}$

12. $\dfrac{z - b}{c} - 1 = \dfrac{z - 2c}{b}$

8. $\dfrac{5}{d} = \dfrac{a}{x}$

13. $\dfrac{3x + 2a}{x - a} - \dfrac{x - 8a}{a - x} = 0$

9. $\dfrac{1}{x} - \dfrac{2}{u} = 3$

14. $\dfrac{2y - c}{y - c} = 2 + \dfrac{y + c}{c - y}$

10. $\dfrac{y}{3b} = 2 + \dfrac{y}{b}$

15. $\dfrac{n^2 + mn - m^2}{mn} - \dfrac{x - 3m}{n} = \dfrac{x + 2n}{m}$

11. $aw + c^2 = a^2 - cw$

16. $\dfrac{y - 2a}{y + 2a} + \dfrac{2a + y}{2a - y} = \dfrac{ay - 3}{y^2 - 4a^2}$

In ex. 17–28, solve for the letter indicated in terms of the remaining letters:

17. $P = 2a + 2b$ Find a.

18. $A = 2a^2 + 4ac$ Find c.

19. $T = 2\pi r + 2\pi rh$ Find h.

20. $A = P + PRT$ Find P.

21. $K = \frac{1}{2}rc$ Find r.

22. $f = \dfrac{mv^2}{r}$ Find r.

23. $F = \dfrac{9C}{5} + 32$ Find C.

24. $T = \dfrac{E}{R + r}$ Find r.

25. $S = \dfrac{n(a + l)}{2}$ Find n.

26. $\dfrac{1}{R} = \dfrac{1}{r} + \dfrac{1}{s}$ Find r.

27. $\dfrac{R}{E} = \dfrac{2\pi rl}{s}$ Find l.

28. $S = \dfrac{a}{1 - r}$ Find r.

ORAL EXERCISES: Fractions

1. The denominator of a certain fraction is 5 more than the numerator of the fraction. If n represents the numerator, what represents the denominator? What represents the fraction?

2. What fraction is obtained when both the numerator and the denominator of the fraction, $\dfrac{x + 1}{x}$, are increased by 2?

3. What fraction is obtained when both members of the fraction, $\frac{11}{15}$, are increased by x. Express the fact that this new fraction equals $\frac{2}{3}$.

4. What is the reciprocal of 3?

5. What is the reciprocal of x?

6. What is the reciprocal of $\frac{5}{7}$?

7. What is the reciprocal of $\dfrac{n}{n-1}$?

8. If Bruce and Ed have respectively b and c darts, how many darts would each have if Bruce gave Ed 6 darts?

9. If x represents the cost of a journey, what represents one half the cost of the journey? What represents one third the cost of the journey?

10. If x represents a certain number, what represents the sum of that number and its reciprocal?

11. The second of two numbers is 3 more than one half the first number. If x represents the first number, what represents the second number?

12. The larger of two numbers exceeds the smaller by c. If x represents the smaller number, what represents one third of the larger number? If y represents the larger number, what represents five sevenths of the smaller number?

E X E R C I S E S : Problems involving fractional equations

1. Five sixths of a certain number is 3 more than three fourths of the number. Find the number.

2. The sum of two thirds of a certain number and one sixth of the number equals 38 diminished by three fourths of the number. Find the number.

3. What number must be added to both the numerator and the denominator of the fraction $\frac{13}{17}$ to make a new fraction whose value equals $\frac{9}{11}$?

4. The sum of a certain number and twice its reciprocal is $\frac{11}{3}$. Find the number.

5. Separate 16 into two parts such that two thirds of the smaller part is 1 less than one half of the larger part.

6. The denominator of a certain fraction is 2 less than three times the numerator of the fraction. If 3 is added to both terms of the fraction, the resulting fraction will equal $\frac{1}{2}$. Find the original fraction.

7. If 5 more than a certain number is divided by 7, the quotient equals 20 less than five sixths of the number. Find the number.

8. If 79 is divided by a certain number, the result is a quotient of 3 and a remainder of 16. Find the number.

9. Bill and John together have a total of $35. If John should give Bill $10, John then would have only one sixth as many dollars as Bill would have. How many dollars does each of the boys have?

10. Mr. King and his son took a short automobile trip. One fifth of the expense of the trip was for transportation, one fourth for meals, and one third for lodging. If they spent $78 for all other items of expense, what was the total cost of the trip?

Elements of motion problems. You remember from your elementary algebra that there are three elements in a motion problem, namely, time, rate (or speed), and distance.

> In a motion problem the product of the time and rate equals the distance, that is,
>
> $$TR = D$$

Solving the formula for T, we get $T = \dfrac{D}{R}$

Solving the formula for R, we get $R = \dfrac{D}{T}$

ORAL EXERCISES: Problems of motion

1. If a man travels 160 mi. in 4 hr., what is his average rate?

2. If a man travels 160 mi. in x hr., what is his average rate?

3. How far can a train travel in 3 hr. at 62 mph.?

4. How far can a car travel in x hours at m miles per hour?

5. Two planes leave the same airport at the same time traveling in opposite directions. If one travels 300 mph. and the other travels 350 mph., how far apart will they be at the end of 1 hr.?

6. If two planes, traveling at x and y miles per hour respectively, leave the same airport at the same time and travel in opposite directions, how far apart will they be in 1 hr.? in 2 hr.?

7. Mr. Smith left Buffalo for Boston; Mr. Brown using the same highway left Boston an hour later for Buffalo. These men traveled until they met. If x represents the number of hours traveled by Mr. Smith, what will represent the number of hours traveled by Mr. Brown? If Mr. Smith traveled 40 mph., what will represent the distance he traveled? If Mr. Brown traveled 35 mph., what will represent the distance he traveled?

How would you represent, in terms of x, the distance from Boston to Buffalo?

	T	R	D
Smith	x	40	?
Brown	?	35	?

8. Bill, an explorer scout, can paddle his canoe in still water at a rate of 5 mph. If the Red River flows at the rate of y miles per hour, how fast can Bill travel downstream? How long will it take him to paddle downstream a distance of 10 mi.? How fast can Bill travel upstream? How long will it take him to paddle upstream a distance of m miles?

$5 =$ rate in miles per hour of paddling in still water
$y =$ rate in miles per hour of Red River

	T	R	D
Downstream	?	?	10
Upstream	?	?	m

E X E R C I S E S : Problems of motion

1. A train left St. Louis at 9:00 A.M. traveling east at an average speed of 40 mph. At 11:00 A.M. a second train left St. Louis traveling west at an average speed of 50 mph. At what time were the two trains 215 mi. apart?

50 mph. ⟵   St. Louis   ⟶ 40 mph.

Hint: Arrange the data in box form.

	T	R	D
1st train	x	40	?
2d train	$x - 2$	50	?

Distance first train travels	plus	distance second train travels	equals	215
?	+	?	=	215

2. Bill left Centerville walking at the rate of 3 mph. One and one half hours later Bob left Centerville on his bicycle riding along the same route at 9 mph. How long did it take Bob to overtake Bill?

Centerville

3. John can paddle his canoe in still water at the rate of 4 mph. In Big River he paddled upstream from his campsite for 3 hr. He made the return trip in 1 hr. What is the rate of flow of Big River?

4. Joe can walk 3 mph. The suburban bus averages 30 mph. How far may Joe walk along the bus route and return by bus if he must make the round trip in 2 hr. and 12 min.? Assume that he is able to board a bus whenever it is necessary for him to begin his return trip.

5. On a recent trip Mr. Jones drove 231 mi. in the same length of time required by Mr. Smith to drive 308 mi. If Mr. Smith's rate of speed exceeded that of Mr. Jones by 13 mph., determine the rate of each.

6. Mr. Williams driving from his home to Centerport averaged 36 mph. He made the return trip by train averaging 48 mph. If traveling time for the round trip was 7 hr., what is the distance between Mr. William's home and Centerport?

7. Two trains leave Memphis at the same time, the first proceeding north and the second proceeding west at a speed 10 mph greater than the speed of the first train. If the trains will be 150 mi. apart at the end of 3 hr., determine the rate of each. Hint: Use the Law of Pythagoras. Solve the quadratic equation by factoring.

ORAL EXERCISES: Problems of mixtures

1. If 20% of an acid solution is pure acid, how much pure acid is there in 10 qt. of the solution?

2. If 10% of an acid solution is pure acid, how much pure acid is there in x quarts of the solution?

3. In x quarts of a mixture of milk and cream there are 8 qt. of milk. How many quarts of cream are in the mixture?

4. What is the value of $(x - 3)$ two-cent stamps?

5. How much pure copper is contained in $(60 - x)$ pounds of alloy that is 25% copper?

6. What is the value of $(100 - x)$ tickets at 40¢ each?

7. What is the amount of pure arnica in a mixture if the druggist mixed x ounces of a solution that is 30% arnica with $(20 - x)$ ounces of a solution that is 25% arnica?

8. What is the total value of x tickets worth 60¢ each and $(120 - x)$ tickets worth $1.00 each?

E X E R C I S E S : Problems of mixtures

1. A candy maker wishes to have a mixture of 80 lb. of chocolate candy to sell for $1.30 per pound. If his chocolate creams are worth $1.00 per pound and his chocolate-covered nuts are worth $1.50 per pound, how many pounds of each should he use in his mixture?

Hint : Arrange the data in box form.

	Pounds	Value per Pound	Total Value
Creams	x	100	$100x$
Nuts	$80 - x$	150	$150(80 - x)$
Mixture	80	130	10,400

Value of creams + value of nuts = value of mixture
$$100x + 150(80 - x) = 10,400$$
Complete the solution.

2. Medium-sized eggs are worth 42¢ per dozen and large-sized eggs are worth 47¢ per dozen. If Mr. Davis sells 12 dozen more of the large-sized eggs than of the medium-sized eggs, and if he receives a total of $35.01 for the eggs, how many dozen of each kind does he sell?

3. Receipts from 570 admissions to the school's "stunt night" program totaled $319.50. If each adult's ticket sold for 75¢ and each child's ticket sold for 25¢, how many of each kind were sold?

4. While at the post office Mrs. Adams purchased $2.39 worth of stamps. The number of 3¢ stamps exceeded four times the number of 6¢ airmail stamps by 1. Also, the number of 3¢ stamps was 13 less than the number of 2¢ stamps. How many stamps of each kind did Mrs. Adams purchase?

5. A druggist wishes to dilute 20 oz. of a 7% solution of iodine with pure alcohol in order to obtain a 4% solution. How much alcohol must he add to the original solution to accomplish this?

Hint : Arrange the data in box form.

	Number of Ounces	Amount of Iodine per Ounce of Solution (per cent)	Amount. of Medicine
Starting solution	20	.07	?
Alcohol added	x	0	0
New solution	$20 + x$	.04	?

The amount of pure iodine remains unchanged by the dilution.

Form the equation and solve.

6. How much water must be evaporated from 30 quarts of 3% salt solution to make a 4% salt solution?

O R A L   E X E R C I S E S : Work problems

1. If Bob can mow the lawn in 3 hr., how much of the lawn can he mow in 1 hr.?

2. If Nick requires x hours to do a job, what fraction of the job can he do in 1 hr.?

3. If Joan needs $(x - 3)$ hours to complete her sewing, what fraction of the job can she do in 2 hr.?

4. If it takes y hours for a company of soldiers to march from their fort to the campsite, what fractional part of the distance will they march in 1 hr.?   in 3 hr.?

5. If Mr. Waters can paint his fence in 4 hr. and his son can paint it in 6 hr., what fraction of the fence can they together paint in x hours?

6. If Carol requires x hours to type a report and Connie requires $(x - 3)$ hours to type the same report, what part of the report can they type together in 1 hr.?   in 5 hr.?

E X E R C I S E S : Work problems

1. An experienced shipping clerk can fill a certain order in 6 hr.   A second, less-experienced clerk, requires 8 hr. to do the same job.   How many hours will be required to fill the order if both clerks work at the same time?

Hint: Arrange the data in box form.

	Number of Hours to Do Whole Job	Fraction of Job Done in One Hour	Number of Hours Worked	Total Fraction of Job Done
Experienced clerk	6	$\frac{1}{6}$	x	$\frac{x}{6}$
Second clerk	8	$\frac{1}{8}$	x	$\frac{x}{8}$

$$\begin{array}{ccccc} \text{Fraction of} & & \text{fraction of} & & \\ \text{job done by ex-} & + & \text{job done by} & = & \text{whole job} \\ \text{perienced clerk} & & \text{second clerk} & & \\ \frac{x}{6} & + & \frac{x}{8} & = & 1 \end{array}$$

Complete the solution.

2. Jack can weed the garden in 5 hr.   His brother can do the same job in 4 hr.   If both boys work together, how long will it take them to weed the garden?

3. It takes 3 days for Mr. Brown and his son working together to pick a bale of cotton. Mr. Brown alone can pick the bale of cotton in 5 days. How long would it take the son to do the job alone?

4. Jack and Joe built a fence. It would have taken Jack working alone 9 hr. to do the job, and it would have taken Joe working alone 12 hr. to do the job. Jack worked 3 hr. before he was joined by Joe. How many hours did they work together in completing the building of the fence?

5. Tom, Edward, and Dan working together can complete a certain job in 4 days. If Tom working alone can do the job in 12 days, and if Edward working alone can do the job in 10 days, how long will it take Dan working alone to do the job?

6. Jane and Mary began typing a report together. Jane, working alone, can type the report in 10 hr.; Mary, working alone, can type the report in 8 hr. Jane became ill after both girls had been working for 2 hr. How much time was required for Mary to complete the job alone?

E X E R C I S E S : Problems about consecutive integers

1. One fourth of the larger of two consecutive integers equals 1 less than two thirds of the result obtained by diminishing the smaller integer by 5. What are the integers?

2. The difference between the squares of two consecutive odd integers is 120. Find the integers.

3. Find two consecutive integers such that the square of the larger exceeds the square of the smaller by 25.

4. There are three consecutive odd integers such that the largest integer divided by 2 less than the smallest integer gives a quotient which is equal to the sum of one thirtieth the smallest integer and one tenth of the remaining integer. Determine the integers (two solutions).

5. There are three consecutive even integers such that the quotient obtained by dividing twice the largest integer by the smallest integer is 3 less than three fifths of the remaining integer. What are the integers?

6. There are three positive consecutive integers such that the square of the largest integer is equal to the sum of the squares of the other two integers. Find the integers.

Magic squares. For centuries mathematicians have found magic squares intriguing. Here are two of them :

1. *Magic multiplication square.* Notice that the product of the numbers in each row is 120, and the product of the numbers in each column is 120.

1	12	10
15	2	4
8	5	3

2. *The Melancholia magic square.* The creator of this magic square is unknown, but the square is shown in Dürer's famous 1514 engraving known as *Melancholia.* The number of each row, each column, and of each of the two diagonals add up to 34.   Similarly, the sum of the four numbers at the corners of the square is 34; also the numbers of the center square add up to 34.

16	3	2	13
5	10	11	8
9	6	7	12
4	15	14	1

Try to construct a magic square of 9 numbers, using the digits 1 to 9 each once, in such a way that the numbers of each row, each column, and each of the two diagonals add up to 15.

EXERCISES: Age problems

1. Peggy is three years younger than Joan. Six years ago Peggy's age was two thirds of Joan's age. What are their present ages?

Hint: Arrange data in box form.

	Present Age	Age 6 Years Ago
Peggy	$x - 3$	$x - 9$
Joan	x	$x - 6$

Peggy's age six years ago $= \frac{2}{3} \times$ Joan's age six years ago

$$x - 9 = \tfrac{2}{3}(x - 6)$$

Complete the solution.

2. The sum of the ages of two girls is 8 yr. Four years hence three times the age of the younger girl divided by the age of the older girl will give a quotient of $2\frac{1}{3}$. Find their present ages.

3. Joe is now 5 yr. old and his father is 30 yr. old. In how many years will Joe be one half as old as his father?

4. The ratio of Albert's age 3 yr. hence to his age 3 yr. ago is $\frac{5}{3}$. What is Albert's present age?

5. Two thirds of my age 6 yr. hence exceeds three fourths of my age 5 yr. ago by a quantity which is 1 less than one third my present age. How old am I?

CHAPTER REVIEW EXERCISES

1. Solve for x: $\dfrac{4x}{5} - \dfrac{x}{4} + \dfrac{3}{2} = \dfrac{7x}{10}$

2. Solve for w: $\dfrac{2}{w-3} = \dfrac{3}{w+2} - \dfrac{1}{w}$

3. Solve for x in terms of a and b: $\dfrac{bx}{2} + b^2 = a^2 - \dfrac{ax}{2}$

4. Solve for F in terms of C: $C = \frac{5}{9}(F - 32)$

5. If a certain number is added to the numerator and subtracted from the denominator of the fraction $\frac{11}{31}$, the resulting fraction will have a value of $\frac{5}{9}$. Find the number.

6. A tiny manmade satellite of the earth is fired upward to a height of 200 mi. from the earth's surface on a two-step rocket. If the first-step rocket travels for 15 sec., and the second-step travels for 20 sec. at a rate 3 mi. per sec. faster than the first rocket, what is the rate of the first rocket?

7. A chemist has two bottles of an acid solution, one of which is 48% acid and the other is 24% acid. How many ounces must he draw from each bottle to prepare 40 oz. of an acid solution that is 30% acid?

8. It would take Mrs. Black 6 hr. less time than her daughter to can all the tomatoes from Mr. Black's garden. Together they could do the job in one third the time it would take the daughter alone. How long would it take each alone?

9. Find four consecutive even integers such that one half the product of the last two is 12 greater than the product of the first two.

10. The sum of the ages of a boy and his sister is 33. In 9 yr. the girl will be $\frac{8}{9}$ of her brother's age. How old is she now?

CUMULATIVE REVIEW EXERCISES

1. From $x^3 - 2x + 4$ subtract the sum of $3x^2 - 2x + 1$ and $2 + x^2$.

2. Subtract $3x - 7$ from the remainder obtained when $x^4 - 2x^3 + x - 7$ is divided by $x^2 + 1$.

3. Using synthetic division, determine the quotient when $x^3 - 2x^2 + x - 3$ is divided by $x - 3$.

4. Simplify: $7x - \{2x - [-(3x - 5)]\}$

5. Solve and check: $(4x + 5)(x - 1) - (2x + 3)^2 = 8$.

In ex. 6–15, factor completely.

6. $a^4b + a^3b^2 - 2a^2b^3$

7. $(m + n)^2 + 2m(m + n)$

8. $81x^4 - 256y^8$

9. $(c - 2d)^2 - (a + d)^2$

10. $5x^2 - 24x - 5$

11. $12x^2 + x - 6$

12. $16b^3 - 2$

13. $ax^{2b} - ay^{2b}$

14. $25a^4 + 16a^2 - 9$

15. $x^3 + 3x^2 - 4$

16. Reduce to lowest terms: $\dfrac{18a^3b^8(a - b)^2}{81a^2b^{10}(b - a)^2}$

17. Multiply as indicated: $\dfrac{c^3 + 8d^3}{c^2 - 4d^2} \cdot \dfrac{c^2 - cd - 2d^2}{c^3d - 2c^2d^2 + 4cd^3}$

18. Solve for y: $\dfrac{5y}{7} - \dfrac{24}{35} = \dfrac{7y}{5}$

19. In dividing his stamps among his friends, Bill gave one fifth of them to Joe, three tenths of them to Bob, and one sixth of them to Jack. If he kept 10 stamps for himself, how many did he have at first?

20. A man travels from town A to town B at an average rate of 40 mph and returns at an average rate of 50 mph. It takes him $\frac{1}{2}$ hr. longer than it would take him if he made the round trip at an average rate of 45 mph. What is the distance from town A to town B?

CHAPTER 6   *Simultaneous Linear Equations*

A coordinate system. In algebra when we wish to locate a point on a flat surface by means of two numbers, we use paper which is ruled horizontally and vertically, dividing the paper into small squares. The point of intersection of two of these ruled lines can be used as a convenient starting point. We call this point the *origin*. Through the origin is drawn a horizontal reference line, called the *x axis*. Also through this

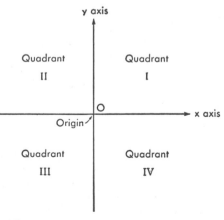

point is drawn a vertical reference line, called the *y axis*. These two axes divide the flat surface into four sections, called *quadrants*. The numbering of these four quadrants begins in the upper right section. They are numbered counterclockwise as shown in the figure on page 110. Distances measured to the right of the origin are positive (+); distances to the left of the origin are negative (−). Distances above the origin are positive; distances below the origin are negative.

Five points are shown on the coordinate system in the adjacent figure. **Point A** is four units to the right (+ 4) of the
y axis; it is also three units above (+ 3) the *x*
axis. These two numbers, 4 and 3, locate or
describe point *A*. **Point B** is five units to the
left (− 5) of the *y* axis and two units above
the *x* axis (+ 2). The numbers − 5 and + 2
locate point *B*. **Point C** is three units to the
left (− 3) of the *y axis;* and, since it lies on
the *x* axis, its distance from the *x* axis is
zero (0). The numbers − 3 and 0 locate

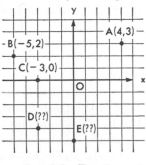

point *C*. Do the numbers − 3 and − 4 locate **point D**? Do 0, − 5 locate **point E**?

Every point on a coordinate system is located by two numbers. The first number is the point's distance to the right or to the left of the *y* axis. Since this distance is measured parallel to the *x* axis, we call the number representing this distance the *x coordinate* of the point, or the *abscissa*. The second number is the point's distance above or below the *x* axis. Since this distance is measured parallel to the *y* axis, we call the number representing this distance the *y coordinate* or the *ordinate* of the point. The two numbers, the coordinates of the point, are written in parentheses with a comma between them. **The first number is always the abscissa; the second number is always the ordinate.** Thus (3, − 4) means the abscissa of the point is + 3, and the ordinate is − 4.

ORAL EXERCISES: Locating points

Referring to the adjacent figure, read
the coordinates of each of the following
points in ex. 1–9.

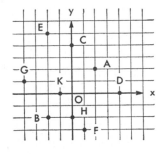

1. *A*		**5.** *E*	
2. *B*		**6.** *F*	
3. *C*		**7.** *G*	
4. *D*		**8.** *H*	
		9. *K*	

10. In which quadrant does each of the following points lie?
   a) $(-2, 3)$ *b)* $(4, -5)$ *c)* $(-6, -1)$ *d)* $(2, 2)$

11. On which axis does each of the following points lie?
   a) $(2, 0)$ *b)* $(0, -2)$ *c)* $(0, 4)$ *d)* $(-7, 0)$

12. State the abscissa of each of the following points.
   a) $(-7, 3)$ *b)* $(-6, 4)$ *c)* $(1\frac{1}{2}, 0)$ *d)* $(.5, .6)$

13. State the ordinate of each of the following points.
   a) $(2, -3)$ *b)* $(-3, 2)$ *c)* $(1\frac{1}{2}, 2\frac{1}{2})$ *d)* $(.4, -5)$

14. How far distant from the x axis is each of the following points?
   a) $(-3, 0)$ *b)* $(-3, -6)$ *c)* $(0, -3)$ *d)* $(6, 3)$

15. How far distant from the y axis is each of the following points?
   a) $(4, 3)$ *b)* $(-5, 2)$ *c)* $(0, -6)$ *d)* $(2.5, 0)$

16. Where does a point lie if
   a) the abscissa is zero?   *b)* the ordinate is zero?
   c) both abscissa and ordinate are zero?

17. In which quadrant does a point lie if
   a) the abscissa and the ordinate are both positive?
   b) the abscissa and the ordinate are both negative?
   c) the abscissa is negative and the ordinate is positive?
   d) the abscissa is positive and the ordinate is negative?

E X E R C I S E S :   Plotting points on a coordinate system

Prepare a coordinate system, labeling the origin 0. Label the axes and indicate a number scale. Plot each of the following points on the coordinate system.

1. A $(3, 5)$ **4.** D $(7, 0)$ **7.** G $(-2\frac{1}{2}, -\frac{1}{2})$
2. B $(0, -4)$ **5.** E $(1, -6)$ **8.** H $(-3\frac{1}{2}, \frac{1}{2})$
3. C $(-2, 4)$ **6.** F $(1.5, 3)$ **9.** K $(-4.5, -3.5)$

The graph of a first-degree equation.   Consider the equation $x + y = 6$, which has two literal numbers, x and y. This equation states that the **sum of x and y is 6.** Since there are endless pairs of numbers whose sum is 6, x may equal any convenient number. For each value of x there is a corresponding value of y. To find this value of y, we solve the equation for y in terms of x. Then we substitute values of x to find the corresponding values of y. Thus,

        Given equation $x + y = 6$
        Solving for y $y = 6 - x$

We substitute values for x in this equation and find the corresponding values of y. The pairs of values are then arranged in a column as shown

x	y
-4	10
-2	8
-1	7
0	6
2	4
6	0

on the right. Thus, if $x = -4$, then $y = 6 - (-4)$ or 10. Similarly, if $x = 2$, then $y = 6 - 2$ or 4. The other pairs of values in the table are obtained in a similar manner. Since x and y vary in value in this equation, we call x and y *variables*. Thus we have an equation in two variables. Since x and y are each raised only to the first power, $x + y = 6$ is a first-degree equation in two variables.

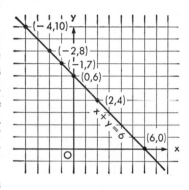

On the coordinate system in the adjacent figure are plotted the six points taken from the above table: $(-4, 10)$, $(-2, 8)$, $(-1, 7)$, $(0, 6)$, $(2, 4)$, and $(6, 0)$. These six points lie on a straight line, and this line has been drawn. If we had plotted other points, whose coordinates satisfy the equation $x + y = 6$, they, too, would lie on this line. This line, then, is the graph of the equation $x + y = 6$. Every pair of values which satisfies the equation $x + y = 6$ are the coordinates of a point on this line; and, conversely, the coordinates of every point on this line satisfy the equation $x + y = 6$. You remember from your work in elementary algebra that:

> The graph of a first-degree equation in two variables is a straight line.

We call a first-degree equation a *linear equation*, because the graph of the equation is a straight line. Since only one straight line can be drawn through two points, it is necessary in drawing the graph of a linear equation to find only two points whose coordinates satisfy the equation. We usually compute and plot a third point whose coordinates satisfy the equation. If this third point lies on the line connecting the first two points, we consider this a check on the drawing of the line.

ILLUSTRATIVE EXAMPLES: Drawing graphs of linear equations

1. Draw the graph of the equation $2x + 3y = 12$.

   Solution. $2x + 3y = 12$

$$y = \frac{12 - 2x}{3}$$

We substitute values for x in this equation to find the corresponding values for y:

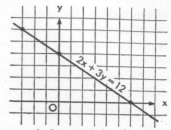

x	y
-3	6
0	4
6	0

These points are plotted in the adjacent figure, and the straight line connecting them is the required graph.

2. Construct the graph of each of the following equations:

      a) $y = 5$ *b)* $x = 4$

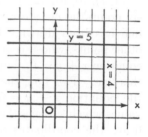

Solution.   *a)* In $y = 5$ the variable x is missing; therefore, the equation may be written in the form $y = 5 + 0x$. For every value of x that we substitute in the equation, y always equals 5. Hence the graph of $y = 5$ is a straight line through $(0, 5)$ parallel to the x axis.

     b) The graph of the equation $x = 4$ is a straight line through $(4, 0)$ parallel to the y axis.

Intercepts.   If the graph of an equation intersects the x axis, the distance from the origin to the point of intersection is the x intercept. Similarly, the distance from the origin to the point where the graph crosses the y axis is the y intercept. To find the x intercept we let $y = 0$ in the equation. To find the y intercept we let $x = 0$ in the equation.

ILLUSTRATIVE EXAMPLE: Using intercepts to graph a line

Construct the graph of $2x - 3y = 6$ by plotting the x and y intercepts.

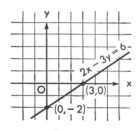

     Solution. In the equation $2x - 3y = 6$ to find the x intercept we let $y = 0$.

Thus $2x - 3(0) = 6$

                $x = 3$

To find the y intercept we let $x = 0$.

x	y
3	0
0	-2

Thus $2(0) - 3y = 6$ $y = -2$

These two points have been plotted in the adjacent figure, and the line connecting them is the required graph.

The constant term of an equation.   Those terms of an equation which do not contain a variable are called *constant* terms.   In the equation $x - 5y = 2$, the constant term is 2.   In the equation $7x + 9y = 0$, there is no constant term.   In any such equation, where there is no constant term, if $x = 0$, then y must also equal zero.   We therefore conclude

> If a linear equation has no constant term, its graph passes through the origin.

ILLUSTRATIVE EXAMPLE: Graphing a linear equation having no constant term

Draw the graph of $5x = 6y$.

x	y
0	0
6	5

Solution. Since the equation $5x = 6y$ has no constant term, its graph passes through the origin. To find the coordinates of one other point, we substitute a value for x and find the corresponding value of y, as shown in the table. These two points have been plotted in the adjacent figure, and the line connecting them is the required graph.

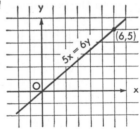

EXERCISES: Graphing linear equations

Draw the graph of each of the following linear equations.
In ex. 1–5 plot three points which satisfy each equation.

1. $x - 3y = 4$ **3.** $3x - 2y = -4$ **5.** $0.4x - 0.3y = -0.2$

2. $2x + 5y = -2$ **4.** $\dfrac{x}{2} - \dfrac{y}{3} = 1$

In ex. 6–10 draw the line parallel to the proper axis.

6. $x = 7$ **8.** $2x = 5$ **10.** $\dfrac{5x}{4} = -3$

7. $y = 4$ **9.** $\frac{4}{5}y = -2$

In ex. 11–15 use the intercept method.

11. $x + y = 8$ **14.** $4x + 5y = 20$

12. $2x - y = 4$ **15.** $3y - 4x = 12$

13. $3y - x = 6$

In ex. 16–20 plot one point, besides the origin, which satisfies each equation.

16. $x = 2y$ **18.** $2x - 3y = 0$ **20.** $0.5x = 0.6y$
17. $y = x$ **19.** $\frac{1}{2}x + \frac{3}{4}y = 0$

Slope.   From sliding down-
hill, from riding a bicycle, or
from hiking you are familiar
with the meaning of **"slope."**
Some slopes are gentle, or
small; some slopes are steep, or large.

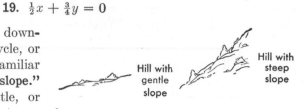

Hill with gentle slope

Hill with steep slope

In the figures below are drawn the graphs of two linear equations. You can readily see that the slope of the graph on the left is gentle, or small, while the slope of the graph on the right is steep, or large. On a coordinate system the slope of a line may be defined as the ratio of the "change in y" to the corresponding "change in x."

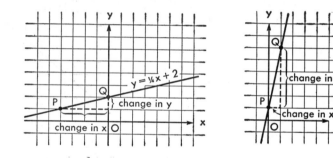

Slope of a graph of a linear equation.   In the adjacent figure the graph of the
equation $x - 2y = 4$ has been drawn. On
the graph the three points P, Q, R are shown
with their respective coordinates. The
"change in x" from P to Q, which is a change
of 4 units to the right $(+4)$ is PS. The
"change in y" from P to Q, which is a change
of two units upward $(+2)$ is SQ. The ratio

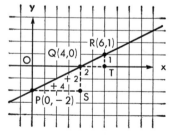

$$\frac{\text{change in } y}{\text{change in } x} = \frac{SQ}{PS} = \frac{+2}{+4} = \frac{1}{2}.$$

Similarly, the change in x from Q to R is QT $(+2)$, and the change in y
from Q to R is TR $(+1)$.   The ratio $\dfrac{\text{change in } y}{\text{change in } x} = \dfrac{TR}{QT} = \dfrac{1}{2}.$ If any

two points on the graph of this equation are joined, the ratio $\dfrac{\text{change in } y}{\text{change in } x}$
will always equal $\frac{1}{2}$.

Solving the equation $x - 2y = 4$ for y in terms of x, we have $y = \frac{1}{2}x - 2$. Notice that in this form the coefficient of the x is $\frac{1}{2}$, which is the slope of the graph. Notice, too, that the constant term of the equation, -2, is the y intercept of the graph.

> If a linear equation is solved for y in terms of x, the coefficient of x is the slope of the graph of the equation, and the constant term is the y intercept of the graph of the equation.

Thus, a linear equation may be expressed in the form
$$y = mx + b$$
where m is the **slope** of the graph of the equation, and b is the **y intercept** of the graph. The form $y = mx + b$ is called the **slope-intercept** form of a linear equation.

ILLUSTRATIVE EXAMPLES: Slope-intercept form of linear equations

1. Express each of the following equations in the form $y = mx + b$, and give the slope and y intercept of the graph of each equation.

a) $3x - y = 1$ b) $2x + y = 6$

Solution. $3x - y = 1$ $2x + y = 6$
$$-y = -3x + 1$$ $$y = -2x + 6$$
$$y = 3x - 1$$ $$m = -2, \quad b = 6$$
$$m = 3 \quad b = -1$$

Slope is 3 and y intercept is -1.   Slope is -2 and y intercept is 6.

2. In each of the following write the linear equation when given the slope and y intercept of its graph.

a) $m = 2 \quad b = 3$ b) $m = \frac{1}{3} \quad b = -1$

Solution. a) $y = mx + b$ b) $y = mx + b$
Substituting $y = 2x + 3$ Substituting $y = \frac{1}{3}x - 1$
                                     Clearing of fractions $3y = x - 3$

EXERCISES: Slope-intercept form of linear equations

In ex. 1–9 at the top of the next page, express each equation in the form $y = mx + b$. Give the slope and y intercept of the graph of each equation.

1. $\frac{x}{5} - y = 2$ 4. $2x + \frac{y}{4} = 5$ 7. $6x + 7y = 6y + 4$

2. $3x + y = x - 8$ 5. $5x + 9 = 1 - 4y$ 8. $4x + 3y = y - 10$

3. $7x + 3y = 6$ 6. $3x + 4y = 12$ 9. $3x + 8y = 16$

In each example of ex. 10–18, the slope and y intercept of the graph of an equation are given. Write the equation.

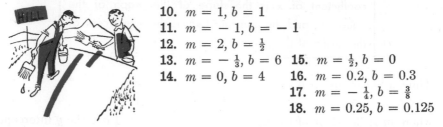

10. $m = 1, b = 1$
11. $m = -1, b = -1$
12. $m = 2, b = \frac{1}{2}$
13. $m = -\frac{1}{3}, b = 6$ 15. $m = \frac{1}{2}, b = 0$
14. $m = 0, b = 4$ 16. $m = 0.2, b = 0.3$
                17. $m = -\frac{1}{4}, b = \frac{3}{8}$
                18. $m = 0.25, b = 0.125$

ILLUSTRATIVE EXAMPLE: Graphing a linear equation in slope-intercept form

Draw the graph of the line whose slope is -3 and whose y intercept is **4.**

Solution. On a system of coordinate axes we plot the y intercept. Since **$b = 4$,** we measure off **4 units upward (plus) from the origin on the y axis** and plot the point P. We know that the **slope of a line** is the ratio **change in y** ⁄ **change in x**. Since the slope is -3, the ratio $\frac{-3}{1}$ indicates for us that the change in y is -3 when the change in x is $+1$. **Starting at point P, we measure 3 units downward (negative) on the y axis and 1 unit to the right (positive) on a line parallel to the x axis** and plot the point Q. We draw a line connecting these points. This is the graph of the equation $y = -3x + 4$.

EXERCISES: Graphing linear equations using the respective slopes and y intercepts

In each example of ex. 1–8 draw the linear graph, given the line's slope, m, and its y intercept, b.

1. $m = 3 \quad b = 5$
2. $m = -2 \quad b = 3$
3. $m = \frac{1}{2} \quad b = -2$
4. $m = -\frac{3}{4} \quad b = 6$

5. $m = \frac{2}{3} \quad b = 0$
6. $m = 0 \quad b = 8$
7. $m = \frac{5}{8} \quad b = -4$
8. $m = 0.2 \quad b = 2.5$

In ex. 9–12, convert each linear equation to the form $y = mx + b$. Then draw the graph of the equation, using the slope and the y intercept.

9. $3x + y = 5$

10. $2y - 5x = 8$

11. $x = 7 - 7y$

12. $4x + 3y = 15$

Solving a pair of linear equations in two unknowns.

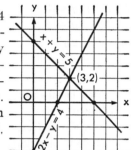

The graphs of the linear equations $2x - y = 4$ and $x + y = 5$, intersect at a point whose coordinates are **(3, 2)**. Since the coordinates of every point on the graph of an equation satisfy the equation, the coordinates (3, 2) of the point of intersection of the two graphs satisfy **both** of the equations.

The pair of values **$x = 3$, $y = 2$ is the solution** of the pair of equations $2x - y = 4$ and $x + y = 5$.

> Two linear equations whose graphs intersect are called *simultaneous linear equations.*

ILLUSTRATIVE EXAMPLE: Solving simultaneous linear equations graphically

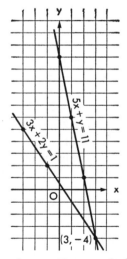

Solve graphically the pair of equations:

$$5x + y = 11$$
$$3x + 2y = 1$$

Solution.

Given equations $5x + y = 11$; $3x + 2y = 1$

Solving for y: $y = 11 - 5x$; $y = \dfrac{1 - 3x}{2}$

Preparing a table of values for each equation:

x	y		x	y
0	11		-3	5
1	6		-1	2
2	1		3	-4

Plotting these points and drawing the graphs of each equation, we find that the coordinates of the point of intersection are **(3, $-$ 4)**.

Thus $x = 3$, $y = -4$ is the required solution.

Check. Given equations $5x + y = 11$ $3x + 2y = 1$

Substituting 3 for x

and -4 for y $5(3) + (-4) \overset{?}{=} 11$ $3(3) + 2(-4) \overset{?}{=} 1$

$11 = 11$ $1 = 1$

E X E R C I S E S : Solving simultaneous linear equations graphically

Solve each of the following pairs of equations by means of graphs.

1. $x - y = 0$ **4.** $x - \ y = -7$ **7.** $x + y = 5$
$\quad\ x + y = 8$ $\quad\ x - 3y = 1$ $\quad\ 3x - y = -9$

2. $\ \ x + y = 3$ **5.** $5x + 2y = 10$ **8.** $2x + 3y = 16$
$\quad\ 2x + y = 8$ $\quad\quad\ y = x + 5$ $\quad\ 3x + 2y = 14$

3. $\ \ x + 2y = 8$ **6.** $\ \ x + 2y = 0$ **9.** $\quad\quad\ x = y$
$\quad\ 3x - \ y = 3$ $\quad\ 3x - 2y = 8$ $\quad\ 4x + 5y = 9$

Inconsistent linear equations.   If the graphs of two equations on the same coordinate system *do not intersect,* then there is no pair of values of the two unknowns that satisfies *both* equations. Hence there is no solution for the pair of equations. We can easily recognize a pair of inconsistent linear equations by writing each equation in slope-intercept form.

I L L U S T R A T I V E   E X A M P L E : Inconsistent equations

Show that the equations $2x - y = -5$ and $4x - 2y = 9$ are inconsistent.

Solution.

We first write each equation in the form $y = mx + b$. Thus

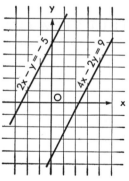

$$2x - y = -5 \qquad\qquad 4x - 2y = 9$$
$$\ \ -y = -2x - 5 \qquad -2y = -4x + 9$$
$$\ \ \ \ y = 2x + 5 \qquad\quad\ \ y = 2x - \tfrac{9}{2}$$

Since $m = 2$ and $b = 5$ the slope of the graph is 2 and the **y** intercept is 5

Since $m = 2$ and $b = -\tfrac{9}{2}$ the slope of the graph is 2 and the **y** intercept is $-\tfrac{9}{2}$

Since these two equations have the same slope, but different y intercepts, the graphs are parallel lines and therefore do not intersect. Thus the equations are inconsistent. The adjacent figure shows the graphs of these equations.

> If the slopes of the graphs of two linear equations are the same, but the y intercepts are different, the graphs are parallel lines.

Dependent linear equations.   When one of a pair of equations can be made **equal to the other,** the equations are called dependent. Their graphs on the same coordinate system **coincide.** Therefore, there is an **unlimited number of solutions** for dependent equations. Thus, the equations $x + y = 5$ and $2x + 2y = 10$ are dependent equations.

ORAL EXERCISES: Types of equations

State whether each of the following pairs of equations is simultaneous, inconsistent, or dependent.

1. $x + y = 4$
$x + y = 8$

2. $x + y = 6$
$x - y = 12$

3. $x + 2y = 5$
$2x + 4y = 10$

4. $x = 4$
$y = 3$

5. $2x - y = 5$
$4x - 6y = 10$

6. $y - x = 6$
$x - y = -6$

7. $x = 3y + 2$
$8 + 6y = 2x$

8. $24 = 8x - 6y$
$24x - 18y = 25$

9. $2x - 13y = 5$
$4x - 13y = 10$

Algebraic methods. Solving two simultaneous linear equations by the graphic method is slow and may give only approximate values for the unknowns. In contrast, the two algebraic methods, known as the **addition-subtraction method** and the **substitution method**, are more rapid and give exact values for the unknowns. The two methods are illustrated in the following examples.

ILLUSTRATIVE EXAMPLE: Addition-subtraction method

Solve for x and y by the addition-subtraction method:

$$5x + 2y = 40$$
$$4x - 3y = 9$$

Solution. In this example let us eliminate y so as to get an equation in x. To do this we multiply the first equation by 3 and the second equation by **2.** This makes the absolute value of the coefficient of y the same in both equations. Adding the equations eliminates the unknown y.

Multiplier	Equation	New Equation
3	$5x + \mathbf{2y} = 40$	$15x + \mathbf{6y} = 120$
2	$4x - \mathbf{3y} = 9$	$8x - \mathbf{6y} = 18$
By addition		$23x \qquad = 138$
		$x = 6$

We substitute the value of x in one of the equations to find the value of y. Substituting 6 for x in the equation

$$5x + 2y = 40$$
$$5(6) + 2y = 40$$

Solving for y $\qquad\qquad\qquad\qquad\qquad\qquad 2y = 10$
$$y = 5$$

The values of the unknowns are $\qquad\quad x = 6 \text{ and } y = 5 \quad$ Answer

Check. Substituting $x = 6$ and $y = 5$ in the equation

$$4x - 3y = 9$$
$$4(6) - 3(5) \overset{?}{=} 9$$
$$24 - 15 \overset{?}{=} 9$$
$$9 = 9 \quad \text{Check}$$

I L L U S T R A T I V E   E X A M P L E :   The substitution method

Solve for x and y by the substitution method:

$$4x - 8y = 5$$
$$8x - 4y = 7$$

Solution. This method is based on the principle that **a quantity may be substituted for its equal in an equation.** In the first equation we find the value of one unknown in terms of the other. We substitute this value in the second equation. This gives an equation in one unknown, which we then solve.

First equation $\qquad\qquad\qquad 4x - 8y = 5$
Solving for x in terms of y $\quad 4x = 5 + 8y$

$$x = \frac{5 + 8y}{4}$$

Substituting $\dfrac{5 + 8y}{4}$ for x in the second equation $8x - 4y = 7$

$$8\left(\frac{5 + 8y}{4}\right) - 4y = 7$$

Clearing of fractions $\qquad\qquad 10 + 16y - 4y = 7$
Solving for y $\qquad\qquad\qquad\qquad\quad 12y = -3$
$$y = -\tfrac{1}{4}$$

To determine x we substitute $-\tfrac{1}{4}$ for y in the equation $x = \dfrac{5 + 8y}{4}$

$$x = \frac{5 - 2}{4}$$
$$x = \tfrac{3}{4}$$

The values of the unknowns are $\qquad x = \tfrac{3}{4}, y = -\tfrac{1}{4}$ Answer

Check. Substituting $x = \tfrac{3}{4}$ and $y = -\tfrac{1}{4}$ in the equation

$$8x - 4y = 7$$
$$8(\tfrac{3}{4}) - 4(-\tfrac{1}{4}) \overset{?}{=} 7$$
$$6 + 1 \overset{?}{=} 7$$
$$7 = 7 \quad \text{Check}$$

EXERCISES : Solving simultaneous linear equations

Solve each of the following either by the addition-subtraction method or by the substitution method.

1. $2x + 5y = 36$
$2x - y = 0$

2. $3x + 5y = 1$
$5x - 2y = 12$

3. $4x + 3y = 17$
$7x - 4y = 2$

4. $x - 3y = -4$
$2x - y = 7$

5. $2x - 5y = -23$
$x = y - 1$

6. $9x + 8y = -24$
$3x - 2y = 6$

7. $7x - 10y = 1$
$x + y = 5$

8. $8x - 5y = 6$
$x = y - 3$

In ex. 9 and 10 clear the equations of decimals; then solve.

9. $0.6x + 0.5y = 1.4$
$0.4x + 0.3y = 1$

10. $0.5x - 0.6y = 0.07$
$0.3x - 0.2y = 0.01$

In ex. 11 and 12 clear the equations of parentheses; then solve.

11. $3(4x - 3y) - 2(2x + 3y) = 1$
$6(x - y) - 5(6x - 9y) = -1$

12. $3(x - 5y) + 1 = 2(3x + 5y)$
$5(3x + 2y) + 2 + 3(10y - 3x) = 0$

In ex. 13–15 clear the equations of fractions; then solve.

13. $\dfrac{10x - 9y}{15} - \dfrac{x + 2y}{4} = \dfrac{12 - 5x + 6y}{4}$

$\dfrac{x + 2y}{2} - \dfrac{3x - y}{5} = \dfrac{x - 75}{15}$

14. $y - 3 + \dfrac{x - 3y}{5} = \dfrac{x - y}{2}$

$\dfrac{5x + 5y}{6} + \dfrac{3x - 3y}{4} = 18$

15. $\dfrac{x + 1}{y - 1} = -\dfrac{16}{9}$

$\dfrac{2x - 3}{3y + 4} = -\dfrac{27}{20}$

Special fractional equations.   In simultaneous equations of the type

$$\frac{a}{x} + \frac{b}{y} = c$$

$$\frac{a'}{x} + \frac{b'}{y} = c'$$

the unknowns appear only in the monomial denominators. Although these equations are not linear, they can be solved by applying the addition-subtraction method.

ILLUSTRATIVE EXAMPLE: Solving special fractional simultaneous equations

Solve for x and y: $\dfrac{3}{2x} + \dfrac{5}{3y} = -\dfrac{19}{36}$

$$\dfrac{4}{3x} - \dfrac{2}{5y} = \dfrac{8}{3}$$

Solution. Each equation is multiplied by a constant to make the numerical coefficients of each term in the denominator equal to 1. We, therefore, multiply each term of the first equation by 36 and each term of the second equation by 15.

Multiplier	Equation	New Equation
36	$\dfrac{3}{2x} + \dfrac{5}{3y} = -\dfrac{19}{36}$	$\dfrac{54}{x} + \dfrac{60}{y} = -19$
15	$\dfrac{4}{3x} - \dfrac{2}{5y} = \dfrac{8}{3}$	$\dfrac{20}{x} - \dfrac{6}{y} = 40$

Using the new equations we eliminate x to solve for y.

1	$\dfrac{54}{x} + \dfrac{60}{y} = -19$	$\dfrac{54}{x} + \dfrac{60}{y} = -19$
10	$\dfrac{20}{x} - \dfrac{6}{y} = 40$	$\dfrac{200}{x} - \dfrac{60}{y} = 400$

Adding $\qquad\qquad\qquad\qquad\qquad\quad \dfrac{254}{x} = 381$

Solving for $x \qquad\qquad\qquad\qquad\qquad\quad x = \dfrac{254}{381}$ or $\dfrac{2}{3}$

Substituting $x = \frac{2}{3}$ in $\qquad \dfrac{4}{3x} - \dfrac{2}{5y} = \dfrac{8}{3}$

$$\dfrac{4}{3(\frac{2}{3})} - \dfrac{2}{5y} = \dfrac{8}{3}$$

Simplifying $\qquad\qquad\qquad 2 - \dfrac{2}{5y} = \dfrac{8}{3}$

$$30y - 6 = 40y$$
$$-10y = 6$$
$$y = -\dfrac{3}{5}$$

The values of the unknowns are: $x = \dfrac{2}{3}$, $y = -\dfrac{3}{5}$ Answer

Check. Substituting these values in $\dfrac{3}{2x} + \dfrac{5}{3y} = -\dfrac{19}{36}$

$$\dfrac{3}{\frac{4}{3}} + \dfrac{5}{-\frac{9}{5}} \overset{?}{=} -\dfrac{19}{36}$$

$$\tfrac{9}{4} - \tfrac{25}{9} \overset{?}{=} -\tfrac{19}{36}$$

$$\dfrac{81 - 100}{36} \overset{?}{=} -\dfrac{19}{36}$$

$$-\tfrac{19}{36} = -\tfrac{19}{36} \quad \text{Check}$$

EXERCISES: Special fractional equations

Solve each of the following pairs of equations by the addition-subtraction method.

1. $\dfrac{1}{r} + \dfrac{1}{s} = 8$

$\dfrac{9}{r} - \dfrac{5}{s} = 2$

2. $\dfrac{1}{x} + \dfrac{1}{y} = 7$

$\dfrac{2}{x} + \dfrac{3}{y} = 17$

3. $\dfrac{1}{m} - \dfrac{1}{n} = 13$

$\dfrac{3}{m} + \dfrac{2}{n} = 19$

4. $\dfrac{5}{x} + \dfrac{3}{y} = 4$

$\dfrac{25}{x} - \dfrac{2}{y} = 3$

5. $\dfrac{2}{3r} - \dfrac{9}{4s} = \dfrac{13}{12}$

$\dfrac{5}{4r} + \dfrac{3}{2s} = \dfrac{1}{8}$

6. $\dfrac{4}{3x} - \dfrac{3}{2y} = -\dfrac{5}{6}$

$\dfrac{3}{4x} - \dfrac{5}{2y} = \dfrac{1}{12}$

7. $\dfrac{3}{2x} + \dfrac{2}{y} = -\dfrac{1}{4}$

$\dfrac{5}{3x} + \dfrac{2}{3y} = -\dfrac{2}{3}$

8. $\dfrac{3}{5m} - \dfrac{5}{3n} + 5 = \dfrac{-7}{15}$

$\dfrac{2}{3m} + \dfrac{6}{5n} - 5 = \dfrac{17}{15}$

Simultaneous literal equations.   These are generally solved by the addition-subtraction method.

ILLUSTRATIVE EXAMPLE: Simultaneous literal equations

Solve for x and y in terms of the other letters

$$mx + ny = m^2 + n^2$$
$$nx + my = 2mn$$

Solution. To solve for x, we eliminate the y terms by multiplying the first equation by m and the second equation by n. Then we subtract the resulting equations.

Multiplier	Equation	New Equation
m	$mx + ny = m^2 + n^2$	$m^2x + mny = m^3 + mn^2$
n	$nx + my = 2\,mn$	$n^2x + mny = 2\,mn^2$

Subtracting	$m^2x - n^2x = m^3 - mn^2$
Factoring	$x(m^2 - n^2) = m(m^2 - n^2)$
Dividing both sides by $m^2 - n^2$	$x = m$
To solve for y we substitute m for x in	$nx + my = 2\,mn$
Substituting	$n(m) + my = 2\,mn$
Combining like terms	$my = mn$
Dividing both sides by m	$y = n$
The values of the unknowns are	$x = m$ and $y = n$ Answer

E X E R C I S E S : Simultaneous literal equations

In each of the following systems of equations solve for x and y in terms of the other letters.

1. $x + y = r$
$x - y = s$

2. $y = m - 2x$
$2x = n + y$

3. $\dfrac{1}{x} + \dfrac{2}{y} = p$
$\dfrac{1}{x} - \dfrac{2}{y} = q$

4. $\dfrac{1}{2x} + \dfrac{1}{y} = a$
$\dfrac{1}{2x} - \dfrac{1}{y} = b$

5. $4x + y = 0$
$6x + 2y = s$

6. $\dfrac{1}{2x} + \dfrac{1}{3y} = 2\,m$
$\dfrac{1}{x} - \dfrac{1}{2y} = \dfrac{m}{2}$

7. $x - 3y = a$
$5x + 6y = 12\,a$

8. $x + ry = s$
$x - sy = r$

9. $mx + ny = m^2 + 2\,mn - n^2$
$nx + my = m^2 + n^2$

10. $px - y = p^2$
$qx - y = q^2$

11. $x - 3by = 4a + b$
$ax + by = a^2 + ab - a$

12. $\dfrac{r}{x} + \dfrac{1}{y} = \dfrac{r + s^2}{rs}$
$\dfrac{s}{x} - \dfrac{1}{y} = \dfrac{1 - s}{r}$

13. $ax + by = a^3 + a^2b - ab^2 + b^3$
$bx - ay = -a^3 + a^2b - ab^2 - b^3$

14. $\dfrac{m}{x} + \dfrac{n}{y} = \dfrac{m^2 + n^2}{m^2 - n^2}$
$\dfrac{n}{x} - \dfrac{m}{y} = \dfrac{m^2 + n^2}{n^2 - m^2}$

Doings of Dimbo. When Dimbo got his first glimpse of the twins who recently moved next door, he forgot what he was doing and went the wrong way.

Can you find the pair that distracted Dimbo in his solution of the following problem? Can you put him back on the right course?

Solve for x and y:

$$3x + 4y = 25$$
$$x + y = 8$$

Dimbo's solution:

Multiplier	Equation	New Equation
1	$3x + 4y = 25$	$3x + 4y = 25$
3	$x + y = 8$	$3x + 3y = 24$
		$7y = 49$
		$y = 7$
	$x + y = 8$	
	$x + 7 = 8$	
	$x = 1$	
Answer:	$x = 1$ and $y = 7$	

Equations in three unknowns. These may be solved by first eliminating one unknown and then solving for the remaining two unknowns by using either the addition-subtraction method or by substitution.

ILLUSTRATIVE EXAMPLE: Solving a set of 3 equations in three unknowns

Solve for x, y, and z in the equations

$$2x + y + z = 17 \quad (1)$$
$$x + 2y + z = 16 \quad (2)$$
$$3x - y - z = 8 \quad (3)$$

Solution. Eliminating the z's using equations (1) and (2)

$$2x + \ y + z = 17$$
$$x + 2y + z = 16$$

Subtracting

$$x - \ y \quad\ \ = 1 \quad (4)$$

Eliminating the z's using equations (2) and (3)

$$x + 2y + z = 16$$
$$3x - \ y - z = 8$$

Adding

$$4x + \ y \quad\ \ = 24 \quad (5)$$

Eliminating the y's using equations (4) and (5)

$$x - y = 1$$
$$4x + y = 24$$
$$5x \quad\ = 25$$

Adding

$$x \quad\ = 5$$

Substituting 5 for x in equation (4)

$$5 - y = 1$$
$$y = 4$$

Substituting 5 for x and 4 for y in equation (1)

$$2x + y + z = 17$$
$$2(5) + 4 + z = 17$$
$$z = 3$$

Therefore $x = 5$; $y = 4$; $z = 3$ Answer

Check.

$$2x + y + z = 17 \qquad x + 2y + z = 16 \qquad 3x - y - z = 8$$
$$10 + 4 + 3 \stackrel{?}{=} 17 \qquad 5 + 8 \ + 3 \stackrel{?}{=} 16 \qquad 15 - 4 - 3 \stackrel{?}{=} 8$$
$$17 = 17 \qquad\qquad 16 = 16 \qquad\qquad 8 = 8$$

EXERCISES: Simultaneous linear equations in three unknowns

Solve each of the following systems of simultaneous linear equations.

1.
$$x + \ y - z = 7$$
$$2x - 3y + z = 5$$
$$x - \ y + z = 5$$

2.
$$x + y + z = 8$$
$$y - z + x = 6$$
$$z - x + y = -2$$

3.
$$x - y + z = 3$$
$$y - z + x = -1$$
$$2z + x - y = 8$$

4.
$$x - 3y + \ z = -2$$
$$2x + \ y - 2z = -2$$
$$3x - 2y + \ z = 2$$

5.
$$5x + 4y + 2z = 35$$
$$4x + 3y - 3z = 25$$
$$3x - 2y + 4z = -45$$

6.
$$x + y = 5$$
$$z - x = 3$$
$$y - z = -2$$

7.
$$x - y = 12$$
$$y - z = 5$$
$$z + x = -17$$

8.
$$x = 19 - y - z$$
$$y = 3x - 10$$
$$z = 2y - 21$$

ORAL EXERCISES: Exchange problems

1. Jack has 75¢ and Bill has 60¢. If Jack gives Bill 25¢, how much money will Bill have? How much money will Jack have left?

2. May has $8 and Eva has $12. If Eva gives May x dollars, how many dollars will May have? How many dollars will Eva have left?

3. Peter received x Christmas cards and Ann received y cards. If Peter gave Ann 5 of his cards, how many cards would Ann have? How many cards would Peter have left?

4. Doris has d books and Jack has j books. If Doris lent Jack 2 books, how many books would Doris have left? How many books would Jack have?

5. A man has $2000 in a savings bank and $5000 in a loan association. If he withdraws d dollars from the loan association and deposits it in the savings bank, how much will he have in the savings bank? How much will he have left in the loan association?

6. A retired teacher has e dollars in endowment insurance and s dollars in stock. If she sells some of her stocks for $5000 and invests the money in more endowment insurance, how many dollars will she have in endowment insurance? in stocks?

ILLUSTRATIVE EXAMPLE: Exchange problem

If Esther gives Richmond 16¢, Richmond will then have twice as much money as Esther has left; but, if Richmond gives Esther 24¢, Esther then will have $\frac{11}{10}$ as much money as Richmond has left. How much did each have originally?

Solution. Arrange the data in box form as follows:

		Number of Cents Each Has Before the Exchange	Number of Cents Each Will Have After the Exchange	Relationship Between the Two Results
First exchange	Esther	e	$e - 16$	$r + 16 = 2(e - 16)$
	Richmond	r	$r + 16$	
Second exchange	Esther	e	$e + 24$	$e + 24 = \frac{11}{10}(r - 24)$
	Richmond	r	$r - 24$	

Simplifying equations

$$r + 16 = 2(e - 16)$$
$$e + 24 = \tfrac{11}{10}(r - 24)$$
$$r + 16 = 2e - 32$$
$$10e + 240 = 11r - 264$$

Writing equations in standard form

$$r - 2e = -48$$
$$-11r + 10e = -504$$

Multiplier	Equation	New Equation
5	$r - 2e = -48$	$5r - 10e = -240$
1	$-11r + 10e = -504$	$-11r + 10e = -504$
	Adding	$-6r \quad = -744$
		$r \quad = 124$

Substituting **124** for r in $\quad r - 2e = -48$

$$124 - 2e = -48$$
$$-2e = -172$$
$$e = 86$$

Esther has 86 cents and Richmond $1.24.   Answer

E X E R C I S E S : Exchange problems

1. A husband and wife each own shares of stock in a company. If the husband gives his wife five of his shares, each will have the same number. If instead, the wife gives her husband 10 of her shares, the husband will have $\frac{5}{2}$ as many shares as his wife has. How many shares did each have originally?

2. Bill and Walt, each with a certain sum of money, go to the beach together. After Walt pays 60¢ for the hamburgers, the money he has left is 40¢ more than that which Bill has. After Bill pays 30¢ for the cokes and ice cream, the money he has left is $\frac{1}{2}$ of that which Walt has left. How much money did each have originally?

3. Wood and Storey are partners in business. If Wood sells $2000 of his holdings to Storey, the holdings of each partner will be the same. If, however, Storey sells a part of his holdings to Wood for $4000, then Wood's holdings will be four times as great as the holdings which Storey has left. What was the share of each in the partnership?

4. Beck and Rawling each have a certain sum of money. After Beck borrowed $10,000 from Rawling, the amount of Beck's money was now one half of that which Rawling had left. If, instead, Rawling had borrowed $10,000 from Beck, Rawling would then have had eight times as much money as Beck had left. How much did each have originally?

5. If 4 students were moved from the first-period division in algebra to the second-period division, the number of students left in the first-period division would be $\frac{5}{8}$ the number in the second-period division. If, instead, 8 students were moved from the second-period division to the first-period division, then the number of students in the first-period division would exceed the number in the second-period division by 12. How many students were in each division originally?

6. At a camp 15 boys were transferred from the tennis squad to the softball squad and, as a result, the number of boys playing softball was $\frac{16}{15}$ of the number playing tennis. Later in the summer, 5 boys were transferred from the softball squad to the tennis squad and, as a result, the number then playing tennis was $\frac{16}{15}$ of the number playing softball. How many boys were on each squad originally?

7. A kennel owner sold a dealer four puppies and as a result the dealer now owns twice as many puppies as the kennel owner. If, instead, the dealer had sold the kennel owner one puppy, each would then have the same number. How many puppies did each have originally?

EXERCISES: Problems about numbers

For an Illustrative Example on solving a problem about numbers see p. 30.

1. Find two numbers such that if three times the first is increased by five times the second, the sum will be 14; and if seven times the first is diminished by nine times the second, the remainder will be 12. Hint: Let x represent the first number and y the second number.

2. Find two numbers such that if one fifth the first is added to one sixth the second, the sum will be $\frac{19}{15}$; and if five thirds the first is diminished by one fifth the second, the remainder will be $\frac{21}{5}$.

3. If the difference between two numbers is multiplied by 5, the product is $\frac{5}{6}$; and if the sum of the numbers is divided by 5, the quotient is $\frac{1}{6}$. Find the numbers.

4. If 10 is subtracted from the numerator of a certain fraction, the resulting fraction equals $-\frac{1}{8}$. If 10 is added to the denominator of the original fraction, the resulting fraction equals $\frac{1}{2}$. What is the original fraction? Hint: Let the original fraction be $\frac{n}{d}$.

5. If 10 is added to the numerator of a certain fraction, the value of the resulting fraction is $\frac{1}{2}$. If 1 is added to the numerator and 10 is subtracted from the denominator, the value of the resulting fraction is $\frac{1}{4}$. What is the original fraction?

6. If the numerator of a fraction is tripled and 11 added to the denominator, the value of the resulting fraction is $\frac{1}{3}$. If, however, 1 is added to the numerator of the original fraction and 5 is added to its denominator, the resulting fraction is $\frac{1}{4}$. Find the original fraction.

7. If 5 is added to double the numerator of a certain fraction and 1 is added to its denominator, the resulting fraction is $\frac{3}{2}$. If, however, 3 is subtracted from triple the denominator of the original fraction and 2 is added to the numerator, the resulting fraction is equal to $\frac{1}{3}$. Find the original fraction.

8. If 1 is subtracted from the numerator of a certain fraction and 4 is subtracted from double the denominator, the result is $\frac{1}{5}$. If, however, 1 is added to triple the numerator of the original fraction and 8 is added to double the denominator, the resulting fraction is equal to $\frac{1}{2}$. Find the original fraction.

9. Find three numbers such that the sum of the first and second is 1; the difference between the second and third is -3; and three times the first less five times the third is -28.

10. The sum of three numbers is 39. Twice the second is 1 more than the first; the sum of the first and the third less three times the second is 3. Find the numbers.

ORAL EXERCISES: Digit problems

1. In the number 492, what is the units digit; the tens digit; the hundreds digit?

2. If the digits of the number 785 were reversed, what would be the new number?

3. What is the sum of the digits of 236?

4. If t is the tens digit and u the units digit of a number, what is the number? What is the sum of the digits? If the digits were reversed, what would be the new number?

ILLUSTRATIVE EXAMPLE: Digit problem

A certain number of two digits is 2 more than three times the sum of its digits. If the number is doubled and increased by 10, the result is the same as if the digits had been reversed. Find the number.

Solution. Let t be the tens digit; let u be the units digit. Then $10t + u$ is the number; $t + u$ is the sum of the digits; and $10u + t$ is the number with the digits in reverse order.

A certain number of two digits	is 2	more than	three times	the sum of its digits
$10t + u$	$= 2$	$+$	3	$(t + u)$

If the number is doubled	and increased by 10	the result is the same as if	the digits had been reversed
$2(10t + u)$	$+ 10$	$=$	$10u + t$

Simplifying each equation
$$10t + u = 2 + 3t + 3u$$
$$20t + 2u + 10 = 10u + t$$

Writing in standard form
$$7t - 2u = 2$$
$$19t - 8u = -10$$

Multiplier	Equation	New Equation
4	$7t - 2u = 2$	$28t - 8u = 8$
1	$19t - 8u = -10$	$19t - 8u = -10$
	Subtracting	$9t = 18$
		$t = 2$

Substituting $t = 2$ in
$$7t - 2u = 2$$
$$14 - 2u = 2$$
$$u = 6$$

The number is $10(2) + 6 = 26$ Answer

Check. Substituting these values in the statement of the problem.

$$26 \overset{?}{=} 2 + 3(2 + 6) \qquad\qquad 2(26) + 10 \overset{?}{=} 62$$
$$26 = 26 \qquad\qquad\qquad\qquad 62 = 62$$

EXERCISES: Digit problems

1. The units digit of a two-digit number is 4 more than the tens digit. The sum of the digits is 10. Find the number.

2. The tens digit of a two-digit number is 5 less than the units digit. The number is 10 more than three times the sum of the digits. Find the number.

3. A certain two-digit number divided by its units digit gives a quotient of 17. The sum of the digits is 13. Find the number.

4. A two-digit number is equal to five times the sum of its digits. If 9 is added to the number, the sum is the number with the digits in reversed order. Find the number.

5. The sum of the digits of a two-digit number is 12. One seventh of the number equals one fourth of the number obtained by reversing the digits. Find the number.

6. In a two-digit number, three times the units digit exceeds the tens digit by 3. Four times the sum of the digits exceeds by 3 the number with the digits in reversed order. Find the number.

7. If the digits of a two-digit number are interchanged, the resulting number is 6 more than seven times the sum of the digits. If the sum of the digits is subtracted from the original number, the difference is **27**. Find the number.

8. The sum of the digits of a three-digit number is 9. Twice the hundreds digit exceeds by 3 the sum of the tens digit and units digit. If 36 is added to the number, the sum is equal to twice the number found by reversing the digits. Find the number.

I L L U S T R A T I V E   E X A M P L E : Combination problem

On one day George played 9 holes of golf and 2 sets of tennis in 2 hr. and 50 min. On another day he played 18 holes of golf and 1 set of tennis in 3 hr. and 40 min. What was his average time to play 1 hole of golf? 1 set of tennis?

Solution. Insert the data of the problem in a box.

		Number of Holes of Golf or Sets of Tennis Played	Time in Minutes for Each Hole or Set Played	Total Time Played in Minutes
First day	Golf	9	g	$9\,g$
	Tennis	2	t	$2\,t$
Second day	Golf	18	g	$18\,g$
	Tennis	1	t	t

George played 9 holes of golf and 2 sets of tennis in 2 hr. and 50 min.

(170 min.)

$$9g \qquad + \qquad 2t \qquad = \qquad 170$$

George played 18 holes of golf and 1 set of tennis in 3 hr. and 40 min.

(220 min.)

$$18g \qquad + \qquad 1t \qquad = \qquad 220$$

Restating the equations $9g + 2t = 170$
$$18g + \ t = 220$$

Multiplier	Equation	New Equation
1	$9g + 2t = 170$	$9g + 2t = 170$
2	$18g + \ t = 220$	$36g + 2t = 440$
	Subtracting	$-27g \quad\ = -270$
		$g \quad\ = 10$

Substituting $g = 10$ in $18g + t = 220$
$$180 + t = 220$$
$$t = 40$$

Time to play 1 hole of golf, 10 min.; 1 set of tennis, 40 min.   Answer

EXERCISES: Combination problems

1. If 2 lb. of tea and 3 lb. of coffee cost $5.22, whereas 3 lb. of tea and 4 lb. of coffee cost $7.36, find the cost of 1 lb. of tea; 1 lb. of coffee.

2. Conrad and Walter had lunch together at the same stand.   Conrad paid $1.44 for his lunch of 4 hamburgers and 3 bottles of milk and Walter paid $1.05 for 3 hamburgers and 2 bottles of milk.   What was the cost of a hamburger?   a bottle of milk?

3. Eugie bought $\frac{1}{2}$ lb. of chocolate peppermints and $1\frac{1}{2}$ lb. of chocolate fruits for $1.98 and Kathy bought 2 lb. of peppermints and $\frac{1}{2}$ lb. of fruits for $1.87.   What was the cost of 1 lb. of peppermints?   1 lb. of fruits?

4. At the first performance given by the school dramatic club, 100 reserved seat tickets and 250 unreserved seat tickets were sold for a total of $260.   At the second performance, 80 reserved seat tickets and 300 unreserved seat tickets were sold for a total of $268.   Find the cost of each kind of ticket.

5. The labor cost of one repair job at the Colony Garage was $18 for 5 hr. of the mechanic's labor and 6 hr. of the assistant's labor.   The cost of a second job was $17.15 for 4 hr. of the mechanic's labor and 7 hr. of the assistant's labor.   How much did each man receive per hour?

6. For a class demonstration Casey combined 5 measures of x liquid with 7 measures of y liquid to form a mixture weighing 184 oz.   The next day he combined 4 measures of x liquid with 9 measures of y liquid to form a mixture weighing 205 oz.   Find the weight of 1 measure of each liquid.

ORAL EXERCISES: Investment problems

1. Express 3% as a fraction.

2. Express $2\frac{1}{2}$% as a fraction in simplest form.

3. Express $4\frac{1}{2}$% as a fraction in simplest form.

4. What is the annual interest of d dollars at 4%?

5. What is the annual income from stocks valued at s dollars and paying 7%?

6. What is the annual income from a business valued at b dollars and paying 9%?

7. What is the annual income from real estate valued at r dollars and paying 8%?

8. If a man borrows x dollars at 3% annual interest and y dollars at $4\frac{1}{2}$% annual interest, how much is the annual interest charge?

ILLUSTRATIVE EXAMPLE: Investment problem

A young married couple, in order to buy a house, borrowed a certain sum of money from the bank at 3% annual interest and a second sum from the local building and loan association at $4\frac{1}{2}$% annual interest. The annual interest charge at the bank exceeded the annual interest charges at the association by \$120. The interest charges at the bank for two years and the interest charges at the association for three years amounted to \$1140. How much money was borrowed from each source?

Solution. Insert the data of the problem in a box, and apply the formula $I = prt$.

		Amount Invested	Rate of Interest Expressed as a Fraction	Time	Total Interest
First arrangement	Bank	b	$\frac{3}{100}$	1	$\frac{3b}{100}$
	Association	a	$\frac{9}{200}$	1	$\frac{9a}{200}$
Second arrangement	Bank	b	$\frac{3}{100}$	2	$\frac{6b}{100}$
	Association	a	$\frac{9}{200}$	3	$\frac{27a}{200}$

The annual interest charge at the bank — minus — the annual interest charge at the association — is — \$120

$$\frac{3b}{100} - \frac{9a}{200} = 120$$

The interest charges at the bank for two years — and — the interest charges at the association for three years — amounted to — \$1140

$$\frac{6b}{100} + \frac{27a}{200} = 1140$$

From the statement of
the problem

$$\frac{3b}{100} - \frac{9a}{200} = 120$$

$$\frac{6b}{100} + \frac{27a}{200} = 1140$$

Clearing of fractions $6b - 9a = 24{,}000$

$12b + 27a = 228{,}000$

Multiplier	Equation	New Equation
2	$6b - 9a = 24{,}000$	$12b - 18a = 48{,}000$
1	$12b + 27a = 228{,}000$	$12b + 27a = 228{,}000$

Subtracting

$-45a = -180{,}000$

$a = 4000$

Substituting $a = 4000$ in

$6b - 9a$	$= 24{,}000$
$6b - 36{,}000$	$= 24{,}000$
$6b$	$= 60{,}000$
b	$= 10{,}000$

Hence $10,000 was borrowed from the bank and $4000 from the building and loan association. Answer

E X E R C I S E S : Investment problems

1. A retired teacher owned real estate which paid her 9% annually on its value. She also owned a paid-up insurance policy which paid 3% annually on the amount of the policy. Her annual income was $2160. Her income from the real estate exceeded the income from the insurance funds by $1440. What was the value of the real estate and the value of the insurance policy?

2. A man invests a part of his capital in bonds paying $4\frac{1}{2}\%$ annually and the remainder in stocks paying $5\frac{1}{2}\%$ annually. From these investments he receives an annual income of $1020. If he had invested in stocks the money he had put into bonds, and if he had invested in bonds the money he had placed in stocks, his annual income would have been $980. How much money did he place in each type of investment?

3. A man invested some money in stock A which paid 7% annually and some money in stock B which paid 5% annually. From these investments he received an annual income of $2600. Had stock A paid 4% and stock B paid 8%, his annual income would have been $2720. How much was invested in each type of stocks?

4. A boy ran a little store of his own in which he sold only soft drinks and candy bars. At the end of his first year he found that he had made 20% on his investments in soft drinks and 25% on his investments in candy. From these investments he received an annual income of $325. He found that his income from his sale of soft drinks exceeded his income from his sale of candy by $75. How much did he invest in each?

5. A girl had an account in a savings bank which paid $2\frac{1}{2}$% annual interest, and she also had bonds which paid 3% annual interest. From these investments she received a yearly income of $27. Her income from the bonds was twice as great as her income from the bank. How much money did she have in the bank? in savings bonds?

ILLUSTRATIVE EXAMPLE: Stream problem

To get camp supplies, Bob was obliged to go downstream 12 mi. and return. Using a motor boat, he required 1 hr. and 12 min. to go down and 2 hr. to return. Find the rate of the boat in still water and the rate of the stream.

Solution. Let b = rate of boat in still water

s = rate of stream

Hence $b + s$ = rate of boat downstream

$b - s$ = rate of boat upstream

Arranging the data in box form and applying the formula

Time (hr.) × Rate (mph) = Distance

	Time	Rate	Distance
Downstream	$1\frac{1}{5}$ or $\frac{6}{5}$	$b + s$	$\frac{6}{5}(b + s)$
Upstream	2	$b - s$	$2(b - s)$

Since the distance is 12 mi., then

Downstream $\frac{6}{5}(b + s) = 12$

Upstream $2(b - s) = 12$

Simplifying $6b + 6s = 60$

$2b - 2s = 12$

Dividing the first equation by 6 $\qquad b + s = 10$

Dividing the second equation by 2 $\qquad b - s = 6$

$$\text{Adding} \quad \overline{2b \qquad = 16}$$

$$b = 8$$

Substituting $b = 8$ in $\qquad b + s = 10$

$$8 + s = 10$$

$$s = 2$$

Hence, the boat's rate in still water is 8 mph; the stream's rate, 2 mph.   Answer

EXERCISES : Stream problems

1. The varsity eight can row the mile course downstream in $3\frac{3}{4}$ min. and the same course upstream in 5 min. Find the rate in miles per hour of the crew in still water and the rate of the stream.

2. A man can row 7 mi. down a stream in 1 hr. and 24 min., and row upstream the same distance in 2 hr. and 20 min. Find the man's rate of rowing in still water and the rate of the stream.

3. An airplane flying with the wind (tail wind) covered a distance of 360 mi. in 1 hr. and 20 min. On the return trip, flying against the wind (head wind) the plane was able to cover only 230 mi. in 1 hr. Find the rate of the plane in still air and the rate of the wind.

4. An airplane flying against a strong wind (head wind) covered a distance of 1000 mi. in 4 hr. and 10 min. On the return trip flying with the wind (tail wind) whose rate was one half that of the head wind, the airplane covered the same distance in 3 hr. and 20 min. Find the rate of the plane in still air and the rate of each wind.

5. A boy in his boat with an outboard motor went 10 mi. downstream in 1 hr. and 15 min. On his return trip his motor could develop only half its power and, as a result, the time required to return was 4 hr. What was the original speed of the boat in still water and what was the rate of the stream?

ILLUSTRATIVE EXAMPLE : Work problem

A father and son working together found that they could wash the windows of their house in $3\frac{3}{5}$ hr. Later in doing the same job the father worked 2 hr. alone and then he was joined by his son and together they finished the job in $2\frac{2}{5}$ hr. How long does it take each to wash the windows alone?

Solution. We arrange the data of the problem in box form.

	Number of Hours to Do the Job Alone	Fractional Part of the Work Done in 1 Hr.	Number of Hours Worked	Fractional Part of Work Completed
Father	f	$\dfrac{1}{f}$	$3\dfrac{3}{5}$ or $\dfrac{18}{5}$	$\dfrac{18}{5f}$
Son	s	$\dfrac{1}{s}$	$3\dfrac{3}{5}$ or $\dfrac{18}{5}$	$\dfrac{18}{5s}$
Father	f	$\dfrac{1}{f}$	$\left(2+2\dfrac{2}{5}\right)$ or $\dfrac{22}{5}$	$\dfrac{22}{5f}$
Son	s	$\dfrac{1}{s}$	$2\dfrac{2}{5}$ or $\dfrac{12}{5}$	$\dfrac{12}{5s}$

$$\underbrace{\text{Part done by father}} + \underbrace{\text{part done by son}} = \underbrace{\text{whole job}}$$

$$\frac{18}{5f} \quad + \quad \frac{18}{5s} \quad = \quad 1$$

$$\frac{22}{5f} \quad + \quad \frac{12}{5s} \quad = \quad 1$$

Simplifying the equations

Multiplier	Equation	New Equation
5	$\dfrac{18}{\mathbf{5}f} + \dfrac{18}{\mathbf{5}s} = 1$	$\dfrac{18}{f} + \dfrac{18}{s} = 5$
5	$\dfrac{22}{\mathbf{5}f} + \dfrac{12}{\mathbf{5}s} = 1$	$\dfrac{22}{f} + \dfrac{12}{s} = 5$

Using the new equation we solve for f by eliminating s

2	$\dfrac{18}{f} + \dfrac{\mathbf{18}}{\mathbf{s}} = 5$	$\dfrac{36}{f} + \dfrac{\mathbf{36}}{\mathbf{s}} = 10$
3	$\dfrac{22}{f} + \dfrac{\mathbf{12}}{\mathbf{s}} = 5$	$\dfrac{66}{f} + \dfrac{\mathbf{36}}{\mathbf{s}} = 15$

$$\text{Subtracting} \qquad -\frac{30}{f} \qquad = -5$$

$$\text{Solving for } f \qquad -30 = -5f$$
$$f = 6$$

Solving for s we substitute **6** for f
in the equation

$$\frac{18}{5f} + \frac{18}{5s} = 1$$

$$\frac{18}{5(6)} + \frac{18}{5s} = 1$$

$$\frac{3}{5} + \frac{18}{5s} = 1$$

$$\frac{18}{5s} = \frac{2}{5}$$

$$s = 9$$

Answering the question, we find the father can wash the windows in 6 hr. and the son can do the same job in 9 hr. Answer

EXERCISES: Work problems

1. Earl and Gary found that when they worked together they could trim the hedge around their lawn in $1\frac{1}{5}$ hr. On one occasion Earl worked 1 hr. and then quit; then Gary finished the job in $1\frac{1}{2}$ hr. more. How long does it take each alone to do the job?

2. Jane and her mother together can paint the woodwork of their living room in 3 hr. Jane began the job, worked 2 hr., and then rested. Her mother then worked for 2 hr. and then was called away. Jane returned and finished the job in 4 more hr. How long does it take each alone to paint the woodwork of the living room?

3. A tank can be filled with gasoline from two different pipes. On one day the tank was filled when the first pipe was open for $\frac{1}{2}$ hr. and the second pipe was open for 1 hr. and 10 min. On another day the tank was filled when the first pipe was open for 3 hr. and the second pipe was open for 20 min. How long does it take each pipe alone to fill the tank?

4. In a factory producing hardware, two machines working together can package for market 100 gross boxes of washers in $2\frac{2}{5}$ hr. On a certain day both machines worked 1 hr. and then the first machine broke down; the job of completing the packaging of 100 gross boxes was done by the second machine in $4\frac{1}{2}$ hr. more. How long does it take each working alone to package 100 gross boxes?

Hint. Packaging 100 gross boxes is one complete job.

5. In a chemical plant a large vat has two pipes entering it, a supply pipe, and another pipe which can be used as a supply pipe or as a drain pipe. When both pipes are used for supply, the vat can be filled in $2\frac{2}{5}$ hr. One day the attendant in error turned the valve on the second pipe to "drain" position, and it required 4 hr. to fill the vat. How long would it take each pipe alone to fill the vat?

6. A pool can be filled with water from three pipes in 2 hr. If only the first and second pipes are open, it takes 2 hr. 24 min. If only the first and third pipes are open, it takes 3 hr. How long would it take each pipe alone to fill the pool?

7. A tank can be filled with gasoline from two pipes and can be emptied by a third pipe. When all the pipes are open, the tank can be filled in 2 hr. If the first pipe is closed and the second and third pipes are open, the tank can be filled in 10 hr. If the third pipe is closed, the first two can fill the tank in 1 hr. How long does it take for the first pipe alone to fill the tank with gasoline? for the second pipe alone? How long does it take the third pipe alone to drain the tank?

The missing sock.   In a laundry a large vat had two drain pipes. With both pipes open the vat could be drained in 2 hr. The smaller pipe alone required 3 hr. longer than the larger pipe. One day the laundress, having failed to remove all the clothes, opened the drain pipes. When she returned 2 hr. later, she found the vat was still half full. In which drain pipe should she look for the missing sock? How long was this pipe clogged?

Determinants.   Simultaneous linear equations can be solved by means of determinants. When numbers are placed in a square array enclosed by two vertical bars, they form a determinant. $\begin{vmatrix} 5 & 4 \\ -2 & 6 \end{vmatrix}$ is a determinant. This determinant, consisting of numbers in two rows (horizontal) and two columns (vertical), is a determinant of the second order. A determinant of three rows and three columns is of the third order, etc.

The top row in a determinant is the first row. The row below the first row is the second row, and so on. The column on the extreme left is the first column. The column to the right of the first column is the second column, and so on. Each number in a row (or column) is an *element* of the determinant. In the following determinant the subscripts of an element indicate the row of the element.

$$\begin{vmatrix} a_1 & b_1 & c_1 \\ a_2 & b_2 & c_2 \\ a_3 & b_3 & c_3 \end{vmatrix}$$

The principal diagonal of a determinant begins at the upper left of the determinant and extends to the lower right. The secondary diagonal of a determinant begins at the upper right and extends to the lower left.

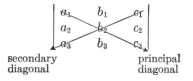

secondary   principal
diagonal   diagonal

The value of a determinant of any order consists of the algebraic sum of all the products which can be formed by taking one element and only one from each row and one element and only one from each column. For example, in a determinant of the second order

$$\begin{vmatrix} a_1 & b_1 \\ a_2 & b_2 \end{vmatrix}$$

the number of possible products of the elements as defined above is two, namely, a_1b_2 and a_2b_1. These products are terms of the expanded determinant. The sign to be given to each term will be explained as we discuss the expansion of each order of determinants. When a determinant is expressed in expanded form, the determinant is said to be developed.

The value of a second order determinant is obtained by subtracting from the product of the elements in the principal diagonal the product of the elements of the secondary diagonal.

ILLUSTRATIVE EXAMPLES: Evaluating determinants

1. Evaluate $\begin{vmatrix} 5 & 4 \\ 2 & 0 \end{vmatrix}$

Solution.

$$\begin{vmatrix} 5 & 4 \\ 2 & 0 \end{vmatrix} = (5)(0) - 4(2)$$

$$= 0 - 8$$

$$= -8 \quad \text{Answer}$$

2. Evaluate $\begin{vmatrix} a & c \\ -b & d \end{vmatrix}$

Solution.

$$\begin{vmatrix} a & c \\ -b & d \end{vmatrix} = ad - (-bc)$$

$$= ad + bc \quad \text{Answer}$$

3. Write as a determinant the difference of two products

$$(2)(3) - (-1)(4)$$

Solution. Since the first product is $(2)(3)$, we reverse our order of evaluating a determinant and insert 2 and 3 as numbers of the principal diagonal. Similarly we insert $(-1)(4)$ as numbers of the secondary diagonal

$$\begin{vmatrix} 2 & -1 \\ 4 & 3 \end{vmatrix} \quad \text{Answer}$$

Note. The value of a second order determinant is not changed if the numbers of a diagonal are changed in position as long as they remain in the diagonal. Thus

$$\begin{vmatrix} 2 & -1 \\ 4 & 3 \end{vmatrix} = \begin{vmatrix} 3 & 4 \\ -1 & 2 \end{vmatrix}$$

3. Write as a determinant $3 - 6$

Solution.

$3 - 6$ may be expressed $(3)(1) - (6)(1)$.
In determinant form

$$\begin{vmatrix} 3 & 6 \\ 1 & 1 \end{vmatrix} \text{ or } \begin{vmatrix} 1 & 1 \\ 6 & 3 \end{vmatrix}$$

$3 - 6$ may also be expressed $(3)(1) - (3)(2)$.
In determinant form

$$\begin{vmatrix} 3 & 3 \\ 2 & 1 \end{vmatrix} \text{ or } \begin{vmatrix} 1 & 2 \\ 3 & 3 \end{vmatrix}$$

Any one solution is sufficient.

EXERCISES: Evaluating determinants

In ex. 1–9 find the value of each second order determinant.

1. $\begin{vmatrix} 6 & 4 \\ 8 & 12 \end{vmatrix}$
4. $\begin{vmatrix} \frac{3}{4} & \frac{1}{16} \\ \frac{1}{2} & \frac{5}{8} \end{vmatrix}$
7. $\begin{vmatrix} \frac{12}{5} & -\frac{1}{10} \\ 18 & -\frac{3}{2} \end{vmatrix}$

2. $\begin{vmatrix} 5 & 0 \\ 7 & 2 \end{vmatrix}$
5. $\begin{vmatrix} -\frac{1}{3} & 5 \\ 0 & \frac{2}{9} \end{vmatrix}$
8. $\begin{vmatrix} 0.2 & -0.8 \\ -0.6 & -0.4 \end{vmatrix}$

3. $\begin{vmatrix} 13 & -11 \\ 6 & 3 \end{vmatrix}$
6. $\begin{vmatrix} \frac{5}{4} & 6 \\ -\frac{9}{8} & 1\frac{1}{2} \end{vmatrix}$
9. $\begin{vmatrix} 6.4 & -0.1 \\ 8.6 & -2 \end{vmatrix}$

In each example of ex. 10–18 find the value of the fraction.

10. $x = \dfrac{\begin{vmatrix} 8 & 5 \\ 7 & 6 \end{vmatrix}}{\begin{vmatrix} 1 & 5 \\ 4 & 6 \end{vmatrix}}$
13. $p = \dfrac{\begin{vmatrix} 0.3 & 0.6 \\ 0.2 & -0.4 \end{vmatrix}}{\begin{vmatrix} -0.5 & -0.4 \\ 0.8 & 0.6 \end{vmatrix}}$
16. $x = \dfrac{\begin{vmatrix} c_1 & b_1 \\ c_2 & b_2 \end{vmatrix}}{\begin{vmatrix} a_1 & b_1 \\ a_2 & b_2 \end{vmatrix}}$

11. $y = \dfrac{\begin{vmatrix} 1 & 8 \\ 4 & 7 \end{vmatrix}}{\begin{vmatrix} 1 & 5 \\ 4 & 6 \end{vmatrix}}$
14. $q = \dfrac{\begin{vmatrix} 0 & 6 \\ -4 & 0 \end{vmatrix}}{\begin{vmatrix} 1 & 8 \\ 0 & -9 \end{vmatrix}}$
17. $y = \dfrac{\begin{vmatrix} a_1 & c_1 \\ a_2 & c_2 \end{vmatrix}}{\begin{vmatrix} a_1 & b_1 \\ a_2 & b_2 \end{vmatrix}}$

12. $z = \dfrac{\begin{vmatrix} \frac{1}{2} & \frac{5}{8} \\ \frac{1}{4} & \frac{1}{8} \end{vmatrix}}{\begin{vmatrix} \frac{1}{2} & -\frac{2}{3} \\ \frac{1}{4} & -\frac{1}{6} \end{vmatrix}}$
15. $r = \dfrac{\begin{vmatrix} -\frac{1}{4} & \frac{1}{10} \\ \frac{1}{2} & -\frac{1}{5} \end{vmatrix}}{\begin{vmatrix} \frac{1}{16} & \frac{1}{10} \\ -\frac{1}{8} & -\frac{1}{2} \end{vmatrix}}$
18. $x = \dfrac{\begin{vmatrix} 2.6 & 1.3 \\ -2.0 & 1.0 \end{vmatrix}}{\begin{vmatrix} 5.2 & -1.0 \\ 2.6 & 2.0 \end{vmatrix}}$

In ex. 19–24, write the given expression in determinant form.

19. $ab - cd$ **22.** $17 - 13$

20. $(6)(8) - (12)(\frac{1}{4})$ **23.** $22 + 15$

21. $(0.2)(0.3) - (0.6)(0.4)$ **24.** $rs + tv$

25. Write a determinant of the second order which has a value of 10.

26. Write a determinant of the second order which has a value of 0.

Solving simultaneous linear equations by determinants.   Using the addition-subtraction method, we shall solve for x and y in the system of equations:

$$a_1x + b_1y = c_1$$
$$a_2x + b_2y = c_2$$

Eliminating the y terms

Multiplier	Equation	New Equation
b_2	$a_1x + b_1y = c_1$	$a_1b_2x + b_1b_2y = b_2c_1$
b_1	$a_2x + b_2y = c_2$	$a_2b_1x + b_1b_2y = b_1c_2$

Subtracting $a_1b_2x - a_2b_1x = b_2c_1 - b_1c_2$

Factoring out the x $x(a_1b_2 - a_2b_1) = b_2c_1 - b_1c_2$

$$x = \frac{b_2c_1 - b_1c_2}{a_1b_2 - a_2b_1}$$

In a similar manner we find $y = \dfrac{a_1c_2 - a_2c_1}{a_1b_2 - a_2b_1}$ when $a_1b_2 - a_2b_1 \neq 0$.

We can express each of these results as a quotient of two determinants.

$$x = \frac{\begin{vmatrix} c_1 & b_1 \\ c_2 & b_2 \end{vmatrix}}{\begin{vmatrix} a_1 & b_1 \\ a_2 & b_2 \end{vmatrix}} \qquad\qquad y = \frac{\begin{vmatrix} a_1 & c_1 \\ a_2 & c_2 \end{vmatrix}}{\begin{vmatrix} a_1 & b_1 \\ a_2 & b_2 \end{vmatrix}}$$

The denominators of both fractions are the same, namely, $\begin{vmatrix} a_1 & b_1 \\ a_2 & b_2 \end{vmatrix}$.

The first column $\begin{smallmatrix} a_1 \\ a_2 \end{smallmatrix}$ consists of the respective coefficients of x, and the

second column $\begin{smallmatrix} b_1 \\ b_2 \end{smallmatrix}$ consists of the respective coefficients of y in the given

simultaneous equations.   Notice that the numerator of the value of x,

namely, $\begin{vmatrix} c_1 & b_1 \\ c_2 & b_2 \end{vmatrix}$ is the same as the denominator $\begin{vmatrix} a_1 & b_1 \\ a_2 & b_2 \end{vmatrix}$ except that

the column $\begin{smallmatrix} c_1 \\ c_2 \end{smallmatrix}$, the constant terms in the original equation, is substituted for the column $\dfrac{a_1}{a_2}$, the coefficients of x, in the original equation.   Simi-

larly, the numerator of the value of y, namely, $\begin{vmatrix} a_1 & c_1 \\ a_2 & c_2 \end{vmatrix}$ is the same as

the denominator $\begin{vmatrix} a_1 & b_1 \\ a_2 & b_2 \end{vmatrix}$ except that the column $\dfrac{c_1}{c_2}$, the constant terms

in the original equations, is substituted for the column $\dfrac{b_1}{b_2}$, the coefficients

of y, in the original equation.

ILLUSTRATIVE EXAMPLE : Solving simultaneous linear equations by determinants

Solve for x and y in the system of equations:
$$2x - 3y = \;\;\; 18$$
$$5x + 6y = -\,9$$

Solution. Apply the formula $\quad x = \dfrac{\begin{vmatrix} c_1 & b_1 \\ c_2 & b_2 \end{vmatrix}}{\begin{vmatrix} a_1 & b_1 \\ a_2 & b_2 \end{vmatrix}}$

where a_1 and a_2 are the respective coefficients of x; b_1 and b_2, the respective coefficients of y; and c_1 and c_2 the respective constant terms.

$$x = \dfrac{\begin{vmatrix} 18 & -3 \\ -9 & 6 \end{vmatrix}}{\begin{vmatrix} 2 & -3 \\ 5 & 6 \end{vmatrix}} = \dfrac{108 - 27}{12 + 15} = \dfrac{81}{27} = 3$$

To solve for y we apply the formula $y = \dfrac{\begin{vmatrix} a_1 & c_1 \\ a_2 & c_2 \end{vmatrix}}{\begin{vmatrix} a_1 & b_1 \\ a_2 & b_2 \end{vmatrix}}$ We already have

the value of the denominator 27, since it is the same as the denominator for the value of x. Substituting values in the numerator,

we have $\qquad\qquad y = \dfrac{\begin{vmatrix} 2 & 18 \\ 5 & -9 \end{vmatrix}}{27} = \dfrac{-18 - 90}{27} = -4$

$$x = 3; \; y = -4. \quad \text{Answer}$$

E X E R C I S E S : Solving simultaneous linear equations by determinants

Solve each of the following systems of equations by determinants.

1. $10x + 6y = -4$
$1.5x + y = -\frac{1}{2}$

2. $6m + 7n = 3$
$2m + 5n = 1$

3. $\frac{7}{3}x - y = 9$
$5x - 6y = 0$

4. $x + \frac{3}{2}y = 2$
$x - 2y = 1$

5. $2p + 3q = 2$
$6p - 3q = 2$

6. $4v - 6w = 8$
$2v - 5w = 4$

7. $3r + 2s = 12$
$2r + 3s = 13$

8. $6x + y = 16$
$5x - y = 6$

9. $2x + 5y = 1$
$\frac{7}{2}x + 3y = 1$

In ex. 10–15 write each system of equations in standard form before solving by determinants.

10. $y - x = 0$
$3y + 30 = 8x$

11. $3m = 43 - 4n$
$n - 2 = m$

12. $2r - 3s = 0$
$3s = 8r - 3$

13. $5p + 7q = 1$
$21q = 10p - 7$

14. $6x = 4y - 1$
$12y - 3x = 8$

15. $3y - 16x = 4$
$8x = 3 - 2y$

Evaluating third order determinants.   To evaluate a third order determinant it is convenient to copy to the right of the determinant the first two columns in this manner :

$$
\begin{vmatrix} a_1 & b_1 & c_1 \\ a_2 & b_2 & c_2 \\ a_3 & b_3 & c_3 \end{vmatrix} \begin{matrix} a_1 & b_1 \\ a_2 & b_2 \\ a_3 & b_3 \end{matrix}
$$

The three positive terms in the expansion of the determinant are obtained by multiplying the terms along each of the following arrows :

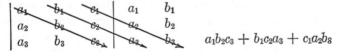

$$a_1 b_2 c_3 + b_1 c_2 a_3 + c_1 a_2 b_3$$

The three negative terms in the expansion of the determinant are obtained by multiplying the terms along each of the following arrows :

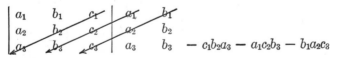

$$- c_1 b_2 a_3 - a_1 c_2 b_3 - b_1 a_2 c_3$$

Therefore, the value of the determinant is :

$$
\begin{vmatrix} a_1 & b_1 & c_1 \\ a_2 & b_2 & c_2 \\ a_3 & b_3 & c_3 \end{vmatrix} = a_1 b_2 c_3 + b_1 c_2 a_3 + c_1 a_2 b_3 - c_1 b_2 a_3 - a_1 c_2 b_3 - b_1 a_2 c_3
$$

ILLUSTRATIVE EXAMPLE: Evaluating a third order determinant

Evaluate:
$$\begin{vmatrix} 2 & -1 & -2 \\ 3 & 2 & 1 \\ 1 & 0 & -3 \end{vmatrix}$$

Solution.

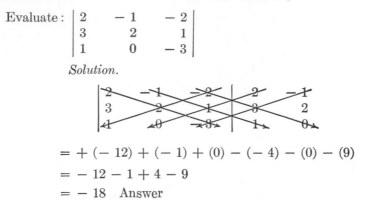

$$= +(-12) + (-1) + (0) - (-4) - (0) - (9)$$
$$= -12 - 1 + 4 - 9$$
$$= -18 \quad \text{Answer}$$

EXERCISES: Evaluating determinants of the third order

Evaluate each of the following:

1.
$$\begin{vmatrix} 1 & -2 & 3 \\ 2 & 0 & -1 \\ 3 & 2 & -3 \end{vmatrix}$$

3.
$$\begin{vmatrix} 0 & 0 & 0 \\ 8 & 9 & 10 \\ -6 & -8 & -7 \end{vmatrix}$$

5.
$$\begin{vmatrix} \frac{1}{2} & 2 & -2 \\ \frac{1}{4} & 4 & -4 \\ \frac{1}{8} & 8 & -8 \end{vmatrix}$$

2.
$$\begin{vmatrix} 0 & -1 & -2 \\ 2 & 3 & 0 \\ 4 & -3 & -4 \end{vmatrix}$$

4.
$$\begin{vmatrix} 0 & 2 & -2 \\ 0 & 3 & -3 \\ 7 & 1 & -1 \end{vmatrix}$$

6.
$$\begin{vmatrix} -\frac{1}{3} & -3 & 6 \\ -\frac{1}{9} & -9 & 0 \\ -\frac{1}{27} & -27 & 3 \end{vmatrix}$$

Solving linear equations in three unknowns by determinants. On page 146 we solved a system of linear equations in x and y and expressed their respective values in determinant form. By following the same methods, a system of linear equations in three unknowns can be solved and the results expressed in determinant form. Without showing the detailed solution we shall state the respective values of x, y, and z in the following equations

$$a_1x + b_1y + c_1z = d_1$$
$$a_2x + b_2y + c_2z = d_2$$
$$a_3x + b_3y + c_3z = d_3$$

$$x = \frac{\begin{vmatrix} d_1 & b_1 & c_1 \\ d_2 & b_2 & c_2 \\ d_3 & b_3 & c_3 \end{vmatrix}}{\begin{vmatrix} a_1 & b_1 & c_1 \\ a_2 & b_2 & c_2 \\ a_3 & b_3 & c_3 \end{vmatrix}} \quad y = \frac{\begin{vmatrix} a_1 & d_1 & c_1 \\ a_2 & d_2 & c_2 \\ a_3 & d_3 & c_3 \end{vmatrix}}{\begin{vmatrix} a_1 & b_1 & c_1 \\ a_2 & b_2 & c_2 \\ a_3 & b_3 & c_3 \end{vmatrix}} \quad z = \frac{\begin{vmatrix} a_1 & b_1 & d_1 \\ a_2 & b_2 & d_2 \\ a_3 & b_3 & d_3 \end{vmatrix}}{\begin{vmatrix} a_1 & b_1 & c_1 \\ a_2 & b_2 & c_2 \\ a_3 & b_3 & c_3 \end{vmatrix}}$$

The determinant denominator of each fraction is the same. The numerator determinant is the same as the denominator determinant except for the following: In the value for x, the d column, made up of the respective constant terms, replaces the a column, the respective coefficients of x. In the value for y, the d column replaces the b column, the respective coefficients of y. In the value of z, the d column replaces the c column, the respective coefficients of z.

ILLUSTRATIVE EXAMPLE: Solving simultaneous linear equations in three unknowns by determinants

Solve for x, y, and z by determinants in the system of equations:

$$3x + 5y = 8$$
$$4x + 7z = 18$$
$$y + z = 3$$

Solution. We rewrite the equations, expressing each in three unknowns and giving a zero coefficient to the unknown which is not in the original equation.

$$3x + 5y + 0z = 8$$
$$4x + 0y + 7z = 18$$
$$0x + y + z = 3$$

Applying the formula

$$x = \frac{\begin{vmatrix} d_1 & b_1 & c_1 \\ d_2 & b_2 & c_2 \\ d_3 & b_3 & c_3 \end{vmatrix}}{\begin{vmatrix} a_1 & b_1 & c_1 \\ a_2 & b_2 & c_2 \\ a_3 & b_3 & c_6 \end{vmatrix}}; \quad x = \frac{\begin{vmatrix} 8 & 5 & 0 \\ 18 & 0 & 7 \\ 3 & 1 & 1 \end{vmatrix}}{\begin{vmatrix} 3 & 5 & 0 \\ 4 & 0 & 7 \\ 0 & 1 & 1 \end{vmatrix}} = \frac{0 + 105 + 0 - 0 - 90 - 56}{0 + 0 + 0 - 0 - 20 - 21}$$

$$\text{Hence } x = \frac{-41}{-41} = 1$$

Similarly

$$y = \frac{\begin{vmatrix} a_1 & d_1 & c_1 \\ a_2 & d_2 & c_2 \\ a_3 & d_3 & c_3 \end{vmatrix}}{-41}; \quad y = \frac{\begin{vmatrix} 3 & 8 & 0 \\ 4 & 18 & 7 \\ 0 & 3 & 1 \end{vmatrix}}{-41} = \frac{54 + 0 + 0 - 0 - 32 - 63}{-41};$$

$$y = \frac{-41}{-41} = 1$$

Similarly

$$z = \dfrac{\begin{vmatrix} a_1 & b_1 & d_1 \\ a_2 & b_2 & d_2 \\ a_3 & b_3 & d_3 \end{vmatrix}}{-41}; \; z = \dfrac{\begin{vmatrix} 3 & 5 & 8 \\ 4 & 0 & 18 \\ 0 & 1 & 3 \end{vmatrix}}{-41} = \dfrac{0 + 0 + 32 - 0 - 60 - 54}{-41};$$

$$z = \dfrac{-82}{-41} = 2$$

$$x = 1, \, y = 1, \, z = 2 \quad \text{Answer}$$

E X E R C I S E S : Solving systems of equations in three unknowns by determinants

Solve each of the following systems of equations by determinants.

1. $x + 2y = 3$
$\qquad 3y + \; z = 2$
$\qquad 3x + 2z = 1$

2. $3x - \; y = 7$
$\qquad 3y - \; z = 5$
$\qquad x - 3z = 0$

3. $2x - y + z = 1$
$\qquad 3x + y + z = 2$
$\qquad x + y + z = 0$

4. $4x + 5y + 9z = 0$
$\qquad 6x - 3y + 3z = 7$
$\qquad 2x + 2y + 6z = 1$

5. $x - 2y + 3z = -3$
$\qquad 2x - 3y - \; z = 7$
$\qquad 3x + \; y - 2z = 6$

6. $x + 2y - \; z = 2$
$\qquad 3x - 2y + 2z = 0$
$\qquad 5x - 4y + 3z = 1$

7. $x + 3y + \; z = 10$
$\qquad x + \; y + 3z = 12$
$\qquad 3x + \; y + \; z = \; 8$

8. $\frac{1}{6}x - \frac{1}{5}y + \frac{1}{4}z = 3$
$\qquad \frac{1}{5}x - \frac{1}{4}y + \frac{1}{5}z = 1$
$\qquad \frac{1}{4}x - \frac{1}{3}y + \frac{1}{2}z = 5$

In ex. 9 and 10 write each system of equations in standard form before solving by determinants.

9. $x + y + 2z = 2$
$\qquad\quad y - 5x = 6z$
$\qquad 4z + 5 - x = y$

10. $z + 4y + 3x = 9$
$\qquad 6x - 10 = 8y - z$
$\qquad\quad 15 - z = -12y$

Solving problems by graphs.   This method of solving problems is used in interception problems of air and surface navigation, in engineering, and in industry, where the greater interest is in the progress of the graph at any given time. For example, in production charts the planned production is plotted, and then the actual production from day to day is plotted on the same axes. The two graphs give a means of comparing the planned schedule with the actual production. In our work we shall use simple problems of motion which illustrate the same principles.

ILLUSTRATIVE EXAMPLES: Solving problems by graphs

1. An automobile left a certain place at 8 A.M. and traveled at the rate of 30 mph. Two hours later a second automobile left the same place and traveled at 60 mph in order to overtake the first. At what time did the second automobile overtake the first and at what distance from the starting point?

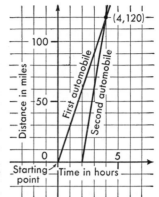

Solution. On graph paper prepare a coordinate system. Let each unit of the horizontal axis represent **one hour of time**; let each unit on the vertical axis represent **10 mi.** of **distance**; let the origin represent the starting point. Since the first automobile travels 30 mph, we measure 1 unit to the right on the horizontal (time) axis to represent one hour and 3 units up (3 × 10) on the line parallel to the vertical (distance) axis to represent 30 mi. and plot the point. We draw the line passing through this point and the origin. The coordinates of each point of this line give the elapsed time in hours and the distance, in miles, covered by the first automobile. Since the second automobile started two hours later, we measure two units to the right on the horizontal axis and plot that point. Also, since the second automobile travels 60 mph, we measure from the point we have just plotted one unit to the right on the time axis to represent one hour and 6 units (6 × 10) up on the line parallel to the distance axis to represent 60 mi. and plot the point. We draw the line passing through the two points. These two lines **intersect** at a point **(4, 120)** Therefore the second automobile overtook the first **4 hr.** after the first had started or at 12:00 noon, at a distance of **120 mi.** from the starting place.

2. Bob and Jack camped on the same river but 50 mi. apart. They planned to get together so Bob broke camp at 7 A.M. and left for Jack's camp making 6 mph in his motor boat. At 8 A.M. Jack broke camp and set out to meet Bob traveling in his motor boat at 4 mph. An hour after starting Jack developed motor trouble and was delayed 2 hr., after which he continued his trip. At what time did he meet Bob and how far had Bob traveled?

Solution. Draw graphs as directed in previous problem. Reading the graph we find they met at approximately **1:10** P.M. at a distance of approximately **36 mi.** from Bob's camp.

E X E R C I S E S : Solving problems by graphs

1. Reading from the graph of illustrative example 1, how far apart were the automobiles *a)* at the time the second automobile started? *b)* one hour after the second automobile started? *c)* $1\frac{1}{2}$ hr. after the second automobile started?

2. Reading the graph of illustrative ex. 2, how far apart were the boys *a)* 2 hr. after Bob had started? *b)* 4 hr. after Bob had started? *c)* 5 hr. after Bob had started?

3. A factory received an order for 100 units of a certain article. One machine can turn out 4 units per hour and a second can turn out 6 units per hour. If the first machine started at 7 A.M. and the second started at 9 A.M., at what time will all the units be made? Use a graph to obtain the solution.

4. If, in problem 3, the machine which made 6 units per hour had broken down after two hours of operation and did not start operating again until three hours later, at what time would all the units have been made? Plot the graph of the problem on the same axes used in problem 3. From the two graphs determine by how much time the total production was delayed due to the breakdown of the machine.

5. A destroyer leaves port at 12 noon making 30 knots on a course due east. Five hours later a helicopter making 90 knots set out from the same port to deliver official papers to the destroyer. Use a graph to determine what time the helicopter overtook the destroyer and at what distance from the port of departure.

6. Two men living in towns 100 mi. apart planned to meet each other at a place between the towns. Because of a traffic jam one man could drive at an average speed of only 20 mph. while the second drove at a rate of 40 mph. One hour after starting, the second car developed engine trouble, was delayed one hour for repairs, and then continued its trip at a rate of 25 mph. If both men left their respective homes at 8:30 A.M., at what time did they meet? Use a graph to obtain the solution.

7. At 4:30 A.M. an advanced radar observation post reported that a plane, 1000 mi. from an airbase, was advancing toward the base at an estimated rate of 400 mph. From the base a plane whose speed is 500 mph was immediately sent out to intercept the first plane. Use a graph to determine at what time the interception is made.

Doings of Dimbo.   When Dimbo's art class was assigned to do an outdoor painting, Dimbo soon found that he had set up his materials on the wrong side of the fence.

What error did Dimbo make in his solution of the following system of linear equations?

Solve for x, y, and z by determinants.

$$2x + y - 4 = 0$$
$$2x - z - 3 = 0$$
$$x + y + z - 2 = 0$$

Dimbo's solution:

CHAPTER REVIEW EXERCISES

1. State whether each pair of equations is simultaneous, inconsistent, or dependent.

a) $x + 3y = 4$ b) $3x - y = 6$ c) $x - 2y = 3$

    $2x + 6y = 5$ $2x + y = 3$ $3x - 6y = 9$

2. The graph of which of the following equations passes through the origin?

a) $x + 2y - 3 = 0$ b) $3x = 4y$ c) $5y = 6x - 7$

3. The graph of the equation $y = 2$ is parallel to what axis?

4. Give the slope and y intercept of the graph of $6x - 2y = 7$.

5. Write the equation whose graph has a slope of $-\frac{2}{3}$ and whose y intercept is 4.

6. Solve graphically for x and y: $x = 3y - 5$
$$x = -2y + 10$$

7. Solve for x and y by the addition-subtraction method
$$3x + 2y = 7$$
$$2x - y = 0$$

8. Solve for r and s by the substitution method
$$r = 1 - 2s$$
$$2r + 6s = -3$$

9. Solve for m and n in the equations $\quad 0.1\,m + 0.6n = 0$
$$0.3\,m - 0.4n = 1.1$$

10. Solve for x and y in the equations $\quad \dfrac{2x - 3}{3x - 7} = \dfrac{6y + 5}{9y + 6}$
$$\dfrac{x - 3y}{x + 3y} = \dfrac{5}{3}$$

11. Solve for x and y in terms of the other letters $\quad x - ay = b$
$$x - by = a$$

12. Solve for x and y in the equations $\quad \dfrac{5}{4x} + \dfrac{2}{3y} = \dfrac{1}{2}$
$$\dfrac{2}{3x} + \dfrac{5}{2y} = -\dfrac{37}{6}$$

13. A student pilot in a light plane flying against a head wind covered a measured distance on the ground of 25 mi. in 15 min. When flying with the wind, he covers a distance of 35 mi. in the same time. At what air speed (rate of plane in calm air) is the pilot flying and what is the rate of the wind?

14. An owner of a garage found that one of his mechanics and the mechanic's assistant can overhaul an engine in 24 hr. of working time. On one occasion the mechanic worked 30 hr. alone on the job, and his assistant completed the job in 15 hr. more. How long does it take each working alone to do the job?

15. A businessman invested a certain amount of money in real estate paying 8% annually and another amount of money in stocks paying $5\frac{1}{2}$% annually. From these investments his yearly income amounted to $4100. If he had invested in stocks the same amount of money he now has in real estate and if he had invested in real estate the same amount of money he now has in stocks, his yearly income would have amounted to $4000. How much money does the man have in real estate? How much money does he have in stocks?

16. A girl, on a visit to her grandmother, traveled 60 mi. by train and 20 mi. by bus. The total cost of her train and bus ticket was $3.25. On her trip home she used a different route going 48 mi. by bus and 32 mi. by train at a total cost of $2.76. What is the cost of travel per mile by train and the cost of travel per mile by bus?

17. Evaluate the determinant $\begin{vmatrix} 5.6 & -2.5 \\ 3.8 & -1.2 \end{vmatrix}$

18. Write as a determinant and evaluate: $(7.9)(0.2) - (1.4)(0.5)$

19. Write a determinant of the second order which has a value of 12.

20. Evaluate the determinant: $\begin{vmatrix} 1.2 & -1 & 0 \\ 4 & 1 & -10 \\ -2.5 & 1 & 5 \end{vmatrix}$

21. Solve the following system of equations by determinants:
$$\tfrac{1}{2}x + \tfrac{1}{3}y = 4$$
$$\tfrac{1}{3}x - \tfrac{1}{4}y = 1$$

22. Solve the following system of equations for y by determinants:
$$2.4x - 3.5y = 1$$
$$1.6y - 4.8z = 1$$
$$6.4x - 6z = 1$$

CUMULATIVE REVIEW EXERCISES

1. Divide $20 - 27a - a^2 + 6a^3$ by $5 - 3a$

2. Factor completely: $18r^2 + 3rs - 6s^2$

3. Factor completely: $a^2x + b^2x - b^2y - a^2y$

4. Simplify: $\dfrac{1}{t^2 - 1} + \dfrac{t}{1 - t} - 1$

5. Solve for y: $\dfrac{3y - 1}{7} - \dfrac{4y + 1}{21} = \dfrac{3y - 2}{3} - \dfrac{10}{3}$

6. Simplify: $\left[5 - \dfrac{a^2 - 19x^2}{a^2 - 4x^2}\right] \div \left[3 - \dfrac{a - 5x}{a - 2x}\right]$

7. Solve for h in terms of the other letters: $A = \dfrac{rm - cr + ch}{2}$

8. Solve for x: $\dfrac{3 - 2x}{x + 3} = \dfrac{26 - x^2}{x^2 - x - 12} - \dfrac{x + 2}{x - 4}$

9. Write the linear equation the slope of whose graph is -3 and whose y intercept is 5. Draw the graph of the equation.

10. Solve the following system of equations for x and y in terms of a and b:

$$3x + 4ay = 8ab$$
$$\frac{x}{a} + 2y = 4b$$

11. Solve the following system of equations for x and y:

$$\frac{5}{x} + \frac{3}{y} = \frac{3}{2}$$
$$\frac{3}{x} = \frac{2}{y} + \frac{4}{15}$$

12. How many quarts of pure water must be evaporated from an 18-qt. solution that is 10% acid in order to make a solution that is 15% acid?

CHAPTER 7 *Ratio, Proportion, and Variation*

Ratio. *The ratio of two numbers* is the indicated division of the two numbers. For example, the ratio of 4 yd. to 3 yd. is $\frac{4}{3}$; the ratio of one dozen units to 5 units is $\frac{12}{5}$; the ratio of 2 hr. to 17 min. is $\frac{120}{17}$ (converting to like units). The ratio $\frac{4}{3}$ may also be written in the form 4 : 3, similarly, the ratio $\frac{a}{b}$ may be written $a : b$. Since a ratio is a fraction, both the numerator and the denominator may be multiplied or divided by the same quantity (except zero) without changing the value of the ratio. For example, the ratio 8 : 12 is equal to the ratio 2 : 3.

E X E R C I S E S : Expressing ratios in simplified form

In ex. 1–8, express each ratio in simplest form.

1. $\frac{9}{12}$ **2.** $\frac{16\,a^3b^4}{24\,a^2b^5}$ **3.** $49\,m^4 : 28n^6$ **4.** $\frac{6}{7} : \frac{8}{9}$ **5.** $2\frac{1}{4} : 3\frac{3}{8}$

6. $\dfrac{p - q}{p^3 - q^3}$ **7.** $(a^2 - \frac{1}{81}) : (\frac{1}{9} - a)$ **8.** $\left(\dfrac{x^2}{y^2} - 1\right) : \left(\dfrac{x^3}{y^3} + 1\right)$

9. Find the ratio of a period of one week to a period of 48 hr.

10. Find the ratio of a nautical mile (6080 ft.) to a statute mile (5280 ft.).

11. Find the ratio of the circumference of a circle to its diameter.

12. Find the ratio of 2 kilowatts of electricity to 500 watts (a kilowatt is 1000 watts).

ILLUSTRATIVE EXAMPLES: Applying ratio to number problems

1. A father bequeathed $36,000 to be divided among his three sons in the continued ratio 3:4:5, with the oldest receiving the largest share and the youngest receiving the smallest. How much did each son receive?

Solution. The money is to be divided in the ratio 3:4:5 or a total of 12 parts. Let each part be x. Then the oldest son receives $5x$, the next son $4x$, and the youngest son $3x$. Hence

$$5x + 4x + 3x = \$36{,}000$$
$$12x = 36{,}000$$
$$x = 3000$$

Therefore $5x = \$15{,}000$, oldest son's share
$4x = \$12{,}000$, second son's share
$3x = \$9000$, youngest son's share

2. Two numbers are in the ratio 2:7. If 6 is added to the first number and 2 is subtracted from the second number, the resulting numbers are in the ratio 5:6. Find the original numbers.

Solution. Let $2x$ and $7x$ represent the original numbers. Then $2x + 6$ and $7x - 2$ represent the resulting numbers.

Since the ratio of these two numbers is 5:6, we have the equation

$$\frac{2x + 6}{7x - 2} = \frac{5}{6}$$

Clearing of fractions $6(2x + 6) = 5(7x - 2)$
Removing parentheses $12x + 36 = 35x - 10$
Hence $-23x = -46$
$$x = 2$$

The original numbers are $\left.\begin{array}{l} 2x = 4 \\ 7x = 14 \end{array}\right\}$ Answer

E X E R C I S E S : Applying ratio to number problems

1. Separate a line 39 in. long into two parts which have the ratio of 4:9.

2. A pencil 6 in. long is divided into lengths in the ratio of 2:3:4 with the respective lengths colored red, white, and blue. How long is the blue length?

3. The halls and stairways of an office building were finished in marble while the floors of the offices were covered with rubberized blocks. How many square feet of each were required if the ratio of the area of the floor space of the halls and stairway to the area of the floor space of the offices was 3:17 and the total floor space was 18,900 sq. ft.?

4. A supermarket is divided into departments for the sale of meats, fruits, groceries, and supplies with the shelf area assigned to each in the ratio 4:3:8:2 respectively. If the total shelf area is 85,000 sq. ft., how much is assigned to each department?

5. Two numbers are in the ratio 3:7. Three times the larger number added to five times the smaller number equals 44. Find the two numbers.

6. Two men worked the same number of hours, but the ratio of their hourly rate of pay was 7:6. If their total pay was $33.80, how much did each receive?

7. A chemist wished to make a mixture of concentrated hydrochloric acid and distilled water so that the ratio of the acid to the water would be 7:2. If the chemist started with 210 cc. of acid, how much water should he add?

8. The ratio of two numbers is 5:6. If 12 is subtracted from each number, the ratio of the resulting numbers is 3:4. Find the numbers.

9. The ratio of Walter's present age to Byron's age is 5:16. Fourteen years ago the ratio of their respective ages was 3:25. What is the present age of each?

10. Six years ago the ratio of Bob's age to Morgan's was 1:4. Six years hence the ratio of their respective ages will be 5:8. What is the present age of each?

11. Eight years hence the ratio of Geoffrey's age to Rowland's age will be 12:5. Four years ago the ratio of their respective ages was 9:2. What is the present age of each?

12. Find the ratio of x to y if $7(x + y) = 9(x - y)$.

Proportion. *A proportion* is an equation which states that one ratio equals another. Thus, $\frac{5}{9} = \frac{10}{18}$ is a proportion. Similarly, $\frac{a}{b} = \frac{c}{d}$ is a proportion. The numbers of a proportion are its *terms*. In $\frac{a}{b} = \frac{c}{d}$, the numbers a, b,

c, and d are respectively the first, second, third, and fourth terms of the proportion. The first and last terms, a and d, are the *extremes;* the second and third terms, b and c, are the *means.* The number d is the *fourth proportional* to a, b, and c.

If the second and third terms of a proportion are the same, as in $\dfrac{a}{b} = \dfrac{b}{c}$, then b is the *mean proportional* between a and c; and c is the *third proportional* to a and b.

Since the proportion $\dfrac{a}{b} = \dfrac{c}{d}$ is a fractional equation, we can clear of fractions by multiplying both members by the lowest common denominator, bd, to obtain $ad = bc$. Thus

> In a proportion the product of the means equals the product of the extremes.

ORAL EXERCISES: Completing proportions

State orally the number that is necessary to replace the question mark in each of the following exercises in order to make the proportion true.

1. $\dfrac{1}{2} = \dfrac{3}{?}$

2. $\dfrac{2}{5} = \dfrac{?}{10}$

3. $\dfrac{4}{?} = \dfrac{12}{9}$

4. $\dfrac{?}{20} = \dfrac{2a}{40}$

5. $\dfrac{3}{5} = \dfrac{?}{25}$

6. $\dfrac{2a}{3b} = \dfrac{4a}{?}$

7. $\dfrac{8}{10} = \dfrac{?}{50}$

8. $\dfrac{?}{1} = \dfrac{1}{a}$

9. $\dfrac{?}{2} = \dfrac{a}{b}$

10. $\dfrac{0}{5} = \dfrac{?}{6}$

ILLUSTRATIVE EXAMPLES: Applying proportion

1. Find the third proportional to 36 and 12.

Solution. Let t represent the third proportional, then

$$\frac{36}{12} = \frac{12}{t}$$

The product of the means equals the product of the extremes

$$36t = 144$$

Simplifying

$$t = 4 \quad \text{Answer}$$

2. What number when added to each of the numbers 4, 12, 8, and 20, will give four numbers which are in proportion?

Solution. Let x be the number to be added.

Stating the proportion $$\frac{4+x}{12+x} = \frac{8+x}{20+x}$$

Simplifying $$80 + 24x + x^2 = 96 + 20x + x^2$$
$$4x = 16$$
$$x = 4 \quad \text{Answer}$$

E X E R C I S E S : Applying proportion

1. Solve for x: $\dfrac{7+x}{17+x} = \dfrac{1}{2}$

2. Solve for y: $\dfrac{3y-7}{2y+8} = \dfrac{4}{9}$

3. In the proportion $\dfrac{r}{s} = \dfrac{t}{v}$, find s if $r = -2$, $t = +3$, and $v = -5$.

4. In the proportion $\dfrac{x}{y} = \dfrac{w}{z}$, find w if $x = -\frac{1}{4}$, $y = \frac{1}{3}$, and $z = -\frac{2}{5}$.

5. Find the third proportional to the numbers 6 and 12.

6. A boy hired a motorcycle for 15 days at the rate of $2.80 a week (7 days). What was his bill?

7. From an 8-oz. jar of instant coffee, a housewife was able to prepare 12 servings of coffee. Assuming she continued to make her coffee of the same strength, find how many servings she could make from a 22-oz. jar.

8. Find the mean proportional between 0.5 and 0.125.

9. What number when subtracted from each of the numbers 13, 23, 4, and 5, will make the resulting members, in that order, a proportion?

10. In one class in mathematics a teacher has 40 students with the ratio of the boys to girls 5:3. After the first semester a certain number of boys dropped out so that the ratio of the number of boys to the number of girls was 7:5. How many boys dropped out?

11. A baseball team has won 20 games and lost 5. If there are still 15 games to be played, how many games can it lose and still make a final average of 0.650?

12. In the Twilight League the Silversmiths at one time had won 8 games and lost 4. They finished the season with an average of 0.800 by winning all the remaining games. How many games were played during the season?

Similar figures are figures which have the same shape. In two similar figures the lengths of lines of one figure and the lengths of lines in corresponding positions in the other figure are proportional.

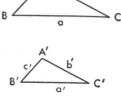

Thus, referring to the similar triangles ABC and $A'B'C'$ in the adjacent figure, we may write the proportions $\dfrac{a}{a'} = \dfrac{b}{b'}$, $\dfrac{a'}{a} = \dfrac{b'}{b}$, and $\dfrac{a}{b} = \dfrac{a'}{b'}$.

These three proportions are equivalent, since each proportion can be converted to the equation: $ab' = a'b$.

I L L U S T R A T I V E   E X A M P L E S :   Applying proportion to similar figures

1. In the similar polygons P and P' at the right, $a = 3$; $b = 2$; $c = 4$; and $d = 5$. If $a' = 3\frac{1}{2}$, find the other sides of polygon P'.

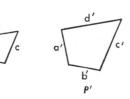

Solution. Since the corresponding sides of similar figures are proportional, then $\dfrac{a}{a'} = \dfrac{b}{b'}$

Substituting

$$\frac{3}{3\frac{1}{2}} = \frac{2}{b'}$$
$$3b' = 7$$
$$b' = \tfrac{7}{3}$$

In like manner

$$\frac{3}{3\frac{1}{2}} = \frac{4}{c'};$$
$$3c' = 14$$
$$c' = \tfrac{14}{3}$$

$$\frac{3}{3\frac{1}{2}} = \frac{5}{d'}$$
$$3d' = \tfrac{35}{2}$$
$$d' = \tfrac{35}{6}$$

E X E R C I S E S :   Applying proportion to similar figures

1. If rt. $\triangle ABC$ is similar to rt. $\triangle A'B'C'$ and if the sides of rt. $\triangle ABC$ are 5 in., 12 in., and 13 in. respectively and the longest side of rt. $\triangle A'B'C'$ is $6\frac{1}{2}$ in., find the remaining sides of rt. $\triangle A'B'C'$.

2. The perimeters of two similar polygons are to each other as any two corresponding sides, that is $\dfrac{p}{p'} = \dfrac{a}{a'}$. If the perimeter and a side of the first polygon are 48 in. and 9 in. respectively, and the corresponding side of the second is 4 in., find the perimeter of the second polygon.

3. The areas of two similar polygons are to each other as the squares of any two corresponding sides, that is, $\dfrac{A}{A'} = \dfrac{a^2}{a'^2}$. If the area and a side of the first polygon are 54 sq. in. and $2\frac{1}{2}$ in. respectively and the corresponding side of the second polygon is $7\frac{1}{2}$ in., find the area of the second polygon.

4. The volumes of two similar right circular cones are to each other as the cubes of their altitudes. If the volume and altitude of the first cone are 81 π cu. in. and 6 in. respectively, and the altitude of the second cone is 4 in., find the volume of the second cone.

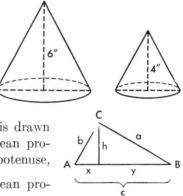

5. If, in a right triangle, the altitude is drawn to the hypotenuse, the altitude is the mean proportional between the segments of the hypotenuse, that is, $\frac{x}{h} = \frac{h}{y}$. Also, either leg is the mean proportional between the hypotenuse and the segment of the hypotenuse adjacent to that leg, that is,

$$\frac{c}{a} = \frac{a}{y}; \qquad \frac{c}{b} = \frac{b}{x}.$$

a) Find h if $x = 5$ in. and $y = 20$ in.
b) Find b if $x = \frac{1}{9}$ ft. and $c = \frac{1}{4}$ ft.
c) Find a if $c = 0.25$ yd. and $y = 0.0625$ yd.

6. The areas of two circles are to each other as the squares of their diameters, that is, $\frac{A}{A'} = \frac{d^2}{d'^2}$. If the area and the diameter of the first circle are 154 sq. in. and 14 in. respectively, and the area of the second circle is $28\frac{2}{7}$ sq. in., find the diameter of the second circle.

7. If, from an external point, a tangent and a secant are drawn to a circle, the tangent is the mean proportional between the secant and its external segment; that is, $\frac{s}{t} = \frac{t}{e}$. Find the tangent, if the secant and its external segment are $24\frac{1}{2}$ in. and $12\frac{1}{2}$ in. respectively.

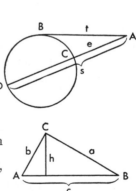

8. If, in a rt. $\triangle$, in the adjacent figure h has been drawn perpendicular to c, then $\frac{a}{h} = \frac{c}{b}$. If the legs, a and b, are respectively 16 in. and 30 in., find h.

9. The areas of two similar triangles are to each other as the squares on any two corresponding sides of the similar triangles. If a side of the first triangle is 8 in. and the corresponding side of the second is 12 in., find the area of the first triangle if the area of the second is 54 sq. in.

The Rule of Three. For a period of about one thousand years, from the ninth to the nineteenth centuries, most mathematics text books showed how to solve certain types of problems by the Rule of Three. Text books especially prepared for the merchants, bankers, and traders in the Mediterranean area and the seaports of Europe contained illustrative examples such as the following: If 15 casks of wine cost \$84, how much would 27 casks cost? In solving the problem the numbers were written in a line in this manner 15 —— 84 —— 27. Then the reader was told to multiply the second term by the third (84·27) and to divide this product by the first term, 15; thus $\frac{84 \cdot 27}{15} = \$151.20$. It was not until the nineteenth century that the Rule of Three was generally recognized as a simple proportion. Today, we would call this rule a proportion and express it in the form $\frac{a}{b} = \frac{c}{x}$ where $a, b,$ and c were known quantities and x, the unknown to be found.

Direct variation.   When the quotient of two variables is a constant, the variables *vary directly*. If x varies directly as y, then for different pairs of values, $\frac{x_1}{y_1} = k$ and $\frac{x_2}{y_2} = k$. This means that whenever x is multiplied by any number, y must be multiplied by the same number. If x is doubled, then y must be doubled. If x is halved, then y must be halved, etc.

Since the left members of the above equations are each equal to k, we have $\frac{x_1}{y_1} = \frac{x_2}{y_2}$. This is equivalent to:

$$\boxed{\frac{x_1}{x_2} = \frac{y_1}{y_2}}$$

ILLUSTRATIVE EXAMPLES: Direct variation

1. If x varies directly as y and $x = 15$ when $y = 4$, find y when $x = 12$.

  Solution.

  Writing the proportion $\dfrac{x_1}{x_2} = \dfrac{y_1}{y_2}$

Substituting the given values for x and y $\dfrac{15}{12} = \dfrac{4}{y}$

Solving for y $15y = 48$

$$y = \dfrac{16}{5} \quad \text{Answer}$$

2. If p varies as q and $p = 0.2$ when $q = 0.35$, find q when $p = 0.8$. Use the "k method."

> *Solution.* Direct variation is implied by the words "varies as".
>
> Writing the formula $\dfrac{p}{q} = k$
>
> Substituting the given values for p and q : $\dfrac{0.2}{0.35} = k$
>
> Simplifying $k = \frac{20}{35}$ or $\frac{4}{7}$
>
> Substituting this value of k and the second value of
> p in the formula, $\dfrac{0.8}{q} = \dfrac{4}{7}$
>
> Solving for q $4q = 5.6$
>
> $\qquad\qquad\qquad\qquad\qquad\qquad q = 1.4$ Answer

EXERCISES: Applying direct variation

1. If x varies directly as y, and $x = 7\frac{1}{2}$ when $y = 10$, find x when $y = 4$.

2. If x varies as y, and $x = 28$ when $y = 7$, find y when $x = 5$.

3. If t varies as v and $t = 0.11$ when $v = 0.33$, find t when $v = 0.55$.

4. If w varies as z and $w = 2\frac{4}{7}$ when $z = \frac{3}{14}$, find z when $w = 2\frac{1}{4}$.

5. If three men working at the same hourly rate are paid a total of $52.08 for a day's work, how much should be paid to five men working at the same hourly rate?

6. The velocity of a falling body varies directly as the time the body has fallen. If the velocity of a falling body is 128 ft. per sec. at the end of the fourth second, what will be its velocity at the end of the tenth second?

7. If the cost of a telephone conversation varies directly as the length of time of the conversation and if the cost including tax for 6 min. is 90¢, what would be the cost for a 9-min. call?

8. The distance through which a body falls from rest varies as the *square* of the time that the body is falling. If a body falls 64 ft. in 2 sec., how far will it fall in 5 sec.?

9. The weight of a sphere of uniform material varies as the *cube* of its diameter. If the weight of a sphere of 2 in. diameter is $2\frac{2}{3}$ lb., what is the weight of a sphere of 3 in. diameter?

10. The amount of water which flows through a circular pipe at a uniform pressure varies as the *square* of the diameter of a cross section of the pipe. If 12 gal. of water a minute flows through a pipe of $1\frac{1}{2}$ in. diameter, how many gallons a minute will flow through a pipe of $1\frac{3}{4}$ in. diameter at the same pressure?

11. The volumes of two cylindrical cans of the same shape vary as the *cubes* of their heights. If a can 6 in. high holds $1\frac{1}{2}$ pints, how many gallons will a similar can 24 in. high hold?

12. In foggy weather certain lighthouses send warnings at the same instant by radio and sound to ships in the neighboring waters. The radio message is received by the ship instantly, but the sound warning is heard later. If a ship is at a distance of $1\frac{1}{4}$ mi. from the lighthouse and receives the sound warning 5 sec. after receiving the radio message, how far distant is a ship which receives the sound warning 7 sec. after the radio message?

Inverse variation. When the product of two variables is a constant, the variables *vary inversely*. If x varies inversely as y, then for different pairs of values, $x_1 y_1 = k$ and $x_2 y_2 = k$. This means that whenever x is multiplied by a number, y must be divided by that same number. If x is doubled, y must be halved. If x is divided by 3, then y must be tripled, etc. Since the left members in the above equations are each equal to k, we have $x_1 y_1 = x_2 y_2$. This is equivalent to

$$\boxed{\dfrac{x_1}{x_2} = \dfrac{y_2}{y_1}}$$

ILLUSTRATIVE EXAMPLES: Inverse variation

1. If x varies inversely as y, and $x = 2$ when $y = 3$, find the value of y when $x = 18$.

Solution. Writing the proportion $\dfrac{x_1}{x_2} = \dfrac{y_2}{y_1}$

Substituting for x_1 and y_1 in the proportion the

first pair of values $\qquad \dfrac{2}{x_2} = \dfrac{y_2}{3}$

Substituting the second value of x $\qquad \dfrac{2}{18} = \dfrac{y}{3}$

Solving for y $\qquad\qquad\qquad 18y = 6$

$\qquad\qquad\qquad\qquad\qquad y = \frac{1}{3}$ Answer

2. If p varies inversely as the cube of q and $p = \frac{1}{2}$ when $q = \frac{1}{3}$, find p when $q = \frac{2}{3}$. Use the "k method."

Solution. Substituting the first values respectively of p and q in the formula $pq^3 = k$, to find the value of k.

Thus
$$\tfrac{1}{2}(\tfrac{1}{3})^3 = k$$
$$(\tfrac{1}{2})(\tfrac{1}{27}) = k$$
$$k = \tfrac{1}{54}$$

Substituting this value of k and the second value of q to find the second value of p.

Thus
$$p(\tfrac{2}{3})^3 = \tfrac{1}{54}$$
$$(p)(\tfrac{8}{27}) = \tfrac{1}{54}$$
$$p = \tfrac{1}{16} \quad \text{Answer}$$

EXERCISES: Inverse variation

1. If x varies inversely as y, and $x = 36$ when $y = 10$, find x when $y = 30$.

2. If r varies inversely as s, and $r = 11$ when $s = 15$, find s when $r = 3$.

3. If m varies inversely as n, and $m = \tfrac{1}{2}$ when $n = \tfrac{5}{8}$, find n when $m = 10$.

4. If t varies inversely as the square of v and $t = 0.2$ when $v = 0.5$, find t when $v = 0.6$. Use the "k method."

5. If a varies inversely as the square root of b and $a = \tfrac{1}{2}$ when $b = \tfrac{1}{16}$, find b when $a = \tfrac{1}{3}$. Use the "k method."

6. A Boston decorator finds that it takes 40 hr. for 2 girls to complete a set of decorative lamp shades. How long would it take 5 girls of equal ability and industry to do the same piece of work?

7. The weights of objects near the earth vary inversely as the squares of their distances from the center of the earth. Assuming the radius of the earth to be 4000 mi., find how much a rocket would weigh 500 mi. above the surface of the earth if, at the surface, it weighed 2000 lb.

8. In many cars the shifting of gears involves the meshing of gears of different numbers of teeth. If the speed of a gear varies inversely as the number of teeth, and 20-tooth gears make 30 revolutions a minute, how many revolutions a minute will a 24-tooth gear make?

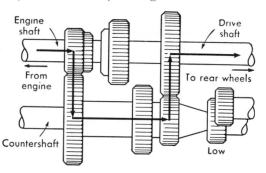

9. The gravitational attraction between two masses varies inversely as the square of the distance between them. If the attraction force between them is 75 lb. when the bodies are 8 ft. apart, find the attraction when the masses are 12 ft. apart.

10. The intensity of illumination from a source of light varies inversely as the square of the distance from the source of the light. If a screen is 10 ft. from the light bulb of a 100-candle power projector, how far, to the nearest foot, should it be placed from the bulb so that the intensity of the illumination on the screen is doubled?

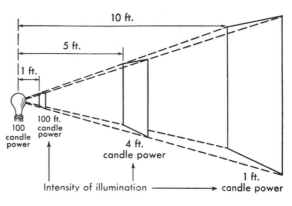

11. The speed of a pulley varies inversely as its diameter. In most automobiles the fan belt passes around the pulleys of the drive shaft, the generator, and the fan respectively. If the drive shaft is making 2400 revolutions per minute (r.p.m.) and the diameters of the pulleys of the drive shaft, the generator, and fan are respectively, 12 in., 6 in., and 4 in., how many revolutions per minute are made *a*) by the generator pulley? *b*) by the fan pulley?

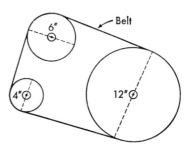

Direct and inverse variation; joint variation.   Frequently a quantity may vary directly as one quantity and inversely as another. For example, if a varies directly as b and inversely as c, we express the proportion $\dfrac{a_1}{a_2} = \dfrac{b_1 c_2}{b_2 c_1}$. Similarly, if a varies inversely as b and directly as c, the proportion is expressed $\dfrac{a_1}{a_2} = \dfrac{b_2 c_1}{b_1 c_2}$. When a *varies jointly* as b and c we mean that a varies directly as b, and a varies directly as c, and the proportion is expressed $\dfrac{a_1}{a_2} = \dfrac{b_1 c_1}{b_2 c_2}$.

ILLUSTRATIVE EXAMPLE: Direct and inverse variation

If m varies directly as n and inversely as p, and $m = 30$ when $n = 7\frac{1}{2}$ and $p = 4$, find m when $n = 15$ and $p = 6$.

Solution. Writing the proportion $\dfrac{m_1}{m_2} = \dfrac{n_1 p_2}{n_2 p_1}$

Substituting the given values $\dfrac{30}{m} = \dfrac{(7\frac{1}{2})6}{15 \cdot 4}$

Simplifying $\dfrac{30}{m} = \dfrac{45}{60}$

$m = 40$ Answer

EXERCISES: Direct and inverse variation; joint variation

1. If x varies directly as y and inversely as z, and $x = 4$ when $y = 6$ and $z = 3$, find x when $y = 8$ and $z = 2$.

2. If r varies inversely as s and directly as t, and $r = 12$ when $t = 10$ and $s = 25$, find s when $r = 6$ and $t = 3$.

3. If p varies jointly as q and r and $p = 20$ when $q = 15$ and $r = 3$, find r when $p = 18$ and $q = 6$.

4. If w varies jointly as x and y and $w = \frac{2}{3}$ when $x = \frac{1}{4}$ and $y = \frac{1}{3}$, find x when $w = \frac{5}{6}$ and $y = \frac{7}{12}$.

5. The area of a triangle varies jointly as a side and the altitude on that side. If the area of a triangle is 0.2 sq. in. when a side is 0.4 in. and its altitude is 1.0 in., find the area when the side is 1.8 in. and its altitude is 0.6 in.

6. The volume of a right circular cone varies jointly as the altitude and the square of the radius of the base. If the volume of the cone is 154 cu. in. when its altitude is 12 in. and the radius of the base is $3\frac{1}{2}$ in., find the altitude when the volume of the cone is 77 cu. in. and the radius of the base is $2\frac{1}{3}$ in.

7. The volume v of a gas varies directly as the absolute temperature t and inversely as the pressure p. If a gas has a volume of 810 cc. at a temperature of 360° A. under a pressure of 780 mm. per square centimeter, find the volume of the gas at a temperature of 300° A. under a pressure of 585 mm. per square centimeter.

8. If a gas has a volume of 120 cu. in. when the temperature is 364° A. and the pressure is 32 lb. per square inch, find the number of pounds pressure per square inch when the volume is 600 cu. in. and the temperature is 455° A. Use relationship given in ex. 7.

9. On an automobile trip the time t in hours of the journey varies directly as the distance d in miles and inversely as the rate r in miles per hour. If you completed a trip of 560 mi. in 14 hr. at the average rate of 40 mph., how much time should you allow yourself for a trip of 540 mi. at an average rate of 45 mph.?

10. The number of volts E in an electric circuit varies jointly as the amount of current in amperes I and the resistance of the circuit in ohms R. If 110 volts are necessary to send a current of 5 amperes through an electric iron with a resistance of 22 ohms, how many volts would be necessary to send a current of 2 amperes through a wire having a resistance of 2 ohms?

ILLUSTRATIVE EXAMPLE: Changing repeating decimals to ratios

Find the ratio which is equal to the repeating decimal $0.252525\cdots$

Solution. Let the unknown ratio be x. Then

$$x = 0.252525\cdots$$

We multiply both members of the equation by 100.

$$100x = 25.252525\cdots$$

From this product we subtract the original decimal in order to get an equation with no decimals.

$$\begin{aligned} 100x &= 25.252525\cdots \\ x &= 0.252525\cdots \\ \hline 99x &= 25 \end{aligned}$$

Solving for x

$$x = \tfrac{25}{99}$$

Substituting our original repeating decimal for x

$$0.252525\cdots = \tfrac{25}{99}$$

The check is left as an exercise for the student.

EXERCISES: Expressing repeating decimals as ratios

Find the ratio which is equal to each of the following repeating decimals.

1. $0.22222\cdots$
2. $0.6666\cdots$
3. $0.8888\cdots$
4. $1.3333\cdots$
5. $2.5555\cdots$

6. $0.848484\cdots$
7. $3.454545\cdots$
8. $4.171717\cdots$
9. $0.231231\cdots$
10. $0.169169\cdots$

CHAPTER   REVIEW   EXERCISES

1. What is the ratio of $18 to 90¢?

2. What is the ratio of $2\frac{3}{4}$ to 0.75?

3. Divide $1000 between Byron and Mabel so that Byron shall receive $13 for every $12 received by Mabel.

4. Two numbers are in the ratio of 2:7. If 1 is added to the first number and 4 is subtracted from the second, the resulting numbers are in the ratio of 1:2. Find the original numbers.

5. If x varies directly as y and $x = \frac{5}{8}$ when $y = \frac{25}{16}$, find x when $y = 7\frac{1}{2}$.

6. If m varies inversely as n and $m = 0.45$ when n equals 0.8, find n when $m = 0.9$.

7. Ten years ago the ratio of a father's age to his son's age was $\frac{21}{5}$ and 10 years hence the ratio of their respective ages will be $\frac{31}{15}$. Find the present age of each.

8. Complete the following statements:

a) If $\dfrac{x}{y} = \dfrac{5}{6}$, then x varies —— as y.

b) If $\dfrac{x}{5} = \dfrac{6}{y}$, then x varies —— as y.

c) If $\dfrac{x_1}{x_2} = \dfrac{y_1 z_1}{y_2 z_2}$, then x varies ——.

d) If $\dfrac{y_1}{y_2} = \dfrac{x_1 z_2}{x_2 z_1}$, then y varies ——.

9. In the adjacent figure $\triangle ADE$ is similar to $\triangle ABC$. If the area of $\triangle ADE = 20$ sq. in., $DE = 4$ in., $BC = 5$ in., find the area of $\triangle ABC$ and the area of the figure $BCED$.

10. Express $2.484848\cdots$ as a ratio.

11. The safe load (W) of a beam varies jointly as its breadth (b) and the square of its depth (d) and inversely as the length (l) between the supporting uprights. If W is 2000 lb. when $b = 5$ in. and $d = 2$ in. and $l = 2$ ft., find W when $b = 3$ in., $d = 1$ in., and $l = 1$ ft.

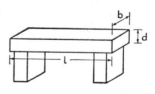

12. In chemistry class David measured out 90 g. of water in a graduated tube. The weight of oxygen in water is 8 times that of the other element, hydrogen. What is the weight of the oxygen in David's graduated tube?

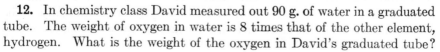

CUMULATIVE REVIEW EXERCISES

1. Divide $20 - 27a - a^2 + 6a^3$ by $5 - 3a$.

2. If $a = -3$, $b = -4$, and $c = 0$, find the value of $2a^3 - a^2b - ab^2 + bc$.

3. Factor: $2r^2 + 7rs - 15s^2$

4. Factor: $4c^2 - 12cd + 9d^2 - 16$

5. Simplify: $\dfrac{1}{a+1} + \dfrac{1}{2a-2} - 1$

6. Solve for x: $\dfrac{13x}{20} = \dfrac{6+x}{4} - \dfrac{1+3x}{10}$

7. Simplify: $\left(x - \dfrac{y^2}{x}\right) \div \left(\dfrac{y}{x} - 1\right)$

8. Solve for x and y in the equations
$$3x - 4y = -16$$
$$x + 6y = 13$$

9. In the formula $S = \dfrac{n}{2}\left[2a + (n-1)d\right]$ solve for d in terms of a, n, and S.

10. Represent the simple interest on d dollars at 4% for 6 mo.

11. If the price of three shirts is c dollars, represent the number of shirts that can be bought for k dollars.

12. If a man can build a log shack in n days, represent the part of the work that is unfinished after he has worked d days. (d is less than n.)

13. Using the slope-intercept method, draw the graph of the equation
$$4x - 2y = 5.$$

14. Two boys assigned to the job of weeding a vegetable garden completed the job in 2 hr. and 24 min. If one boy had worked alone for 3 hr. and then quit, the second boy could have completed the job in 2 more hours. Find the time it would have required each boy working alone to weed the garden.

15. A man's annual income of $2072.50 was derived from a part interest in a store and from government bonds. The bonds paid $2\frac{3}{8}\%$ interest annually and the store investment yielded an $8\frac{1}{2}\%$ return annually. The annual interest from the store exceeded the annual interest from the bonds by $647.50. How much had he in each investment?

16. The income of a family was budgeted for food, shelter, clothing, and for miscellaneous needs in the continued ratio of $10:3:2:1$. If the income was \$3600, how much was assigned for each account?

17. If x varies jointly as the square root of y and the cube root of z and $x = 6$ when $y = 9$ and $z = 8$, find x when $y = 4$ and $z = 64$.

18. If x varies directly as the square of y and inversely as the cube of z and $x = 2$ when $y = 3$ and $z = 5$, find x when $y = \frac{1}{2}$ and $z = \frac{3}{2}$.

19. Solve the following system of equations by use of determinants:

$$3x - 2.1y = 1$$
$$2x + 0.5y = 3$$

CHAPTER 8   *Exponents*

Exponents in elementary algebra.   You have already learned that an exponent is a small number written to the right of, and above, a second number called the base. When the exponent is a positive whole number, it indicates the number of times the base is used as a factor. Thus x^4 means $x \cdot x \cdot x \cdot x$.   Later, in this chapter you will find that we can use negative numbers, zero, or fractions as exponents.

Laws of exponents.   You have already learned the method for multiplying two expressions having the same base. The product is this same base written with an exponent obtained by adding the original exponents. In symbol form, the *multiplication law* of exponents is

$$\boxed{x^a \cdot x^b = x^{a+b}}$$

You have learned, too, the method for dividing two expressions having the same base. The quotient is this same base written with an exponent obtained by subtracting the exponent of the divisor from the exponent of the dividend. In symbol form, the *division law* of exponents is

$$\frac{x^a}{x^b} = x^{a-b}$$

The *law for raising a product to a power* can be expressed in symbol form

$$(xy)^n = x^n y^n$$

The proof of this law is the following:

From the definition of exponent
$$(xy)^n = \underbrace{xy \cdot xy \cdot xy \cdots xy}_{n \text{ factors}}$$

Rearranging the factors
$$= \underbrace{x \cdot x \cdot x \cdots x}_{n \text{ factors}} \cdot \underbrace{y \cdot y \cdot y \cdots y}_{n \text{ factors}}$$

Again, from the definition of exponent
$$(xy)^n = x^n y^n$$

The *law for raising a quotient to a power* can be expressed in symbol form

$$\left(\frac{x}{y}\right)^n = \frac{x^n}{y^n}$$

The proof of this law is the following:

From the definition of exponent
$$\left(\frac{x}{y}\right)^n = \underbrace{\frac{x}{y} \cdot \frac{x}{y} \cdot \frac{x}{y} \cdots \frac{x}{y}}_{n \text{ factors}}$$

Multiplying the fractions in the right member
$$= \frac{x \cdot x \cdot x \cdots x \ (n \text{ factors})}{y \cdot y \cdot y \cdots y \ (n \text{ factors})}$$

Again, from the definition of exponent
$$\left(\frac{x}{y}\right)^n = \frac{x^n}{y^n}$$

The *involution law* of exponents, that is, the law for raising to a power a quantity that already represents a number raised to a power, can be expressed in symbol form as:

$$(x^a)^b = x^{ab}$$

The proof of this law is the following:

From the definition of $(x^a)^b = \underbrace{x^a \cdot x^a \cdot x^a \cdots x^a}_{b \text{ factors}}$
exponent

Applying the multipli-
cation law $\qquad = x^{a+a+a+\cdots+a}$ (b terms)

Simplifying $\qquad (x^a)^b = x^{ab}$

The *evolution law* of exponents, that is, the law for obtaining a root of a quantity that already represents a number raised to a power, can be expressed in symbol form as:

$$\sqrt[b]{x^a} = x^{\frac{a}{b}}$$

The proof of this law is the following:

Beginning with the iden-
tity $\qquad x^a = x^{\frac{ab}{b}}$

Applying the involution
law in reverse $\qquad x^a = \left(x^{\frac{a}{b}}\right)^b$

From the definition of
exponent $\qquad = \underbrace{x^{\frac{a}{b}} \cdot x^{\frac{a}{b}} \cdot x^{\frac{a}{b}} \cdots x^{\frac{a}{b}}}_{b \text{ factors}}$

Since the bth root of a
quantity is defined
as one of the b like
factors of that
quantity, we have $\sqrt[b]{x^a} = x^{\frac{a}{b}}$

Remembering the laws of exponents. An easy way to remember the multiplication, division, involution, and evolution laws for exponents is the list below of the six fundamental arithmetic operations. We arrange these six operations in order:

Addition	Subtraction
Multiplication	Division
Involution (raise to a power)	Evolution (take a root)

Exponents are a device aimed at simplifying mathematics. This list of six operations shows how that results. These operations are arranged in order of complexity. In the multiplication law notice that the exponents are only added. Addition is one step simpler than multiplication. In the involution law the exponents are only multiplied. Multiplication is one step simpler than raising to a power. In order to perform an operation with an expression containing exponents, it is necessary only to apply to the exponents that operation which is written above the required operation in the above list. This then requires that we use a simpler operation on the exponents than the process itself implies.

By remembering this list of six operations in their correct order the student will always know, in working with exponents, how to treat the exponents. Since there is no operation written above "addition" or its opposite, "subtraction," the student is reminded that, unless the terms are like terms, they cannot be added or subtracted.

ILLUSTRATIVE EXAMPLES: Applying the laws of exponents

1. Multiply: $x^5 \cdot x^2$

Solution. By the multiplication law $\quad x^5 \cdot x^2 = x^{5+2}$
$$= x^7 \quad \text{Answer}$$

2. Divide: $x^8 \div x^2$

Solution. By the division law $\quad x^8 \div x^2 = x^{8-2}$
$$= x^6 \quad \text{Answer}$$

3. Simplify: $(x^2 y^3)^4$

Solution. By the law for raising a product to a power $\quad (x^2 y^3)^4 = (x^2)^4 \cdot (y^3)^4$

By the involution law $\quad = x^8 y^{12} \quad \text{Answer}$

4. Simplify: $\left(\dfrac{x^3}{y}\right)^5$

Solution. By the law for raising a quotient to a power $\quad \left(\dfrac{x^3}{y}\right)^5 = \dfrac{(x^3)^5}{y^5}$

By the involution law $\quad = \dfrac{x^{15}}{y^5} \quad \text{Answer}$

5. Simplify : $(x^3)^4$

      Solution. By the involution law $(x^3)^4 = x^{3 \cdot 4}$

                                                    $= x^{12}$ Answer

6. Simplify : $\sqrt[3]{x^{12}}$

      Solution. By the evolution law $\sqrt[3]{x^{12}} = x^{\frac{12}{3}}$

                                                    $= x^4$ Answer

ORAL EXERCISES: Applying laws of exponents

In exercises 1–10 multiply as indicated :

1. $x^2 \cdot x^4$ **5.** $x^b \cdot x^c$ **9.** $y^2 \cdot y^n$
2. $y^3 \cdot y^4$ **6.** $y^5 \cdot y^3$ **10.** $y^{2a} \cdot y^b$
3. $a^7 \cdot a^3 \cdot a^4$ **7.** $x^r \cdot x^s$
4. $x^a \cdot x^{2a}$ **8.** $y^m \cdot y^{3m}$

In exercises 11–20 divide as indicated :

11. $x^6 \div x^2$ **15.** $x^{3a} \div x^a$ **19.** $y^{2n} \div y^4$
12. $x^7 \div x^3$ **16.** $y^5 \div y^3$ **20.** $y^r \div y^s$
13. $x^{12} \div x^{10}$ **17.** $y^{4a} \div y^a$
14. $x^5 \div x$ **18.** $x^m \div x^n$

EXERCISES: Applying laws of exponents

In exercises 1–5 multiply as indicated :

1. $(x^{n+1})(x^{n-1})$ **3.** $(y^{3a})(y^{5a})$ **5.** $(x^{r+5})(x^{2r-3})$
2. $(x^{2n})(x^{4n})$ **4.** $(x^{2r-1})(x^{3r+1})$

In exercises 6–10 divide as indicated :

6. $\dfrac{x^{2a}}{x^{a-1}}$ **8.** $\dfrac{x^{3n+1}}{x^{2n+1}}$ **10.** $\dfrac{x^{n+1}}{x^{n-1}}$

7. $\dfrac{x^{2n}}{x^{2n-1}}$ **9.** $\dfrac{x^{n+5}}{x^n}$

Simplify each of the following :

11. $(x^3)^2$ **17.** $\sqrt[4]{x^{12}}$ **23.** $(-a^4bc^5)^4$ **27.** $\left(\dfrac{x^a}{y^b}\right)^y$
12. $(x^5)^3$ **18.** $\sqrt[3]{x^9}$
13. $(x^7)^n$ **19.** $\sqrt{x^{10a}}$ **24.** $(x^ay^bc)^3$
14. $(x^a)^{n+1}$ **20.** $\sqrt{x^6y^2}$ **25.** $(-xyz^2)^5$ **28.** $\left(\dfrac{r^7}{s^3}\right)^{2p}$
15. $(-x^2)^3$ **21.** $(xy^4)^2$
16. $\sqrt[3]{x^6}$ **22.** $(a^2b^3c)^3$ **26.** $\left(\dfrac{x^2}{y}\right)^3$ **29.** $\left(\dfrac{x^{2n}}{y^{3m}}\right)^{2k}$

The zero exponent. In applying the division law of exponents in previous exercises, you may have noticed that in every case the exponent of the dividend was greater than the exponent of the divisor, except in those cases where the exponents were literal numbers. If we apply the division law to the problem $x^5 \div x^5$, we obtain as a quotient x^{5-5} or x^0. Notice that the result contains a *zero exponent*.

We know that $$\frac{x^5}{x^5} = 1$$

From the division law we find that $$\frac{x^5}{x^5} = x^0$$

Therefore $$\mathbf{x^0 = 1}$$

Similarly $6^0 = 1$; $(rs)^0 = 1$; $m^0 = 1$.

This leads us to the definition of the zero exponent:

> Any quantity, except zero, raised to a zero power is equal to 1.

The negative exponent. If we apply the division law of exponents to the problem $x^2 \div x^5$, we obtain as a quotient x^{2-5} or x^{-3}. Notice that the result contains a *negative exponent*.

We know that $$\frac{x^2}{x^5} = \frac{x \cdot x}{x \cdot x \cdot x \cdot x \cdot x} = \frac{1}{x^3}$$

From the division law we find $$\frac{x^2}{x^5} = x^{-3}$$

Therefore $$\mathbf{x^{-3} = \frac{1}{x^3}}$$

Similarly it can be proved that $$x^{-5} = \frac{1}{x^5}; \quad y^{-1} = \frac{1}{y}$$

In general,

From the multiplication law $$x^{-m} \cdot x^m = x^0$$

From the meaning of the zero exponent $$x^{-m} \cdot x^m = 1$$

Dividing by x^m $$\mathbf{x^{-m} = \frac{1}{x^m}}$$

This leads us to the definition of a negative exponent:

> A number raised to a negative power is equal to the reciprocal of the number raised to the same power with a positive sign.

The fractional exponent.   In applying the evolution law of exponents, that is, in taking the root of a number raised to a power, you may have noticed that in previous exercises the exponent of the radicand was always a multiple of the index of the radical.   If we apply the evolution law to $\sqrt[3]{x^2}$, we obtain as a result $x^{\frac{2}{3}}$. Notice that this result contains a *fractional exponent*.   This leads us to the definition of the fractional exponent:

> The denominator of a fractional exponent of a number denotes the principal root of the number.   The numerator denotes the power to which the root of the number is to be raised.

In $x^{\frac{3}{5}}$, the **5** indicates the **fifth** root of x: $\sqrt[5]{x}$.   The **3** indicates the **third power** (cube) of $\sqrt[5]{x}$: $(\sqrt[5]{x})^3$.   The result is the same if x is first raised to the indicated power (numerator of the fractional exponent) and then the indicated root (denominator of the fractional exponent) is taken. In $x^{\frac{3}{5}}$, the **3** indicates the **cube** of x: x^3.   The **5** indicates the **fifth root** of x^3: $\sqrt[5]{x^3}$.   Hence $\sqrt[5]{x^3} = (\sqrt[5]{x})^3$.

Powers of unity.   No matter how many times 1 is multiplied by itself, the result is always 1.   For this reason, 1 with any positive whole number as an exponent is equal to 1.   From our meaning for the zero exponent we know that 1^0 equals 1.   Since any root of 1 must equal 1, we know that 1 with a positive fractional exponent equals 1.

It is left as an exercise for the student to prove, from the meaning of a negative exponent, that 1 raised to a negative power is equal to 1 also. Therefore: for any value of x, $1^x = 1$.   We can state this:

> 1 raised to any power is equal to 1.

I L L U S T R A T I V E   E X A M P L E S : Finding the value of exponential expressions

1. Simplify: $(\frac{2}{3})^0$; 1^p; 3^{-2}.

> *Solution.* Any quantity, except zero, raised to the zero power is equal to 1. $(\frac{2}{3})^0 = 1$
>
> 1 raised to any power is equal to 1 $1^p = 1$
>
> A number raised to a negative power is equal to the reciprocal of the number raised to the same power with a positive sign. $3^{-2} = (\frac{1}{3})^2$
> $$= \tfrac{1}{9}$$

2. Simplify: $(\frac{4}{9})^{-\frac{3}{2}}$

> *Solution.* Since a number raised to a negative power is equal to the reciprocal of the number raised to the same power with a positive sign, therefore $(\frac{4}{9})^{-\frac{3}{2}} = (\frac{9}{4})^{\frac{3}{2}}$
>
> The denominator of a fractional exponent of a number indicates a root. The numerator of the fractional exponent of the number indicates a power of the number.
>
> Therefore $(\frac{9}{4})^{\frac{3}{2}} = (\sqrt{\frac{9}{4}})^3$
>
> Taking the square root $= (\frac{3}{2})^3$
>
> Raising to the third power $= \frac{27}{8}$ Answer

3. Express with a radical sign and an integral exponent: $x^{\frac{4}{5}}$

> *Solution.* The denominator of the fractional exponent $\frac{4}{5}$ indicates the fifth root of x. The numerator indicates the fourth power of x. Therefore, $x^{\frac{4}{5}} = \sqrt[5]{x^4}$ Answer

4. Express with fractional exponents: $\sqrt[5]{b^2c^3}$

> *Solution.* Because the fifth root is indicated, the denominator of the fractional exponents must be 5.
> $$\sqrt[5]{b^2c^3} = b^{\frac{2}{5}}c^{\frac{3}{5}}   \text{Answer}$$

5. Express with a positive exponent: x^{-1}

> *Solution.* Since a number raised to a negative power is equal to the reciprocal of the number raised to the same power with a positive sign,
>
> therefore $x^{-1} = \left(\frac{1}{x}\right)^{+1}$
> $$= \frac{1}{x}$$

ORAL EXERCISES: Finding the value of exponential expressions

Find the value of each of the following:

1. a^0
2. 3^0
3. $(2x)^0$
4. $5x^0$
5. 1^3
6. 1^{-5}

7. 1^{x+y}
8. $4^{\frac{3}{2}}$
9. $27^{\frac{2}{3}}$
10. $(\frac{2}{3})^{-1}$
11. $49^{\frac{1}{2}}$
12. $125^{\frac{1}{3}}$

13. $64^{\frac{1}{6}}$
14. $(32)^{-\frac{1}{5}}$
15. $(\frac{1}{3})^{-2}$
16. $(-8)^{\frac{1}{3}}$
17. $(4)^{-1}$
18. 5^{-3}

EXERCISES: Finding the value of exponential expressions

Find the value of each of the following:

1. $(-27)^{\frac{2}{3}}$
2. $(\frac{2}{3})^{-3}$
3. $(\frac{27}{8})^{\frac{1}{3}}$
4. $64^{\frac{5}{6}}$

5. $(3^{10})^{\frac{1}{5}}$
6. $(4^{\frac{1}{6}})^3$
7. $25^{\frac{3}{2}}$
8. $(8^5 \cdot 3^{10})^{\frac{1}{5}}$

9. $(1.44)^{\frac{1}{2}}$
10. $(.001)^{\frac{1}{3}}$
11. $(.25)^{\frac{1}{2}}$
12. $(.09)^{\frac{1}{2}}$

In ex. 13–20 express each with a radical sign and an integral exponent:

13. $x^{\frac{3}{5}}$
14. $a^{\frac{5}{2}}$
15. $x^{\frac{5}{6}}$

16. $y^{\frac{2}{3}}$
17. $a^{\frac{1}{2}}$
18. $x^{\frac{5}{4}}$

19. $b^{\frac{3}{2}}$
20. $s^{\frac{1}{3}}$

In ex. 21–28 express each with a fractional exponent:

21. $\sqrt{x}$
22. $\sqrt[3]{y}$
23. $\sqrt{x^3}$

24. $\sqrt[5]{x^3}$
25. $\sqrt[3]{x^2}$
26. $\sqrt[3]{y^5}$

27. $\sqrt{a^5}$
28. $\sqrt[4]{x^7}$

In ex. 29–36 express each with a positive exponent:

29. x^{-2}

30. y^{-3}

31. $\dfrac{1}{x^{-2}}$

32. $\dfrac{1}{x^{-\frac{2}{3}}}$

33. $m^{-\frac{1}{2}}$

34. $\dfrac{1}{n^{-3}}$

35. $\dfrac{1}{y^{-\frac{1}{2}}}$

36. $\left(\dfrac{x}{y}\right)^{-2}$

ILLUSTRATIVE EXAMPLES: Simplifying exponential expressions

1. Find the value of : $(\frac{3}{5})^{-2} \cdot (\frac{3}{5})^5$

$\quad$ *Solution.* By the multiplication law $(\frac{3}{5})^{-2} \cdot (\frac{3}{5})^5 = (\frac{3}{5})^3$

$$= \tfrac{27}{125}$$

2. Write with positive exponents and simplify : $\dfrac{x^{-2} - y^{-2}}{x^{-2} + y^{-2}}$

$\quad$ *Solution.* Given the expression $\dfrac{x^{-2} - y^{-2}}{x^{-2} + y^{-2}}$

Writing each term of the numerator and each term of the $\dfrac{\dfrac{1}{x^2} - \dfrac{1}{y^2}}{\dfrac{1}{x^2} + \dfrac{1}{y^2}}$
denominator as reciprocals with positive exponents

Combining fractions in numerator, and combining frac- $\dfrac{\dfrac{y^2 - x^2}{x^2 y^2}}{\dfrac{y^2 + x^2}{x^2 y^2}}$
tions in denominator

Multiplying the numerator by the reciprocal of the de- $\dfrac{y^2 - x^2}{x^2 y^2} \cdot \dfrac{x^2 y^2}{y^2 + x^2}$
nominator

Dividing the numerator and the denominator by the like $\dfrac{y^2 - x^2}{y^2 + x^2}$
factor

3. Write with positive exponents and simplify : $\dfrac{a^{-2} b^3 c^{-5}}{a^3 b^{-1} c}$

$\quad$ *Solution.* Given expression $\dfrac{a^{-2} b^3 c^{-5}}{a^3 b^{-1} c}$

Writing with positive exponents $\dfrac{\dfrac{1}{a^2} \cdot b^3 \cdot \dfrac{1}{c^5}}{\dfrac{a^3 c}{b}}$

Multiplying the numerator by the reciprocal of the de- $\dfrac{b^3}{a^2 c^5} \cdot \dfrac{b}{a^3 c}$
nominator

$$= \dfrac{b^4}{a^5 c^6}$$

Note: A fraction of this type when both numerator and denominator
are monomials, can be simplified more rapidly by moving all **factors** in
the numerator with negative exponents to the denominator, and all factors in the denominator with negative exponents to the numerator and
making the signs of the exponents positive.

$$\dfrac{a^{-2} b^3 c^{-5}}{a^3 b^{-1} c} = \dfrac{b^3 b}{a^2 a^3 c c^5} = \dfrac{b^4}{a^5 c^6}$$

4. Perform the indicated operation and write the simplified result with positive exponents:

$$(2x^{\frac{4}{3}} - 9x^{\frac{2}{3}} - 5x + 19x^{\frac{1}{3}} + 7x^{\frac{5}{3}} - 6x^2) \div (2x^{\frac{2}{3}} - x - 3x^{\frac{4}{3}})$$

Solution. By long division:

$$
\begin{array}{r}
\text{divisor} \qquad\qquad\qquad x^{-\frac{1}{3}} - 4 \;\;\; - 3x^{\frac{1}{3}} + 2x^{\frac{2}{3}} \quad \text{quotient} \\
\hline
2x^{\frac{2}{3}} - x - 3x^{\frac{4}{3}}\,\big|\,2x^{\frac{4}{3}} - 9x^{\frac{2}{3}} - 5x + 19x^{\frac{1}{3}} + 7x^{\frac{5}{3}} - 6x^2 \quad \text{dividend} \\
2x^{\frac{4}{3}} - \;\;\; x^{\frac{2}{3}} - 3x \\
\hline
- 8x^{\frac{2}{3}} - 2x + 19x^{\frac{1}{3}} \\
- 8x^{\frac{2}{3}} + 4x + 12x^{\frac{1}{3}} \\
\hline
- 6x + 7x^{\frac{1}{3}} + 7x^{\frac{5}{3}} \\
- 6x + 3x^{\frac{1}{3}} + 9x^{\frac{5}{3}} \\
\hline
4x^{\frac{4}{3}} - 2x^{\frac{5}{3}} - 6x^2 \\
4x^{\frac{4}{3}} - 2x^{\frac{5}{3}} - 6x^2 \\
\hline
0
\end{array}
$$

The result, $x^{-\frac{1}{3}} - 4 - 3x^{\frac{1}{3}} + 2x^{\frac{2}{3}}$, expressed with positive exponents is:

$$\frac{1}{x^{\frac{1}{3}}} - 4 - 3x^{\frac{1}{3}} + 2x^{\frac{2}{3}} \quad \text{Answer}$$

E X E R C I S E S :   Evaluating quantities with special exponents

In ex. 1–10 find the value of each example:

1. $2^3 \cdot 2^0$

2. $1^n \div 3^0$

3. $(x^3)^0$

4. $\left(\frac{2}{3}\right)^{-2} \cdot \left(\frac{2}{3}\right)^0$

5. $\left(\frac{1}{2}\right)^{-4} \cdot \left(\frac{2}{5}\right)^{-3}$

6. $\left(\frac{1}{16}\right)^{-\frac{5}{4}} \cdot (32)^{-\frac{2}{5}}$

7. $\left(\frac{8}{27}\right)^{-\frac{2}{3}} \cdot \left(\frac{81}{16}\right)^{-\frac{3}{4}}$

8. $\left(\frac{1}{125}\right)^{-\frac{1}{3}} \cdot \left(\frac{49}{16}\right)^{\frac{3}{2}}$

9. $\left(\frac{64}{27}\right)^{-\frac{2}{3}} \cdot \left(\frac{9}{16}\right)^{-\frac{3}{2}}$

10. $16^{\frac{3}{4}} - 4^0 + \left(\frac{9}{4}\right)^{-\frac{3}{2}}$

In ex. 11–30 write each expression with positive exponents and simplify if possible:

11. bx^{-5}

12. $x^{-3}y^2$

13. $\dfrac{x^2}{y^{-2}}$

14. $\dfrac{a^2b^{-3}}{c}$

15. $\dfrac{a^{-2}b^{-2}}{c^{-2}}$

16. $-3x^{-1}$

17. $\dfrac{-2x}{-3y^{-1}}$

18. $\dfrac{a^3}{b^{-1}c^2}$

19. $\dfrac{2x}{-y^{-2}}$

20. $\dfrac{x^{-1}}{x^2}$

21. $\dfrac{x^{-2}yz^{-3}}{xy^2z^{-4}}$

22. $\dfrac{a^{-5}b}{-5}$

23. $\dfrac{x}{y} + \dfrac{y^{-1}}{x^{-1}}$

24. $(x + y)^{-1}$

25. $(x^{-2})^{-3}$

26. $a^{-1} - b^{-1}$

27. $x^{-1} + y^{-1}$

28. $xy^{-1} + x^{-1}y$

29. $\dfrac{x^{-1}}{y} + \dfrac{y^{-1}}{x}$

30. $-3^{-1}x^{-1}$

In ex. 31–72 perform the indicated operations of each exercise and write the simplified result with positive exponents.

31. $x^{\frac{1}{3}} \cdot x^{\frac{2}{3}}$

32. $x^{\frac{1}{2}} \cdot x^{\frac{3}{4}}$

33. $x^{\frac{2}{3}} \cdot x^{\frac{1}{3}}$

34. $y^{\frac{1}{3}} \cdot y^{\frac{1}{3}} \cdot y^{\frac{1}{3}}$

35. $a^{\frac{5}{3}} \div a^{\frac{2}{3}}$

36. $b^{\frac{5}{6}} \div b^{\frac{1}{2}}$

37. $a^5 \cdot a^{\frac{1}{5}}$

38. $a^4 \div a^{\frac{1}{4}}$

39. $a \cdot a^{\frac{1}{2}} \cdot a^{\frac{1}{3}}$

40. $x^{-a} \cdot x^a$

41. $x^{a-b} \cdot x^{b-a}$

42. $x^3 \div x^0$

43. $x^{-\frac{3}{2}} \div x^{-\frac{1}{2}}$

44. $x^3 \cdot x^{-2}$

45. $x^4 \div x^{-4}$

46. $x^{\frac{1}{4}} \cdot x^{\frac{1}{2}} \div x^{\frac{3}{4}}$

47. $(x^{\frac{1}{2}} - y^{\frac{1}{2}})(x^{\frac{1}{2}} + y^{\frac{1}{2}})$

48. $(x - x^{-1})^2$

49. $x^{3a}(x^a + x^{-a})$

50. $(x^{-1} + y^{-1})(x^{-1} - y^{-1})$

51. $(x^{-a} + y^{-a})(x^{-a} - y^{-a})$

52. $\dfrac{x^{-2} + y^{-2}}{x^{-2}}$

53. $\dfrac{a^{-3}b^{-3}}{a^{-3} + b^{-3}}$

54. $\dfrac{a^{-2} - b^{-2}}{a^{-1} - b^{-1}}$

55. $(m^{-2} - 5\,m^{-1} - 6) \div (m^{-1} - 6)$

56. $(x - y) \div (x^{\frac{1}{2}} - y^{\frac{1}{2}})$

57. $(x - y) \div (x^{\frac{1}{3}} - y^{\frac{1}{3}})$

58. $(2a^{\frac{1}{2}} + 3a^{\frac{1}{4}} + 5)(3a^{\frac{1}{2}} - 2a^{\frac{1}{4}})$

59. $(a^{\frac{3}{2}} - ab^{\frac{1}{2}} + a^{\frac{1}{2}}b - b^{\frac{3}{2}}) \div (a + b)$

60. $\left(\dfrac{a^2b}{64\,a^{-3}b^{\frac{4}{3}}}\right)^{-\frac{1}{3}}$

61. $(a^3b^6c^2)^{\frac{2}{3}}$

62. $(a^4b^{-2}c^{-\frac{4}{5}})^{-\frac{1}{2}}$

63. $(x^{\frac{4}{5}}y^{-8}z^{-1})^{-\frac{3}{4}}$

64. $(x^{\frac{1}{3}}y^{2s}z^2)^s$

65. $(x^{-\frac{2}{3}}y^{-8}z^4)^{-\frac{3}{4}}$

66. $\sqrt{a^2b^{-4}c^{-10}}$

67. $\sqrt[3]{-a^{12}b^9c^{-15}}$

68. $\left(\dfrac{2a^{-1}b^2}{3\,a^3b^{-\frac{1}{2}}}\right)^3$

69. $\left(\dfrac{a^{\frac{1}{3}}b^{\frac{1}{2}}c^0}{a^{-1}b^{\frac{2}{3}}c^2}\right)^6$

70. $\sqrt[3]{\dfrac{8a^{12}b^0}{27\,x^6z^{-3}}}$

71. $\left(\dfrac{x^6y^{-9}z^{-3}}{8\,a^{-\frac{3}{4}}b^0}\right)^{-\frac{2}{3}}$

72. $\sqrt[5]{\dfrac{a^5s^{-10}t^{\frac{5}{2}}}{a^{10}s^{-5}t^{-\frac{5}{2}}}}$

Standard (or scientific) notation of numbers. The sciences of chemistry, physics, astronomy, and engineering often use very large and very small numbers. For example, the number of molecules in 2 grams of hydrogen is **606,000,000,000,000,000,000,000.** Scientists find it more convenient to write this number as **6.06 × 10²³.** You have long ago learned that to multiply a number by 10 it is necessary to move the decimal point one place to the right. To multiply a number by 10^{23}, therefore, is equivalent to moving the decimal point 23 places to the right. In this large number the zeros following the 606 are merely used to help locate the decimal point. They are not significant figures; the only significant figures are 606. To write a large number, the scientist writes the significant figures as a number between 1 and 10. In this case, he writes the significant figures as 6.06. Then he locates the decimal point by multiplying this figure by a power of 10, as 6.06×10^{23}.

Scientists treat very small numbers in a similar manner. The distance between the atomic layers of a crystal of rock salt is **.0000000281** centimeters. The scientist writes this number as **2.81 × 10⁻⁸.** You know that to divide a number by 10, or to multiply the number by 10^{-1}, it is necessary only to move the decimal point one place to the left. To multiply a number by 10^{-8}, therefore, is equivalent to moving the decimal point 8 places to the left. In this small number the zeros preceding the 281 are merely used to help locate the decimal point. They are not significant figures; the only significant figures are 281. Because the scientist writes the significant figures as a number between 1 and 10, he writes these 2.81; but to locate the decimal point he must multiply this number by a power of 10; therefore, he writes 2.81×10^{-8}.

I L L U S T R A T I V E   E X A M P L E S : Using standard (or scientific) notation

1. Express in standard notation: 3,100,000,000

> *Solution.* The significant figures are **31**; written as a number between 1 and 10, this is 3.1. To locate the decimal point, we must multiply by 10^9.
> $$3,100,000,000 = 3.1 \times 10^9$$

2. Express in standard notation: .00000000052

> *Solution.* The significant figures are 52. Written as a number between 1 and 10, this is 5.2. To locate the decimal point, we must multiply by 10^{-10}.
> $$.00000000052 = 5.2 \times 10^{-10}$$

3. Write without exponents: 1.65×10^8

> *Solution.* To multiply by 10^8 is to move the decimal point 8 places to the right.
> $$1.65 \times 10^8 = 165,000,000$$

4. Write without exponents: 4.02×10^{-6}

    Solution. To multiply by 10^{-6} is to move the decimal point 6 places to the left.

$$4.02 \times 10^{-6} = .00000402$$

Googol and googolplex. The newest names for large numbers, invented in 1940, are googol and googolplex. A googol is defined as the number 1 followed by one hundred zeros.

$$\text{A googol} = 10^{100}$$

A googolplex is the name given to the number 1 followed by a googol of zeros.

$$\text{A googolplex} = 10^{\,1\ \text{googol}}$$

As yet there has not been found any practical application for numbers of this size. The total number of raindrops that fall on the earth in a century is not as great as a googol. The total number of words that have ever been spoken on this earth is not as great as a googol.

    A googolplex is so large that if a person were to start writing the number here on the earth and continued writing zeros to the farthest star with a zero every inch of the way he would not reach a googolplex. He could, however, save a lot of time and energy by using that great time-saver, the exponent, if he wrote a googolplex as

$$10^{10^{100}}.$$

E X E R C I S E S : Using standard (or scientific) notation

    In ex. 1–10 express each in standard notation:

1. 2,560,000,000
2. 30,150,000,000
3. 9,700,000,000,000
4. .0000000808
5. .00000000091

6. .00000000000011
7. 1,101,000,000,000
8. 8,003,000,000,000
9. .000000000109
10. .000000002

    In ex. 11–16 write each without exponents:

11. 3.5×10^{8}
12. 2.01×10^{-7}
13. 2.69×10^{10}

14. 3.7×10^{11}
15. 1.05×10^{-6}
16. 9.1×10^{-7}

Doings of Dimbo.   On Dimbo's first ski-
ing excursion he met with misfortune
and landed upside down.

Can you find Dimbo's error in the
following problem?

What is the correct answer?

Simplify : $\left(\dfrac{a^2 b^8}{c^{-3}}\right)^{-\frac{1}{2}}$

Dimbo's solution :

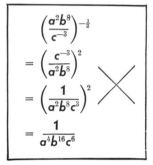

$$\left(\dfrac{a^2 b^3}{c^{-3}}\right)^{-\frac{1}{2}}$$

$$= \left(\dfrac{c^{-3}}{a^2 b^8}\right)^{2}$$

$$= \left(\dfrac{1}{a^2 b^8 c^3}\right)^{2}$$

$$= \dfrac{1}{a^4 b^{16} c^6}$$

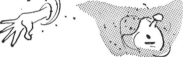

CHAPTER REVIEW EXERCISES

1. Write with a radical sign and integral exponents : $y^{\frac{3}{5}}$

2. Write with a fractional exponent : $\sqrt[3]{x^7}$

3. Find the value of : $(\frac{1}{3})^{-3} \cdot (\frac{3}{4})^{-2}$

4. Simplify : $(\frac{27}{8})^{\frac{2}{3}} + (5x)^0 - 5b^0 + 4^{-\frac{1}{2}}$

5. Multiply as indicated : $(6 a^3 b^{\frac{1}{3}} c^{n+1})(- 2 a^{-1} b^{\frac{2}{3}} c^{1-n})$

6. Divide as indicated : $(x^{\frac{1}{2}} y^{-\frac{2}{3}}) \div (x^{-\frac{3}{2}} y^{\frac{1}{3}})$

7. Write with standard (or scientific) notation :
   a) 371,000,000,000
   b) .00000079

8. Simplify : $\left(\dfrac{5^{-1} a^{\frac{1}{3}}}{a^{-\frac{2}{3}}}\right)^{-2}$

9. Multiply as indicated : $(x^{\frac{2}{3}} - x^{\frac{1}{3}} + 1)(x^{\frac{1}{3}} + 1)$

10. Divide as indicated : $(2 a^{\frac{4}{3}} - 3 a + 5 a^{\frac{2}{3}} - 3 a^{\frac{1}{3}} + 2) \div (a^{\frac{2}{3}} - a^{\frac{1}{3}} + 1)$

CUMULATIVE REVIEW EXERCISES

1. Express algebraically : the reciprocal of the sum of two numbers,
x and y, diminished by twice the sum of their reciprocals.

2. Find the value of S in $S = \dfrac{a - ar^n}{1 - r}$ if $a = 16$, $r = \frac{1}{2}$, $n = 4$.

3. Reduce to lowest terms: $\dfrac{x^2 + 4x}{2x}$

4. If x varies inversely as the cube of y, and $x = 9$ when $y = 4$, what does x equal when $y = 3$?

5. Factor: $x^{2a} - y^{-4b}$

6. Find the slope and y intercept of the graph of $y - 3x = 7$.

7. If the point $(3, -2)$ lies on the line $2x - y = k$ what value must k have?

8. Solve for x and y: $\dfrac{4}{3x} - \dfrac{1}{9y} = \dfrac{1}{3}$

$$\dfrac{3}{4x} - \dfrac{2}{y} = -\dfrac{7}{4}$$

9. Solve for x in terms of a and b: $1 - \dfrac{x}{a} = \dfrac{x}{b}$

10. Use the factor theorem to factor: $2x^3 - 11x^2 + 17x - 6$.

11. In a vat there are 80 pints of a solution which is 20% alcohol. How much pure alcohol must be added to produce a solution which is 30% alcohol?

12. If $y = 27$, find the numerical value of

$$\left(\dfrac{1}{4y}\right)^0 - y^{-\frac{1}{3}} + 5y^{\frac{1}{3}}$$

CHAPTER 9   *Radicals*

Roots and radicals.   You have already learned that the square root of a number is one of two equal factors of that number. The cube root of a number is one of three equal factors of the number. In general, then, we can say that the nth root of a number is one of n equal factors of that number.

To indicate the nth root of x, we write $\sqrt[n]{x}$. The number n is the **index** of the radical sign. The cube root of x is written $\sqrt[3]{x}$; here the index is 3. In the case of the square root of x, written $\sqrt{x}$, the index, although it is not written, is understood to be 2.

The index denotes the order of the radical. The following are radicals of the second order: $\sqrt{3x}$, $\sqrt{2}$, $\sqrt{13}$. If the index is 3, the radical is of the third order, as $\sqrt[3]{11}$, $\sqrt[3]{17}$, etc. In general, if the index is n, the radical is of the nth order.

The number within a radical sign is known as the *radicand*. In the expression $\sqrt{5x}$ the radicand is $5x$. Frequently the whole expression, $\sqrt{5x}$ or $\sqrt[n]{x}$ or $\sqrt{x+y}$, is called a *radical*.

Simplifying radicals.   A radical can be simplified by the following operations:

1. Reducing the radicand. This can be done by removing from the radicand all factors whose indicated root can be found.

2. Reducing the order of the radical as much as possible.

3. Making the radicand integral by eliminating all fractions under the radical sign.

I L L U S T R A T I V E   E X A M P L E S : Reducing the radicand

1. Simplify: $\sqrt[3]{64}$

       Solution. Since $4 \cdot 4 \cdot 4 = 64$, then 4 is one of the three equal factors of 64. Therefore $\sqrt[3]{64} = 4$ Answer

2. Simplify: $\sqrt{128}$

       Solution. The largest square that is a factor of 128 is 64. $\sqrt{128} = \sqrt{2 \cdot 64}$. Since the square root of 64 is 8, we remove the 64 from the radical and write 8 as a coefficient of the radical. $\sqrt{128} = 8\sqrt{2}$ Answer

3. Simplify: $2\sqrt[3]{54\,x^5yz^4}$

       Solution. $2\sqrt[3]{54x^5yz^4} = 2\sqrt[3]{27 \cdot 2 \cdot x^3 \cdot x^2 \cdot y \cdot z^3 \cdot z}$

       Removing from the radical sign
those factors which are cubes

$$= 2 \cdot 3 \cdot x \cdot z\sqrt[3]{2x^2yz}$$
$$= 6xz\sqrt[3]{2x^2yz} \text{ Answer}$$

E X E R C I S E S : Reducing radicands

Simplify the following by reducing the radicands as much as possible:

1. $\sqrt{8}$	10. $\sqrt[3]{16}$	19. $\sqrt[3]{32x^4}$
2. $\sqrt{225}$	11. $\sqrt[3]{54}$	20. $\sqrt[3]{27\,a^3b}$
3. $\sqrt{18}$	12. $\sqrt[3]{81}$	21. $2\sqrt[3]{54\,x^4}$
4. $\sqrt{50}$	13. $5\sqrt[3]{40}$	22. $6x^2\sqrt[3]{250\,x^5}$
5. $\sqrt{75}$	14. $2x\sqrt{9\,x^2}$	23. $2a\sqrt{98x^2y^3}$
6. $2\sqrt{90}$	15. $3\sqrt{16\,a^2x}$	24. $\frac{1}{2}\sqrt{128}$
7. $\sqrt{72}$	16. $2x\sqrt{50\,a^2x^2}$	25. $\sqrt[4]{16}$
8. $\sqrt{147}$	17. $5\sqrt{200\,ab^2}$	26. $\frac{1}{2}\sqrt[4]{32}$
9. $\sqrt[3]{8}$	18. $\sqrt[3]{16x^3}$	27. $\frac{1}{6}\sqrt[4]{81}$

28. $2x\sqrt[4]{162\,x^4}$

29. $\sqrt[6]{64\,a^6b}$

30. $-\,a\sqrt{72\,ab^3}$

31. $-\,2\sqrt[3]{54\,x^3}$

32. $\sqrt[3]{-\,27\,x^3y^5}$

33. $\sqrt{a^2 + 2ab + b^2}$

    Hint: Factor the radicand.

34. $x\sqrt{4\,x^3 + 12\,ax^2 + 9\,a^2x}$

35. $\sqrt{(x^2 - y^2)(x + y)}$

36. $\sqrt{(x^3 - y^3)(x^2 - y^2)}$

ILLUSTRATIVE EXAMPLES: Reducing the order of the radical

1. Simplify: $\sqrt[4]{9}$.

        Solution. Since $9 = 3^2$, we have $\sqrt[4]{9} = \sqrt[4]{3^2}$

        Writing with a fractional exponent $= 3^{\frac{2}{4}}$

        Reducing the fractional exponent $= 3^{\frac{1}{2}}$

        Writing with a radical sign $= \sqrt{3}$ Answer

2. Simplify: $\sqrt[6]{81}$.

        Solution. $\sqrt[6]{81} = \sqrt[6]{3^4}$

                             $= 3^{\frac{4}{6}}$

                             $= 3^{\frac{2}{3}}$

                             $= \sqrt[3]{3^2}$

                             $= \sqrt[3]{9}$ Answer

3. Simplify: $2x\sqrt[8]{x^{12}}$.

        Solution. $2x\sqrt[8]{x^{12}} = 2x\sqrt[8]{x^8 \cdot x^4}$

                           $= 2x \cdot x\sqrt[8]{x^4}$

                           $= 2x^2\sqrt[8]{x^4}$

                           $= 2x^2 \cdot x^{\frac{4}{8}}$

                           $= 2x^2 \cdot x^{\frac{1}{2}}$

                           $= 2x^2\sqrt{x}$ Answer

EXERCISES: Reducing the order of the radical

Simplify the following by reducing the order of the radical as much as possible.

1. $\sqrt[4]{4}$

2. $\sqrt[4]{49}$

3. $\sqrt[6]{27}$

4. $\sqrt[6]{16}$

5. $\sqrt[4]{25}$

6. $\sqrt[6]{64}$

7. $\sqrt[4]{25\,a^2}$

8. $\sqrt[6]{125\,x^3}$

9. $\sqrt[6]{36\,x^2y^4}$

10. $\sqrt[6]{64\,s^4}$

11. $3\sqrt[4]{81\,x^4}$

12. $5x\sqrt[8]{x^{12}}$

13. $3y\sqrt[6]{y^9}$

14. $4a\sqrt[4]{100\,a^6}$

15. $2a\sqrt[6]{3^n}$

16. $\sqrt[n]{x^{2n}y^{3n}}$

17. $\sqrt[4]{a^{4n}}$

18. $\sqrt[n]{2^n y^{2n}}$

ILLUSTRATIVE EXAMPLES: Making the radicand integral

1. Simplify: $\sqrt{\frac{2}{3}}$.

> *Solution.* Given example $\qquad\qquad \sqrt{\frac{2}{3}}$
>
> Multiplying the fraction under the radical sign by $\frac{3}{3}$ to make the
>
> denominator a square
> $$= \sqrt{\frac{2}{3} \cdot \frac{3}{3}}$$
> $$= \sqrt{\frac{6}{9}}$$
>
> Factoring the radicand
> $$= \sqrt{6 \cdot \frac{1}{9}}$$
>
> Removing the square factor
> $$= \frac{1}{3}\sqrt{6} \quad \text{Answer}$$

2. Simplify: $\sqrt[3]{\frac{x}{y^2}}$.

> *Solution.* Given example $\qquad\qquad \sqrt[3]{\frac{x}{y^2}}$
>
> Multiplying the fraction under the radical sign by $\frac{y}{y}$ to make the
>
> denominator a cube
> $$= \sqrt[3]{\frac{xy}{y^3}}$$
> $$= \sqrt[3]{xy\left(\frac{1}{y^3}\right)}$$
> $$= \frac{1}{y}\sqrt[3]{xy} \quad \text{Answer}$$

3. Simplify: $\sqrt{\frac{3}{8}}$

> *Solution.* $\qquad\qquad\qquad \sqrt{\frac{3}{8}}$
> $$= \sqrt{\frac{3}{8} \cdot \frac{2}{2}}$$
> $$= \sqrt{\frac{6}{16}}$$
> $$= \frac{1}{4}\sqrt{6} \quad \text{Answer}$$

EXERCISES: Making the radicand integral

Simplify the following by making the radicand integral:

1. $\sqrt{\frac{1}{4}}$ **2.** $\sqrt{\frac{2}{5}}$ **3.** $\sqrt{\frac{3}{7}}$

4. $2\sqrt{\frac{2}{5}}$

5. $3x\sqrt{\frac{6}{x}}$

6. $2x^2\sqrt{\frac{5}{x^3}}$

7. $\sqrt[3]{\frac{1}{9}}$

8. $\sqrt[3]{\frac{5}{2}}$

9. $\sqrt[3]{\frac{3}{5}}$

10. $\sqrt[4]{\frac{1}{8}}$

11. $2x\sqrt[3]{\frac{5}{x^2}}$

12. $5x\sqrt[4]{\frac{6}{x^3}}$

13. $\frac{1}{2}\sqrt{\frac{3}{5}}$

14. $\frac{2}{3}\sqrt{\frac{3}{4}}$

15. $\frac{4}{3}\sqrt[3]{\frac{3}{4}}$

16. $\sqrt{\frac{x^2}{12}}$

17. $\sqrt[3]{\frac{x^3}{9}}$

18. $\frac{3}{x}\sqrt{\frac{4x^3}{5}}$

19. $\sqrt{\frac{5x}{3y}}$

20. $5\sqrt{\frac{x^2y}{8}}$

21. $\sqrt[3]{\frac{64x^6y^2}{27a^5b^3}}$

22. $\sqrt[4]{\frac{16x^5y^6}{a^3b^3}}$

23. $\sqrt[n]{\frac{x^{2n}}{y^{n-1}}}$

24. $\sqrt[n]{\frac{y^{3n}}{x^{n-2}}}$

Addition and subtraction of radicals. *Similar* radicals, or *like* radicals, are those radical expressions of the same order in which the radicands are the same. Therefore, $\sqrt{5}$, $3\sqrt{5}$, $-2\sqrt{5}$ are like radicals. $\sqrt{3}$ and $\sqrt[3]{3}$ are *not* like radicals since they are of different orders. $\sqrt{2x}$ and $\sqrt{3x}$ are not like radicals since the radicands are *not* the same. *Only like radicals can be combined by addition and subtraction.* We can combine like radicals by adding their coefficients and annexing their common radical. When we collect the like terms in the expression $x + 3x - 2x$, we obtain $2x$. In the same way, when we combine the like radicals $\sqrt{5} + 3\sqrt{5} - 2\sqrt{5}$, we obtain $2\sqrt{5}$.

ILLUSTRATIVE EXAMPLES: Adding and subtracting radicals

1. Simplify: $\sqrt{32} + \sqrt{128} - \sqrt{18} + \sqrt{50}$

    Solution.

    Given example $\sqrt{32} + \sqrt{128} - \sqrt{18} + \sqrt{50}$

    Simplifying each radical $4\sqrt{2} + 8\sqrt{2} - 3\sqrt{2} + 5\sqrt{2}$

    Combining like radicals $14\sqrt{2}$ Answer

2. Simplify: $18\sqrt{\frac{1}{3}} + \sqrt{12} - \sqrt{75}$

Solution.

Given example

$$18\sqrt{\tfrac{1}{3}} + \sqrt{12} - \sqrt{75}$$
$$\tfrac{18}{3}\sqrt{3} + 2\sqrt{3} - 5\sqrt{3}$$
$$3\sqrt{3} \quad \text{Answer}$$

ORAL EXERCISES: Combining like radicals

Simplify by combining like radicals.

1. $6\sqrt{3} + 2\sqrt{3}$
2. $8\sqrt{2} - 7\sqrt{2}$
3. $4\sqrt{a} + \sqrt{a}$
4. $2\sqrt{x} - \sqrt{x} + 3\sqrt{y}$
5. $6\sqrt{ab} - 3\sqrt{ab}$

6. $9\sqrt{5} - 4\sqrt{3} + 2\sqrt{5} - \sqrt{3}$
7. $4\sqrt{x} + 3\sqrt{y} - 2\sqrt{x}$
8. $6\sqrt{3} + 7\sqrt{3} - 2\sqrt{3} + \sqrt{x}$
9. $\sqrt{a} + \sqrt{b} + \sqrt{a} + \sqrt{c}$
10. $2\sqrt{a} - 3\sqrt{b} + 5\sqrt{a} + \sqrt{b}$

EXERCISES: Adding and subtracting radicals

Simplify each radical expression and combine like radicals.

1. $\sqrt{72} - \sqrt{50} + \sqrt{8}$
2. $\sqrt{12} + \sqrt{75} - \sqrt{27}$
3. $3\sqrt{20} - \sqrt{45} + \frac{1}{4}\sqrt{80}$
4. $\frac{1}{2}\sqrt{4x} - \frac{1}{3}\sqrt{9x} + \frac{1}{4}\sqrt{64x}$
5. $\sqrt[3]{16} + 2\sqrt[3]{54}$
6. $4\sqrt[3]{\frac{1}{2}} + \sqrt[3]{32}$
7. $\sqrt[3]{24} - \sqrt[3]{\frac{1}{9}} + 3\sqrt[3]{81}$
8. $\sqrt{\frac{1}{30}} + \sqrt{\frac{5}{6}} - \sqrt{\frac{6}{5}}$

9. $15\sqrt{\frac{1}{5}} - 3\sqrt{45}$
10. $6\sqrt{40} + 3\sqrt{\frac{5}{8}} - 2\sqrt{\frac{5}{2}}$
11. $2\sqrt{18} - 3\sqrt{32} + 2\sqrt{128}$
12. $3\sqrt{80} + 2\sqrt{32} - 2\sqrt{45} - 4\sqrt{20}$
13. $\sqrt[3]{3x} + \sqrt[3]{81x} - \sqrt{45x} + \sqrt[3]{54x}$
14. $5\sqrt{\frac{3}{5a}} - 3\sqrt{\frac{5}{3a}}$
15. $\sqrt[5]{64} + \sqrt[5]{2} + \sqrt[5]{486}$
16. $\sqrt[4]{512} - \sqrt[4]{162} + \sqrt[4]{32}$

Multiplication of radicals of the same order.   The product of the square roots of two non-negative numbers is equal to the square root of the product of those numbers. That is

$$\sqrt{a} \cdot \sqrt{b} = \sqrt{ab}, \text{ where } a \text{ and } b \text{ are not both negative.}$$

Similarly, the product of the cube roots of two numbers is equal to the cube root of the product of those numbers. That is

$$\sqrt[3]{a} \cdot \sqrt[3]{b} = \sqrt[3]{ab}$$

We can carry this principle still further to fourth roots, to fifth roots, and, in general, to nth roots. The product of the nth roots of two numbers is equal to the nth root of the product of those numbers. That is

$$\sqrt[n]{a} \cdot \sqrt[n]{b} = \sqrt[n]{ab}$$

ILLUSTRATIVE EXAMPLES: Multiplying radicals of the same order

1. Simplify: $5\sqrt{3} \cdot 2\sqrt{6}$

        Solution. Given example $5\sqrt{3} \cdot 2\sqrt{6}$
        Multiply the coefficients,
        $5 \cdot 2 = 10$ $10\sqrt{3}\,\sqrt{6}$
        Multiply the radicands $10\sqrt{18}$
        Reduce the radicand $10\sqrt{9 \cdot 2} = 10 \cdot 3\sqrt{2}$
                                      $= 30\sqrt{2}$ Answer

2. Simplify: $(2\sqrt{5} + \sqrt{3})(3\sqrt{5} - \sqrt{3})$

        Solution.

    Given example $(2\sqrt{5} + \sqrt{3})(3\sqrt{5} - \sqrt{3})$
    By the FOIL method $6\sqrt{25} - 2\sqrt{15} + 3\sqrt{15} - \sqrt{9}$
    Simplifying $30 - 2\sqrt{15} + 3\sqrt{15} - 3$
                              $27 + \sqrt{15}$ Answer

EXERCISES: Multiplying radicals of the same order

Simplify:

1. $\sqrt{3}\,\sqrt{2}$

2. $\sqrt{3}\,\sqrt{6}$

3. $\sqrt{6}\,\sqrt{2}$

4. $3\sqrt{2}\,\sqrt{18}$

5. $\sqrt[3]{16}\,\sqrt[3]{4}$

6. $\sqrt[3]{9}\,\sqrt[3]{3}$

7. $2\sqrt{50}\,\sqrt{8}$

8. $(\sqrt{5})^2$

9. $(\sqrt{3x})^2$

10. $3\sqrt{3}\,\sqrt{21}$

11. $(4\sqrt{3})^2$

12. $5\sqrt{3x} \cdot 2\sqrt{6x}$

13. $(\sqrt{x-2})^2$

14. $(4\sqrt{x-1})^2$

15. $5\sqrt{3a^2} \cdot 3\sqrt{25a}$

16. $\sqrt{a+b}\,\sqrt{a-b}$

17. $(\sqrt[3]{5a})^3$

18. $\sqrt[5]{8}\,\sqrt[5]{4}$

19. $\sqrt[4]{27}\,\sqrt[4]{6}$

20. $2\sqrt[3]{x-y}\,\sqrt[3]{(x-y)^2}$

21. $(\sqrt{2} + \sqrt{3})(\sqrt{2} - \sqrt{3})$

22. $(\sqrt{5} - \sqrt{3})(\sqrt{5} + \sqrt{3})$

23. $(2\sqrt{3} - \sqrt{2})^2$

24. $(3\sqrt{5} - \sqrt{2})^2$

25. $(2\sqrt{7} - 3\sqrt{3})^2$

26. $(2\sqrt{5} - 3\sqrt{3})(3\sqrt{5} + \sqrt{3})$

27. $(5 - \sqrt{2})(5 + \sqrt{2})$

28. $(4 + \sqrt{3})^2$

29. $(2\sqrt{7} - 3)^2$

30. $(\sqrt{x-1} + 2)(\sqrt{x-1} - 2)$

31. $(1 - \sqrt{x})^2$

32. $(7 - \sqrt{x})^2$

33. $(\sqrt{x+1} - 2)^2$

34. $(3 - \sqrt{2x-1})^2$

35. $(\sqrt{x+1} + \sqrt{x-2})^2$

36. $(\sqrt{x-5} - 6)^2$

37. $(\sqrt{2x-1} + \sqrt{3x})^2$

38. $(1 - \sqrt{5x+4})^2$

Division of radicals of the same order.   If the square root of a number is divided by the square root of a second number, the result is the square root of the quotient of those numbers.   That is

$$\frac{\sqrt{a}}{\sqrt{b}} = \sqrt{\frac{a}{b}},$$ where a and b are not both negative.

Similarly, if the cube root of a number is divided by the cube root of a second number, the result is the cube root of the quotient of those numbers. That is

$$\frac{\sqrt[3]{a}}{\sqrt[3]{b}} = \sqrt[3]{\frac{a}{b}}$$

We can carry this principle to fourth roots, to fifth roots, and, in general, to nth roots.   If the nth root of a number is divided by the nth root of a second number, the result is the nth root of the quotient of those numbers. That is

$$\frac{\sqrt[n]{a}}{\sqrt[n]{b}} = \sqrt[n]{\frac{a}{b}}$$

I L L U S T R A T I V E   E X A M P L E S :   Dividing monomial radicals of the same order

1. Simplify : $\dfrac{15\sqrt{40}}{3\sqrt{8}}$

Solution. Given example	$\dfrac{15\sqrt{40}}{3\sqrt{8}}$
Dividing the coefficients	$\dfrac{5\sqrt{40}}{\sqrt{8}}$
Dividing the radicands	$5\sqrt{\dfrac{40}{8}}$
Reducing the fraction	$5\sqrt{5}$ Answer

2. Simplify : $6\sqrt[3]{135} \div \sqrt[3]{5}$

Solution. Given example	$6\sqrt[3]{135} \div \sqrt[3]{5}$
Dividing the radicands	$6\sqrt[3]{\dfrac{135}{5}}$
Reducing the fraction	$6\sqrt[3]{27}$
Taking the indicated root	$6 \cdot 3$
	18 Answer

3. Simplify: $3\sqrt[4]{2} \div \sqrt[4]{54}$

   Solution. Given example $3\sqrt[4]{2} \div \sqrt[4]{54}$

    Dividing the radicands $3\sqrt[4]{\dfrac{2}{54}}$

    Reducing the fraction $3\sqrt[4]{\dfrac{1}{27}}$

    Making the radicand integral $3\sqrt[4]{\dfrac{1}{27} \cdot \dfrac{3}{3}}$

              $3\sqrt[4]{\dfrac{3}{81}}$

              $3 \cdot \dfrac{1}{3}\sqrt[4]{3}$

              $\sqrt[4]{3}$ Answer

E X E R C I S E S : Dividing monomial radicals of the same order

Perform the indicated divisions.

1. $\sqrt{8} \div \sqrt{2}$ **7.** $\sqrt[3]{54} \div \sqrt[3]{2}$

2. $\sqrt{20} \div \sqrt{5}$ **8.** $\sqrt[3]{16} \div \sqrt[3]{2}$ **14.** $\dfrac{3\sqrt[3]{4}}{2\sqrt[3]{16}}$

3. $\sqrt{75} \div \sqrt{3}$ **9.** $\sqrt[3]{40x} \div \sqrt[3]{5x}$

4. $6\sqrt{15} \div 2\sqrt{5}$ **10.** $9\sqrt{45} \div 3\sqrt{5}$ **15.** $\dfrac{4\sqrt[3]{2}}{3\sqrt[3]{48}}$

5. $\sqrt{128} \div \sqrt{32}$ **11.** $7\sqrt{21} \div \sqrt{7}$

6. $\sqrt{8a^3} \div \sqrt{2a}$ **12.** $15\sqrt{75} \div 5\sqrt{3}$ **16.** $\dfrac{6\sqrt[4]{3}}{5\sqrt[4]{243}}$

            13. $\dfrac{6\sqrt{32}}{\sqrt{64}}$ **17.** $\dfrac{3\sqrt[5]{2}}{5\sqrt[5]{16}}$

                      18. $\sqrt[3]{250x^5} \div \sqrt[3]{2x^2}$

                      19. $4\sqrt[4]{80x^5} \div \sqrt[4]{5x}$

                      20. $6\sqrt[3]{x^7y^5} \div 2\sqrt[3]{xy^2}$

Two equals one? The following proof demonstrates that 2 is equal to 1. Of course, there must be an error. Can you find it?

Let $M = N$

Multiplying each member by M $\qquad M^2 = MN$

Subtracting N^2 $\qquad M^2 - N^2 = MN - N^2$

Factoring $\qquad (M + N)(M - N) = N(M - N)$

Dividing by $M - N$ $\qquad M + N = N$

Substituting N for its equal M $\qquad 2N = N$

Dividing by N $\qquad 2 = 1$

Multiplication of radicals of different orders.   To multiply radicals of different orders it is necessary to change them all to the same order.   The radicals should be converted to equivalent expressions containing fractional exponents.   Change all these fractional exponents to equivalent fractions having the same denominator.   Rewrite the equivalent fractional exponents in radical form.   Then proceed as in multiplication of radicals of the same order.

ILLUSTRATIVE EXAMPLE: Multiplying radicals of different orders

Multiply $\sqrt{6}$ by $\sqrt[3]{5}$

Solution.   Converting to fractional exponents $\sqrt{6} = 6^{\frac{1}{2}}$ and $\sqrt[3]{5} = 5^{\frac{1}{3}}$
Changing the fractional exponents to equivalent fractions, having like denominators $\qquad 6^{\frac{1}{2}} = 6^{\frac{3}{6}}$ and $5^{\frac{1}{3}} = 5^{\frac{2}{6}}$

Rewriting these in radical form $\qquad 6^{\frac{3}{6}} = \sqrt[6]{6^3} = \sqrt[6]{216}$

and $\quad 5^{\frac{2}{6}} = \sqrt[6]{5^2} = \sqrt[6]{25}$

The product is $\qquad \sqrt[6]{216} \cdot \sqrt[6]{25} = \sqrt[6]{216 \cdot 25} = \sqrt[6]{5400}$ Answer

EXERCISES: Multiplying radicals of different orders

Multiply as indicated :

1. $\sqrt{3} \cdot \sqrt[3]{2}$
2. $\sqrt[3]{3} \cdot \sqrt[4]{2}$
3. $\sqrt{5} \cdot \sqrt[3]{2}$
4. $\sqrt[3]{10} \cdot \sqrt{5}$

5. $\sqrt{2} \cdot \sqrt[3]{2}$
6. $\sqrt{2} \cdot \sqrt[5]{2}$
7. $\sqrt[3]{5} \cdot \sqrt{2}$
8. $\sqrt[3]{3} \cdot \sqrt[6]{2}$

9. $\sqrt[6]{3} \cdot \sqrt[3]{4}$
10. $\sqrt[5]{3} \cdot \sqrt{3}$
11. $\sqrt[6]{a} \cdot \sqrt[4]{a}$
12. $\sqrt[3]{a^2} \cdot \sqrt[4]{a^3}$

Division of radicals of different orders.   To divide radicals of different order, it is necessary first to change the radicals to the same order.

ILLUSTRATIVE EXAMPLE: Dividing radicals of different orders

Divide: $\sqrt[3]{4} \div \sqrt[6]{2}$.

Solution.	$\sqrt[3]{4} = 4^{\frac{1}{3}} = 4^{\frac{2}{6}} = \sqrt[6]{16}$
Given example	$\sqrt[3]{4} \div \sqrt[6]{2}$
Substituting	$\sqrt[6]{16} \div \sqrt[6]{2}$
Dividing	$\sqrt[6]{8}$
	$\sqrt[6]{2^3}$
	$\sqrt{2}$ Answer

EXERCISES: Dividing radicals of different orders

Divide as indicated:

1. $\sqrt[4]{6} \div \sqrt[6]{2}$ 5. $\sqrt{5} \div \sqrt[3]{5}$ 9. $\sqrt{8} \div \sqrt[3]{3}$

2. $\sqrt{8} \div \sqrt[3]{4}$ 6. $\sqrt[3]{2} \div \sqrt[4]{2}$ 10. $\sqrt[3]{3} \div \sqrt{2}$

3. $\sqrt[3]{4} \div \sqrt{2}$ 7. $\sqrt[4]{8} \div \sqrt{2}$ 11. $\sqrt[3]{x} \div \sqrt[6]{x}$

4. $\sqrt{6} \div \sqrt[3]{3}$ 8. $\sqrt[6]{12} \div \sqrt[3]{2}$ 12. $\sqrt{a^3} \div \sqrt[4]{a^3}$

Real and imaginary numbers. All numbers are either *real* or *imaginary*. An *imaginary* number is the indicated even root of a negative number. The following numbers are imaginary: $\sqrt{-5}$, $\sqrt{-\frac{1}{2}}$, $\sqrt[4]{-3}$, $\sqrt[6]{-\frac{2}{3}}$. The imaginary number $\sqrt{-5}$ means a number which, when multiplied by itself, is equal to the negative number, -5. Probably the meaning of these numbers was not clear for many years and, for that reason, they were given the unfortunate name of imaginary numbers. The student should not let the name "imaginary number" lead him to believe that such numbers are not of any practical value. Many of the problems of the electrical engineer are most conveniently solved with the aid of imaginary numbers.

All numbers that are not imaginary are real. All the numbers that you have used in your arithmetic and earlier algebra have been real numbers. The following numbers are real: 7, $\frac{1}{3}$, -5, $\sqrt[3]{3}$, $\sqrt{11}$, π, $-\frac{3}{7}$.

Real numbers: rational and irrational. All real numbers are either rational or irrational. **A *rational* number is one that can be represented as a ratio of two whole numbers.** The following numbers are rational: $\frac{3}{5}$, $2\frac{1}{2}$, -11, 0.26, $\sqrt{\frac{4}{9}}$, $\sqrt{25}$.

Those real numbers that are not rational (that is, numbers that cannot be represented as a fraction with integral numerator and denominator) are called *irrational*. The following numbers are irrational: $\sqrt{7}$, $\sqrt{13}$,

π, $\sqrt[3]{-17}$. In a radical of the second order, if the radicand is a square, the number is rational. If the radicand is positive but not a square, the number is irrational. Similarly, in a radical of the third order, if the radicand is a cube, the number is rational. If the radicand is not a cube, the number is irrational.

ORAL EXERCISES: Nature of numbers

Identify the following numbers as real or imaginary. If they are real, tell if they are rational or irrational.

1. $7\frac{1}{3}$	**5.** $2\frac{7}{19}$	**9.** $\sqrt{-6\frac{1}{2}}$	**13.** π
2. $-6\frac{1}{2}$	**6.** $\sqrt{36}$	**10.** $\frac{2}{9}$	**14.** $\sqrt{-1}$
3. $\sqrt{13}$	**7.** $\sqrt[3]{-11}$	**11.** $-\frac{3}{5}$	**15.** $\sqrt[3]{-1}$
4. $\sqrt{-5}$	**8.** $\sqrt[4]{-10}$	**12.** $\sqrt{-7}$	**16.** $\sqrt{11}$

Rational denominators.   If an irrational number in a denominator is replaced by a rational number without changing the fraction's value, the fraction has been simplified. This procedure is known as *rationalizing the denominator* and is demonstrated in the following examples.

ILLUSTRATIVE EXAMPLES: Rationalizing monomial denominators

1. Rationalize the denominator of the following expression: $\dfrac{2}{\sqrt{3}}$

$\qquad$ *Solution.* Given example $\dfrac{2}{\sqrt{3}}$

To make the denominator a rational number, we must eliminate the radical. We can do this by multiplying both the numerator and the denominator by $\sqrt{3}$.

$$\frac{2}{\sqrt{3}} \cdot \frac{\sqrt{3}}{\sqrt{3}}$$
$$\tfrac{2}{3}\sqrt{3} \quad \text{Answer}$$

2. Rationalize the denominator of the following expression: $\dfrac{5x}{\sqrt[3]{x^2}}$

$\qquad$ *Solution.* Given example $\dfrac{5x}{\sqrt[3]{x^2}}$

$$\frac{5x}{\sqrt[3]{x^2}} \cdot \frac{\sqrt[3]{x}}{\sqrt[3]{x}}$$

Multiplying $\dfrac{5x\sqrt[3]{x}}{\sqrt[3]{x^3}}$

$\dfrac{5x\sqrt[3]{x}}{x}$

$5\sqrt[3]{x}$ Answer

3. Rationalize the denominator of the following expression: $\dfrac{15}{\sqrt{20}}$

Solution.   Given example $\dfrac{15}{\sqrt{20}}$

$\dfrac{15}{\sqrt{20}} \cdot \dfrac{\sqrt{5}}{\sqrt{5}}$

$\dfrac{15\sqrt{5}}{\sqrt{100}}$

$\dfrac{15\sqrt{5}}{10}$

$\dfrac{3\sqrt{5}}{2}$ Answer

EXERCISES: Rationalizing monomial denominators

Rationalize the denominators of each of the following:

1. $\dfrac{\sqrt{5}}{\sqrt{2}}$ 6. $\dfrac{\sqrt{2}}{\sqrt{3}}$ 11. $\dfrac{5\sqrt{6}}{2\sqrt{3}}$ 16. $\dfrac{2\sqrt[3]{9}}{\sqrt[3]{3}}$

2. $\dfrac{5}{\sqrt{3}}$ 7. $\dfrac{\sqrt{7}}{\sqrt{3}}$ 12. $\dfrac{3\sqrt{7}}{2\sqrt{5}}$ 17. $\dfrac{5\sqrt[3]{4}}{\sqrt[3]{2}}$

3. $\dfrac{8}{\sqrt{2}}$ 8. $\dfrac{\sqrt{11}}{\sqrt{6}}$ 13. $\dfrac{15\sqrt{6}}{3\sqrt{5}}$ 18. $\dfrac{5\sqrt[3]{10}}{3\sqrt[3]{2}}$

4. $\dfrac{21}{\sqrt{7}}$ 9. $\dfrac{2\sqrt{3}}{\sqrt{5}}$ 14. $\dfrac{\sqrt[3]{5}}{\sqrt[3]{9}}$ 19. $\dfrac{3}{\sqrt[3]{10}}$

5. $\dfrac{35}{\sqrt{5}}$ 10. $\dfrac{5\sqrt{6}}{\sqrt{5}}$ 15. $\dfrac{\sqrt[3]{6}}{\sqrt[3]{4}}$ 20. $\dfrac{5\sqrt[4]{6}}{\sqrt[4]{27}}$

Rationalizing binomial denominators.   Two binomial radical expressions are *conjugates* if they differ only in the sign which connects their terms. Thus, $2 - \sqrt{3}$ and $2 + \sqrt{3}$ are conjugate radical expressions; $\sqrt{2} + \sqrt{5}$ and $\sqrt{2} - \sqrt{5}$ are also conjugate radical expressions.

> The product of two conjugate radical expressions is a rational number.
>
> $$(\sqrt{a} + \sqrt{b})(\sqrt{a} - \sqrt{b}) = a - b$$

If a fraction contains a binomial denominator that is not rational, the denominator can be made rational by multiplying it by its conjugate. In order not to change the value of the fraction, the numerator must be multiplied by the same quantity that is used to multiply the denominator.

ILLUSTRATIVE EXAMPLE: Rationalizing a binomial denominator

Rationalize the denominator of $\dfrac{6 - \sqrt{2}}{4 - 3\sqrt{2}}$.

Solution. Given example $\qquad \dfrac{6 - \sqrt{2}}{4 - 3\sqrt{2}}$

Multiplying the numerator and the denominator by the conjugate of the denominator $\qquad \dfrac{6 - \sqrt{2}}{4 - 3\sqrt{2}} \cdot \dfrac{4 + 3\sqrt{2}}{4 + 3\sqrt{2}}$

Multiplying by the FOIL method $\qquad \dfrac{24 + 18\sqrt{2} - 4\sqrt{2} - 6}{16 + 12\sqrt{2} - 12\sqrt{2} - 18}$

Collecting terms $\qquad \dfrac{18 + 14\sqrt{2}}{-2}$

Reducing the fraction $\qquad -9 - 7\sqrt{2}$ Answer

EXERCISES: Rationalizing binomial denominators

Rationalize the denominator of the following fractions. Where possible, simplify the resulting fraction by reducing it.

1. $\dfrac{4}{3 - \sqrt{5}}$

2. $\dfrac{\sqrt{5}}{\sqrt{3} + \sqrt{2}}$

3. $\dfrac{14}{2\sqrt{3} + 5}$

4. $\dfrac{\sqrt{3} - \sqrt{2}}{\sqrt{3} + \sqrt{2}}$

5. $\dfrac{2 + \sqrt{2}}{5 + 3\sqrt{2}}$

6. $\dfrac{\sqrt{6}}{\sqrt{5} - \sqrt{3}}$

7. $\dfrac{2\sqrt{3} - 3\sqrt{2}}{2\sqrt{3} + 3\sqrt{2}}$

8. $\dfrac{\sqrt{3} + \sqrt{5}}{\sqrt{5} - \sqrt{3}}$

9. $\dfrac{5\sqrt{5} + 3\sqrt{3}}{\sqrt{5} - \sqrt{3}}$

10. $\dfrac{a + b\sqrt{x}}{a - b\sqrt{x}}$

14. $\dfrac{a + \sqrt{a+1}}{a - \sqrt{a-1}}$

11. $\dfrac{2\sqrt{3} + 3\sqrt{7}}{3\sqrt{3} - 2\sqrt{7}}$

15. $\dfrac{\sqrt{x+1} - 2}{\sqrt{x+1} + 2}$

12. $\dfrac{3\sqrt{7} - 2\sqrt{5}}{2\sqrt{7} - 3\sqrt{5}}$

16. $\dfrac{\sqrt{a^2 + b^2} - \sqrt{a^2 - b^2}}{\sqrt{a^2 + b^2} + \sqrt{a^2 - b^2}}$

13. $\dfrac{3\sqrt{a} + 2\sqrt{b}}{\sqrt{a} - 2\sqrt{b}}$

Square root of binomial radical expressions. If we square $\pm(\sqrt{a} + \sqrt{b})$, we obtain $a + 2\sqrt{ab} + b$, or $(a + b) + 2\sqrt{ab}$. Therefore, the square roots of $(a + b) + 2\sqrt{ab}$ are $\pm(\sqrt{a} + \sqrt{b})$. Similarly, the square roots of $(a + b) - 2\sqrt{ab}$ are $\pm(\sqrt{a} - \sqrt{b})$. We can use these facts to find the square roots of some binomial radical expressions as shown in the following illustrative example.

ILLUSTRATIVE EXAMPLE: Finding the square root of a binomial radical expression

Find $\sqrt{9 - 3\sqrt{8}}$.

Solution. Given the example
$$\pm\sqrt{9 - 3\sqrt{8}}$$

We first express the radicand in the form $(a + b) \pm 2\sqrt{ab}$
$$\pm\sqrt{9 - \sqrt{9\cdot8}}$$

Put the 3 under the radical sign to become 9
$$\pm\sqrt{9 - \sqrt{9\cdot2\cdot\mathbf{4}}}$$

Factor 4 out of the radicand so that 2 may be taken out from under the radical sign.
$$\pm\sqrt{9 - 2\sqrt{9\cdot2}}$$
$$\pm\sqrt{9 - 2\sqrt{\mathbf{18}}}$$

Therefore, $(a + b)$ must equal 9 and ab must equal 18. Two numbers whose sum is 9 and whose product is 18 are 6 and 3.
The required square roots, therefore, are
$$\pm(\sqrt{6} - \sqrt{3}) \quad \text{Answer}$$

Check. $9 - 3\sqrt{8} \overset{?}{=} (\sqrt{6} - \sqrt{3})^2$ $\quad 9 - 3\sqrt{8} = (-\sqrt{6} + \sqrt{3})^2$
$$\overset{?}{=} 6 - 2\sqrt{18} + 3 \qquad\qquad \overset{?}{=} 6 - 2\sqrt{18} + 3$$
$$\overset{?}{=} 9 - 2\sqrt{18} \qquad\qquad\quad \overset{?}{=} 9 - 2\sqrt{18}$$
$$\overset{?}{=} 9 - \sqrt{4\cdot2\cdot9} \qquad\qquad \overset{?}{=} 9 - \sqrt{4\cdot2\cdot9}$$
$$= 9 - 3\sqrt{8} \text{ Check} \qquad\qquad = 9 - 3\sqrt{8} \text{ Check}$$

EXERCISES: Finding square roots of binomial radical expressions

Find the square roots of each binomial radical expression in ex. 1–10.

1. $11 - 2\sqrt{30}$

2. $6 + \sqrt{32}$

3. $17 - 2\sqrt{72}$

4. $7 + \sqrt{40}$

5. $8 - \sqrt{28}$

6. $30 + 10\sqrt{5}$

7. $12 - 6\sqrt{3}$

8. $18 + 4\sqrt{18}$

9. $7 + 4\sqrt{3}$

10. $14 + 6\sqrt{5}$

11. Simplify: $\pm \sqrt{14 + 8\sqrt{3}}$

12. Simplify: $\pm \sqrt{10a + 2\sqrt{25a^2 - b^2}}$

Doings of Dimbo. Dimbo learned that sawing wood was much easier when he used the whole saw, handle as well as the blade.

Can you find what handle Dimbo should have used in his solution of the following problem? What is the correct answer?

Rationalize the denominator of $\dfrac{\sqrt{3}}{\sqrt{3} + 2}$.

Dimbo's solution:

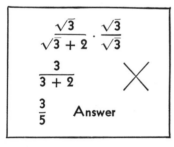

$$\frac{\sqrt{3}}{\sqrt{3} + 2} \cdot \frac{\sqrt{3}}{\sqrt{3}}$$

$$\frac{3}{3 + 2}$$

$$\frac{3}{5} \quad \text{Answer}$$

The imaginary unit. Since every imaginary number can be written as the product of a real number and $\sqrt{-1}$, the $\sqrt{-1}$ is considered to be the imaginary unit; we frequently represent it as i.

$$\sqrt{-9} = \sqrt{9} \cdot \sqrt{-1} = 3\sqrt{-1} \text{ or } 3i$$

$$\sqrt{-15} = \sqrt{15} \cdot \sqrt{-1} = \sqrt{15}\, i \text{ or } i\sqrt{15} \quad \text{To avoid con-}$$

fusion and misreading, it is customary to place the i before the radical.
The first four powers of i are:

$$i = \sqrt{-1}$$
$$i^2 = -1$$
$$i^3 = i^2 \cdot i \text{ or } -i$$
$$i^4 = i^2 \cdot i^2 = (-1)^2 = +1$$

Beyond i^4 the values of the powers of i repeat over and over again in the
order $i, -1, -i, +1$.

I L L U S T R A T I V E   E X A M P L E : Evaluating expressions containing powers of i

Simplify: $(i^{16} - i^{29})^3$

Solution.
$$i^{16} = (i^4)^4 = (+1)^4 = +1$$
$$i^{29} = i^{28} \cdot i = (i^4)^7 \cdot i = 1^7 \cdot i = i$$
$$(i^{16} - i^{29})^3 = (1 - i)^3 = 1 - 3i + 3i^2 - i^3$$
$$= 1 - 3i + 3(-1) - (-i)$$
$$= 1 - 3i - 3 + i$$
$$= -2 - 2i \quad \text{Answer}$$

Note. A simple method of evaluating a power of i is to divide mentally
the exponent of i by 4:

If there is no remainder, the i term equals 1. $i^{36} = 1.$
If the remainder is 1, the i term equals i. $i^{17} = i.$
If the remainder is 2, the i term equals -1. $i^{30} = -1.$
If the remainder is 3, the i term equals $-i$. $i^{11} = -i.$

E X E R C I S E S : Evaluating expressions containing powers of i

Simplify the following:

1. i^{15} 4. i^{99} 7. $(i^{29} - i^{32})^3$ 10. $i^{100} - i^{96} + i^{92} - i^{88}$
2. $i^{71} - i^{49}$ 5. $(i^{20} - i^{19})^2$ 8. $(i^{53} + i^{61})^2$
3. i^{37} 6. $(i^{13})^3 - (i^{14})^2$ 9. $i^{14} + i^{15} + i^{16}$

Operations with imaginary numbers.   To perform operations with imaginary
numbers it is helpful to convert the imaginary number into the product
of a real number and i. In performing any operation the i should be treated
as if it were any other letter. As a final step in simplification all the powers
of i above 1 should be converted to their equivalent, $\pm i$ or ± 1.

A binomial, one of whose terms is real and the other imaginary, is called
a *complex number*. Thus, the following are complex numbers: $3 + \sqrt{-5}$,
$-2 - 7i, \frac{3}{2} - \sqrt{-2}$, etc.

I L L U S T R A T I V E   E X A M P L E S :   Operating with imaginary and complex numbers

1. Simplify : $\sqrt{-5} \cdot \sqrt{-3}$

$\qquad$ *Solution.* $\qquad$ $\sqrt{-5} = \sqrt{5} \cdot \sqrt{-1} = i\sqrt{5}$

$\qquad\qquad\qquad\qquad$ $\sqrt{-3} = \sqrt{3} \cdot \sqrt{-1} = i\sqrt{3}$

$\qquad\qquad\qquad$ $\sqrt{-5} \cdot \sqrt{-3} = (i\sqrt{5})(i\sqrt{3}) = i^2\sqrt{15}$

Since $i^2 = -1$ $\qquad\qquad\qquad\qquad\qquad\qquad$ $= -\sqrt{15}$ $\quad$ Answer

2. Multiply : $(3 + \sqrt{-5})(2 - \sqrt{-2})$

Solution. $3 + \sqrt{-5} = 3 + i\sqrt{5}$ and $2 - \sqrt{-2} = 2 - i\sqrt{2}$

Therefore $\quad$ $(3 + \sqrt{-5})(2 - \sqrt{-2}) = (3 + i\sqrt{5})(2 - i\sqrt{2})$

Multiplying $\qquad\qquad\qquad\qquad$ $= 6 + 2i\sqrt{5} - 3i\sqrt{2} - i^2\sqrt{10}$

Since $i^2 = -1$ $\qquad\qquad\qquad\quad$ $= 6 + 2i\sqrt{5} - 3i\sqrt{2} + \sqrt{10}$

$\qquad\qquad\qquad\qquad\qquad\qquad\qquad\qquad\qquad\qquad$ Answer

3. Find the square root of the complex number $-3 - 2i\sqrt{10}$

Solution. Refer to Illustrative Example, page 204.

Given complex number $\qquad\qquad\qquad\qquad$ $-3 - 2i\sqrt{10}$

Expressing i as $\sqrt{-1}$ $\qquad\qquad\qquad\qquad$ $-3 - 2\sqrt{-1} \cdot \sqrt{10}$

Multiplying $\qquad\qquad\qquad\qquad\qquad\quad$ $-3 - 2\sqrt{-10}$

Two numbers whose product is -10 and whose sum is -3 are -5 and $+2$.

Therefore $\qquad\quad$ $\pm \sqrt{-3 - 2i\sqrt{10}} = \pm(\sqrt{-5} - \sqrt{2})$ $\quad$ Answer

Imaginary numbers.
Originally these numbers were called fictitious or impossible and were rejected as having no meaning. By the seventeenth century mathematicians accepted them as numbers and tried to define them geometrically. René Descartes was the first to use the term "imaginary" in referring to a number which was not "real." Leonard Euler introduced the letter i to represent $\sqrt{-1}$. Later Augustin Louis Cauchy gave us the name "complex number."

E X E R C I S E S : Operating with imaginary and complex numbers

In ex. 1–24 perform the operation indicated and simplify the result if possible.

1. $\sqrt{-5} \cdot \sqrt{-2}$

2. $\sqrt{-5} \cdot \sqrt{-5}$

3. $\sqrt{-2} \cdot \sqrt{-24}$

4. $2i \cdot 5i$

5. $-3i \cdot 6i$

6. $2i\sqrt{3} \cdot 5i\sqrt{2}$

7. $5i\sqrt{5} \cdot i\sqrt{3}$

8. $\sqrt{-27} \cdot \sqrt{-3}$

9. $(3\sqrt{-2})^2$

10. $(2i\sqrt{5})^2$

11. $\sqrt{-25} + \sqrt{-16} + \sqrt{-9}$

12. $2\sqrt{-18} - \sqrt{-50}$

13. $5\sqrt{-27} + 2\sqrt{-12}$

14. $(i\sqrt{2} + 3)^2$

15. $(5 - 2i)^2$

16. $(\sqrt{-2} - \sqrt{-3})^2$

17. $(\sqrt{3} - \sqrt{-2})(\sqrt{3} + \sqrt{-2})$

18. $(2i + 5)(2i - 5)$

19. $(7 - 2\sqrt{-3})(4 + 2\sqrt{-3})$

20. $\dfrac{2a + \sqrt{-b}}{3a - \sqrt{-b}}$

21. $\dfrac{1 + 2\sqrt{-3}}{2\sqrt{3} - \sqrt{-3}}$

22. $\dfrac{\sqrt{2 + 3i} + \sqrt{2 - 3i}}{\sqrt{2 - 3i} + \sqrt{2 + 3i}}$

23. $\dfrac{3 - 2i}{4 + i}$

24. $\dfrac{1 + \sqrt{-9}}{2 - \sqrt{-4}}$

In ex. 25–32 find the square roots of each of the complex numbers.

25. $8 + 2\sqrt{-9}$

26. $-3 - 2\sqrt{-4}$

27. $3 - 4i$

28. $5 + 12i$

29. $7 - 24i$

30. $9 - 40i$

Radical equations.   Equations in which the unknown occurs in a radicand are called radical equations. To solve equations that contain radicals of the second order, it is necessary first to arrange the terms in the equation so that one member consists of a single radical. Then both members should be squared, applying the axiom: *Like powers of equals are equal.*

After the resulting equation is solved, each root should be checked in the original equation. All the *extraneous* roots, that is, roots which do not check in the original equation, should be discarded.

Extraneous roots are sometimes introduced into an equation by the process of squaring both members.

As an example, if $\qquad x = -2$

Squaring both members $\qquad x^2 = 4$

Solving for x $\qquad x = \pm 2$

Of these two roots, $+2$ and -2, only -2 checks in the original equation. The extraneous root, $+2$, was introduced into the equation when both members were squared. This simple example illustrates the necessity always to:

> Check every root whenever both members of an equation are squared in the process of solution.

ILLUSTRATIVE EXAMPLE: Solving a radical equation

Solve the equation $\sqrt{x^2 + 5} + x = 5$.

Solution.

Given equation $\qquad \sqrt{x^2 + 5} + x = 5$

Transposing to make the left member consist of a single radical $\qquad \sqrt{x^2 + 5} = 5 - x$

Squaring both members $\qquad x^2 + 5 = 25 - 10x + x^2$

Collecting terms $\qquad 10x = 20$

$\qquad x = 2$

Checking this root in the original equation $\qquad \sqrt{4 + 5} + 2 \overset{?}{=} 5$

$\qquad 3 + 2 = 5 \quad$ Check

$\qquad x = 2 \quad$ Answer

EXERCISES: Solving radical equations

Solve each of the following equations. Remember that it is necessary to check each root in the original equation.

1. $\sqrt{x} = 3$

2. $\sqrt{x - 2} = 2$

3. $6 = \sqrt{x + 11}$

4. $\sqrt{x - 1} + 4 = 0$

5. $x - 1 = \sqrt{x^2 - 11}$

6. $\sqrt{3x - 2} = 4$

7. $\sqrt{4x} = 2\sqrt{2x - 3}$

8. $\sqrt{3x + 1} = \sqrt{2x + 6}$

9. $3\sqrt{x + 1} = \sqrt{6}$

10. $\sqrt[3]{x - 5} = 2$

Hint. Cube each member.

11. $3 = 2\sqrt{5x - 4} + 11$

12. $\sqrt{4x^2 + 7} = 2x - 7$

13. $\sqrt[3]{x^3 + 12x^2} = x + 4$

14. $\dfrac{x + 14}{2} = \sqrt{\dfrac{x^2}{4} - 7}$

15. $x = 8 - \sqrt{x^2 - 8}$

16. $\sqrt{2 - x} + \sqrt{3 - x} = \dfrac{3}{\sqrt{3 - x}}$

Hint. Clear of fractions by multiplying both members by $\sqrt{3 - x}$.

17. $\dfrac{\sqrt{2}}{2\sqrt{x}} = \dfrac{\sqrt{x}}{\sqrt{2x} + \sqrt{8}}$

18. $\dfrac{\sqrt{x} + 7}{\sqrt{x} + 1} = \dfrac{\sqrt{x} + 1}{\sqrt{x} - 1}$

19. $\dfrac{\sqrt{x} + 55}{\sqrt{x} + 7} = \dfrac{\sqrt{x} - 5}{\sqrt{x} - 8}$

20. $\dfrac{24}{\sqrt{x} + \sqrt{x - 12}} = \sqrt{x}$

ILLUSTRATIVE EXAMPLE: Solving a radical equation by squaring both members twice

Solve for x: $\sqrt{x + 7} - \sqrt{x - 5} - 2 = 0$

Solution. Given equation $\qquad\qquad \sqrt{x + 7} - \sqrt{x - 5} - 2 = 0$

Transposing terms to make the left member a single radical $\qquad \sqrt{x + 7} = \sqrt{x - 5} + 2$

Squaring both members $\qquad\qquad x + 7 = (x - 5) + 4\sqrt{x - 5} + 4$

Collecting terms $\qquad\qquad\qquad\qquad 8 = 4\sqrt{x - 5}$

Dividing by 4 $\qquad\qquad\qquad\qquad\quad 2 = \sqrt{x - 5}$

Squaring again $\qquad\qquad\qquad\qquad\quad 4 = x - 5$

$\qquad\qquad\qquad\qquad\qquad\qquad\qquad 9 = x$

Checking $x = 9$ in the original equation

$$\sqrt{9 + 7} - \sqrt{9 - 5} - 2 \overset{?}{=} 0$$
$$4 - 2 - 2 \overset{?}{=} 0$$
$$0 = 0 \quad \text{Check}$$
$$x = 9 \quad \text{Answer}$$

EXERCISES: Solving radical equations by squaring both members twice

Solve each of the following equations, remembering to check each root in the original equation.

1. $\sqrt{x - 9} = 1 - \sqrt{x}$

2. $7 - \sqrt{x} = \sqrt{x - 7}$

3. $3 + \sqrt{x - 6} = \sqrt{x + 9}$

4. $3 - \sqrt{x - 6} = \sqrt{x + 9}$

5. $7 - \sqrt{3x + 10} = \sqrt{3x - 11}$

6. $7 + \sqrt{3x + 10} = \sqrt{3x - 11}$

7. $2 + \sqrt{5x + 6} = \sqrt{5x + 34}$ **10.** $1 - \sqrt{7x + 18} = \sqrt{7x + 1}$

8. $\sqrt{x + 1} - \sqrt{x - 2} - 1 = 0$ **11.** $\sqrt{4x + 20} + \sqrt{x} = \sqrt{x + 60}$

9. $1 - \sqrt{5x + 4} = \sqrt{5x - 9}$ **12.** $\sqrt{x - 2} - \sqrt{x + 2} = \sqrt{2x}$

VOCABULARY REVIEW. (Chapters 1-9)

You should know the meaning of and be able to spell each of the following words or groups of words.

abscissa	linear equation
absolute value	mean proportional
axiom	mixed expression
binomial conjugate radical expressions	order of a radical
complex fraction	ordinate
complex number	principal square root
conditional equation	proportion
cube root	quadrants
dependent linear equations	quadratic equation
direct variation	radical equation
evolution	radical sign
extraneous root	radicand
fourth proportional	ratio
function	rational
identity	real
imaginary number	repeating decimals
imaginary unit	scientific notation
inconsistent linear equations	significant figures
index of a radical	similar figures
integral	similar radicals
inverse variation	simultaneous linear equations
involution	slope
irrational	square root
joint variation	synthetic division
like radicals	third proportional

CHAPTER REVIEW EXERCISES

Simplify each exercise of ex. 1–6.

1. $\frac{1}{3}\sqrt[3]{81}$ **3.** $\sqrt[4]{25}$ **5.** $\sqrt{\frac{3}{7}}$

2. $\sqrt{250}$ **4.** $2x\sqrt[6]{x^3}$ **6.** $2x\sqrt{\dfrac{5}{x}}$

7. Which of the following numbers are imaginary?

$$-5 \qquad -2\tfrac{1}{2} \qquad \pi \qquad \sqrt{-4} \qquad \sqrt{-\tfrac{6}{7}}$$

8. Which of the following numbers are rational?

$$\sqrt{3} \qquad -2\tfrac{1}{2} \qquad 0.689 \qquad \sqrt{-7} \qquad \sqrt{\tfrac{2}{3}}$$

9. Rationalize the denominator: $\dfrac{6\sqrt{3}}{2\sqrt{6}}$.

10. Simplify: $\tfrac{3}{4}\sqrt{\tfrac{2}{9}} + \sqrt[3]{250} - \sqrt{\tfrac{1}{2}} - \sqrt[3]{54}$

11. Multiply: $(3 + 2\sqrt{5})(3 - 2\sqrt{5})$

12. Multiply: $(2\sqrt{3} + 3\sqrt{2})(5\sqrt{3} - 2\sqrt{2})$

13. What is the square of $(\sqrt{x+2} - \sqrt{3x})$?

14. Divide: $5\sqrt{15} \div 3\sqrt{3}$

15. Divide: $\sqrt[3]{16x^4} \div \sqrt[3]{2x}$

16. Rationalize the denominator of $\dfrac{2\sqrt{3} - 5\sqrt{2}}{3\sqrt{3} + 2\sqrt{2}}$.

17. Find the square roots of $11 + 6\sqrt{2}$.

18. Multiply: $\sqrt{2} \cdot \sqrt[3]{6}$

19. Divide: $\sqrt[5]{4} \div \sqrt{2}$

20. Solve: $\sqrt{x+3} = \sqrt{2x-3}$

21. Solve: $\sqrt{x+2} + \sqrt{x} = \dfrac{3}{\sqrt{x+2}}$

22. Simplify: $(i^{17} + 2i^{37})^4$

23. Simplify: $\sqrt{-15} \cdot \sqrt{-4}$

24. Simplify: $(2 + 5i)(3 - 4i)$

25. Simplify: $\dfrac{3 - 2i}{6 + 5i}$

26. Find the square roots of $12 + 16i$.

CUMULATIVE REVIEW EXERCISES

1. Write a formula for the charge C for a telephone conversation of 9 min., if the charge for the first 3 min. is 65¢ and each additional minute costs k cents.

2. Write the equation of a straight line that is parallel to the line $y = 3x - 5$ and which has a y intercept of 4.

3. If $2^x = 13$, what is the value of 2^{x+1}?

4. Factor completely: $am^2 - bm^2 + b - a$

5. If $f(x) = x^3 - 3x^2 + 2x - 5$, what is the value of $f(0)$?

6. Simplify: $\dfrac{\dfrac{a}{b} - 3}{9 - \dfrac{a^2}{b^2}}$

7. What is the square of $(3\sqrt{5} - 2\sqrt{3})$?

8. Solve for x: $(x - 7)^{\frac{1}{2}} = 1$

9. Simplify: $\dfrac{4 + \sqrt{-100}}{2}$

10. Rationalize the denominator: $\dfrac{\sqrt{3} + 2\sqrt{2}}{\sqrt{3} + \sqrt{2}}$

11. Solve for x and y: $a(x - y) = x + y$
$$\frac{1}{y - a} = \frac{1}{a - x}$$

12. If $f(x) = \dfrac{x - 4}{x}$, what happens to the value of $f(x)$ as x increases from $+1$ to $+4$?

13. The volume of a cone varies jointly as the area of its base and the height. If the volume is 36 cu. in. when the area of the base is 18 sq. in. and the height is 6 in., what is the height of a cone whose volume is 70 cu. in. and the area of whose base is 21 sq. in.?

14. A man made a gift of 10% of his salary to charitable organizations. On this gift and on an additional gift of $3000 he paid no taxes. On the remainder of his salary he paid an income tax of 20%, which amounted to $1920. What was his salary?

15. Evaluate the determinant:

$$\begin{vmatrix} 3 & -1 & 3 \\ 2 & -2 & 3 \\ 4 & -1 & -1 \end{vmatrix}$$

CHAPTER 10 *Quadratic Equations In One Unknown*

Degree of an equation.   When an equation in one unknown letter contains only positive integral powers of this unknown letter, and if it does not contain this unknown letter in any denominator, then the degree of the equation is the same as the exponent of the highest power of this unknown letter.   Thus we have:

Equation	Highest Power of the Unknown	Degree of the Equation
$4x + 9 = 0$	1	first
$2x + 7 = 5x^2$	2	second
$x^3 - 1 = 6x^2$	3	third

Quadratic equations.   An equation of the second degree is called a *quadratic equation*.   The general form of a quadratic equation in one unknown is

$$ax^2 + bx + c = 0$$

where a, b, and c represent known numbers, and x represents the unknown number.   In this equation either b, or c, or both b and c can be equal to zero.   The coefficient a cannot be equal to zero; if it were, the resulting equation would be an equation of the first degree.   The following are quadratic equations in the form $ax^2 + bx + c = 0$:

$$3x^2 + 5x - 2 = 0 \qquad\qquad 6y^2 - 7y = 0$$
$$4x^2 - 25 = 0 \qquad\qquad 5x^2 = 0$$

If, in a quadratic equation in the form $ax^2 + bx + c = 0$, either b or c is zero, the equation is an **incomplete** quadratic equation.   The following incomplete quadratic equations do not contain the first power of the unknown (b is zero):

$$x^2 - 12 = 0 \qquad 4y^2 = 9 \qquad ax^2 + c = 0$$

The following incomplete quadratic equations do not contain a constant term (c is zero):

$$5x^2 - 4x = 0 \qquad 8y^2 = y \qquad ax^2 + bx = 0$$

If a quadratic equation contains a term with the unknown raised to the second power, a term with the unknown to the first power, and a constant term, it is said to be a **complete** quadratic equation.   Thus

$$y^2 - y - 30 = 0,\ x^2 = 6 - 4x,\ \text{and}\ ax^2 + bx + c = 0$$

are examples of complete quadratic equations.

Solving quadratic equations by the factor method.   We have already solved quadratic equations by the factor method (p. 59).   If a quadratic equation is readily factorable, this is the easiest method of solving the equation.   You remember that the factor method is based on the principle that if the product of two numbers is zero, then either one or both of the factors must be zero.   The following examples review the factor method.

I L L U S T R A T I V E   E X A M P L E S :   Solving quadratic equations by the factor method

1. Solve for x: $4x^2 - 3x = 0$

Solution. Given	$4x^2 - 3x = 0$
Factoring	$x(4x - 3) = 0$
Setting each factor equal to zero	$x = 0$ and $4x - 3 = 0$
Solving for x	$x = 0$ and $x = \frac{3}{4}$ Answers

2. Solve for x: $(x + 2)(x - 3) = 24$

Solution. Given	$(x + 2)(x - 3) = 24$
Simplifying	$x^2 - x - 6 = 24$
Collecting	$x^2 - x - 30 = 0$
Factoring	$(x + 5)(x - 6) = 0$
Setting each factor equal to zero	$x + 5 = 0$ and $x - 6 = 0$
Solving for x	$x = -5$ and $x = 6$ Answers

3. Solve for x: $\dfrac{4}{x - 1} - 2 = \dfrac{3x}{x^2 - 1}$

Solution. Given	$\dfrac{4}{x - 1} - 2 = \dfrac{3x}{x^2 - 1}$
Clearing of fractions	$4(x + 1) - 2(x^2 - 1) = 3x$
Simplifying	$4x + 4 - 2x^2 + 2 = 3x$
Collecting	$-2x^2 + x + 6 = 0$
Multiplying both members by -1	$2x^2 - x - 6 = 0$
Factoring	$(2x + 3)(x - 2) = 0$
Setting each factor equal to zero	$2x + 3 = 0$ and $x - 2 = 0$
Solving for x	$x = -\frac{3}{2}$ and $x = 2$ Answers

Check. By inspection find that neither root, when substituted for x in the original equation, would make the value of a denominator equal to zero. Thus both answers are valid.

E X E R C I S E S : Solving quadratic equations by the factor method

Solve each of the following equations by the factor method.

1. $x^2 + 5x = 0$

2. $3x^2 - 2x = 0$

3. $y^2 - 16 = 0$

4. $4x^2 - 25 = 0$

5. $6y^2 = 30y$

6. $x^2 + x - 6 = 0$

7. $y^2 + 5 = 6y$

8. $t^2 + 8t + 12 = 0$

9. $y^2 - y = 42$

10. $2x^2 + 5x - 12 = 0$

11. $3x^2 - 10 = x$

12. $10y^2 - 29y + 10 = 0$

13. $6z^2 - 20 = 19z$

14. $(x + 2)(x - 3) = 24$

15. $x^2 + 108 = 3x(x + 2)$

16. $x(x - 4) - (2x + 1)(x + 1) = 5$

17. $x^2 = \dfrac{9x + 5}{2}$

18. $x + 5 = \dfrac{27}{x - 1}$

19. $x + \dfrac{1}{x} = \dfrac{10}{3}$

20. $\dfrac{x}{6} + 2 = \dfrac{15}{2x}$

21. $\dfrac{x - 3}{x} = \dfrac{4}{x + 5}$

22. $\dfrac{x}{x + 1} = \dfrac{2x}{x + 3}$

23. $\dfrac{x}{6} + \dfrac{6}{2x - 1} = \dfrac{3}{2}$

24. $2(x - 2) + \dfrac{x - 1}{x - 4} = 0$

Incomplete quadratic equations.   Any quadratic equation in the form $ax^2 + bx = 0$ can be solved by the factor method; that is, we can solve every quadratic equation which does not contain a constant term by the factor method. Let us now consider a method of solving an incomplete quadratic equation which does not contain the unknown raised to the first power; that is, a quadratic equation in the form $ax^2 + c = 0$.   We shall apply the following axiom:

Like roots of equals are equal.

I L L U S T R A T I V E   E X A M P L E S : Solving quadratic equations

1. Solve for x: $3x^2 + 2 = 11 - x^2$

    Solution. Given equation $3x^2 + 2 = 11 - x^2$

    Applying the addition axiom $3x^2 + x^2 = 11 - 2$

    Collecting like terms $4x^2 = 9$

    Applying the division axiom $x^2 = \frac{9}{4}$

    Taking the square root of both members $x = \pm \frac{3}{2}$.

    Thus $x = \frac{3}{2}$ and $x = -\frac{3}{2}$ Answers

2. Solve for x: $(x - \frac{3}{2})^2 = \frac{11}{4}$

    Solution. Although this equation will be a complete quadratic equation if the binomial is squared, it can be solved in its present form by the method demonstrated in the above example.

    Given equation $(x - \frac{3}{2})^2 = \frac{11}{4}$

    Taking the square root of both members $x - \dfrac{3}{2} = \pm \dfrac{\sqrt{11}}{2}$

Completing the solution $x = \dfrac{3}{2} \pm \dfrac{\sqrt{11}}{2}$

$$x = \dfrac{3 \pm \sqrt{11}}{2}$$

Thus $x = \dfrac{3 + \sqrt{11}}{2}$ and $x = \dfrac{3 - \sqrt{11}}{2}$ Answers

E X E R C I S E S : Solving quadratic equations

Solve each of the following, expressing irrational roots in simplest radical form.

1. $x^2 = 49$

2. $x^2 - 36 = 0$

3. $x^2 - 10 = 90$

4. $4y^2 = 25$

5. $5x^2 - 11 = 5 - 4x^2$

6. $16y^2 = 169 - 9y^2$

7. $144 - 29z^2 = 20z^2$

8. $x^2 - 9 = 1 - x^2$

9. $7 - y^2 = -1$

10. $3y^2 - 17 = 8$

11. $4x^2 - 12 = x^2 + 15$

12. $8x^2 = 60 - 7x^2$

13. $\dfrac{25x^2}{4} = 7$

14. $\dfrac{64}{y^2} = 27$

15. $\dfrac{y}{5} = \dfrac{3}{2y}$

16. $(x - 1)^2 = 9$

17. $(x - 5)^2 = 64$

18. $(x - 2)^2 = 25$

19. $(y + 4)^2 = 81$

20. $(x - 6)^2 = 36$

21. $(y - 3)^2 = 10$

22. $(2x - 3)^2 = 8$

23. $(3x + 1)^2 = 12$

24. $(5x - 3)^2 - 6 = 0$

25. $(x - \tfrac{1}{2})^2 = \tfrac{9}{4}$

26. $(x + \tfrac{1}{2})^2 = \tfrac{15}{4}$

27. $\dfrac{4}{x + 2} = \dfrac{x - 2}{8}$

28. $\dfrac{x + 3}{1 - x} = \dfrac{4}{x - 7}$

29. $\dfrac{x - 8}{75} = \dfrac{3}{x + 8}$

30. $\dfrac{2y + 7}{y + 2} = \dfrac{3y - 1}{3y - 8}$

31. $\dfrac{4x + 5}{2x - 3} = \dfrac{3x + 1}{x - 3}$

32. $\dfrac{3x - 5}{2} = \dfrac{12}{3x + 5}$

O R A L   R E V I E W   E X E R C I S E S : Forming trinomial squares

What quantity must be added to each of the following binomials to make it a trinomial square?

1. $x^2 + 10x$

2. $y^2 - 18y$

3. $y^2 - 2y$

4. $x^2 + 5x$

5. $z^2 - 9z$

6. $y^2 - 5y$

7. $x^2 + \frac{2}{5}x$

8. $y^2 - \frac{4y}{7}$

9. $y^2 + \frac{1}{2}y$

10. $x^2 + \frac{2x}{3}$

11. $x^2 - bx$

12. $x^2 + \frac{b}{a}x$

Solving quadratic equations by completing the square.   Let us consider quadratic equations that cannot be solved by the factor method; for example, the equation $x^2 + 6x - 3 = 0$. We can solve such an equation, or any other quadratic equation, by a method called "completing the square." The first illustrative example which follows shows the solution of the equation $x^2 + 6x - 3 = 0$ by this method. Notice that in the solution the left member is made a trinomial square by adding the necessary quantity, which must also be added to the right member. Because the term added completes the trinomial square in the left member, this method of solving a quadratic equation is called *completing the square.*

I L L U S T R A T I V E   E X A M P L E S : Solving quadratic equations by completing the square

1. Solve for x by completing the square, expressing the answers in simplest radical form: $x^2 + 6x - 3 = 0$.

Solution.

Given equation

$$x^2 + 6x - 3 = 0$$

Transposing the constant term to the right member

$$x^2 + 6x = 3$$

We make the left member a trinomial square by adding 9 (the square of half the coefficient of x); we must also add 9 to the right member

$$x^2 + 6x + 9 = 3 + 9$$

Expressing the left member as the square of a binomial; collecting terms in the right member $(x + 3)^2 = 12$

Taking the square
root of both members $x + 3 = \pm \sqrt{12}$

Solving for x $x = -3 \pm \sqrt{12}$

Simplifying $x = -3 \pm 2\sqrt{3}$ Answers

2. Solve for x by completing the square, expressing the answers to the nearest hundredth : $2x^2 - 6x - 1 = 0$.

Solution.

Given equation $2x^2 - 6x - 1 = 0$

Transposing the constant
term to the right member $2x^2 - 6x = 1$

Dividing each term by 2,
the coefficient of x^2 $x^2 - 3x = \frac{1}{2}$

Adding $\frac{9}{4}$, the square of
half the coefficient of x,
to both members $x^2 - 3x + \dfrac{9}{4} = \dfrac{1}{2} + \dfrac{9}{4}$

Expressing the left mem-
ber as the square of a binomial ; adding the frac-
tions in the right member $(x - \frac{3}{2})^2 = \frac{11}{4}$

Taking the square root
of both members $x - \dfrac{3}{2} = \pm \dfrac{\sqrt{11}}{2}$

Solving for x $x = \dfrac{3}{2} \pm \dfrac{\sqrt{11}}{2}$

The roots of the equation
in radical form are $\mathbf{x = \dfrac{3 \pm \sqrt{11}}{2}}$

Replacing $\sqrt{11}$ by its approximate decimal value
(p. 467) $x = \dfrac{3 \pm 3.317}{2}$

Simplifying $x = \dfrac{6.317}{2}$ and $x = \dfrac{-0.317}{2}$

               $x = 3.159$ and $x = -0.159$

To the nearest
hundredth $\mathbf{x = 3.16}$ **and** $\mathbf{x = -0.16}$ Answers

E X E R C I S E S : Solving quadratic equations by completing the square

Solve each equation in ex. 1–12 by completing the square, expressing irrational answers in simplest radical form.

1. $x^2 + 3x - 2 = 0$

2. $x^2 + 5x - 3 = 0$

3. $x^2 - x - 30 = 0$

4. $x^2 - 6x + 4 = 0$

5. $x^2 - 4x - 2 = 0$

6. $x^2 + 8x + 4 = 0$

7. $2x^2 + 6x - 1 = 0$

8. $3x = 11 + \dfrac{4}{x}$

9. $\dfrac{x}{3x - 1} + \dfrac{1}{1 + 3x} = 0$

10. $2x + \dfrac{3}{x - 3} = 0$

11. $\dfrac{3x}{x + 2} + \dfrac{1}{2x + 4} = \dfrac{1}{x^2 + 2x}$

12. $\dfrac{2}{x - 3} - 1 = \dfrac{2}{x}$

Solve each equation in ex. 13–24 by completing the square, expressing irrational answers correct to the nearest hundredth.

13. $x^2 - 3x + 1 = 0$

14. $x^2 - x - 5 = 0$

15. $x^2 + 7x - 3 = 0$

16. $x^2 - 8x + 5 = 0$

17. $2x^2 + 3x - 4 = 0$

18. $4x^2 - 7x + 2 = 0$

19. $3x^2 + 8x = 10$

20. $2x + 4 + \dfrac{1}{x} = 0$

21. $\dfrac{10x + 4}{x^2} = 3$

22. $5x - \dfrac{2}{x - 1} = 0$

23. $\dfrac{3}{x + 2} + 4 = \dfrac{3}{x}$

24. $\dfrac{x - 3}{2x - 2} - \dfrac{x + 2}{3x + 3} + \dfrac{7}{6x^2 - 6} = 0$

Derivation of the formula for solving quadratic equations. We can solve the general quadratic equation

$$ax^2 + bx + c = 0$$

by completing the square. The roots of this equation will be expressed in terms of the coefficients a, b, and c. This gives us a formula that may be used to solve any quadratic equation in one unknown. Using this formula is a more efficient method of solving quadratic equations than by completing the square. We derive the formula as follows:

General quadratic equation $ax^2 + bx + c = 0$

Transposing the constant to the right member $ax^2 + bx = -c$

Dividing each term by a, the coefficient of x^2

$$x^2 + \frac{b}{a}x = -\frac{c}{a}$$

Adding the square of half the coefficient of x to both members

$$x^2 + \frac{b}{a}x + \frac{b^2}{4a^2} = \frac{b^2}{4a^2} - \frac{c}{a}$$

Expressing the left member as the square of a binomial; adding the fractions in the right member

$$\left(x + \frac{b}{2a}\right)^2 = \frac{b^2 - 4ac}{4a^2}$$

Taking the square root of both members

$$x + \frac{b}{2a} = \frac{\pm\sqrt{b^2 - 4ac}}{2a}$$

Solving for x

$$x = -\frac{b}{2a} \pm \frac{\sqrt{b^2 - 4ac}}{2a}$$

$$x = \frac{-b \pm \sqrt{b^2 - 4ac}}{2a}$$

Observe that in the formula $x = \dfrac{-b \pm \sqrt{b^2 - 4ac}}{2a}$ we have expressed the roots of the general quadratic equation $ax^2 + bx + c = 0$ in terms of the coefficients a, b, and c. We can write every quadratic equation in one unknown in the form $ax^2 + bx + c = 0$; by inspection we can determine the values of a, b, and c. We can then substitute these values in the formula to obtain the roots of the equation.

Notice that the formula contains a square root radical. In solving some quadratic equations, the number under this radical will be negative. As we saw in Chapter 9, the indicated square root of a negative number is imaginary. When a quadratic equation has imaginary roots, it means that there are no real numbers which will satisfy the equation.

ILLUSTRATIVE EXAMPLES: Determining values for a, b, and c in quadratic equation $ax^2 + bx + c = 0$

1. Determine the values of a, b, and c in the quadratic equation $5x^2 - 3 = 2x$.

Solution. Given equation written with all terms on one side of the equal sign and in descending powers of x

$$5x^2 - 2x - 3 = 0$$

Comparing this equation with the general quadratic equation

$$ax^2 + bx + c = 0$$

We observe that

$$a = 5, \ b = -2, \text{ and } c = -3$$

2. Determine the values of a, b, and c in the quadratic equation $mx^2 + x^2 - 3mx + m + 5 = 0$.

Solution. In the given equation there are two terms containing x^2; to find the coefficient of x^2 we factor these two terms

$$(m + 1)x^2 - 3mx + m + 5 = 0$$

Comparing this equation with the general quadratic equation

$$ax^2 + bx + c = 0$$

We conclude that $a = m + 1, b = -3m$, and $c = m + 5$

ORAL EXERCISES: Determining values in quadratic formula

In each of the following, state the values of a, b, and c for use in the quadratic formula $x = \dfrac{-b \pm \sqrt{b^2 - 4ac}}{2a}$.   The letters x and y represent the unknowns.

1. $2x^2 + 3x + 4 = 0$

2. $4x^2 + 2x - 3 = 0$

3. $3x^2 - 5x + 2 = 0$

4. $7y^2 - 6y - 5 = 0$

5. $y^2 + 10y - 8 = 0$

6. $6x^2 - 1 = 4x$

7. $9y + 3y^2 = 16$

8. $12 - 3y + 2y^2 = 0$

9. $3x^2 - 14 = 0$

10. $mx^2 - 2mx + 4 = 0$

11. $(a - b)x^2 + cx = d$

12. $2px^2 - (p + q)x - r = 0$

13. $2ax - x^2 + bx = 5$

14. $x^2 - ax + bx^2 - p = 0$

15. $x^2 + x - mx^2 + nx + p = 0$

16. $px^2 + q(x^2 + 1) = x$

ILLUSTRATIVE EXAMPLES: Solving quadratic equations by the formula

1. Solve for x by using the quadratic formula, expressing the answers in simplest radical form: $2x^2 - 6x + 3 = 0$.

Solution. Given $\qquad\qquad\qquad 2x^2 - 6x + 3 = 0$

We observe that $\qquad\qquad a = 2, b = -6$, and $c = 3$

The quadratic formula is $\qquad\qquad\qquad x = \dfrac{-b \pm \sqrt{b^2 - 4ac}}{2a}$

Substituting 2 for a, -6 for b, and 3 for c $\qquad x = \dfrac{6 \pm \sqrt{36 - 4(2)(3)}}{2(2)}$

Simplifying
$$x = \frac{6 \pm \sqrt{36 - 24}}{4}$$

$$x = \frac{6 \pm \sqrt{12}}{4}$$

$$x = \frac{6 \pm 2\sqrt{3}}{4}$$

Dividing numerator and denominator by 2 $x = \dfrac{3 \pm \sqrt{3}}{2}$ Answers

2. Solve for y by using the quadratic formula, expressing the answers to the nearest hundredth: $4y^2 + 5y = 3$.

Solution. Given $4y^2 + 5y = 3$

Writing the equation in
the form $ax^2 + bx + c = 0$ $4y^2 + 5y - 3 = 0$

We observe that $a = 4, b = 5,$ and $c = -3$

The quadratic formula is $y = \dfrac{-b \pm \sqrt{b^2 - 4ac}}{2a}$

Substituting $y = \dfrac{-5 \pm \sqrt{25 - 4(4)(-3)}}{2(4)}$

Simplifying $y = \dfrac{-5 \pm \sqrt{25 + 48}}{8}$

$$y = \frac{-5 \pm \sqrt{73}}{8}$$

Replacing $\sqrt{73}$ by its approximate
decimal value p. 467. $y = \dfrac{-5 \pm 8.544}{8}$

Evaluating $y = \dfrac{3.544}{8}$ and $y = \dfrac{-13.544}{8}$

$$y = 0.418 \text{ and } y = -1.693$$

To the nearest hundredth $y = 0.42$ and $y = -1.69$ Answers

3. Solve for x by using the quadratic formula, expressing the answers in simplest radical form: $4x^2 - 8x + 13 = 0$.

Solution. Given equation $4x^2 - 8x + 13 = 0$

We observe that $a = 4, b = -8,$ and $c = 13$

Substituting in the formula we have $x = \dfrac{8 \pm \sqrt{64 - 4(4)(13)}}{2(4)}$

Simplifying $x = \dfrac{8 \pm \sqrt{64 - 208}}{8}$

$$x = \frac{8 \pm \sqrt{-144}}{8}$$

$$x = \frac{8 \pm 12\sqrt{-1}}{8}$$

$$x = \frac{2 \pm 3\sqrt{-1}}{2} \quad \text{or} \quad x = \frac{2 \pm 3i}{2} \quad \text{Answers}$$

E X E R C I S E S : Solving quadratic equations by using the quadratic formula

Solve each of the following by the quadratic formula. Express irrational answers in simplest radical form except in those problems for which your teacher may direct you to express the answers in decimal form.

1. $2x^2 - 3x - 4 = 0$
2. $3x^2 + 6x + 1 = 0$
3. $y^2 - 4y + 2 = 0$
4. $5x^2 - x - 3 = 0$
5. $4x^2 - 4x - 15 = 0$
6. $y^2 + 2y + 2 = 0$
7. $3x^2 + 5x - 2 = 0$
8. $4x^2 - 8x + 3 = 0$
9. $6y^2 - 3y - 4 = 0$
10. $2x^2 - 6x + 5 = 0$
11. $2x^2 + 10x + 3 = 0$
12. $9x^2 + 9x - 1 = 0$
13. $y^2 - 19y + 34 = 0$
14. $4x^2 - 12x + 5 = 0$
15. $6x^2 = 2x + 1$
16. $5x^2 - 6x = 0$
17. $y + 6 = 4y^2$

18. $x^2 - 4x + 13 = 0$
19. $10x = 3x^2 + 5$
20. $2x^2 + 6x = -3$
21. $8x^2 = 7x$
22. $8y - 2y^2 = 1$
23. $4x^2 + 9 = 8x$
24. $\dfrac{3x}{4} = \dfrac{1}{x}$
25. $\dfrac{x^2 + 1}{13} - \dfrac{x}{6} = 0$
26. $\dfrac{3}{5x - 2} = 2x$
27. $\dfrac{5}{x} = \dfrac{5}{x - 3} - 2$
28. $\dfrac{x - 2}{x + 2} + \dfrac{x + 3}{x - 3} = \dfrac{10x^2 - 4x + 7}{x^2 - x - 6}$
29. $\dfrac{y + 2}{y + 1} + \dfrac{y - 2}{y - 1} = \dfrac{2y^2 - y + 3}{1 - y^2}$

I L L U S T R A T I V E   E X A M P L E S : Solving literal quadratic equations

1. Solve for x in terms of a and b: $x^2 - 2ax + bx - 2ab = 0$

Solution. Given equation $x^2 - 2ax + bx - 2ab = 0$

Factoring the four terms by grouping
two-and-two $(x^2 - 2ax) + (bx - 2ab) = 0$
$$x(x - 2a) + b(x - 2a) = 0$$
$$(x - 2a)(x + b) = 0$$

Setting each factor equal to zero
and solving for x $x = 2a \quad \text{and} \quad x = -b \quad \text{Answers}$

2. Solve for x in terms of a and b: $ax^2 + 2bx - ax - b = 0$

Solution. Given equation $ax^2 + 2bx - ax - b = 0$

The left member of the equation cannot be factored. To solve by formula, we first write the equation in the form $Ax^2 + Bx + C = 0$

$$ax^2 + (2b - a)x - b = 0$$

We observe that the values of A, B, and C to be used in the formula are $A = a$, $B = (2b - a)$, and $C = -b$

Substituting these values in the formula, we have

$$x = \frac{-(2b - a) \pm \sqrt{(2b - a)^2 - 4(a)(-b)}}{2a}$$

Simplifying

$$x = \frac{-(2b - a) \pm \sqrt{4b^2 - 4ab + a^2 + 4ab}}{2a}$$

$$x = \frac{-(2b - a) \pm \sqrt{a^2 + 4b^2}}{2a} \quad \text{Answers}$$

EXERCISES: Solving literal quadratic equations

Solve each of the following equations for x in terms of the other letters.

1. $x^2 - a^2 = 0$
2. $ax^2 - bx = 0$
3. $6x^2 + 3a^2 = 5x^2 + 4a^2$
4. $5x^2 - a^2 = 3x^2 + 17a^2$
5. $a^2x^2 - 1 = 0$
6. $x^2 + ax - 2a^2 = 0$
7. $x^2 - bx - 6b^2 = 0$
8. $x^2 + 2bx - 15b^2 = 0$

9. $2x^2 + 3a^2 = 7ax$
10. $5bx = 6x^2 + b^2$
11. $a^2x^2 - 3abx + 2b^2 = 0$
12. $x^2 = (a - b)^2$
13. $x^2 - a^2 - 2ab - b^2 = 0$
14. $(x - 2a)^2 - b^2 = 0$
15. $x^2 - a^2 - 2bx + b^2 = 0$
16. $(x - a)^2 + 5(x - a) + 4 = 0$
17. $\dfrac{x}{a} - 1 - \dfrac{b}{a} + \dfrac{b}{x} = 0$
18. $\dfrac{2(x^2 - 1)}{ab} - \dfrac{4x}{a} = \dfrac{x}{b}$
19. $\dfrac{x^2 - b^2}{a - b} = x$
20. $\dfrac{x(x - a)}{a - b} - a - b = 0$

A quadratic function in one unknown. The expression $ax^2 + bx + c$ is a function of x, and, as x takes on different values, the function $ax^2 + bx + c$ takes on corresponding values. In the quadratic function $ax^2 + bx + c$, the letter a represents any constant except zero; the letters b and c represent any constants. The function is quadratic since it contains only integral powers of the unknown letter, and since the highest power of this unknown is 2. The following are examples of quadratic functions in one unknown:

$$4x^2 + 2x - 3 \qquad 3x^2 - 8x \qquad 5x^2 + 6$$

The graph of a quadratic function in the form $ax^2 + bx + c$.   Let us consider the function $x^2 + 2x - 3$. Since x is a variable, we may substitute different values for x in the function $x^2 + 2x - 3$ and find the corresponding value of the function. Thus: If $x = 0$, then $x^2 + 2x - 3 = 0 + 0 - 3 = -3$
If $x = 1$, then $x^2 + 2x - 3 = 1 + 2 - 3 = 0$
If $x = 2$, then $x^2 + 2x - 3 = 4 + 4 - 3 = 5$
and so we could continue.

The fact that $x^2 + 2x - 3$ is a function of x may be expressed as $f(x) = x^2 + 2x - 3$ or $y = x^2 + 2x - 3$. The latter form states that "y is a function of x." We proceed to construct the graph of $y = x^2 + 2x - 3$ by substituting values for x and computing the corresponding values of y, which will also be the corresponding values of the function. A convenient manner for setting up these calculations for the points to be used in plotting the graph is shown below:

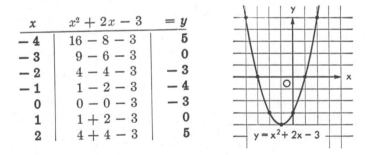

x	$x^2 + 2x - 3$	$= y$
-4	$16 - 8 - 3$	5
-3	$9 - 6 - 3$	0
-2	$4 - 4 - 3$	-3
-1	$1 - 2 - 3$	-4
0	$0 - 0 - 3$	-3
1	$1 + 2 - 3$	0
2	$4 + 4 - 3$	5

$y = x^2 + 2x - 3$

These calculations give us the coordinates of seven points on the graph of $y = x^2 + 2x - 3$. The points are plotted and connected by a smooth curve. This curve is a *parabola*.

Solving a quadratic equation graphically.   By reading the abscissas of the graph of $y = x^2 + 2x - 3$ where y equals zero, we can determine the roots of the quadratic equation $x^2 + 2x - 3 = 0$. We know that $y = 0$ at every point on the x axis. We find that the graph of $y = x^2 + 2x - 3$ intersects the x axis at the points where $x = -3$ and $x = 1$. Therefore $y = 0$ when $x = -3$, and $y = 0$ when $x = 1$. Hence the roots of the equation $x^2 + 2x - 3 = 0$ are $x = -3$ and $x = 1$.

> When the graph of $y = ax^2 + bx + c$ intersects the x axis at two points, the x coordinate of each of these points is a root of the equation
> $$ax^2 + bx + c = 0.$$

In those cases where the parabolic graph of $y = ax^2 + bx + c$ just touches (is tangent to) the x axis, the equation $ax^2 + bx + c = 0$ has two equal roots. The two roots are equal to the x coordinate of the point where the parabola is tangent to the x axis.

In those cases where the parabolic graph of $y = ax^2 + bx + c$ neither intersects the x axis nor is tangent to the x axis, the roots of $ax^2 + bx + c = 0$ are imaginary. A method of solving for these roots is discussed on pages 229 and 230.

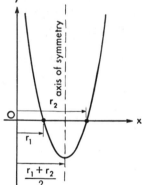

The abscissa of the vertex of a parabola. The vertex of a parabola is that point at which the direction of the parabola changes from downward to upward, or vice versa. This point is sometimes called the turning point. The parabola in the adjacent figure represents the graph of $y = ax^2 + bx + c$. The abscissas of the points where the graph intersects the x axis are the roots of the equation $ax^2 + bx + c = 0$. The axis of the parabola, shown as the axis of symmetry on the figure, intersects the x axis at a point midway between these two points. The axis of the parabola intersects the curve itself at the vertex. Therefore, the abscissa of the vertex is the average of r_1 and r_2, the roots of the equation; that is, $x = \dfrac{r_1 + r_2}{2}$

Since $r_1 = \dfrac{-b - \sqrt{b^2 - 4ac}}{2a}$ and $r_2 = \dfrac{-b + \sqrt{b^2 - 4ac}}{2a}$,

then $\dfrac{r_1 + r_2}{2} = \dfrac{\dfrac{-b - \sqrt{b^2 - 4ac}}{2a} + \dfrac{-b + \sqrt{b^2 - 4ac}}{2a}}{2} = \dfrac{-b}{2a}$

> The abscissa of the vertex of the parabola, whose equation is $y = ax^2 + bx + c$ is $-\dfrac{b}{2a}$.

Finding graphically imaginary roots of a quadratic equation.   The abscissa of the vertex of the parabola whose equation is $y = ax^2 + bx + c$, hereafter labeled x_v, is equal to $-\dfrac{b}{2a}$. Substituting this value for x in the equation, we find that the ordinate, hereafter labeled y_v, of the vertex is

$$y_v = \frac{4ac - b^2}{4a}$$

The roots of the equation $ax^2 + bx + c = 0$ are, as we learned,

$$x = \frac{-b \pm \sqrt{b^2 - 4ac}}{2a}$$

Written as two terms, these roots are

$$-\frac{b}{2a} \pm \frac{\sqrt{b^2 - 4ac}}{2a} \quad \text{or} \quad -\frac{b}{2a} \pm \sqrt{\frac{b^2 - 4ac}{4a^2}}$$

If the roots are complex numbers, the real part must be $-\dfrac{b}{2a}$ and the imaginary part must be $\sqrt{\dfrac{b^2 - 4ac}{4a^2}}$. Notice that the real part is equal to x_v, the abscissa of the vertex. But $\sqrt{\dfrac{b^2 - 4ac}{4a^2}} = \sqrt{-1} \cdot \sqrt{\dfrac{4ac - b^2}{4a^2}}$ or $i\sqrt{\dfrac{4ac - b^2}{4a^2}}$. Notice that this radicand is equivalent to $\dfrac{y_v}{a}$, where y_v is the ordinate of the vertex.

ILLUSTRATIVE EXAMPLES:
Solving quadratic equations graphically

1. By use of a graph estimate the roots of $2x^2 + 3x - 4 = 0$.

Solution. We set $2x^2 + 3x - 4 = y$. We draw the parabola represented by this equation. This parabola crosses the x axis approximately at $x = -2.4$ and $x = 0.9$.

The roots of the given equation are approximately $x = -2.4$ ⎫
$\qquad\qquad\qquad\qquad\; x = 0.9$ ⎬ Answers

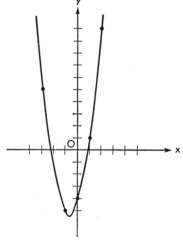

2. By use of a graph estimate the roots of $4x^2 - 20x + 25 = 0$.

Solution. We set $4x^2 - 20x + 25 = y$. We draw the parabola represented by this equation. This parabola is tangent to the x axis at $x = 2.5$. The roots of the given equation are:

$$\left.\begin{array}{l} x = 2.5 \\ x = 2.5 \end{array}\right\} \text{ Answers}$$

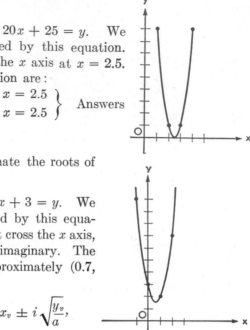

3. By use of a graph estimate the roots of $3x^2 - 4x + 3 = 0$.

Solution. We set $3x^2 - 4x + 3 = y$. We draw the parabola represented by this equation. Since the graph does not cross the x axis, the roots of the equation are imaginary. The turning point (vertex) is approximately $(0.7, 1.7)$.

Substituting in the formula $x_v \pm i\sqrt{\dfrac{y_v}{a}}$,

we estimate the roots to be approximately

$$x = 0.7 \pm i\sqrt{\frac{1.7}{3}}$$
$$x = 0.7 \pm i\sqrt{0.6} \quad \text{Answer}$$

E X E R C I S E S : Estimating roots of quadratic equations from graphs

By drawing the appropriate parabolas, estimate the roots of the following equations from the graphs.

1. $x^2 - 4x - 5 = 0$

2. $x^2 - 4 = 0$

3. $x^2 + 2x = 0$

4. $x^2 - 2x - 6 = 0$

5. $x^2 + 6x + 5 = 0$

6. $x^2 - 4x + 4 = 0$

7. $x^2 - 10x + 25 = 0$

8. $4x^2 - 4x - 3 = 0$

9. $2x^2 + 3x - 1 = 0$

10. $2x^2 - 3x - 9 = 0$

11. $3x^2 + 4x - 3 = 0$

12. $x^2 + 3x + 3 = 0$

13. $x^2 + x + 2 = 0$

14. $x^2 - 3x + 5 = 0$

15. $2x^2 + x + 3 = 0$

16. $3x^2 - 2x + 1 = 0$

Summary: Solving quadratic equations.   There are four standard methods of solving a quadratic equation in one unknown:

1. *The factor method.* This is usually the easiest method if it can be applied. It cannot be used to solve every quadratic equation.

2. *The method of completing the square.* This method has its greatest value in deriving the formula for the solution of quadratic equations. It can be used to solve every quadratic equation, but it is a longer and less efficient method than the formula.

3. *The formula method.* This is the most efficient method for solving a quadratic equation that cannot be solved by the factor method. It can be used to solve every quadratic equation.

4. *The graphic method.* This method has its greatest value in showing us a way to solve equations of higher degree in one unknown. Usually it gives only approximate answers.

REVIEW EXERCISES: Solving quadratic equations

Solve each of the following equations by any of the four standard methods; express irrational answers in simplest radical form.

1. $x^2 - x - 20 = 0$

2. $x^2 + 10x + 21 = 0$

3. $2x^2 + x - 6 = 0$

4. $x^2 - 9a^2 = 0$

5. $2y^2 + 5y = 0$

6. $x^2 - 8x - 2 = 0$

7. $2x^2 - 6x + 1 = 0$

8. $2y^2 - 7ay + 3a^2 = 0$

9. $x^2 - x + 1 = 0$

10. $3x^2 - 12x + 5 = 0$

11. $x^2 + 10 = 20x$

12. $15y^2 - 2y = 1$

13. $4y^2 + 5 = 10y$

14. $10 + 11y - 6y^2 = 0$

15. $3x^2 + 5x = 7$

16. $2 + 6x^2 + 7x = 0$

17. $2 = 8x - 5x^2$

18. $3x^2 - 4x + 3 = 0$

19. $12x^2 - x = 6$

20. $35x^2 - 2 = 3x$

21. $(x + 3)(x - 5) = 9$

22. $(9 + x)(3 - 4x) = 35$

23. $(2 - y)(1 + y) = y - 7$

24. $(x + 2)(2x + 3) = 6$

25. $\dfrac{2}{x} = \dfrac{x}{x + 4}$

26. $\dfrac{x + 4}{4} = \dfrac{x}{x + 2}$

27. $\dfrac{4}{x - 6} - 1 = \dfrac{8}{x}$

28. $\dfrac{5}{2x - 1} + 2 = \dfrac{x + 3}{2}$

29. $\dfrac{5x - 1}{x^2 - 1} - \dfrac{3x + 1}{1 - x} = \dfrac{5x}{1 + x}$

30. $\dfrac{24}{y} = \dfrac{30}{y - 2} + 1$

31. $\dfrac{35}{y - 2} - 2 = \dfrac{35}{y}$

32. $\dfrac{56}{1-y} + \dfrac{50}{y} = 1$

34. $\dfrac{y+a}{y} - \dfrac{y}{y-a} = 4$

33. $\dfrac{y}{2} + \dfrac{a}{2} - b - \dfrac{ab}{y} = 0$

35. $y^2 - a^2 = b^2 - 2ab$

EXERCISES: Number problems

The student may wish to study the illustrative example on page 30 before attempting these problems. In the problems that follow all the equations are quadratic, leading to two correct answers.

1. The square of a certain number is 18 more than seven times the number. Find the number.

2. If a number is subtracted from twice the square of the number, the result is 21. Find the number.

3. The product of two consecutive even integers is 168. Find the integers.

4. The product of two consecutive odd integers is 99. Find the integers.

5. The sum of a number and its reciprocal is $1\frac{3}{6}$; find the number.

6. If a number, minus its reciprocal, equals $2\frac{1}{10}$, find the number.

7. The sum of a number and three times its reciprocal is $6\frac{1}{2}$. Find the number.

ILLUSTRATIVE EXAMPLE: Geometry problems

The area of a picture, its border, and its frame together is 180 sq. in. If the dimensions of the picture are 6 in. by 9 in., and if the width of the border is twice the width of the frame, what is the width of the frame?

Solution. In the adjacent figure x represents the width of the frame, and $2x$ represents the width of the border.

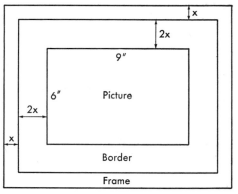

The dimensions of the largest rectangle are $6 + 6x$ and $9 + 6x$. Thus the area of the largest rectangle is $(6 + 6x)(9 + 6x)$. Since the largest rectangle includes the picture, the border, and the frame, its area is 180 sq. in.

The equation is $\qquad$ $(6 + 6x)(9 + 6x) = 180$

Removing parentheses $\qquad$ $54 + 90x + 36x^2 = 180$

Collecting terms $\qquad$ $36x^2 + 90x - 126 = 0$

Dividing by 18 $\qquad$ $2x^2 + 5x - 7 = 0$

Factoring $\qquad$ $(2x + 7)(x - 1) = 0$

Solving for x $\qquad$ $2x + 7 = 0$ and $x - 1 = 0$

$$x = -\tfrac{7}{2} \text{ and } x = 1$$

Since x represents the width of the frame, the answer $-\tfrac{7}{2}$ is not an acceptable answer. The width of the frame is 1 in. Answer.

EXERCISES: Geometry problems

1. The length of a rectangle is 1 ft. less than twice the width of the rectangle. If the area of the rectangle is 120 sq. ft., what are its dimensions?

2. The base of a triangle is 4 ft. less than twice its altitude. Find the base and altitude if the area of the triangle is 48 sq. ft.

3. The side of one square is 5 ft. greater than the side of a second square. Twice the area of the smaller is 34 sq. ft. less than the area of the larger. Find the side of each square.

4. One side of a square is decreased by 2 ft. and another side of the square is increased by 5 ft. to form a rectangle. If the area of the rectangle is 78 sq. ft., find the side of the square.

5. The diagonal of a rectangle is 15 in. and the length of the rectangle is 3 in. longer than its width. Find the dimensions of the rectangle. Hint: Apply the Law of Pythagoras.

6. A rectangular picture is 5 in. longer than it is wide. It is surrounded by a frame 2 in. wide. The area of the picture and the frame together is 456 sq. in. What are the dimensions of the picture?

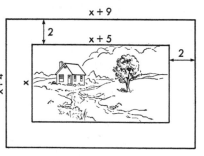

7. A man has enough wire netting to enclose a rectangular plot whose length is 10 ft. less than twice its width. He finds, however, that if he uses the netting to enclose a *square* plot, the area of the enclosure will be increased by 100 sq. ft. How many feet of netting has he?

8. Two chords intersect within a circle. The segments of the first chord are 9 in. and 4 in. If the other chord is 15 in. long, find the two segments of the second chord. Hint: If two chords intersect within a circle, the product of the segments of one is equal to the product of the segments of the other. Thus $ab = cd$.

Doings of Dimbo. Dimbo certainly didn't pay much attention to where he was going this time. Where did he go wrong, and what are the correct answers?

    Problem:
    Solve for x: $(x - 3)(x - 4) = 20$

    Dimbo's solution

$$(x - 3)(x - 4) = 20$$
$$x - 3 = 20 \quad x - 4 = 20$$
$$x = 23 \quad \text{and} \quad x = 24$$
$$\text{Answers}$$

EXERCISES: Motion problems

1. A man traveled a distance of 240 mi. and then returned in a total time of 9 hr. If his rate returning was 12 mph greater than his rate going, what were his rates each way?

Hint:

	T	R	D
Going	$\dfrac{240}{x}$	x	240
Returning	$\dfrac{240}{x + 12}$	$x + 12$	240

Equation: Time going + time returning = 9 hr.

2. A girl skated across a 6-mi. lake and back in $2\frac{1}{2}$ hr. If her rate returning was 2 mph less than her rate going, find her rate each way.

3. Two men drive their cars a distance of 495 mi. One travels at an average rate that is 10 mph faster than the other's rate and completes the distance in 2 hr. less time. Find the speed of each.

4. A man drove 200 mi. at a certain rate, and then he drove 100 mi. at a rate 10 mph slower. Had he driven the entire distance at the faster rate, his time for the entire trip would have been $\frac{1}{2}$ hr. less. Find his original rate.

5. A bomber, leaving from its home base, travels at a certain rate for the first 300 mi. Then its rate is increased by 50 mph. The fighter escort, starting $\frac{1}{2}$ hr. after the bomber, travels at the rate of 400 mph. The planes will arrive together at the destination, 1000 mi. from home base. Find the rate at which the bomber started.

ILLUSTRATIVE EXAMPLE: Problem involving products of numbers

In driving a distance of 480 mi., a man found that his car used a certain number of gallons of gasoline. Had he been able to travel 4 mi. more on each gallon, he could have made the trip using 6 gal. less. How many gallons of gasoline did the man actually use on his trip?

Solution. We let x represent the number of gallons of gasoline actually used. Since he traveled 480 mi., then $\dfrac{480}{x}$ represents the number of miles per gallon. If he had used 6 gal. less, he would have used $x - 6$ gallons; the number of miles per gallon would then have been $\dfrac{480}{x - 6}$. We can tabulate this information as follows:

	Number of gallons	Number of miles traveled	Miles per gallon
Actual case	x	480	$\dfrac{480}{x}$
If	$x - 6$	480	$\dfrac{480}{x - 6}$

The statement of the problem tells us that $\dfrac{480}{x-6}$ is 4 more than $\dfrac{480}{x}$,

Hence we write the equation
$$\frac{480}{x-6} = \frac{480}{x} + 4$$

Dividing by 4
$$\frac{120}{x-6} = \frac{120}{x} + 1$$

Clearing of fractions
$$120x = 120(x-6) + x(x-6)$$

Removing parentheses
$$120x = 120x - 720 + x^2 - 6x$$

Simplifying
$$-x^2 + 6x + 720 = 0$$

Solving for x
$$x^2 - 6x - 720 = 0$$
$$(x-30)(x+24) = 0$$
$$x = 30 \text{ and } x = -24$$

Both of these values of x will satisfy the equation, but the value -24 has no meaning in the statement of the original problem, since the man could not have used a negative number of gallons. We therefore discard the -24. Answering the question, we find that the man used 30 gal. of gasoline on his trip.

E X E R C I S E S : **Problems involving products of numbers**

1. A man bought two farms for $2800 each. The larger contained 10 acres more than the smaller, but he paid $5 more per acre for the smaller than for the larger. How many acres did each farm contain?

2. A man bought a certain number of shares of stock for $4000. When the price advanced $25 a share, he sold all but 10 shares for $4200. How many shares did he buy?

3. The 600 members of the senior class of a high school were seated in rows, with each row containing the same number of seats. If there had been 5 more seats in each row, they could have been seated in 4 rows less. How many seats are there in each row?

4. Each of two wires weighs 5 lb. One of the wires is 40 ft. longer than the other, and its weight per foot is $\frac{1}{6}$ lb. less than that of the other. Find the length of each wire.

5. A grocer bought a certain number of packages of cookies for $15. After throwing away 20 packages that were crushed, he sold the remaining packages at 10¢ apiece more than he paid for them, and made a profit of $5. How many packages did he buy?

6. A man bought some oranges for $7.20. If he had paid 12¢ less per dozen, he could have bought 2 doz. more for the same money. How many dozen oranges did he buy?

EXERCISES : Work problems

The student may wish to study the Illustrative Example on page 105 before attempting these work problems. Although these problems lead to quadratic equations, there is only one correct answer in each case.

1. A man and his son working together can paint a barn in 4 days. The man alone could paint the barn in 6 days less time than the boy could do the job alone. How long would it take each to paint the barn alone?

2. Two machines working together can complete a job in $1\frac{7}{8}$ hr. The slower machine requires 2 hr. more than the other machine to do the job alone. How much time is needed for each machine to do this job alone?

3. It takes a man 2 days less than a boy to gather the wheat on a certain farm. However, if 4 men and 5 boys work at the same time, the wheat can be gathered in 1 day. How long would it take a man alone to gather this wheat?

4. Three boys, Allen, Bob, and Carl, can polish a car together in 1 hr. 20 min. To polish the car alone, Carl would take twice as long as Allen and 2 hr. longer than Bob. How long would it take each to do the job alone?

5. A pool has two supply pipes and one drain pipe. The first supply pipe requires 2 hr. longer than the second supply pipe to fill the pool alone. The time required to empty the pool by the drain pipe is twice the time required by the second supply pipe to fill the pool. If all pipes are open, the pool can be filled in 4 hr. 48 min. If only the drain pipe is open, how long will it take to empty the pool?

Radical equations.   In Chapter 9 we solved radical equations containing square roots by squaring both members of the equation once or more times to remove the radical containing the unknown. You will remember that before squaring both members of the equation the form of the equation was changed, if necessary, so that one radical was alone in one member. The radical equations in this chapter can be solved by this same method, but the resulting equations here will be quadratic rather than first-degree equations.

ILLUSTRATIVE EXAMPLE : Solving radical equations

Solve for x : $\sqrt{4x - 1} - \sqrt{2x - 1} = 1$

Solution. Given equation with the second radical transposed to the right member

$$\sqrt{4x - 1} = 1 + \sqrt{2x - 1}$$

Squaring both members

$$4x - 1 = 1 + 2\sqrt{2x - 1} + 2x - 1$$

Transposing all terms in the right
member, except the radical, to
the left member and collecting $\qquad 2x - 1 = 2\sqrt{2x - 1}$

Squaring both members $\qquad (2x - 1)^2 = 4(2x - 1)$

Removing parentheses $\qquad 4x^2 - 4x + 1 = 8x - 4$

Solving for x $\qquad 4x^2 - 12x + 5 = 0$
$$(2x - 5)(2x - 1) = 0$$
$$x = \tfrac{5}{2} \text{ and } x = \tfrac{1}{2}$$

Since we have squared both members of the equation, we may have
introduced new roots which do not satisfy the original equation. Hence
we do not know, until we have checked, whether or not $\tfrac{5}{2}$ and $\tfrac{1}{2}$ are roots
of the original equation.

Substituting $\tfrac{5}{2}$ for x in the original
  equation

$$\sqrt{4(\tfrac{5}{2}) - 1} - \sqrt{2(\tfrac{5}{2}) - 1} \overset{?}{=} 1$$

$$\sqrt{10 - 1} - \sqrt{5 - 1} \overset{?}{=} 1$$

$$3 - 2 = 1 \quad \text{Check}$$

Substituting $\tfrac{1}{2}$ for x in the
  original equation

$$\sqrt{4(\tfrac{1}{2}) - 1} - \sqrt{2(\tfrac{1}{2}) - 1} \overset{?}{=} 1$$

$$\sqrt{2 - 1} - \sqrt{1 - 1} \overset{?}{=} 1$$

$$1 - 0 = 1 \quad \text{Check}$$

The roots of the equation are $x = \tfrac{5}{2}$ and $x = \tfrac{1}{2}$. Answer

EXERCISES: Solving radical equations

Solve each of the following equations. Remember that it is necessary
to check your answers if you have squared both members of the equation

1. $\sqrt{x^2 + 24} = 7$

2. $\sqrt{10x^2 - 9x} = 3$

3. $\sqrt{2x^2 - 5x} = 5$

4. $4\sqrt{x - 3} = x$

5. $5 - \sqrt{x + 7} = x$

6. $3 + \sqrt{x + 3} = x$

7. $\sqrt{2x + 7} = \sqrt{x + 2}$

8. $3 + \sqrt{2x - 6} = \sqrt{5x}$

9. $3\sqrt{x} + \sqrt{x - 24} = 16$

10. $\dfrac{\sqrt{x + 2}}{x} = \dfrac{3}{\sqrt{x + 2}}$

11. $\sqrt{1 - 2x} + 2 = \sqrt{1 - 6x}$

12. $\sqrt{x + 4} - \sqrt{x - 3} = 1$

13. $\sqrt{x + 2} + \sqrt{3 - x} = 3$

14. $\sqrt{2x + 8} + 2\sqrt{x + 5} = 2$

15. $\sqrt{2x - 1} - \sqrt{x - 1} = 1$

16. $\sqrt{3x - 5} - \sqrt{2x + 3} = 1$

17. $x + 2\sqrt{x + 2} - 1 = 0$

18. $\sqrt{x + 1} + \sqrt{3x + 1} - 2 = 0$

19. $\sqrt{x} + \sqrt{x - 6} = \dfrac{3}{\sqrt{x - 6}}$

20. $2\sqrt{x + 4} - \sqrt{x + 11} = \dfrac{6}{\sqrt{x + 4}}$

21. $\dfrac{5x - 1}{1 + \sqrt{5x}} = 1 + \dfrac{\sqrt{5x} - 1}{2}$

22. $\sqrt{x - 1} + \sqrt{6 + x} = \sqrt{5x - 1}$

23. $\sqrt{6x + 1} + \sqrt{2 - 2x} - \sqrt{7x + 6} = 0$

24. $\sqrt{2x + 3} - \sqrt{x + 1} = \sqrt{5x - 14}$

Equations in quadratic form.   Some equations that are not true quadratics can be put into quadratic form and solved by a method used for the solution of quadratic equations. In the equation $x^4 + 5x^2 - 14 = 0$, if we substitute y for x^2, the equation takes the form $y^2 + 5y - 14 = 0$. Similarly in $6x^{\frac{1}{2}} + x^{\frac{1}{4}} - 1 = 0$, if we substitute y for $x^{\frac{1}{4}}$, the equation takes the form $6y^2 + y - 1 = 0$. In like manner $3(x - 2)^4 + (x - 2)^2 - 2 = 0$ may take the form $3y^2 + y - 2 = 0$ where y is substituted for $(x - 2)^2$. After the equations in terms of y are solved, the quantity for which y has been substituted can readily be found.

ILLUSTRATIVE EXAMPLE: Solving an equation expressed in quadratic form

Solve for x: $x^{\frac{4}{3}} - 5x^{\frac{2}{3}} + 4 = 0$

$\qquad$ *Solution.* Given equation $\qquad x^{\frac{4}{3}} - 5x^{\frac{2}{3}} + 4 = 0$

$\qquad$ Let y represent $x^{\frac{2}{3}}$, then y^2
$\qquad$ represents $x^{\frac{4}{3}}$

$\qquad$ Substituting $\qquad\qquad\qquad\qquad y^2 - 5y + 4 = 0$

$\qquad$ Factoring $\qquad\qquad\qquad\qquad (y - 4)(y - 1) = 0$

$\qquad$ Solving for y $\qquad\qquad\qquad y = 4 \qquad y = 1$

$\qquad$ But $x^{\frac{2}{3}} = y$, hence $\qquad\qquad x^{\frac{2}{3}} = 4 \qquad x^{\frac{2}{3}} = 1$

$\qquad$ Cubing both members of
$\qquad$ each equation $\qquad\qquad\qquad x^2 = 64 \qquad x^2 = 1$

$\qquad$ Solving for x $\qquad\qquad\qquad\quad x = \pm 8 \qquad x = \pm 1$

$\qquad$ Check. Substituting (± 8) for x in the given equation:

$$x^{\frac{4}{3}} - 5x^{\frac{2}{3}} + 4 = 0$$
$$(\pm 8)^{\frac{4}{3}} - 5(\pm 8)^{\frac{2}{3}} + 4 \stackrel{?}{=} 0$$
$$16 \quad - 5(4) \quad + 4 \stackrel{?}{=} 0$$
$$0 = 0$$

Substituting ± 1 for x in the given equation

$$x^{\frac{4}{3}} - 5x^{\frac{2}{3}} + 4 = 0$$
$$(\pm 1)^{\frac{4}{3}} - 5(\pm 1)^{\frac{2}{3}} + 4 \overset{?}{=} 0$$
$$1 \quad - 5 \qquad + 4 \overset{?}{=} 0$$
$$0 = 0$$

All four values of x satisfy the original equation. Hence the roots of $x^{\frac{4}{3}} - 5x^{\frac{2}{3}} + 4 = 0$ are $x = 8$, $x = -8$, $x = 1$, and $x = -1$. Answer

E X E R C I S E S : Solving equations in quadratic form

Solve each of the following equations:

1. $x^4 - 5x^2 + 4 = 0$

2. $x^4 - 13x^2 + 36 = 0$

3. $x - 6x^{\frac{1}{2}} + 5 = 0$

4. $x + x^{\frac{1}{2}} - 6 = 0$

5. $3x^{\frac{1}{2}} + x^{\frac{1}{4}} - 14 = 0$

6. $x^{\frac{2}{3}} + x^{\frac{1}{3}} - 2 = 0$

7. $x^6 + 7x^3 - 8 = 0$

8. $x^{-2} + 2x^{-1} - 8 = 0$

9. $x^{\frac{4}{3}} - 10x^{\frac{2}{3}} + 9 = 0$

10. $3x^{\frac{2}{3}} - 4x^{\frac{1}{3}} - 4 = 0$

11. $4x^{\frac{4}{3}} - 17x^{\frac{2}{3}} + 4 = 0$

12. $3x^{-\frac{2}{3}} - 5x^{-\frac{1}{3}} + 2 = 0$

13. $(x - 3) + 3(x - 3)^{\frac{1}{2}} - 10 = 0$

14. $2(x - 5)^2 - 5(x - 5) + 3 = 0$

15. $(4x + 5) - 3(4x + 5)^{\frac{1}{2}} - 10 = 0$

16. $(x - 2)^4 - 13(x - 2)^2 + 36 = 0$

C H A P T E R   R E V I E W   E X E R C I S E S

1. Solve each of the following quadratic equations.

a) $x^2 - 36 = 0$

b) $2x^2 = 9x$

c) $2x^2 - 7x - 15 = 0$

d) $x^2 - 7x - 15 = 0$

e) $x(x + 5) = 2(6 - x)$

f) $\dfrac{1}{x - 1} - \dfrac{1}{x} = \dfrac{1}{6}$

2. Solve each of the following for x in terms of a and b.

a) $2x^2 - ax - 4bx + 2ab = 0$

b) $x^2 - 2ax + a^2 - b^2 = 0$

3. Plot the graph of $y = x^2 - 2x - 4$; estimate the roots of $x^2 - 2x - 4 = 0$

4. Plot the graph of $x^2 + 2x + 2 = y$; estimate the roots of $x^2 + 2x + 2 = 0$

5. Solve for x: $\sqrt{3x + 7} = 1 + \sqrt{6x}$

6. Solve for x: $x^{\frac{2}{3}} - 7x^{\frac{1}{3}} - 8 = 0$

7. Solve for x: $.125x^2 - .75x + 1 = 0$

8. Solve the equation $ax^2 + bx + c = 0$ for x in terms of a, b, and c by the method of completing the square.

9. A car traveled 85 mi. in $1\frac{1}{2}$ hr. For the first 60 mi. it traveled at a rate 10 mph faster than the rate for the remainder of the trip. Find the two rates at which the car traveled.

10. It takes 6 hr. for the water from two faucets together to fill a tank. It takes the larger 5 hr. less time than the smaller to fill the tank alone. How many hours will it take each faucet alone to fill the tank?

CUMULATIVE REVIEW EXERCISES

1. Factor: $ax^2 + 2ax - 3a$.

2. Solve for x and y: $y = 2x + 11$
$$3x - y + 14 = 0$$

3. Solve for x: $3x - \dfrac{2(7 + x)}{3} = 0$

4. Solve for x: $x - \sqrt{x + 1} = 5$

5. Simplify: $\dfrac{4}{9 - x^2} + \dfrac{2}{x - 3}$

6. Simplify: $(3\sqrt{2})(2\sqrt{3})$

7. Simplify the following expression, writing your result with positive exponents:

$$\left(\frac{a^0 b c^{-3}}{a^{-2} b^2 c^3}\right)^{-2}$$

8. Simplify: $(2 - 3\sqrt{5})(2 + 3\sqrt{5})$.

9. If $A = \frac{1}{2}h(x + y)$, solve for x in terms of the other letters.

10. A man has two sums of money invested at interest, one at 4% and the other at 5%. Together they yield $750 a year. If each rate were 1 per cent higher, his annual return from the two investments would be $915. How much money is invested at each rate?

11. The hypotenuse of a right triangle is 50 in., and one leg is 34 in. longer than the other. Find the two legs of the triangle.

12. Two boys, each in his own car, drove over the same highways from their school in Connecticut to a fishing village in Maine, a distance of 288 mi. The rate of the first boy averaged 3 mph faster than the rate of the second. As a result, the first boy covered the distance in 24 min. less time than that required by the second boy to cover the same distance. What was the rate of each boy?

CHAPTER 11   *Theory of Quadratic Equations; Inequalities*

Inequalities.   In mathematics we often find it necessary to express relationships between numbers that are not equal. An *inequality* is a statement that two numbers are unequal. We may state the inequality between two unequal numbers x and y in three ways: by using the symbol $\neq$ (is not equal to), the symbol $>$ (is greater than), and the symbol $<$ (is less than). Thus we may say:

1. The numbers x and y are unequal: $x \neq y$
2. The number x is greater than the number y: $x > y$
3. The number x is less than the number y: $x < y$

We can express the fact that x is a *positive* number by using the notation $x > 0$. Similarly, we can express the fact that x is a *negative* number by using the notation $x < 0$.

The discriminant.   On page 222 it was shown that the two roots of the general quadratic equation $ax^2 + bx + c = 0$ are

$$\frac{-b + \sqrt{b^2 - 4ac}}{2a} \quad \text{and} \quad \frac{-b - \sqrt{b^2 - 4ac}}{2a}$$

Notice that the denominators of the two roots are the same. Furthermore, the numerators are the same except for the fact that in the first root the quantity $\sqrt{b^2 - 4ac}$ is *added to* $-b$, and in the second root the quantity $\sqrt{b^2 - 4ac}$ is *subtracted from* $-b$. The expression $b^2 - 4ac$, which appears under the radical, is called the *discriminant* of the equation $ax^2 + bx + c = 0$.

In the quadratic equation

$$ax^2 + bx + c = 0,$$

the discriminant is

$$b^2 - 4ac$$

The nature, or character, of the roots of a quadratic equation.   The roots of a quadratic equation may be real numbers or they may be imaginary numbers. If the roots are real numbers, they may be rational numbers or they may be irrational numbers. Finally, the two roots may be equal or they may be unequal. The value of the discriminant, $b^2 - 4ac$, enables us to determine the nature, or character, of the roots of a quadratic equation without solving the equation; that is, the value of the discriminant enables us to determine whether the roots of the equation are real or imaginary, rational or irrational, equal or unequal. In the following discussion, we assume that the coefficients a, b, and c in the equation $ax^2 + bx + c = 0$ are real and rational numbers.

1. If the value of the discriminant is a negative number, that is, if $b^2 - 4ac < 0$, then each of the two roots of the equation contains the indicated square root of a negative number. This means that the roots of the equation are imaginary.

If $b^2 - 4ac < 0$, the roots of the equation $ax^2 + bx + c = 0$ are imaginary.

2. If the value of the discriminant is zero, that is, if $b^2 - 4ac = 0$, then the two roots of the equation are identical, since one is $\dfrac{-b + 0}{2a}$ and the other is $\dfrac{-b - 0}{2a}$. Furthermore, since a and b are real and rational numbers, the two roots are real and rational.

> If $b^2 - 4ac = 0$, the roots of the equation
> $ax^2 + bx + c = 0$ are real, rational, and equal.

3. If the value of the discriminant is a positive number, that is, if $b^2 - 4ac > 0$, then the roots of the equation are unequal, since one is $\dfrac{-b + \sqrt{b^2 - 4\,ac}}{2a}$ and the other is $\dfrac{-b - \sqrt{b^2 - 4ac}}{2a}$. Furthermore, the roots are real since the radicand is a positive number. If $b^2 - 4ac$ is a square, the roots of the equation are rational; if $b^2 - 4ac$ is not a square, the roots are irrational.

> If $b^2 - 4ac > 0$, the roots of the equation
> $ax^2 + bx + c = 0$ are real, unequal, and
> 1) rational if $b^2 - 4ac$ is a square,
> 2) irrational if $b^2 - 4ac$ is not a square.

ILLUSTRATIVE EXAMPLES: Determining the nature of roots of a quadratic equation

1. Determine the nature of the roots of the equation $2x^2 + 7x - 15 = 0$ without solving the equation.

Solution. Referring to the general quadratic equation $ax^2 + bx + c = 0$, we observe in the given equation $2x^2 + 7x - 15 = 0$ that $a = 2$, $b = 7$, and $c = -15$.

Substituting these values in the discriminant we have
$$b^2 - 4ac = 49 - 4(2)(-15)$$
$$= 49 + 120$$
$$= 169$$

Since $b^2 - 4ac > 0$, the roots of the equation are real and unequal; also since 169 is a square, the roots are rational. Therefore the roots of the equation $2x^2 + 7x - 15 = 0$ are real, rational, and unequal.

2. Determine the nature of the roots of the equation $4x^2 - 12x + 9 = 0$ without solving the equation.

Solution. We observe that $a = 4$, $b = -12$, and $c = 9$

Substituting these values in the discriminant we have
$$b^2 - 4ac = 144 - 4(4)(9)$$
$$= 144 - 144$$
$$= 0$$

Since $b^2 - 4ac = 0$, the roots of the equation $4x^2 - 12x + 9 = 0$ are real, equal, and rational.

3. Determine the nature of the roots of the equation $2x^2 - x + 3 = 0$ without solving the equation.

Solution. We observe that $a = 2, b = -1$, and $c = 3$

Substituting these values in the discriminant we have

$$b^2 - 4ac = 1 - 4(2)(3)$$
$$= 1 - 24$$
$$= -23$$

Since $b^2 - 4ac < 0$, the roots of the equation $2x^2 - x + 3 = 0$ are imaginary.

4. Determine the value(s) of m for which the roots of the equation $x^2 - mx + m + 3 = 0$ will be equal.

Solution. If the roots of a quadratic equation are equal, we know that the discriminant, $b^2 - 4ac$, must have the value zero.

In the equation $\qquad\qquad x^2 - mx + m + 3 = 0$
we observe that $\qquad a = 1, b = -m$, and $c = m + 3$

Substituting these values in the discriminant we have $\qquad b^2 - 4ac = (-m)^2 - 4(1)(m + 3)$

We substitute zero for $b^2 - 4ac$ and solve for m

$$0 = m^2 - 4m - 12$$
$$0 = (m - 6)(m + 2)$$
$$m = 6 \text{ and } m = -2 \quad \text{Answers}$$

Check. If $m = 6$, the original equation is $\qquad x^2 - 6x + 6 + 3 = 0$

Simplifying $\qquad\qquad\qquad x^2 - 6x + 9 = 0$

Solving for x $\qquad\qquad (x - 3)(x - 3) = 0$
$$x = 3 \text{ and } x = 3 \quad \text{Hence the equation has equal roots.}$$

If $m = -2$, the original equation is $\qquad x^2 - (-2)x + (-2) + 3 = 0$

Simplifying $\qquad\qquad\qquad x^2 + 2x + 1 = 0$

Solving for x $\qquad\qquad (x + 1)(x + 1) = 0$
$$x = -1 \text{ and } x = -1 \quad \text{Hence the equation has equal roots.}$$

EXERCISES: Determining the nature of the roots of a quadratic equation

In each of ex. 1–21 determine the nature of the roots of the equation without solving the equation.

1. $x^2 + 6x - 2 = 0$
2. $x^2 - 5x + 7 = 0$
3. $x^2 + 11x + 30 = 0$
4. $x^2 - 18x + 81 = 0$
5. $4x^2 - 20x + 25 = 0$
6. $3x^2 + 2x + 5 = 0$
7. $2x^2 - 3x - 5 = 0$
8. $5x^2 - 7x - 1 = 0$
9. $3x^2 - 10 = 0$
10. $5x^2 + 7x = 0$
11. $4x^2 - 12x + 9 = 0$

12. $x^2 - 4x - 21 = 0$
13. $2x^2 - 3x + 2 = 0$
14. $3x^2 + 7x - 2 = 0$
15. $6x^2 + 5x = 6$
16. $6x^2 + x = 40$
17. $2x^2 + 11 = 7x$
18. $7x^2 = 8x - 3$
19. $5x^2 + 4x = 1$
20. $7x - 4 = 3x^2$
21. $2x^2 = 11x + 21$

In each of ex. 22–33 find the value(s) of m that will make the roots of the equation equal.

22. $x^2 + 2mx + 25 = 0$
23. $x^2 - 12x + 9m = 0$
24. $9x^2 + (m + 4)x + 1 = 0$
25. $m^2x^2 + (3m + 12)x + 9 = 0$
26. $x^2 + 4mx + m + 14 = 0$
27. $x^2 + (m - 3)x + m = 0$

28. $4x^2 - 2(m + 5)x + m^2 = 0$
29. $(2m - 3)x^2 - 7mx + 49 = 0$
30. $x^2 + 2mx + 6x - 4m = 0$
31. $(m + 1)x^2 + mx - 1 = 0$
32. $3x^2 + 10x + m + 3 = 0$
33. $4x^2 + 6mx + 2x + 4m + 13 = 0$

The sum of the roots of a quadratic equation.   The two roots of the general quadratic equation $ax^2 + bx + c = 0$ are

$$r_1 = \frac{-b + \sqrt{b^2 - 4ac}}{2a} \quad \text{and} \quad r_2 = \frac{-b - \sqrt{b^2 - 4ac}}{2a}$$

If we add these two roots, we have:

$$r_1 + r_2 = \frac{-b + \sqrt{b^2 - 4ac} - b - \sqrt{b^2 - 4ac}}{2a}$$

$$= \frac{-2b}{2a}$$

$$= -\frac{b}{a}$$

The sum of the roots of the quadratic equation

$$ax^2 + bx + c = 0 \text{ is } -\frac{b}{a}.$$

The product of the roots of a quadratic equation.   If we multiply the two roots of a quadratic equation, we have:

$$r_1 r_2 = \left(\frac{-b + \sqrt{b^2 - 4ac}}{2a} \right)\left(\frac{-b - \sqrt{b^2 - 4ac}}{2a} \right)$$

$$= \frac{b^2 - (b^2 - 4ac)}{4a^2}$$

$$= \frac{4ac}{4a^2}$$

$$= \frac{c}{a}$$

The product of the roots of the quadratic equation

$$ax^2 + bx + c = 0 \text{ is } \frac{c}{a}.$$

ILLUSTRATIVE EXAMPLES: Finding the sum and product of the roots of a quadratic equation

1. Without solving the equation $3x^2 - 5x + 4 = 0$, find the sum of the roots and the product of the roots.

Solution. We know that the sum of the roots of the quadratic equation $ax^2 + bx + c = 0$ is $-\frac{b}{a}$; we know that the product of the roots is $\frac{c}{a}$.

In the given equation $\qquad 3x^2 - 5x + 4 = 0$

We observe that $\qquad a = 3, b = -5, \text{ and } c = 4$

Hence the sum of the roots is $\qquad -\frac{b}{a} = \frac{5}{3}$

The product of the roots is $\qquad \frac{c}{a} = \frac{4}{3}$ $\left.\begin{array}{c}\\[4pt]\\[4pt]\end{array}\right\}$ Answer

2. In the equation $2x^2 - 3mx + 2x + m^2 = 0$, for what values of m will the sum of the roots be equal to the product of the roots?

Solution. Writing the equation in standard form $\qquad 2x^2 - (3m - 2)x + m^2 = 0$

We know that the sum of the roots is $\qquad -\frac{b}{a} = \frac{3m - 2}{2}$

The product of the roots is $\qquad \frac{c}{a} = \frac{m^2}{2}$

Since the sum of the roots is to be equal to the product of the roots

$$\frac{3\,m - 2}{2} = \frac{m^2}{2}$$

Multiplying by 2 and transposing

$$m^2 - 3\,m + 2 = 0$$

Solving for m

$$(m - 2)(m - 1) = 0$$

$$m = 2 \quad \text{and} \quad m = 1 \quad \text{Answers}$$

E X E R C I S E S : Finding the sum and product of the roots of a quadratic equation

In ex. 1–16 find the sum of the roots and the product of the roots of each equation without solving the equation.

1. $2x^2 + 3x + 4 = 0$

2. $5x^2 - 4x + 1 = 0$

3. $6x^2 + 8x - 9 = 0$

4. $9x^2 + 2 = 0$

5. $8x^2 - 5x = 0$

6. $7x^2 - 35x + 10 = 0$

7. $3x^2 - 6 = 7x$

8. $4x - 11 = 2x^2$

9. $12 - 3x - 2x^2 = 0$

10. $10x - 5x^2 = 1$

11. $6x^2 = 18x - 4$

12. $15x^2 + 20 + 18x = 0$

13. $2ax^2 - 3bx + p = 0$

14. $m^2x^2 - nx - p = 0$

15. $ax^2 - x + bx^2 + 5 = 0$

16. $p - x^2 + q - x + rx^2 = 0$

17. In the equation $3x^2 - (3\,m + 2)x + m^2 = 0$, for what values of m will the sum of the roots be equal to twice the product of the roots?

18. In the equation $x^2 + mx - 5x + 1 - m^2 = 0$, for what values of m will the sum of the roots be 10 more than the product of the roots?

19. In the equation $2\,mx^2 - m^2x + x + 3 = 0$, for what values of m will the sum of the roots be equal to five times the product of the roots?

20. In the equation, $3x^2 - 6\,mx + 2\,m^2 + 4(x - 2) = 0$, for what values of m will the product of the roots be equal to twice the sum of the roots?

Forming a quadratic equation whose roots are given.   Since both members of an equation can be divided by the same number, we can write the general quadratic equation $ax^2 + bx + c = 0$ in the form $x^2 + \dfrac{b}{a}x + \dfrac{c}{a} = 0$.

In this form, we observe that the coefficient of the x^2 term is one; the coefficient of the x term is the negative of the sum of the roots, and the constant term is the product of the roots. If we let s represent the sum of the roots and p represent the product of the roots, we have,

$$x^2 - \left(-\frac{b}{a}\right)x + \left(\frac{c}{a}\right) = 0$$

sum of the roots   product of the roots

$$x^2 - sx + p = 0$$

$$x^2 - sx + p = 0$$

This gives us a convenient method of forming a quadratic equation when we are given the roots of the equation.

ILLUSTRATIVE EXAMPLES: Forming quadratic equations when given the roots

1. Write the quadratic equation whose roots are 5 and -7.

Solution. In the equation $\qquad\qquad\qquad x^2 - sx + p = 0$
s represents the sum of the roots and p represents the product of the roots. We are given the roots 5 and -7.
Thus we have $\qquad\qquad\qquad s = 5 - 7 = -2$
$$p = 5(-7) = -35$$
Substituting $\qquad\qquad\qquad x^2 - (-2)x + (-35) = 0$
Simplifying $\qquad\qquad\qquad\qquad x^2 + 2x - 35 = 0 \qquad$ Answer

2. Write, and simplify, the quadratic equation whose roots are $\dfrac{2 \pm \sqrt{5}}{3}$.

Solution. Finding s $\qquad\qquad\qquad s = \dfrac{2 + \sqrt{5}}{3} + \dfrac{2 - \sqrt{5}}{3}$

$$s = \tfrac{4}{3}$$

Finding p $\qquad\qquad\qquad p = \left(\dfrac{2 + \sqrt{5}}{3}\right)\left(\dfrac{2 - \sqrt{5}}{3}\right)$

$$p = \dfrac{4 - 5}{9}$$

$$p = -\tfrac{1}{9}$$

Substituting in the equation $\qquad x^2 - sx + p = 0$
We have $\qquad\qquad\qquad\qquad x^2 - \tfrac{4}{3}x - \tfrac{1}{9} = 0$
Simplifying $\qquad\qquad\qquad\qquad 9x^2 - 12x - 1 = 0 \qquad$ Answer

EXERCISES: Forming quadratic equations whose roots are given

In each of the following, write and simplify the quadratic equation which will have the given pair of roots.

1. 4, 2

2. 5, -4

3. 8, -7

4. $-9, -4$

5. $\tfrac{1}{2}, 3$

6. $\tfrac{1}{4}, -2$

7. $\tfrac{1}{2}, \tfrac{2}{3}$

8. $\tfrac{3}{4}, -\tfrac{1}{4}$

9. 0, 5

10. 9, -9

11. 0, $-\tfrac{1}{2}$

12. $\tfrac{3}{5}, -\tfrac{3}{2}$

13. $a, -3a$

14. $\dfrac{b}{2}, \dfrac{3b}{2}$

15. $a - b, a + b$

16. $3a - b, 3b - a$

17. $-\sqrt{2}, \sqrt{2}$

18. $3 + \sqrt{2}, 3 - \sqrt{2}$

19. $\dfrac{2 \pm \sqrt{3}}{2}$ **23.** $\dfrac{a \pm \sqrt{b}}{2}$

20. $\dfrac{-1 \pm 2\sqrt{5}}{2}$ **24.** $a \pm bi$

25. $\dfrac{2 \pm \sqrt{-3}}{3}$

21. $2 \pm \sqrt{-1}$

22. $-3 \pm 2i$ **26.** $\dfrac{2 \pm 3\sqrt{-5}}{4}$

Absolute and conditional inequalities.   Just as equations may be identical or conditional, inequalities (defined on p. 242) may be absolute or conditional. All numerical inequalities are absolute, thus $10 > -3$ and $4 < 6$ are absolute inequalities. An inequality which contains one or more letters is an *absolute inequality* if it is true for all real values of the letters involved. An inequality such as $x^2 + 4 > 0$ is an absolute inequality since it is true for all real values of x, because x^2 is always greater than zero.

A *conditional inequality* is one that does not hold true for all real values of the letter or letters involved. An inequality such as $x + 1 > 3$ is conditional. This inequality is true for all numbers greater than 2, but it is not true for the number 2, nor for any number less than 2. In order to solve a conditional inequality it is necessary to find the range of numbers for which the inequality is true. This is similar to solving a conditional equation. To solve inequalities, we shall use the following axioms.

Axioms on inequalities

1. If equals are added to unequals, the sums are unequal in the same order.

$$\text{Examples} \qquad \begin{array}{c} 9 > 4 \\ 3 = 3 \\ \hline 12 > 7 \end{array} \qquad \begin{array}{c} 2 > -5 \\ 6 = 6 \\ \hline 8 > 1 \end{array}$$

2. If equals are subtracted from unequals, the remainders are unequal in the same order.

$$\text{Examples} \qquad \begin{array}{c} 7 > 5 \\ 2 = 2 \\ \hline 5 > 3 \end{array} \qquad \begin{array}{c} 4 > 1 \\ -3 = -3 \\ \hline 7 > 4 \end{array}$$

3. If unequals are multiplied (or divided) by *positive* equals, the products (or quotients) are unequal in the same order.

Examples $-2 > -6$ $8 > 6$
$3 = 3$ $2 = 2$

Multiplying $3(-2) > 3(-6)$ Dividing $\frac{8}{2} > \frac{6}{2}$
$-6 > -18$ $4 > 3$

4. If unequals are multiplied (or divided) by *negative* equals, the products (or quotients) are unequal in the *reverse order*.

Examples
$$10 > 7$$
$$-3 = -3$$

$$8 > -6$$
$$-2 = -2$$

Multiplying $\quad -3(10) < (-3)(7)$ Dividing $\quad -\dfrac{8}{2} < \dfrac{-6}{-2}$

$$-30 < -21$$

$$-4 < 3$$

The first two axioms on inequalities tell us that we may add equal quantities to, or subtract equal quantities from, both members of an inequality without changing the order of the inequality (the direction of the inequality sign). Adding the same quantity to or subtracting the same quantity from both members of an inequality is similar to the process of adding the same quantity to or subtracting the same quantity from both members of an equation. For example

Given the inequality	$x + 5 > 6$
Subtracting 5 from both members	$x > 1$
Similarly in the inequality	$2 > 1 - x$
Adding x to both members	$2 + x > 1$
Subtracting 2 from both members	$x > -1$

ILLUSTRATIVE EXAMPLES: Solving inequalities of the first degree

1. Solve for x: $2x - 7 > 8 - 3x$

$\quad$ *Solution.* Given inequality $\quad 2x - 7 > 8 - 3x$

Adding $3x + 7$ to both members $\quad 2x + 3x > 8 + 7$

Collecting $\qquad\qquad\qquad\qquad\qquad 5x > 15$

Dividing both members by 5 $\qquad\quad x > 3$ Answer

2. Solve for x: $3x + 9 > 5x + 13$

$\quad$ *Solution.* Given inequality $\quad 3x + 9 > 5x + 13$

Subtracting $5x + 9$ from both members $\qquad 3x - 5x > 13 - 9$

Collecting $\qquad\qquad\qquad\qquad\quad -2x > 4$

Dividing both members by -2 $\qquad\quad x < -2$ Answer

ORAL EXERCISES: Inequalities

For each blank in the solution of the following inequalities, state the axiom on inequalities that has been applied in the adjacent step.

1. $3x - 9 > 6$
   $3x > 15$ _____
   $x > 5$ _____

4. $8x + 12 > -4$
   $8x > -16$ _____
   $x > -2$ _____

2. $\dfrac{x}{2} < 4 + \dfrac{x}{6}$
   $3x < 24 + x$ _____
   $2x < 24$ _____
   $x < 12$ _____

5. $\dfrac{x}{4} < 6 - \dfrac{x}{8}$
   $2x < 48 - x$ _____
   $3x < 48$ _____
   $x < 16$ _____

3. $12 - 2x > 5x + 26$
   $-7x > 14$ _____
   $x < -2$ _____

6. $9 + 2x < 3x - 12$
   $-x < -21$ _____
   $x > 21$ _____

EXERCISES: Solving inequalities of the first degree

Solve each of the following.

1. $5x - 2 > 4x + 3$
2. $6x + 8 < 6 + 5x$
3. $3x + 7 < 32 - 2x$
4. $x + 6 > 5x - 6$
5. $3x - 2 < x + 6$
6. $2x + 4 > 5x + 10$
7. $3x - 6 + 2x > 6x - 6$
8. $12 - 3x < 2x + 8 - 1$

9. $8x + 1 - 3x > 15 - x$

10. $\dfrac{x}{3} < \dfrac{5x}{6} + 3$

11. $\dfrac{2x}{3} + 5 + \dfrac{x}{2} > \dfrac{x}{3} + 3$

12. $\dfrac{2x - 1}{3} - x < 1 - \dfrac{x - 1}{2}$

Inequalities of the second degree.   Some inequalities of the second degree can be solved by factoring. If we wish to solve $x^2 - x < 12$, we would first subtract 12 from both members in order to make one member equal to zero.

$$x^2 - x - 12 < 0$$

Factoring, we find $(x - 4)(x + 3) < 0$

This inequality states that the product of $x - 4$ and $x + 3$ must be negative. We know, then, that one factor must be positive and the other must be negative, in order that the product be negative.

The value of x cannot be 4 or -3. If it were, the product $(x - 4)(x + 3)$ would equal zero. Therefore, if any values of x satisfy the given inequality, they must be values other than 4 and -3. The other possible values of x are:

I. x is less than the smaller: $x < -3$

II. x is greater than the smaller and less than the larger: $-3 < x < 4$

III. x is greater than the larger: $x > 4$

We, therefore, check all of these three possibilities.

I. If $x < -3$, then $x - 4$ is negative, and $x + 3$ is negative. Then $(x - 4)(x + 3)$ is positive, because the product of two negative numbers is positive. Therefore, x cannot be less than -3.

II. If $-3 < x < 4$, then $x - 4$ is negative, and $x + 3$ is positive. Then $(x - 4)(x + 3)$ is negative. Hence all values of x between -3 and 4 are solutions for the given inequality.

III. If $x > 4$, then $x - 4$ is positive, and $x + 3$ is positive. Then $(x - 4)(x + 3)$ is positive. Therefore, x cannot be greater than 4.

The only values of x that satisfy this inequality are $-3 < x < 4$.

ILLUSTRATIVE EXAMPLE: Solving a second-degree inequality by factoring

Solve for x: $3x^2 - 18x > 21$

Solution. Given inequality $3x^2 - 18x > 21$

Subtracting 21 from both members $3x^2 - 18x - 21 > 0$

Factoring completely $3(x - 7)(x + 1) > 0$

Dividing both members by 3 $(x - 7)(x + 1) > 0$

$$x \neq 7 \text{ and } x \neq -1$$

I. If $x < -1$, then $\begin{cases} x - 7 \text{ is negative} \\ x + 1 \text{ is negative} \end{cases}$. Thus $(x - 7)(x + 1) > 0$.

Any value of x less than -1 satisfies the inequality.

II. If $-1 < x < 7$, then $\begin{cases} x - 7 \text{ is negative} \\ x + 1 \text{ is positive} \end{cases}$. Thus $(x - 7)(x + 1) < 0$.

These values of x do not satisfy the inequality.

III. If $x > 7$, then $\begin{cases} x - 7 \text{ is positive} \\ x + 1 \text{ is positive} \end{cases}$. Thus $(x - 7)(x + 1) > 0$. Any value of x greater than 7 satisfies the inequality.

The solution of the inequality is $\left. \begin{array}{l} x < -1 \\ \text{and } x > 7 \end{array} \right\}$ Answers

EXERCISES: Solving inequalities of the second degree by factoring

Solve each of the following:

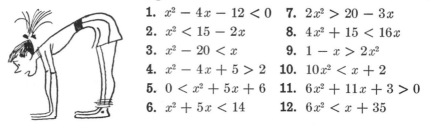

1. $x^2 - 4x - 12 < 0$
2. $x^2 < 15 - 2x$
3. $x^2 - 20 < x$
4. $x^2 - 4x + 5 > 2$
5. $0 < x^2 + 5x + 6$
6. $x^2 + 5x < 14$

7. $2x^2 > 20 - 3x$
8. $4x^2 + 15 < 16x$
9. $1 - x > 2x^2$
10. $10x^2 < x + 2$
11. $6x^2 + 11x + 3 > 0$
12. $6x^2 < x + 35$

The graph method for solving second-degree inequalities.   Many inequalities of the second degree cannot be solved by factoring. However, if the coefficients are numerical, the inequalities can be solved by graphical methods. If we wish to find values of x that will satisfy the inequality

$$x^2 - 5x - 4 < 0,$$

we can graph the equation $y = x^2 - 5x - 4$. Since we are trying to find all values of x that will make $x^2 - 5x - 4$ negative, we need only to read from the graph of the equation those values of x that will make y negative.

ILLUSTRATIVE EXAMPLE:
Solving a second-degree inequality by graph

Solve for x: $2x^2 + 5x < 4$

Solution.   Given inequality
$$2x^2 + 5x < 4$$

Subtracting 4 from both members
$$2x^2 + 5x - 4 < 0$$

Setting the left member equal to y
$$y = 2x^2 + 5x - 4$$

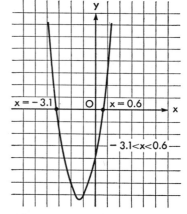

Graphing this equation of a parabola, we find that all values of x between -3.1 and 0.6 will make y negative. Since $y = 2x^2 + 5x - 4$, then $-3.1 < x < 0.6$ is true for $2x^2 + 5x - 4 < 0$.

Note that these limiting values for x, both -3.1 and 0.6, are not exact. In this problem the limiting values of x are irrational numbers, which cannot be found exactly from the graph. However, if the equation $2x^2 + 5x - 4 = 0$ is solved, it is found that these limiting values of x are exactly $\dfrac{-5 \pm \sqrt{57}}{4}$.

E X E R C I S E S : Solving second-degree inequalities by graphing

1. By drawing the graph of $y = x^2 + 4x + 3$:
    a) Find the values of x that satisfy $x^2 + 4x + 3 > 0$.
    b) Find the values of x that satisfy $x^2 + 4x + 3 < 0$.
    c) Find the roots of the equation $x^2 + 4x + 3 = 0$.
2. Solve by graph for x: $2x^2 - 7x > 4$
3. Solve by graph for x: $2x^2 + 7x < -1$
4. Draw the graph of $y = x^2 + x + 2$. What does this graph tell you about the solution of $x^2 + x + 2 > 0$?
5. Show by a graph that no real value of x will satisfy the inequality $x + 1 < -x^2$.
6. Determine from a graph the largest integral value of x that will satisfy the inequality $13x - 2x^2 > 18$.

I L L U S T R A T I V E   E X A M P L E : Applying inequalities in solving problems

For what values of m will the roots of the equation $x^2 - mx + m + 3 = 0$ be real and unequal?

Solution. If the roots of a quadratic equation are real and unequal, we know that the discriminant, $b^2 - 4ac$, must be greater than zero. Substituting the values from the equation in the discriminant we have $\quad b^2 - 4ac = (-m)^2 - 4(1)(m + 3)$

Since $b^2 - 4ac > 0$ $\hspace{4.5cm} m^2 - 4m - 12 > 0$

Factoring $\hspace{6cm} (m - 6)(m + 2) > 0$

$$m \neq 6 \text{ and } m \neq -2$$

I. If $m < -2$, then $\begin{cases} m - 6 \text{ is negative} \\ m + 2 \text{ is negative} \end{cases}$. Thus $(m - 6)(m + 2) > 0$.

All values of m less than -2 *satisfy* the inequality.

II. If $-2 < m < 6$, then $\begin{cases} m - 6 \text{ is negative} \\ m + 2 \text{ is positive} \end{cases}$. Thus $(m - 6)(m + 2) < 0$.

All values of m between -2 and 6 *do not satisfy* the inequality.

III. If $m > 6$, then $\begin{cases} m - 6 \text{ is positive} \\ m + 2 \text{ is positive} \end{cases}$. Thus $(m - 6)(m + 2) > 0$.

All values of m greater than 6 *satisfy* the inequality.

The solution of the inequality is $\left.\begin{matrix} m < -2 \\ m > 6 \end{matrix}\right\}$ Answers

E X E R C I S E S : Applying inequalities in solving problems

In ex. 1–4, find the values of m for which the roots of each equation will be real and unequal.

1. $x^2 + 2mx + 25 = 0$ 3. $4x^2 - 2mx + m^2 - 10x = 0$

2. $9y^2 + my + 4y + 1 = 0$ 4. $mx^2 + mx = 1 - x^2$

In ex. 5–8, find the values of m for which the roots of each equation will be imaginary.

5. $x^2 - 12x + 9m = 0$ 7. $2my^2 - 7my = 3y^2 - 49$

6. $x^2 + 4mx + m + 14 = 0$ 8. $4(x^2 + m) + 13 + 2x + 6mx = 0$

R E V I E W   E X E R C I S E S

1. Solve the equation : $2x^2 - 5x + 4 = 0$
    a) Are the roots real or imaginary?
    b) Find the discriminant.
    c) Is the discriminant real or imaginary?
    d) Is the discriminant rational or irrational?

2. Solve the equation : $4x^2 - 20x + 25 = 0$
    a) Are the roots real or imaginary?
    b) Are the roots equal or unequal?
    c) Are the roots rational or irrational?
    d) Find the discriminant.
    e) Is the discriminant real or imaginary?

3. What value must k have in order that the graph of each of the following be tangent to the x axis?
    a) $y = x^2 - kx + 16$
    b) $kx^2 + 6x + 9 = y$
    c) $kx^2 + 16x + 16 = y$
    d) $9x^2 - 24x + k = y$

4. In the equation $y = x^2 + 4x + k$ what values may k have in order that the graph of the equation may not intersect the x axis?

5. In the equation $y = x^2 + 9x + k$ what values may k have in order that the graph of the equation may neither be tangent to the x axis nor intersect the x axis?

6. In the equation $4x^2 + 3x = k$ what value must k have if one of the roots is $\frac{3}{2}$?

7. Write the quadratic equation the sum of whose roots is -3 and the product of whose roots is 8.

8. If the constant term and the numerical coefficients of the unknown of a quadratic equation are real,

    a) can the *discriminant* ever be imaginary? Give a reason for your answer.

    b) can the *roots* ever be imaginary? Give a reason for your answer and state what relationship must exist among the coefficients and the constant term.

9. From the information given us in the equation $5x^2 + 3x - 2 = 0$ pair the numbers in the first column below with the word or group of words from the second column which describe these numbers.

-1	a root
$-\frac{3}{5}$	another root
$-\frac{2}{5}$	the discriminant
$\frac{2}{5}$	the sum of the roots
-2	the product of the roots
3	a numerical coefficient
5	another numerical coefficient
49	the constant term

10. In the equation $2x^2 + 3x - k = 0$ what value must k have if the product of the roots is -4?

11. In the equation $3kx^2 - 2x + 3 = 0$ what value must k have if the sum of the roots is 6?

12. If the roots of a quadratic equation are 3 and -5, what is the sum of the roots? What is the product of the roots? What is the equation?

13. What is the largest integral value of k that will make the roots imaginary in $(6 + x)^2 - 3 = 2k$?

In ex. 14–16, without solving the equation, determine whether the roots indicated for the respective equations are correct.

14. $5x + 21 = 6x^2$ $x = \frac{7}{3}, -\frac{2}{3}$

15. $3x^2 - 7x = 2$ $x = \frac{1}{3}, 2$

16. $2 + 3x - 7x^2 = 0$ $x = \dfrac{3 \pm \sqrt{65}}{14}$

17. If one root of $2x^2 + 3x - 2 = 0$ is -2, find the other root without solving the equation.

CHAPTER REVIEW EXERCISES

1. Determine the nature of the roots of each of the following:

a) $3x^2 - 4x - 1 = 0$ c) $4x^2 - 36x + 81 = 0$

b) $y^2 - 16y + 65 = 0$ d) $2x^2 + 9x - 56 = 0$

2. Write and simplify the quadratic equation whose roots are:

a) 3 and -5 c) $3 \pm 2\sqrt{5}$

b) $\dfrac{2a}{3}$ and $-\dfrac{a}{2}$ d) $\dfrac{2 \pm i}{4}$

3. Find the sum of the roots and the product of the roots of each of the following:

a) $2x^2 - 3x + 4 = 0$ c) $4x^2 = 8x$

b) $3x^2 - 16 = 0$ d) $x^2 - r = qx$

4. For what values of m will the roots of the equation $x^2 - 2m(x - 4) = 15$ be equal?

5. Solve for x: $\dfrac{5 + x}{2} + 2 > \dfrac{6 - x}{3}$

6. Solve for x: $x^2 + 3x < 10$

7. For what values of m will one root of the equation $2x^2 - (m + 2)x - m^2 = 5$ be equal to 6?

8. For what values of m will the roots of the equation $3x^2 + 10x + m + 3 = 0$ be

     a) imaginary?   b) real and unequal?

9. In the equation $y = x^2 - kx + 81$, what must be the value of k in order that the graph of the equation be tangent to the x axis?

10. In the equation $y = x^2 + 12x + k$, what values may k have in order that the graph of the equation may neither be tangent to the x axis nor intersect the x axis?

CUMULATIVE REVIEW EXERCISES

1. Multiply: $3x(2x - 5)(3x + 2)$

2. Simplify and combine: $\sqrt{28} - \sqrt{63} + \sqrt{112}$

3. Solve for t in terms of the other letters: $at^2 = -\frac{1}{2}bt$

4. Solve for y in terms of x: $x^2 + 4y^2 = 100$

5. Factor: $m^2 + 6n - 1 - 9n^2$

6. If $\frac{1}{2}x - \frac{2}{3}y = 0$, find the ratio of x to y.

7. How many positive integers satisfy the inequality $5x + 1 < 3x + 8$?

8. Solve for x: $\dfrac{4x^4 + 9}{37x} = x$

9. Solve for x: $\dfrac{2x - 14}{x^2 + 3x - 28} + \dfrac{2 - x}{4 - x} + \dfrac{x - 3}{x + 7} = 0$

10. Solve for x and y: $\dfrac{2}{3x} + \dfrac{3}{5y} = 5$

$$\dfrac{1}{6x} + \dfrac{7}{10y} = -3$$

11. In the equation $kx^2 + 2mx = 2p$, if $k = 4$, what relation must hold between m and p so that the values of x are real?

12. Simplify: $\dfrac{(-a^{\frac{3}{4}}b^2c^{n-3})(3abc^{3-n})}{(-a^{\frac{5}{6}}b^{-3})}$

13. Find the value of $32^{\frac{2}{5}} - (\frac{1}{27})^{-\frac{1}{3}} + 1^{2m} - (5x^2)^0$

14. There are two numbers such that the second divided by the first gives the quotient 3 and remainder 5, while 9 times the first is 11 more than 2 times the second. What are the numbers?

15. Solve the following system of equations by use of determinants:

$$2x - y + 3z = 20$$
$$x + y + z = 3$$
$$x - 2y - 2z = -3$$

16. Estimate the roots of $x^2 + 3x + 4 = 0$ from the graph of $y = x^2 + 3x + 4$.

CHAPTER 12   *Graphs of Quadratic Equations in Two Variables*

Standard forms of quadratic equations in two variables. In this chapter we shall study the graphs of equations, each of which is represented by one of the following standard forms of quadratic equations in two variables:

$$y = ax^2 + bx + c \qquad ax^2 + by^2 = c \qquad x^2 + y^2 = r^2$$
$$x = ay^2 + by + c \qquad ax^2 - by^2 = c \qquad xy = k$$

Parabola. In Chapter 10 we used parabolas to solve quadratic equations in one unknown. We found that the graphs of equations in the form $y = ax^2 + bx + c$ were parabolas.

A *parabola* can be defined as the path in a plane traced by a point that is always equidistant from a given fixed point and a given fixed line.

In the adjacent figure, F is the given fixed point (called the focus) and d is the given fixed line (called the directrix). Each of the points labeled P is equidistant from F and from line d; that is, the line drawn from any point P to F is equal to the perpendicular line drawn from the same point P to line d.

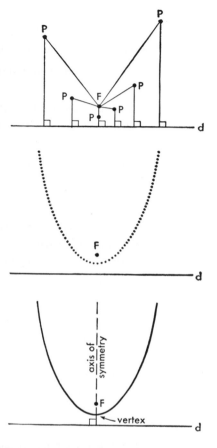

The second figure shows a great many more such points, and we can see the general shape of the curve that will contain all of the points equidistant from line d and from F. The third figure shows the curve containing these points; this curve is a parabola.

The line through F which is perpendicular to line d is called the axis of symmetry of the parabola. If you folded the paper along the axis of symmetry, the left part of the curve would coincide with the right part.

The point at which the axis of symmetry intersects the parabola is the *vertex* of the parabola. The vertex of the parabola is also called the "turning point" of the curve. As we trace the curve in the adjacent figure from left to right, the curve stops decreasing (falling) at the vertex and begins increasing (rising). At this point, the curve "turns" from a downward to an upward direction.

> The graph of an equation in the form
> $$y = ax^2 + bx + c,$$
> where a, b, and c can have any real value except that a cannot equal 0, is a parabola with its axis of symmetry perpendicular to the x axis.

Examples of equations of the form $y = ax^2 + bx + c$ are:

$y = 2x^2 + 3x - 4$, $y = \frac{2}{3}x^2 + \frac{7}{3}$, $y = \frac{1}{2}x^2 + 2$,   and $y = 4x^2$

ILLUSTRATIVE EXAMPLE: Finding the coordinates of the vertex of a parabola

Find the coordinates of the vertex of the parabola whose equation is $y = 2x^2 - 6x + 1$, and describe the location of its axis of symmetry.

Solution. Given equation $\qquad y = 2x^2 - 6x + 1$

We observe that $\qquad\qquad\qquad a = 2 \quad \text{and} \quad b = -6$

On page 228 we found that the x coordinate of the vertex is

$$x = -\frac{b}{2a}$$

Substituting -6 for b and 2 for a

$$x = -\frac{-6}{2(2)}$$

Simplifying $\qquad\qquad\qquad\qquad x = \tfrac{3}{2}$

To find the y coordinate of the vertex, we substitute $\tfrac{3}{2}$ for x in the original equation

$$y = 2x^2 - 6x + 1$$
$$y = 2(\tfrac{3}{2})^2 - 6(\tfrac{3}{2}) + 1$$
$$y = 2(\tfrac{9}{4}) - 9 + 1$$
$$y = 4\tfrac{1}{2} - 8$$
$$y = -3\tfrac{1}{2}$$

The coordinates of the vertex are $(1\tfrac{1}{2}, -3\tfrac{1}{2})$. Answer

The axis of symmetry of the parabola is a line through the point $(1\tfrac{1}{2}, -3\tfrac{1}{2})$ drawn perpendicular to the x axis. The equation of the axis of symmetry is $x = \tfrac{3}{2}$.

ORAL EXERCISES: Parabolas

1. State the equation of the axis of symmetry of the graph of each of the following equations:

a) $y = x^2 - 4x + 6$

b) $y = 2x^2 + 6x - 3$

c) $y = 7x^2$

d) $y = 3x^2 - 15x$

e) $y = 4x^2 - 24$

2. For which of the following does the y axis coincide with the axis of symmetry of the equation's graph?

a) $y = x^2 - 8x + 4$

b) $y = 2x^2 + 7x - 14$

c) $y = 9x^2$

d) $y = 5x^2 + 20x$

e) $y = x^2 + 32$

3. For which of the following equations does the graph pass through the origin?

a) $y = x^2 + 2x + 5$ c) $y = 5x^2$ e) $y = x^2 - 36$

b) $y = 2x^2 + 8x - 3$ d) $y = 3x^2 - 18x$

4. Find the y coordinate of the vertex of the graph of each of the following equations:

    a) $x^2 + 6x + 18 = y$ when the x coordinate is -3.

    b) $x^2 - 4x - 3 = y$ when the x coordinate is 2.

    c) $x^2 + 8x + 32 = y$ when the x coordinate is -4.

    d) $x^2 - 4x = y$ when the x coordinate is 2.

    e) $2x^2 + 12x = y$ when the x coordinate is -3.

    f) $3x^2 + y = 2x$ when the x coordinate is $-\frac{1}{3}$.

In ex. 5–12, state at what points the graph of each of the following equations intersects the x axis. Do not draw the graph.

5. $y = x^2 - x$ **8.** $y = x^2 + 5x$ **11.** $y = 4x^2 + 20x$

6. $y = x^2 - 2x$ **9.** $y = 3x^2 - 6x$ **12.** $y = 7x^2 + 14x$

7. $y = x^2 + x$ **10.** $y = 2x^2 - 8x$

In ex. 13–24, state at what point the graph of each of the following equations is tangent to the x axis. Do not draw the graph.

13. $y = x^2$ **17.** $y = (x + 5)^2$ **21.** $y = x^2 - 2x + 1$

14. $y = (x - 1)^2$ **18.** $y = (2x - 1)^2$ **22.** $y = x^2 + 2x + 1$

15. $y = (x - 3)^2$ **19.** $y = (3x - 4)^2$ **23.** $y = 4x^2 - 12x + 9$

16. $y = (x + 2)^2$ **20.** $y = (5x + 4)^2$ **24.** $y = 25x^2 + 60x + 36$

ILLUSTRATIVE EXAMPLE: Drawing the graph of an equation in the form $y = ax^2 + bx + c$

Draw the graph of the equation $y = 3x^2 - 4x - 6$.

Solution. Since the graph of the equation is a parabola, we first find the x coordinate of the vertex by evaluating the

expression
$$x = -\frac{b}{2a}$$

Substituting -4 for b and 3 for a
$$x = -\frac{-4}{2(3)}$$

Simplifying
$$x = \tfrac{2}{3}$$

We find the y coordinate by substituting $\tfrac{2}{3}$ for x in the equation

$$y = 3x^2 - 4x - 6$$
$$y = 3(\tfrac{2}{3})^2 - 4(\tfrac{2}{3}) - 6$$
$$y = -7\tfrac{1}{3}$$

To construct the axis of symmetry (whose equation is $x = \frac{2}{3}$), we draw a line through the vertex ($\frac{2}{3}$, $-7\frac{1}{3}$) parallel to the y axis.

Before we can draw the graph of the equation, we must find the coordinates of enough points to determine the curve, selecting values of x on both sides of the axis of symmetry. We then plot these points and join them with a smooth curve.

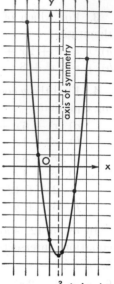

x	$3x^2 - 4x - 6$	y
-2	$12 + 8 - 6$	14
-1	$3 + 4 - 6$	1
0	$0 - 0 - 6$	-6
$\frac{2}{3}$	$\frac{4}{3} - \frac{8}{3} - 6$	$-7\frac{1}{3}$
1	$3 - 4 - 6$	-7
2	$12 - 8 - 6$	-2
3	$27 - 12 - 6$	9

E X E R C I S E S : Drawing the graph of an equation in the form $y = ax^2 + bx + c$

In drawing the graph of each of the following equations find first the coordinates of the vertex of the graph and draw the axis of symmetry. Find the coordinates of enough points to determine the curve by selecting values of x on both sides of the axis of symmetry.

1. $y = x^2 - 2x - 5$
2. $y = x^2$
3. $y = x^2 - 4x + 3$
4. $y = x^2 - 4$
5. $y = x^2 - 8x + 16$
6. $y = x^2 - 3x - 5$
7. $y = x^2 + 18x + 75$

8. $y = x^2 + 5x$
9. $y = 6 - x - x^2$
10. $y = 8 - 3x - x^2$
11. $y = 3x^2 - x - 4$
12. $x^2 - 15x + y + 50 = 0$
13. $x^2 - 3x - y + 1 = 0$
14. $2x^2 + x - 3y + 3 = 0$

> The graph of an equation in the form
> $$x = ay^2 + by + c,$$
> where a, b, and c can have any real value except that a cannot equal 0, is a parabola with its axis of symmetry perpendicular to the y axis. The y coordinate of the vertex of the parabola is $-\dfrac{b}{2a}$.

Examples of equations in the form $x = ay^2 + by + c$ are:
$$x = 2y^2 + 3y - 5;\ x = y^2 + 6;\ x = 2y^2 - 5;\ \text{and}\ x = 3y^2$$

ORAL EXERCISES: Parabolas

In ex. 1–8, state at what points the graph of each of the following equations intersects the y axis. Do not draw the graph.

1. $x = y^2 - y$

2. $x = y^2 - 3y$

3. $x = y^2 + y$

4. $x = y^2 + 4y$

5. $x = 5y^2 - 15y$

6. $x = 3y^2 - 12y$

7. $x = 4y^2 + 8y$

8. $x = 9y^2 + 27y$

In ex. 9–20, state at what point the graph of each of the following equations is tangent to the y axis. Do not draw the graph.

9. $x = y^2$

10. $x = (y - 1)^2$

11. $x = (y - 4)^2$

12. $x = (y + 3)^2$

13. $x = (y + 7)^2$

14. $x = (3y - 1)^2$

15. $x = (4y - 3)^2$

16. $x = (6y + 5)^2$

17. $x = y^2 - 4y + 4$

18. $x = y^2 - 12y + 36$

19. $x = 9y^2 - 30y + 25$

20. $x = 49y^2 + 28y + 4$

ILLUSTRATIVE EXAMPLE: Drawing the graph of an equation in the form $x = ay^2 + by + c$

Draw the graph of the equation $x = y^2 - 9y + 14$.

Solution. Since the graph of the equation is a parabola we first find the y coordinate of the

vertex by evaluating the expression $y = -\dfrac{b}{2a}$

Substituting -9 for b and 1 for a $y = -\dfrac{-9}{2(1)}$

Simplifying $y = 4\tfrac{1}{2}$

We find the x coordinate by substituting $4\tfrac{1}{2}$ for y
in the equation

$$x = y^2 - 9y + 14$$
$$x = (4\tfrac{1}{2})^2 - 9(4\tfrac{1}{2}) + 14$$
$$x = -6\tfrac{1}{4}$$

To construct the axis of symmetry (whose equation is $y = 4\tfrac{1}{2}$), we draw a line through the vertex $(-6\tfrac{1}{4}, 4\tfrac{1}{2})$ perpendicular to the y axis. Before we can draw the graph of the equation, we must find the coordinates of enough points to determine the curve, selecting values for y on both sides of the axis of symmetry. We then plot these points and join them with a smooth curve.

y	$y^2 - 9y + 14$	x
1	$1 - 9 + 14$	6
2	$4 - 18 + 14$	0
3	$9 - 27 + 14$	-4
4	$16 - 36 + 14$	-6
$4\frac{1}{2}$	$\frac{81}{4} - \frac{81}{2} + 14$	$-6\frac{1}{4}$
5	$25 - 45 + 14$	-6
6	$36 - 54 + 14$	-4
7	$49 - 63 + 14$	0
8	$64 - 72 + 14$	6

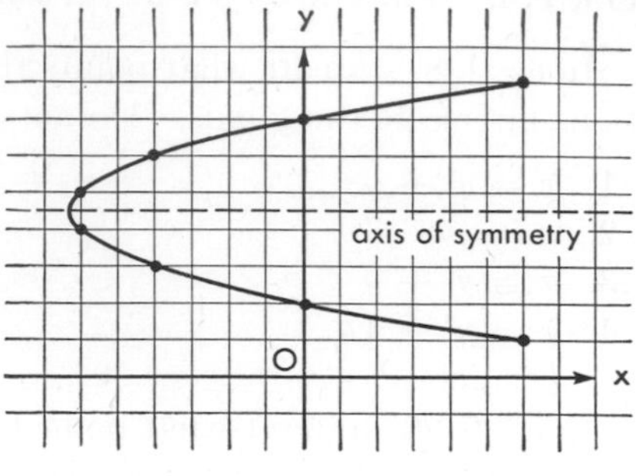

axis of symmetry

EXERCISES: Drawing the graph of an equation in the form $x = ay^2 + by + c$

In drawing the graph of each of the following equations find first a co-ordinate of the vertex of the graph and draw the axis of symmetry. Find the coordinates of enough points to determine the curve by selecting values of y on both sides of the axis of symmetry.

1. $x = y^2 - y + 1$
2. $x = y^2 - 6y + 10$
3. $x = y^2$
4. $x = y^2 - 4y + 4$
5. $x = y^2 - 3y + 6$
6. $x = y^2 - 6$

7. $x = y^2 + 3y$
8. $x = 6 - y - y^2$
9. $x = y^2 + 18y + 75$
10. $y^2 - x - 3y + 1 = 0$
11. $3y^2 - x - y - 4 = 0$
12. $2y^2 - 3x + y + 3 = 0$

The circle. A circle can be defined as the path in a plane traced by a point that is always a given fixed distance from a given fixed point. In the adjacent figure C is the given fixed point (called the center) and each of the points labeled P is the same fixed distance from C. The second figure shows the circle containing all of these points.

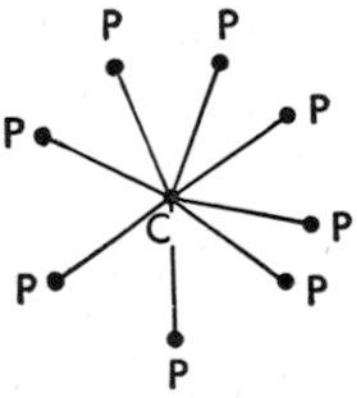

When you draw a circle with a compass, the metal point of the compass is the given fixed point (the center), and the point of the pencil, as it moves, is held in a position so that it is always the same fixed distance (the radius distance) from the center.

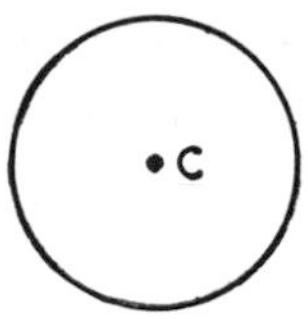

The graph of an equation in the form $x^2 + y^2 = r^2$, where r can have any real value, is a circle whose center is at the origin and whose radius is r.

Examples of equations in the form $x^2 + y^2 = r^2$ are:

$$x^2 + y^2 = 16 \qquad x^2 + y^2 = \tfrac{25}{4} \qquad x^2 + y^2 = 10$$

ILLUSTRATIVE EXAMPLE: Drawing the graph of an equation in the form $x^2 + y^2 = r^2$

Draw the graph of the equation $x^2 + y^2 = 25$.

Solution. From the form of the equation, we know that the graph is a circle whose center is at the origin and whose radius is 5 units. We can easily draw the graph with a compass. It is good experience, however, to verify this by plotting some points that lie on the graph. To do this, we first solve the given equation for y in terms of x:

$$x^2 + y^2 = 25$$
$$y^2 = 25 - x^2$$
$$y = \pm\sqrt{25 - x^2}$$

We substitute values for x and find the corresponding values for y:

x	$\pm\sqrt{25 - x^2}$		y
0	$\pm\sqrt{25 - 0}$		± 5
1	$\pm\sqrt{25 - 1}$	$= \pm\sqrt{24}$	± 4.9
2	$\pm\sqrt{25 - 4}$	$= \pm\sqrt{21}$	± 4.6
3	$\pm\sqrt{25 - 9}$	$= \pm\sqrt{16}$	± 4
4	$\pm\sqrt{25 - 16}$	$= \pm\sqrt{9}$	± 3
5	$\pm\sqrt{25 - 25}$		0
-1	$\pm\sqrt{25 - 1}$	$= \pm\sqrt{24}$	± 4.9
-2	$\pm\sqrt{25 - 4}$	$= \pm\sqrt{21}$	± 4.6
-3	$\pm\sqrt{25 - 9}$	$= \pm\sqrt{16}$	± 4
-4	$\pm\sqrt{25 - 16}$	$= \pm\sqrt{9}$	± 3
-5	$\pm\sqrt{25 - 25}$		0

Since the equation contains x raised to the second power only, the substitution of $+1$ or -1 for x gives the same value for y; similarly for $+2$ or -2, $+3$ or -3, etc.

Notice that if we let x have any value larger than 5, the corresponding value for y is imaginary.

EXERCISES: Drawing the graph of an equation in the form $x^2 + y^2 = r^2$

Draw the graph of each of the following equations.

1. $x^2 + y^2 = 100$ **2.** $x^2 + y^2 = 36$ **3.** $x^2 + y^2 = 64$

4. $x^2 + y^2 = 6\frac{1}{4}$ **7.** $4x^2 + 4y^2 = 81$ **10.** $3x^2 + 3y^2 = 20$

5. $x^2 + y^2 = 50$ **8.** $9x^2 + 9y^2 = 196$ **11.** $\frac{1}{2}x^2 = 20 - \frac{1}{2}y^2$

6. $x^2 + y^2 = 20$ **9.** $2x^2 + 2y^2 = 49$ **12.** $\dfrac{35 - 2y^2}{2} = x^2$

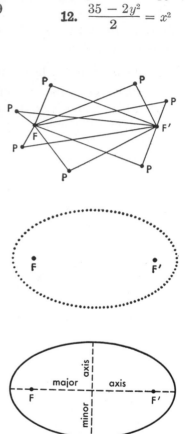

The ellipse. An ellipse can be defined as the path in a plane traced by a point which moves so that the sum of the distances from the point to two fixed points is a constant. In the adjacent figure, the two fixed points are F and F' (each of these points is called a *focus*). The points labeled P are plotted in such a way that the sum of the distances from each point P to F and F' is a fixed length; that is, $FP + PF'$ remains constant.

The second figure shows a great many more such points, and we can see the general shape of the curve that will contain all the points satisfying this condition. The third figure shows the curve containing these points; this curve is an ellipse.

The line drawn through the foci F and F', when extended to meet the curve, is called the *major axis* of the ellipse. This is an axis of symmetry; if the paper is folded along this axis, the upper and lower parts of the ellipse will coincide. The line which is the perpendicular bisector of the major axis and which is terminated by the ellipse is called the *minor axis* of the ellipse; the minor axis is also an axis of symmetry. The point of intersection of the major axis and the minor axis is the *center* of the ellipse.

The graph of an equation in the form $ax^2 + by^2 = c$, where a, b, and c can have any real positive values and $a \neq b$, is an ellipse whose center is at the origin and whose major and minor axes lie along the x and y axes.

Examples of equations in the form $ax^2 + by^2 = c$ are:

$$x^2 + 6y^2 = 54 \qquad 9x^2 + 4y^2 = 36 \qquad 12x^2 + 25y^2 = 300$$

ILLUSTRATIVE EXAMPLE: Drawing the graph of an equation in the form $ax^2 + by^2 = c$

Draw the graph of the equation $4x^2 + 9y^2 = 36$.

Solution. We first find the points at which the graph intersects the two coordinate axes.

Given equation	$4x^2 + 9y^2 = 36$
If $x = 0$, we have	$0 + 9y^2 = 36$
	$y = \pm 2$ (y intercepts)

The graph intersects the y axis at $(0, 2)$ and $(0, -2)$.

If $y = 0$, we have	$4x^2 + 0 = 36$
	$x = \pm 3$ (x intercepts)

The graph intersects the x axis at $(3, 0)$ and $(-3, 0)$.

Solving the given equation for y in terms of x:

$$9y^2 = 36 - 4x^2$$
$$y^2 = \frac{36 - 4x^2}{9}$$
$$y = \frac{\pm \sqrt{36 - 4x^2}}{3}$$

We substitute values of x and find the corresponding values for y:

x	$\dfrac{\pm \sqrt{36 - 4x^2}}{3}$	y
1	$\dfrac{\pm \sqrt{36 - 4}}{3} = \dfrac{\pm \sqrt{32}}{3}$	± 1.9
2	$\dfrac{\pm \sqrt{36 - 16}}{3} = \dfrac{\pm \sqrt{20}}{3}$	± 1.5
-1	$\dfrac{\pm \sqrt{36 - 4}}{3} = \dfrac{\pm \sqrt{32}}{3}$	± 1.9
-2	$\dfrac{\pm \sqrt{36 - 16}}{3} = \dfrac{\pm \sqrt{20}}{3}$	± 1.5

EXERCISES: Drawing the graph of an equation in the form $ax^2 + by^2 = c$

Draw the graph of each of the following equations.

1. $x^2 + 4y^2 = 36$ **2.** $4x^2 + 25y^2 = 100$ **3.** $9x^2 + 16y^2 = 144$

4. $16x^2 + 25y^2 = 400$ **6.** $x^2 + 10y^2 = 100$ **8.** $6x^2 + 9y^2 = 54$
5. $25x^2 + 9y^2 = 225$ **7.** $12x^2 + 25y^2 = 300$ **9.** $16x^2 + 10y^2 = 160$

Constructing an ellipse mechanically.
An ellipse can be constructed mechanically with two thumb tacks, a piece of string, a pencil and paper. Each end of the string is tied to a tack and the tacks are placed at F and F' on a sheet of paper with the string not stretched. The string is then pulled taut with the point of a pencil, as shown in the adjacent figure.

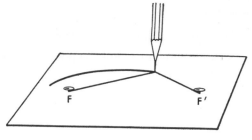

As the pencil is moved, keeping the string taut, it traces out an ellipse. By varying the length of the string and the distance between F and F', we can draw ellipses of different sizes and shapes.

The hyperbola. A hyperbola can be defined as the path in a plane traced by a point which moves so that the difference between the distances from the point to two fixed points is a constant. In the adjacent figure the two fixed points are F and F'. Each of these points is called a *focus*. The points labeled P or P' are plotted in such a way that the difference of the distances from each point P to F and F' is a fixed length; that is, $FP - PF'$ and $F'P' - P'F$ remain constant.

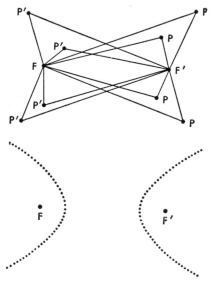

The second figure shows a great many more such points and we can see the general shape of the curve that will contain all the points satisfying this condition. The figure on the next page shows the curve containing these points. The curve is a hyperbola.

A hyperbola consists of two parts called the *branches* of the hyperbola. The line through the foci, FF', is the *transverse axis* of the hyperbola; the perpendicular bisector of FF' is the *conjugate axis*. The hyperbola is symmetric with respect to these axes. The point of intersection of the two axes is the *center* of the hyperbola. The two points where the transverse axis intersects the hyperbola are the *vertices*.

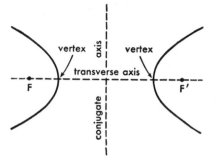

The graph of an equation in the form $ax^2 - by^2 = c$ is a hyperbola whose center is at the origin and whose axes are the x and y axes; a and b can have any real positive values; c cannot equal 0,

---

Examples of equations in the form $ax^2 - by^2 = c$ are:

$$x^2 - y^2 = 9 \qquad 2x^2 - y^2 = 18 \qquad 4x^2 - 9y^2 = -36$$

ILLUSTRATIVE EXAMPLE: Drawing the graph of an equation in the form $ax^2 - by^2 = c$

Draw the graph of the equation $x^2 - y^2 = 9$.

Solution. We first find the points at which the graph intersects the coordinate axes.

Given equation $\qquad\qquad x^2 - y^2 = 9$

If $x = 0$, we have $\qquad\quad 0 - y^2 = 9$
$$y^2 = -9$$
$$y = \pm \sqrt{-9} \quad \text{(The } y \text{ intercepts are imaginary ; the graph does not cross the } y \text{ axis.)}$$

If $y = 0$, we have $\qquad\quad x^2 - 0 = 9$
$$x = \pm 3 \quad (x \text{ intercepts})$$

Solving the equation for y in terms of x:

$$x^2 - 9 = y^2$$

$$y = \pm \sqrt{x^2 - 9}$$

We substitute values for x and find the corresponding values for y:

x	$\pm \sqrt{x^2 - 9}$	y
4	$\pm \sqrt{16 - 9} = \pm \sqrt{7}$	± 2.6
5	$\pm \sqrt{25 - 9} = \pm \sqrt{16}$	± 4
6	$\pm \sqrt{36 - 9} = \pm \sqrt{27}$	± 5.2
-4	$\pm \sqrt{16 - 9} = \pm \sqrt{7}$	± 2.6
-5	$\pm \sqrt{25 - 9} = \pm \sqrt{16}$	± 4
-6	$\pm \sqrt{36 - 9} = \pm \sqrt{27}$	± 5.2

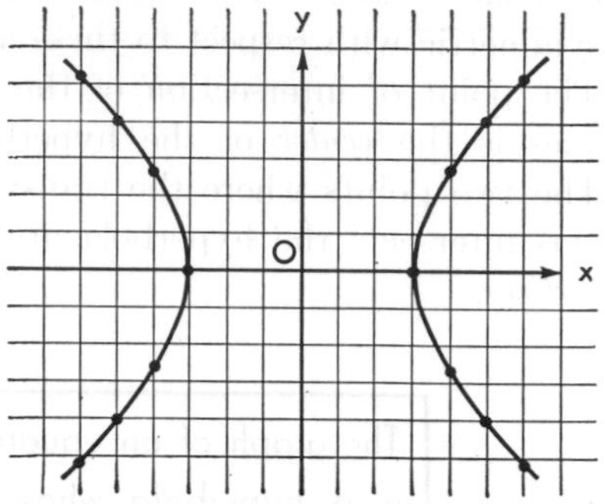

Note: If a and b are positive, the graph of an equation in the form $ax^2 - by^2 = c$ will intersect the x axis when c is positive, and it will intersect the y axis when c is negative.

E X E R C I S E S : Drawing the graph of an equation in the form $ax^2 - by^2 = c$

Draw the graph of each of the following equations:

1. $x^2 - y^2 = 4$ 4. $x^2 - y^2 = 18$ 7. $y^2 - x^2 = 9$

2. $x^2 - y^2 = 16$ 5. $x^2 - 4y^2 = 36$ 8. $y^2 - 4x^2 = 9$

3. $x^2 - y^2 = 25$ 6. $4x^2 - 9y^2 = 36$ 9. $25x^2 - 4y^2 = 100$

The graph of every equation in the form $xy = k$, where k can have any real value except that k cannot equal 0, is a hyperbola whose branches lie in diagonally opposite quadrants.

Examples of equations in the form $xy = k$ are:

$$xy = 12 \qquad xy = -8 \qquad xy = \tfrac{25}{4}$$

ILLUSTRATIVE EXAMPLE: Drawing the graph of an equation in the form $xy = k$

Draw the graph of the equation $xy = 12$.

Solution. Solving the equation for y in terms of x: $y = \dfrac{12}{x}$

We substitute values for x and find the corresponding value for y:

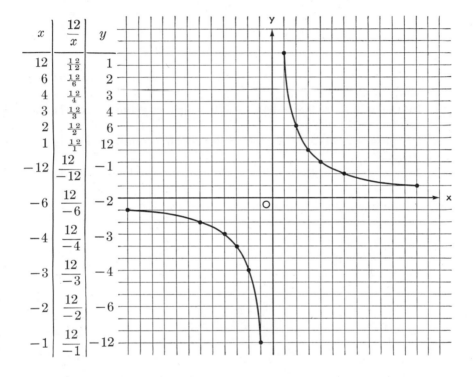

x	$\dfrac{12}{x}$	y
12	$\frac{12}{12}$	1
6	$\frac{12}{6}$	2
4	$\frac{12}{4}$	3
3	$\frac{12}{3}$	4
2	$\frac{12}{2}$	6
1	$\frac{12}{1}$	12
-12	$\dfrac{12}{-12}$	-1
-6	$\dfrac{12}{-6}$	-2
-4	$\dfrac{12}{-4}$	-3
-3	$\dfrac{12}{-3}$	-4
-2	$\dfrac{12}{-2}$	-6
-1	$\dfrac{12}{-1}$	-12

Note: If k is positive, $xy = k$ represents a hyperbola with its branches in the first and third quadrants. If k is negative, $xy = k$ represents a hyperbola with its branches in the second and fourth quadrants.

EXERCISES: Drawing the graph of an equation in the form $xy = k$

Draw the graph of each of the following equations:

1. $xy = 12$

2. $xy = 8$

3. $xy = -4$

4. $xy = 10$

5. $xy + 18 = 0$

6. $x = \dfrac{16}{y}$

7. $xy - 15 = 0$

8. $20 - xy = 0$

9. $24 + xy = 0$

ORAL EXERCISES: Identifying graphs

In ex. 1–25 identify the graph of each equation:

1. $x^2 + y^2 = 25$
2. $x + y = 25$
3. $xy = 25$
4. $x^2 - y^2 = 25$
5. $x^2 + y = 25$
6. $x - y^2 = 25$
7. $2x^2 + y^2 = 25$
8. $x^2 + 2y^2 = 25$
9. $x^2 - 2y^2 = 25$

10. $-2xy = 25$
11. $x^2 - y - 9 = 0$
12. $x^2 - y^2 - 9 = 0$
13. $x^2 + y^2 - 9 = 0$
14. $x - y^2 + 9 = 0$
15. $2x^2 + y^2 - 9 = 0$
16. $x = \dfrac{1}{4y}$
17. $x = \frac{1}{4}y$

18. $x^2 = \frac{1}{4}y$
19. $x^2 - y^2 = \frac{1}{4}$
20. $x^2 + y^2 = \frac{1}{4}$
21. $x^2 + 4y^2 = \frac{1}{4}$
22. $(x + y)(x - y) = 8$
23. $(x + 3)^2 = y$
24. $x = (3 - y)(2 + y)$
25. $2x - y = 3$

26. In the graph of $25x^2 + 16y^2 = 400$ which coordinate axis is the major axis?

27. In the graph of $9x^2 + 64y^2 = 576$ which coordinate axis is the major axis?

28. In the graph of $25x^2 - 16y^2 = 400$ which coordinate axis is the conjugate axis?

29. In the graph of $64y^2 - 9x^2 = 576$ which coordinate axis is the conjugate axis?

30. The branches of the graph of $xy = 6$ lie in which quadrants?

31. The branches of the graph of $xy = -8$ lie in which quadrants?

32. The branches of the graph of $x^2 - y^2 = 25$ lie in which quadrants?

33. The branches of the graph of $y^2 - x^2 = 49$ lie in which quadrants?

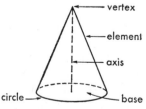

Conic sections. More than 2000 years ago the Greek mathematicians were familiar with the curves represented by quadratic equations in two variables. These curves are all conic sections. Each one can be represented as the intersection of a plane with a conical surface.

The adjacent figure is a right circular cone with various

Right Circular Cone

Conical Surface

parts appropriately labeled. An element of a cone is a straight line drawn
from any point on the base to the vertex. If all the elements are extended
through the vertex, there results another curved surface. This surface
(upper nappe) along with the first cone (lower nappe) compose a conical
surface. A conical surface may extend indefinitely in both directions.

If the surface of a right circular cone is cut by a plane
perpendicular to the axis of
the cone (not at the vertex),
the intersection is a circle.

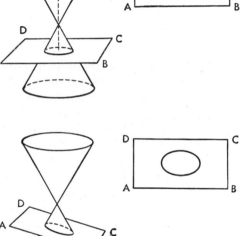

If the surface of a right circular cone is cut by a plane
oblique to the axis and cutting all elements (not at the
vertex), the intersection is an
ellipse.

If the surface of a right circular cone is cut by a plane
parallel to an element, the intersection is a parabola.

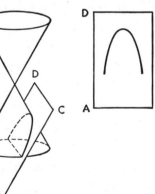

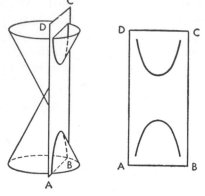

If the surface of a right circular cone is cut by a plane not parallel to any element and intersecting both nappes, the intersection is a hyperbola.

Special cases. Since equations of the form $x^2 + y^2 = r^2$ represent circles with the center at the origin and a radius of r, the equation $x^2 + y^2 = 0$ must represent a circle with a radius of 0. Therefore, this equation represents a single point, the origin. This equation is often called a *point circle*.

Equations of the form $x^2 + y^2 = r^2$, in which r^2 is negative, cannot be represented on a Cartesian coordinate system, because the radius is of imaginary length. These equations are often called *imaginary circles*.

Equations of the form $ax^2 + by^2 = c$ represent ellipses. When $c = 0$, this equation represents a *point ellipse*. This point, too, is the origin. When c is negative, the equation represents an *imaginary ellipse*.

Equations of the form $ax^2 - by^2 = c$ represent hyperbolas. When $c = 0$, this equation represents a pair of straight lines. If $ax^2 - by^2 = 0$, then $(x\sqrt{a} - y\sqrt{b})(x\sqrt{a} + y\sqrt{b}) = 0$. The pair of straight lines would have the equations: $x\sqrt{a} - y\sqrt{b} = 0$

$$x\sqrt{a} + y\sqrt{b} = 0$$

Equations of the form $xy = k$ represent hyperbolas. When $k = 0$, this equation represents the coordinate axes. If $xy = 0$, then $x = 0$ and $y = 0$. The equation of the x axis is $y = 0$. The equation of the y axis is $x = 0$.

CHAPTER REVIEW EXERCISES

1. What are the coordinates of the vertex of the parabola whose equation is $y = x^2 - 6x + 7$?

2. Write the equation of the circle whose center is at the origin and whose radius is 5 units.

3. Draw an ellipse using a piece of string about 4 inches in length and two thumb tacks. (Hint: refer to page 270.)

4. Does the graph of the equation $4x^2 - y^2 = 24$ pass through the point $(2\frac{1}{2}, -1)$?

5. The graph of which one of the following equations passes through the origin?

a) $xy = 4$ c) $x + y = 4$
b) $y = 2x^2 + 4$ d) $4x = y^2$

6. Do the graphs of the equations $x^2 + y^2 = 25$ and $xy = -12$ intersect at the point $(3, -4)$?

7. What is the graph of $x^2 + y^2 = 0$?
8. What is the graph of $xy = 0$?
9. What is the graph of $4x^2 - 9y^2 = 0$?

In ex. 10–13 give the equation of the axis of symmetry of the graph of each equation.

10. $y = x^2 - 6x + 8$ **12.** $x = 3y^2$
11. $y = 2x^2$ **13.** $x = y^2 - 6y - 9$

In ex. 14–19, draw the graph of each equation.

14. $x^2 + y^2 = 16$ **17.** $4x^2 - y^2 = 36$
15. $xy = 24$ **18.** $9x^2 + 25y^2 = 144$
16. $y^2 = 12x$ **19.** $x = y^2 + 2y - 4$

CUMULATIVE REVIEW EXERCISES

1. Factor completely $x^2 - 6xy - 18yz - 9z^2$.

2. Simplify and collect: $4\sqrt{\dfrac{3}{8}} - \dfrac{4}{\sqrt{6} + \sqrt{2}} + \dfrac{1}{2^{-\frac{1}{2}}}$

3. The time of exposure necessary to photograph a given object varies as the square of the distance of the object from the source of the light. When the light is 6 ft. from the object, an exposure of $\frac{1}{4}$ sec. is required. Where must the light be placed when an exposure of $\frac{1}{16}$ sec. is used?

4. Solve for x: $\sqrt{x+1} + \sqrt{3x-5} = 4$

5. Solve for x, y, and z:
$$x - y - z = 10$$
$$2x + y - z = 11$$
$$x + y + 2z = -3$$

6. For what value(s) of k will the roots of $2x^2 + (k-1)x + 2 = 0$ be a) equal? b) imaginary?

7. Without solving the equation, determine the sum, the product, and the nature of the roots of the equation $2x^2 - 3x = 4$.

8. In the equation $x(3x - 1) = 6$ find the value of the roots correct to the nearest hundredth.

9. Form the quadratic equation whose roots are $\dfrac{2 \pm i\sqrt{3}}{3}$.

10. Find the coordinates of the turning point (vertex) of the graph of equation $x = y^2 - 2y - 3$.

11. Identify the graph of   *a)* $x^2 = 4 - 2y^2$ *b)* $\dfrac{10}{x} = y$

12. Mr. Roberts left his home to keep an appointment with his lawyer in a city 144 mi. away. After driving 80 mi. at an average rate of speed which would enable him to arrive at his destination at the exact time of his appointment, Mr. Roberts was delayed for 30 min. because of a washout on the road. After the delay Mr. Roberts increased his average speed by 16 mph. and, as a result, arrived at his destination 10 min. after the time of his appointment. At what average rate of speed did Mr. Roberts drive before his delay?

CHAPTER 13   *Systems of Quadratic Equations*

Systems of equations involving quadratics.   In Chapter 6 we solved systems of equations in two unknowns in which the equations were of the first degree. We first solved them graphically, and then we solved them algebraically. In this chapter we shall solve systems of equations in two unknowns in which one equation is, or both equations are, of the second degree. We shall solve them both graphically and algebraically.

A system involving a linear equation and a quadratic equation.   Let us first consider a system of equations in two unknowns of which one is linear and the other is quadratic. To solve these equations graphically we draw the graph of both equations on the same coordinate system and estimate the coordinates of the point, or points, of intersection of the two graphs. In solving simultaneous linear equations in Chapter 6, the two straight-line graphs could intersect at most in one point only, resulting in one solution and only one. However, a straight line can intersect a circle, an ellipse, a parabola, or a hyperbola in two points. Hence in a system of a linear equation and a quadratic equation there can be as many as two solutions.

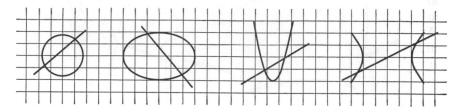

A straight line may be tangent to (touch) a circle, an ellipse, a parabola, or a hyperbola at a point. In any one of these cases there are still two solutions to the system of equations, but these two solutions are the same.

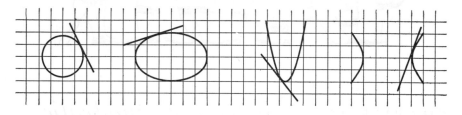

Finally, it is possible that a straight line may neither intersect the circle, the ellipse, the parabola, or the hyperbola nor be tangent to any one of these. In these cases the two solutions are said to be imaginary.

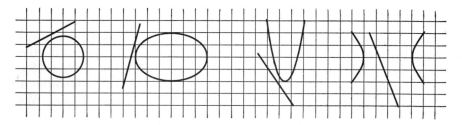

ILLUSTRATIVE EXAMPLE: Solving graphically a system involving a linear equation and a quadratic equation

Solve graphically the system of equations:
$$5x - 3y = 15$$
$$x^2 + y^2 = 25$$

Solution. On a coordinate system we draw the graph of the equation $5x - 3y = 15$. This graph is a straight line; the intercepts are $x = 3$ and $y = -5$.

On the same coordinate system we draw the graph of the equation $x^2 + y^2 = 25$. This graph is a circle, whose center is at the origin and whose radius is 5.

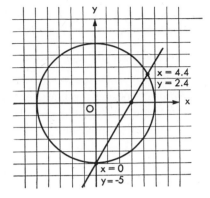

We estimate the coordinates of the points of intersection of the two graphs. When $x = 0$, $y = -5$; and when x is about 4.4, y is about 2.4.

The solutions are:

$$x = 0 \quad \text{and} \quad y = -5$$
$$x = 4.4 \quad \text{and} \quad y = 2.4$$

} Answers

Notice that the graphic solution may give only approximate answers. Actually the exact answers (found by algebraic methods, described later in this chapter) are $x = 4\frac{7}{17}$ and $y = 2\frac{6}{17}$.

EXERCISES: Solving graphically systems involving linear and quadratic equations

Solve graphically each of the following systems of equations.

1. $x - y = 7$
$x^2 + y^2 = 169$

2. $xy = 12$
$2x - y + 2 = 0$

3. $x - y = 2$
$y = x^2 - 2x - 6$

4. $x^2 - y^2 = 16$
$x + 3y + 4 = 0$

5. $2x^2 + 3y^2 = 72$
$9x + 8y + 13 = 0$

6. $xy = -6$
$x - y + 5 = 0$

7. $x^2 + y^2 = 100$
$x + y = 2$

8. $y = x^2 - 5$
$2x + y + 2 = 0$

9. $9y^2 - 16x^2 = 144$
$20x = 9y$

10. $3y = x^2 - 13$
$8x - 7y = 56$

11. $xy = -9$
$x - y - 6 = 0$

12. $4x^2 + 9y^2 = 45$
$x + y = 6$

The algebraic solution of a system involving a linear equation and a quadratic equation. In solving such a system of equations we use the substitution method which we have previously used in solving simultaneous linear equations. We solve the linear equation for one of the unknowns in terms of the other, and then we substitute this expression in the quadratic equation.

ILLUSTRATIVE EXAMPLE: Solving algebraically a system involving a linear equation and a quadratic equation

Solve algebraically the system of equations:
$$2x^2 - y^2 = 2$$
$$x + y = 1$$

Solution. Solving the linear equation for y in terms of x

$$y = 1 - x$$

In the quadratic equation we substitute $1 - x$ for y

$$2x^2 - y^2 = 2$$
$$2x^2 - (1 - x)^2 = 2$$

Removing parentheses

$$2x^2 - 1 + 2x - x^2 = 2$$

Collecting

$$x^2 + 2x - 3 = 0$$

Factoring

$$(x + 3)(x - 1) = 0$$

Hence

$$x = -3 \quad \text{and} \quad x = 1$$

To find the corresponding values for y, we substitute in the equation $y = 1 - x$. Thus if $x = -3$, $y = 4$; if $x = 1$, $y = 0$. **Answers**

EXERCISES: Solving algebraically systems involving linear and quadratic equations

Solve algebraically each of the following systems of equations.

1. $x^2 + y^2 = 100$
$\quad x + y = 2$

2. $xy = 12$
$\quad x - 2y = 2$

3. $y = x^2 - 5$
$\quad 2x + y = -2$

4. $9x^2 - 16y^2 = 144$
$\quad 9x - 20y = 0$

5. $x^2 + y^2 = 25$
$\quad 4x - 3y = -25$

6. $x - y = 2$
$\quad y^2 - 4 = 2x$

7. $y = 2x - x^2$
$\quad x - y = 6$

8. $x^2 + 4y^2 = 25$
$\quad 2x = 3y$

9. $x^2 - y^2 = 3$
$\quad 2x - y = 0$

10. $2x - 2y = 5$
$\quad 4x^2 + 3y^2 = 12$

11. $x - y = 2$
$\quad x^2 - xy + 3y^2 = 37$

12. $x - y = 5$
$\quad 6x + xy + 6y = 0$

13. $x + y + 2 = 0$
$\quad x^2 + 4x + y^2 + 4y + 4 = 0$

14. $4x^2 + 9y^2 = 45$
$\quad 4x - 3y + 25 = 0$

15. $2x^2 + 3y^2 = 30$
$\quad 3x - y = 7$

16. $y = x^2 - 4x + 2$
$\quad x - y = 2$

17. $3x - 6y = 8$
$\quad 2x^2 = 3y + 2x + 5$

A system of quadratic equations.   If we have a pair of quadratic equations in two unknowns, we can solve them graphically by drawing the graph of each on the same coordinate system and estimating the coordinates of the points of intersection.   The graphs can intersect at most in **four**

points (four solutions), but they may intersect in three or two points, in one point, or they may not intersect.   The following figures show a circle and a parabola intersecting in four, three, or two points, in one point, and not intersecting.

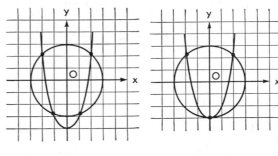

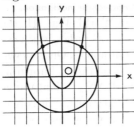 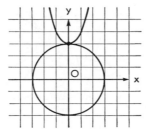 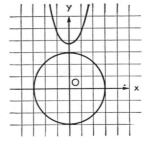

ILLUSTRATIVE   EXAMPLE: Solving graphically a system of quadratic equations

Solve graphically the system of equations:

$$x^2 + 2y^2 = 43$$
$$x^2 - y^2 = 16$$

Solution.   On a coordinate system we draw the graph of the ellipse $x^2 + 2y^2 = 43$.   On the same coordinate system we draw the graph of the hyperbola $x^2 - y^2 = 16$.   These graphs intersect in four points.   The coordinates of each of these points satisfy both equations.   Therefore the four solutions are:

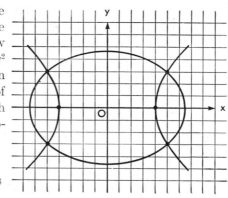

$$
\left.
\begin{aligned}
x &= 5, & y &= 3 \\
x &= 5, & y &= -3 \\
x &= -5, & y &= 3 \\
x &= -5, & y &= -3
\end{aligned}
\right\} \text{Answers}
$$

E X E R C I S E S :   Solving graphically systems of quadratic equations

Solve graphically each of the following systems of equations.

1. $x^2 + y^2 = 25$
     $xy = 12$

2. $3x^2 + y^2 = 12$
     $xy = -6$

3. $y = x^2 + 3x - 6$
     $xy = 8$

4. $y = x^2 - 5$
     $x^2 + y^2 = 25$

5. $x^2 + y^2 = 13$
     $x^2 - y^2 = 5$

6. $x^2 - y^2 = 9$
     $xy = 20$

7. $x^2 + y^2 = 25$
     $4x^2 + y^2 = 25$

8. $2x^2 - y^2 = 2$
     $y = 2x^2 - 12$

9. $xy = -4$
     $y = x^2 + 3x - 3$

10. $x^2 + y^2 = 16$
      $4x^2 + 9y^2 = 36$

11. $x^2 + y^2 = 25$
      $x = 8 - y^2$

12. $y = x^2 - 4x + 4$
      $x = y^2 - 8y + 17$

13. $2y^2 - x^2 = 2$
      $2x = y^2 + 6$

14. $x^2 + 4y^2 = 4$
      $x^2 - 4y^2 = 4$

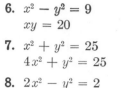

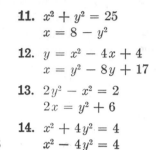

Long-range navigation.
In World War II the use of radar was very common.   One special use of radar, known as LORAN   (long-range navigation),   involved the intersection of two hyperbolas.   Several miles apart on shore were placed two stations, which served as the foci of a hyperbola.   These stations each sent out simultaneously impulses which were received by the LORAN equipment on board a ship.   Using the definition of a hyperbola, and by measuring the difference between the arrival times of these impulses on a "scope," or screen, the ship's navigator was able to plot a hyperbola, on which the ship was located.   If then the LORAN equipment was able to pick up the impulses from another pair of stations on shore, the navigator could determine another hyperbola on which the ship was located.   The intersections of the two curves marked the ship's position.   Since two hyperbolas can intersect in as many as four points, "dead reckoning" was used to obtain some general idea of the ship's locality.   From this the proper point of intersection was selected.

Solving systems of quadratic equations by the addition-subtraction method.   The addition-subtraction method, which we previously used in solving systems of linear equations, can often be applied in solving systems of quadratic equations.   This method can be used if both of the equations are in the form $ax^2 \pm by^2 = c$, or if one equation is in this form while the other equation is in the form $ax^2 + by = c$ or $ay^2 + bx = c$. Since the graphs of quadratic equations (circles, ellipses, parabolas, and hyperbolas) can intersect in four points, there can be as many as four solutions.

ILLUSTRATIVE EXAMPLES: Solving systems of quadratic equations by the addition-subtraction method

1. Solve by the addition-subtraction method: $\begin{aligned} x^2 + 2y^2 &= 18 \\ 2x^2 - y^2 &= 31 \end{aligned}$

Solution. To eliminate the terms containing y^2, we multiply the second equation by 2 and then add the two equations:

Multiplier	Equation	New Equation
1	$x^2 + 2y^2 = 18$	$x^2 + 2y^2 = 18$
2	$2x^2 - y^2 = 31$	$4x^2 - 2y^2 = 62$
By addition		$5x^2 \qquad\quad = 80$
		$x^2 = 16$
		$x = \pm 4$

To find the corresponding values for y, we first substitute 4 for x in one of the original equations; then we substitute -4 for x:

When $x = 4$	When $x = -4$
$x^2 + 2y^2 = 18$	$x^2 + 2y^2 = 18$
$(4)^2 + 2y^2 = 18$	$(-4)^2 + 2y^2 = 18$
$16 + 2y^2 = 18$	$16 + 2y^2 = 18$
$2y^2 = 2$	$2y^2 = 2$
$y^2 = 1$	$y^2 = 1$
$y = \pm 1$	$y = \pm 1$

Pairing these values, we have: $\left.\begin{aligned} x &= 4, & y &= 1 \\ x &= 4, & y &= -1 \\ x &= -4, & y &= 1 \\ x &= -4, & y &= -1 \end{aligned}\right\}$ Answers

2. Solve by the addition-subtraction method: $\begin{aligned} x^2 - y^2 &= 6 \\ x^2 - y &= 12 \end{aligned}$

Solution. To eliminate the terms containing x^2, we subtract the second equation from the first:

Given equations
$$\begin{aligned} x^2 - y^2 &= 6 \\ x^2 - y &= 12 \end{aligned}$$

Subtracting $\qquad\qquad\qquad -y^2 + y = -6$

Solving for y $\qquad\qquad\quad y^2 - y - 6 = 0$

$$(y - 3)(y + 2) = 0$$

$$y = 3 \quad \text{and} \quad y = -2$$

To find the corresponding values for x, we substitute each of these values for y in one of the original equations:

When $y = 3$
$$x^2 - y = 12$$
$$x^2 - 3 = 12$$
$$x^2 = 15$$
$$x = \pm \sqrt{15}$$

When $y = -2$
$$x^2 - y = 12$$
$$x^2 + 2 = 12$$
$$x^2 = 10$$
$$x = \pm \sqrt{10}$$

Pairing these values, we have:
$$\left. \begin{array}{l} x = \sqrt{15}, \quad y = 3 \\ x = -\sqrt{15}, \; y = 3 \\ x = \sqrt{10}, \quad y = -2 \\ x = -\sqrt{10}, \; y = -2 \end{array} \right\} \text{Answers}$$

E X E R C I S E S : Solving systems of quadratic equations by the addition-subtraction method

Solve each of the following systems by the addition-subtraction method.

1. $x^2 + 2y^2 = 33$
$x^2 - y^2 = 21$

2. $3x^2 + y^2 = 19$
$5x^2 + y^2 = 21$

3. $2x^2 + 4y^2 = 19$
$5x^2 - 12y^2 = 42$

4. $x^2 + y^2 = 5$
$x^2 - y = 3$

5. $x^2 + y^2 = 25$
$x = 13 - y^2$

6. $8x^2 + y^2 = 36$
$x^2 + 3y^2 = 108$

7. $4x^2 - 5y^2 = 21$
$3x^2 + 4y^2 = 39$

8. $x^2 - y^2 = 16$
$y^2 + 36 = 9x$

9. $7x^2 + 8y^2 = 32$
$9x^2 - 4y^2 = 9$

10. $9x^2 + 4y^2 = 13$
$6x^2 + 2y^2 = 7\frac{1}{6}$

11. $18x^2 + 2y^2 = 34$
$9x^2 - y^2 + 15 = 0$

12. $2y^2 - x^2 = 2$
$2x = y^2 - 7$

13. $x^2 + y^2 - 169 = 0$
$109 - 7y = x^2$

14. $4x^2 + 9y^2 = 98$
$36x^2 - 36y^2 = 245$

15. $4x^2 - 11y^2 = 25$
$2x^2 + 3y^2 = 12\frac{1}{2}$

16. $x^2 + y^2 = 100$
$32x = 3y^2$

17. $4x^2 - 5y^2 = 12$
$3x^2 - 2y^2 = 30$

18. $y^2 - x^2 = 3$
$x^2 - 3y + 5 = 0$

19. $3x^2 - 2y^2 = 5$
$5x^2 - 6y^2 = 19$

20. $x^2 + y^2 + 6x - 25 = 0$
$x^2 + y^2 + 5x - 23 = 0$

Solving a system of quadratic equations by the substitution method. We have already used the substitution method to solve a system of a linear equation and a quadratic equation. This method may be applied readily to a system of quadratic equations if one of the equations is in the form $xy = k$. The equation $xy = k$ can be solved for either x or y in terms of the other letter, and this expression can then be substituted in the other equation.

The substitution method may also be used in combination with the addition-subtraction method as shown in the second illustrative example which follows.

ILLUSTRATIVE EXAMPLES: Solving a system of quadratic equations by the substitution method

1. Solve by the substitution method:

$$x^2 + y^2 = 29$$
$$xy = 10$$

Solution. Solving the second equation for y in terms of x we have, $\qquad y = \dfrac{10}{x}$

Substituting this value for y in the first equation $\qquad x^2 + y^2 = 29$

we have $\qquad x^2 + \left(\dfrac{10}{x}\right)^2 = 29$

Solving for x $\qquad x^2 + \dfrac{100}{x^2} = 29$

$$x^4 + 100 = 29\,x^2$$
$$x^4 - 29\,x^2 + 100 = 0$$
$$(x^2 - 25)(x^2 - 4) = 0$$
$$x^2 = 25 \quad \text{and} \quad x^2 = 4$$
$$x = 5,\ -5,\ 2,\ -2$$

To find the corresponding values for y, we substitute in the equation $y = \dfrac{10}{x}$:

$$\left.\begin{array}{ll} x = 5, & y = 2 \\ x = -5, & y = -2 \\ x = 2, & y = 5 \\ x = -2, & y = -5 \end{array}\right\} \text{Answers}$$

2. Solve by using both methods:

$$xy + 10x = 1800$$
$$xy + 10y = 2000$$

Solution. By subtracting the second equation from the first, we obtain a first degree equation in x and y. We can then solve this equation for either x or y in terms of the other letter and substitute in either of the original equations.

Given equations	$xy + 10x = 1800$
	$\underline{xy + 10y = 2000}$
Subtracting	$10x - 10y = -200$
Dividing by 10	$x - y = -20$
Solving for x in terms of y	$x = y - 20$
Substituting this value for x in the second equation	$(y - 20)y + 10y = 2000$
Solving for y	$y^2 - 20y + 10y - 2000 = 0$
	$y^2 - 10y - 2000 = 0$
	$(y - 50)(y + 40) = 0$
	$y = 50 \quad \text{and} \quad y = -40$

To find the corresponding values for x we substitute in the equation $x = y - 20$:

$$\left. \begin{array}{ll} y = 50, & x = 30 \\ y = -40, & x = -60 \end{array} \right\} \text{Answers}$$

E X E R C I S E S : Solving systems of quadratic equations by the substitution method

Solve each of the following systems algebraically.

1. $x^2 + y^2 = 20$
$\quad xy = 8$

2. $xy = 60$
$\quad x^2 + y^2 = 169$

3. $x^2 + y^2 = 37$
$\quad xy = 6$

4. $xy = -6$
$\quad xy + x + 3y = 1$

5. $2x^2 + y^2 = 41$
$\quad xy = -12$

6. $x^2 - y^2 = 16$
$\quad xy = 15$

7. $x + xy = 77$
$\quad y + xy = 80$

8. $xy - 7x = 60$
$\quad xy - 6y = 80$

9. $2xy + y = -36$
$\quad xy - 3x = -5$

10. $2x - xy = 24$
$\quad 2y - xy = 50$

11. $4x^2 + xy + y + 2 = 0$
$\quad 4x^2 + xy + 2x - 1 = 0$

12. $x^2 - y^2 + 3x - 14 = 0$
$\quad x^2 - y^2 - 2y - 9 = 0$

13. $3x - 2y + 2xy = 3$
$\quad 2x - 3y + xy = 4$

14. $2xy - 9x - 5$
$\quad 3xy + 16y = 4$

15. $3x^2 + 3y^2 + 3xy = 1$
$\quad 3x^2 + 3y^2 - 6xy = 3$

16. $x^2 + 4y^2 = 40$
$\quad xy = 6$

Doings of Dimbo.   While in the country Dimbo lost out on the fun when he overlooked a low-hanging branch. What is wrong with his solution of the following problem?

Solve graphically:
$$xy = 6$$
$$y = 7 - x^2$$

Dimbo's solution:

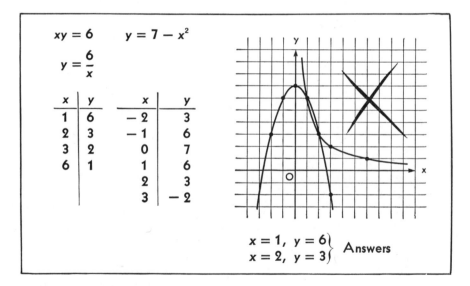

$xy = 6$		$y = 7 - x^2$	

$$y = \frac{6}{x}$$

x	y		x	y
1	6		− 2	3
2	3		− 1	6
3	2		0	7
6	1		1	6
			2	3
			3	− 2

$$\left. \begin{array}{l} x = 1,\ y = 6 \\ x = 2,\ y = 3 \end{array} \right\} \text{Answers}$$

ILLUSTRATIVE EXAMPLES: Problems involving quadratic equations in two unknowns

1. A rectangular sheet of tin containing 400 sq. in. is made into an open box containing 312 cu. in. by cutting out a 6-in. square from each corner of the sheet and folding up the sides. Find the dimensions of the original sheet of tin.

Solution. Let x represent the number of inches in the length of the sheet and y represent the number of inches in its width.

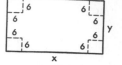

Since the area of the original sheet is 400 sq. in., we have the equation $xy = 400$.

The dimensions of the box that is formed by cutting out 6-in. squares and folding up the sides are: $x - 12$, $y - 12$, and 6. Since the volume of the box is 312 cu. in., we have the equation $(x - 12)(y - 12)(6) = 312$.

Our equations are therefore
$$\begin{cases} xy = 400 \\ (x - 12)(y - 12)(6) = 312 \end{cases}$$

Solving the first equation for y in terms of x
$$y = \frac{400}{x}$$

Substituting this expression for y in the second equation
$$(x - 12)\left(\frac{400}{x} - 12\right)(6) = 312$$

Dividing by 6
$$(x - 12)\left(\frac{400 - 12x}{x}\right) = 52$$

Multiplying by x $\qquad (x - 12)(400 - 12x) = 52x$

Clearing of parentheses $\qquad 400x - 12x^2 - 4800 + 144x = 52x$

Multiplying by -1, collecting terms
$$12x^2 - 492x + 4800 = 0$$

Dividing by 12
$$x^2 - 41x + 400 = 0$$

Factoring
$$(x - 25)(x - 16) = 0$$

Solving for x
$$x = 25 \quad \text{and} \quad x = 16$$

To find the corresponding values of y, we substitute in the equation $y = \dfrac{400}{x}$.

If $x = 25$, $y = \frac{400}{25} = 16$; if $x = 16$, $y = \frac{400}{16} = 25$.

The dimensions of the rectangular sheet of tin are 25 by 16. **Answer.**

2. In the equation $mx^2 - 8x + m + 1 = 0$, for what values of m will one root be three times the other root?

Solution. Let one root be r; then the other root is $3r$.

The sum of the roots of the given equation is $\dfrac{8}{m}$; therefore we have the equation
$$r + 3r = \frac{8}{m}.$$

The product of the roots of the given equation is $\dfrac{m + 1}{m}$; therefore we have the equation
$$r(3r) = \frac{m + 1}{m}.$$

In this pair of equations, we solve the first equation for r in terms of m and substitute in the second:

$$4r = \frac{8}{m}$$

$$r = \frac{2}{m}$$

Substituting in the equation, $\qquad 3r^2 = \frac{m+1}{m}$

we have $\qquad 3\left(\frac{2}{m}\right)^2 = \frac{m+1}{m}$

$$\frac{3\left(\frac{4}{m^2}\right) = \frac{m+1}{m}}{m}$$

Solving for m $\qquad m^2 + m = 12$

$$m^2 + m - 12 = 0$$
$$(m+4)(m-3) = 0$$
$$m = -4 \quad \text{and} \quad m = 3 \quad \text{Answers}$$

E X E R C I S E S : Problems involving quadratic equations in two unknowns

Number problems

1. Find two numbers such that the sum of their squares is 117, and the difference between their squares is 45.

2. Find two numbers such that the square of the smaller, increased by 17, equals six times the larger; while twice the smaller, increased by three times the larger, equals 47.

3. Twice a certain number, increased by three times a second number, gives a sum of 37. The sum of the squares of the two numbers is 106. Find the two numbers.

4. Find two numbers such that three times the first is 11 greater than the second, and three times the square of the first is 47 greater than the square of the second.

Geometric problems

5. Find the dimensions of a rectangle whose perimeter is 36 in. and whose area is 80 sq. in.

6. The sum of the perimeters of two unequal squares is 104 ft., and the sum of their areas is 356 sq. ft. Find a side of each square.

7. A man has three square flower beds all of the same size. He has a fourth square flower bed of a different size. The sum of the areas of the four beds is 208 sq. ft., and the sum of their perimeters is 112 ft. Find the size of the flower beds.

8. A plot of land consists of two adjacent square lots as shown in the figure. The total area of the two plots is 765 sq. yd., and the length of fence around the outside is 120 yd. Find the length of a side of each square.

9. A rectangular sheet of tin can be made into a box with an open top by cutting a square from each corner and folding up the sides. If 1-in. squares are cut out, the volume of the box will be 180 cu. in.; if 2-in. squares are cut out, the volume will be 256 cu. in. Find the dimensions of the original sheet of tin.

10. A gardener has two square flower beds. If he divides the first bed into small squares 2 ft. on a side and the second bed into small squares $1\frac{1}{3}$ ft. on a side and puts a plant in the center of each square, he finds that the number of plants needed is 1525. If he divides the first bed into small squares $2\frac{1}{2}$ ft. on a side and the second bed into small squares 2 ft. on a side, the number of plants needed is 800. Find the lengths of the sides of the two beds.

11. The sides of a triangle are 13, 14, and 15. Referring to the adjacent figure, find the length x of the altitude to the side 14.

Hint: Use the Pythagorean Theorem twice.

12. The sides of a triangle are 10, 17, and 21. Find the length of the altitude drawn to the side 21.

Digit problems. Before attempting ex. 13–17, the student may wish to study the Illustrative Example on p. 132.

13. If a number of two digits is divided by the sum of its digits, the quotient is 2, and the remainder is 2. If the number is multiplied by the sum of its digits, the product is 112. Find the number.

14. The tens digit of a two-digit number is 1 more than the units digit. Twice the square of the number formed by reversing the digits is 34 more than the square of the original number. Find the original number.

15. The product of the digits of a two-digit number is 18. The larger digit is 1 less than five times the smaller digit. Find the number.

16. There is a certain two-digit number such that the square of the tens digit decreased by the square of twice the units digit equals the amount by which the number itself exceeds 60. The tens digit is 1 more than twice the units digit. Find the number.

17. Twice the product of the digits of a certain two-digit number is equal to the number itself. If the number formed by reversing the digits is divided by the sum of the digits, the quotient is 7. Find the number.

Problems involving products of numbers

18. A camera dealer made a profit of $300 on the sale of some cameras. Another dealer sold twice as many cameras and, though making a profit of $5 less on each camera, made a total profit of $400. How many cameras did the first dealer sell, and what was his profit on each camera?

Hint:

	No. Sold	Profit on Each	Total Profit
Dealer 1	x	y	300
Dealer 2	$2x$	$y - 5$	400

Equations: $(x)(y) = 300$
$(2x)(y - 5) = 400$

19. A man sold a number of television sets. If he had charged $50 more for each set, he would have received $16,000. If he had sold 10 more sets at the original price, he would have received $17,500. Find the number of sets that he sold and the price of each set.

20. A telephone company is planning to extend a line of poles for a distance of $\frac{1}{4}$ mi. If they place them at the customary interval, they will need 1 pole more than they have on hand. If they make the interval 44 ft. less, they will need 2 more poles. How many poles have they on hand?

21. A farmer pressed 1800 lb. of fiber into bales. If he had made the bales of the usual weight, he would have had 1 more bale. On the other hand, if he had made each bale 60 lb. less than the usual weight, he would have had two more bales. How many bales did he make?

22. A dealer bought some "grade A" basketballs. If he had bought the same number of "grade B," which cost $4 less apiece, he would have paid only $720. On the other hand, if he had bought 15 less basketballs of "grade A," he would also have paid only $720. How many balls did he buy? How much did each ball cost?

Investment problems

23. The annual income from a certain investment is $225. If the amount invested had been $500 less and the rate had been 1% more, the annual income would have been $240. What is the amount invested and at what rate?

24. The simple interest on $10,000 for a certain number of years at a certain rate is $3200. If the time were 3 years less and the rate were 2% more, the simple interest would be $3000. Find the time and the rate.

25. The annual interest on a certain sum of money is $210. If the sum were $600 less and the rate were 1% more, the annual interest would be $33 more. Find the principal and the rate.

26. If a bank lends a sum of money at 6% for a certain time, the interest will exceed the loan by $200. If the bank were to lend it at 5% for half the time, the loan would exceed the interest by $500. What is the principal that the bank lends?

Relationship of roots to coefficients. See Illustrative Example No. 2 on p. 290.

27. For what values of m will one root of the equation $x^2 - 2mx + 5m + 8 = 0$ be three times the other root?

28. For what values of m will one root of the equation $x^2 - mx - 8x + 7m + 2 = 0$ be twice the other root?

29. For what values of m will one root of the equation $x^2 - 2mx + m^2 - 4 = 0$ be twice the other root?

Motion problems

30. A train travels a certain distance in a scheduled time. If it were to travel 12 mph. faster, it would take 1 hr. less time. If it were to travel 8 mph. slower, it would take 1 hr. more time. What is the distance?

31. A man took an automobile trip for a vacation. If he had traveled 40 mi. less each day, it would have taken him 2 more days to cover the same distance. If he had traveled 60 mi. more each day, it would have taken him 2 days less. How many miles did he travel?

32. A plane left field A for B. After traveling $1\frac{1}{2}$ hr., it was still 200 mi. from its destination. If the plane could have traveled 80 mph. faster, it could have made the entire trip in 20 min. less time than it will take at its actual rate. Find the distance A to B and the plane's rate.

33. The time required for a trip of 240 mi. downstream on a steamer is 3 hr. less than the time required for the upstream trip. A boat whose rate is 4 mph. less than that of the steamer required 5 hr. more for the upstream trip than for the downstream trip. Find the rate of the river.

CHAPTER REVIEW EXERCISES

In ex. 1–10 solve each pair of equations graphically.

1. $x^2 + y^2 = 36$
  $x - 2y + 6 = 0$

2. $xy = 6$
  $x - 3y + 3 = 0$

3. $4x^2 + 9y^2 = 180$
$4x - 3y + 36 = 0$

4. $x - y = 9$
$xy = -9$

5. $3y = x^2 - 13$
$2x + 3y = -5$

6. $y^2 - x^2 = 9$
$2x - y = 3$

7. $x^2 + y^2 = 100$
$xy = -48$

8. $x^2 - y^2 = 7$
$x^2 + y^2 = 25$

9. $4x^2 + 9y^2 = 45$
$x = y^2 + 2$

10. $2x^2 - y^2 = 2$
$y = x^2 + 3$

In ex. 11–18 solve each pair of equations algebraically.

11. $x^2 + y^2 = 13$
$3x - 2y = 0$

12. $xy = -8$
$x + 4y = 4$

13. $y^2 - x^2 = 16$
$3x - y = 4$

14. $x + y = 2$
$x^2 - 4y^2 - 3x + 4y + 8 = 0$

15. $3x^2 + 2y^2 = 30$
$7x^2 - 3y^2 = 1$

16. $xy = -6$
$3x^2 + y^2 = 21$

17. $x^2 - 2y^2 = 6$
$y^2 + 2x + 3 = 0$

18. $3y^2 - 3xy + x^2 = 2$
$xy = 4$

19. Find two numbers such that the square of the first increased by twice the square of the second is 59, and their product is -15.

20. A man is planning to enlarge the rectangular play area for his child. If he increases the width by 10 ft., the area will be 750 sq. ft. If, on the other hand, he increases the length by 5 ft., the area will be 600 sq. ft. What is the present area?

21. If a number of two digits is divided by the sum of the digits, the quotient is 4. If it is multiplied by the sum of the digits, the product is **576.** What is the number?

22. A group of girls is planning to decorate the club room. To have a decorator supply the materials and do the work would cost them $320. If they buy the material and do the work themselves, it will cost only $160. They decide to admit 4 more girls to the club and to do the work themselves, thus saving each girl $12, based on the original estimate of $320. How many girls were in the original group?

23. What relationship exists between m and p in $x^2 - 2px - 2m = 0$ if one root is two greater than the other root?

24. A man walked a certain distance. If he had walked 1 mph slower, it would have taken him 1 hr. longer. If he had walked $\frac{1}{2}$ mph faster, he would have arrived 20 min. earlier. What was his actual rate, and how far did he walk?

CUMULATIVE REVIEW EXERCISES

1. Simplify: $(2a - b) - (a - 3b) + [-(2a + b) + (3a - b)]$.

2. Solve for x: $\frac{1}{2}(x + 1) - \frac{2x - 1}{3} = \frac{1}{x}$.

3. If $f(x) = 3x^3 - x - 1$, find the value of $f(-2)$.

4. Factor: $16x^3 - 2$.

5. If $(a - b)(c + d)x = (b - a)(d + c)$, find the value of x.

6. Simplify: $\left(a + \dfrac{p^2}{a - p}\right) \div \left(a - \dfrac{(a - p)p^2}{a^2 + p^2}\right)$.

7. If a varies directly as b and inversely as $\sqrt{c}$, and if $a = 2$ when $b = 3$ and $c = 4$, what will c equal when $a = 1$ and $b = 2$?

8. Evaluate the expression $x(x^x + 1^x)^{x+1}$ if $x = 2$.

9. Solve for x in terms of k: $3k\sqrt{x - 1} - k^2 = 0$.

10. If the roots of the equation $y^2 + my + p = 0$ are $3 \pm \sqrt{2}$, find the value of m and p.

11. Find the coordinates of the vertex of the graph of the equation $2y = (x - 3)^2$.

12. Name the graphs of the following equations and find their intercepts:

$\quad\quad a)\ x^2 + 3y^2 = 9 \quad\quad\quad\quad b)\ x - y^2 - 2 = 0$

13. The area of a rectangle is 40 sq. ft. If the number of feet in the length is halved and the number of feet in the width is squared, the area of the new rectangle that is formed is 100 sq. ft. Find the dimensions of the original rectangle.

14. Evaluate the determinant:

$$\begin{vmatrix} 3 & 1 & 2 \\ 1 & 0 & -1 \\ 0 & 2 & -3 \end{vmatrix}$$

CHAPTER 14   *Arithmetic and*
Geometric Progressions

Sequences.   When you learned to count 1, 2, 3, 4, 5, $\cdots$, you began your study of *sequences*.   Later when you learned to count by "twos," that is, 2, 4, 6, 8, $\cdots$, you were still dealing with sequences.   When you learned the multiplication tables, the numbers 3, 6, 9, 12, $\cdots$, and 4, 8, 12, 16, $\cdots$, formed sequences.

> A sequence is a succession of numbers arranged in a definite order such that each number is derived from the preceding numbers according to a fixed rule.

In our work in this chapter we shall deal with two kinds of sequences usually called *arithmetic progressions* (abbreviation, A.P.) and *geometric progressions* (abbreviation, G.P.).

Arithmetic progressions. An arithmetic progression is a sequence of numbers in which each number after the first can be found by adding the same number to the preceding number. Each number of the progression is called a *term*. The number which is added to each term is called the *common difference*, and this difference may be either positive or negative.

The following sequences are in arithmetic progression, and d is the common difference.

$$1, 2, 3, 4, 5, \cdots \qquad\qquad d = 1$$
$$2, 4, 6, 8, \cdots \qquad\qquad d = 2$$
$$-3, 0, 3, 6, \cdots \qquad\qquad d = 3$$
$$-\tfrac{1}{2}, -1, -\tfrac{3}{2}, -2, \cdots \qquad\qquad d = -\tfrac{1}{2}$$
$$-\sqrt{a}, 0, \sqrt{a}, 2\sqrt{a}, \cdots \qquad\qquad d = \sqrt{a}$$

Notice that in each sequence the second term minus the first equals the third term minus the second. In fact, throughout the progression the difference between any two consecutive terms remains the same. Conversely, if the difference between every two consecutive terms in a sequence is the same, the sequence is an arithmetic progression.

ORAL EXERCISES: Recognizing arithmetic progressions

State whether or not each of the following sequences is an arithmetic progression. If it is, give the value of the common difference.

1. $10, 20, 30, \cdots$

2. $28, 23\tfrac{1}{2}, 20, \cdots$

3. $0, -3, -6, \cdots$

4. $-100, -1, 98, \cdots$

5. $-6, -4\tfrac{1}{2}, -3, \cdots$

6. $-5, +5, -15, \cdots$

7. $5.1, 0, -5.1, \cdots$

8. $2, 4, 8, \cdots$

9. $\tfrac{1}{2}, \tfrac{1}{4}, \tfrac{1}{8}, \cdots$

10. $\dfrac{1}{\sqrt{3}}, \dfrac{2}{\sqrt{3}}, \dfrac{3}{\sqrt{3}}, \cdots$

EXERCISES: Recognizing arithmetic progressions

In ex. 1–10 state whether or not each sequence is an arithmetic progression. If it is, give the value of the common difference.

1. $5, 2\tfrac{11}{16}, \tfrac{3}{8}, \cdots$

2. $\sqrt{\tfrac{1}{3}}, \sqrt{3}, 5\sqrt{\tfrac{1}{3}}, \cdots$

3. $\dfrac{\sqrt{3}}{2}, \dfrac{\sqrt{3}+1}{2}, \dfrac{\sqrt{3}+2}{2}, \cdots$

4. $-8, -1\tfrac{1}{3}, 5\tfrac{1}{3}, \cdots$

5. $4\tfrac{2}{3}, -\tfrac{8}{9}, -6\tfrac{4}{9}, \cdots$

6. $\sqrt{2}, \sqrt{4}, \sqrt{6}, \cdots$

7. $\sqrt{3}, 3\sqrt{3}, 6\sqrt{3}, \cdots$

8. $\tfrac{1}{3}, -\tfrac{2}{3}, \tfrac{3}{3}, \cdots$

9. $\sqrt{4}, \sqrt{9}, 4, \cdots$

10. $1, 0.1, 0.01, \cdots$

11. The sequence $-7a,$ ____, $3a, 8a,$ ____ is an arithmetic progression. What is the common difference? What are the second and fifth terms respectively?

12. If the sequence ____, ____, ____, $a + b$, ____ is an arithmetic progression and the common difference is a, what are the first, second, third, and fifth terms respectively?

13. In the arithmetic progression $\frac{\sqrt{2}}{2}$, ____, $\frac{5\sqrt{2}}{2}$ what is the missing term?

14. In the arithmetic progression ____, $\frac{\sqrt{3}}{8}$, $\frac{\sqrt{3}}{4}$ what is the missing term?

The formula for the last term of an arithmetic progression.   Let us represent the first term of an arithmetic progression by a; the common difference by d; the number of terms by n.

Number of the term:	1	2	3	4	$\cdots$
An arithmetic progression:	a	$a + d$	$a + 2d$	$a + 3d$	$\cdots$

Notice that each term consists of an a to which is added a certain number of d's.   The coefficient of d in each term is always 1 less than the number of the term.   Hence, the coefficient of d in the nth term is $(n - 1)$.   If we call the nth term the "last" term and represent it by l, we have

$$l = a + (n - 1)d$$

I L L U S T R A T I V E   E X A M P L E S : Applying the formula
$l = a + (n - 1)\, d$

1. Find the 19th term in the progression 2, 6, 10, $\cdots$

    Solution.   In this arithmetic progression $a = 2$; $d = 4$; $n = 19$

Writing the formula for l	$l = a + (n - 1)d$
Substituting	$l = 2 + (19 - 1)4$
	$l = 2 + 72$
	$l = 74$

                                 The 19th term is 74.   Answer

2. In an arithmetic progression, $a = 100$, $l = 10$, $n = 19$, find d.

    Solution.   Writing the formula for the last term $l = a + (n - 1)d$

Substituting $\qquad\qquad\qquad 10 = 100 + (19 - 1)d$

Solving for d $\qquad\qquad\quad\ 10 = 100 + 18d$

$$- 18d = 90$$

$$d = -5 \quad \text{Answer}$$

EXERCISES: Applying the formula $l = a + (n-1)d$

1. Find the tenth term in the progression 5, 7, 9, $\cdots$

2. Find the seventh term in the progression 7, 13, 19, $\cdots$

3. Find the last term in the progression $-12, -9, -6, \cdots$ to 8 terms.

4. Find the forty-first term in the progression $-16, -11, -6, \cdots$

5. Find the nth term in the progression $\frac{7}{2}, \frac{9}{2}, \frac{11}{2}, \cdots$ when $n = 9$.

6. Find the last term in the progression $-\frac{8}{5}, -1, -\frac{2}{5}, \cdots$ to 16 terms.

7. Find the tenth term in the progression $-5\sqrt{a}, -3\sqrt{a}, -\sqrt{a}, \cdots$

8. Find the last term in the progression $b, b - 2c, b - 4c, \cdots$ to 12 terms.

9. Find the twenty-eighth term in the progression

$$\frac{c - d}{3}, \quad c - d, \quad \frac{5c - 5d}{3}, \cdots$$

10. Find the nth term in the progression

$$\frac{\sqrt{b} - 1}{b}, \quad \frac{\sqrt{b} - 2}{b}, \quad \frac{\sqrt{b} - 3}{b}, \cdots$$

11. If $n = 21$, $d = 2$, and $l = 89$, find a.

12. If $l = -61$, $a = -4$, and $n = 20$, find d.

13. If $d = \frac{1}{3}$, $a = 2$, and $l = 8\frac{2}{3}$, find n.

14. If $a = 3$, $n = 271$, and $l = 93$, find d.

15. If the twenty-first term of an arithmetic progression is -103 and the first term is -3, find the common difference.

16. If the first and last terms of an arithmetic progression are respectively 2 and 83 and the common difference is 9, how many terms are in the progression?

17. If the first and last terms of an arithmetic progression are r and s, respectively, and the number of terms is 3, find the common difference in terms of r and s and write the first three terms of the progression.

18. If the last term of an arithmetic progression of 13 terms is $\frac{8}{3}$ and the common difference is $\frac{1}{12}$, find the first term.

ILLUSTRATIVE EXAMPLE: Determining an arithmetic progression when two particular terms are given

If the third term of an arithmetic progression is 23 and the sixth term is 47, write the first three terms of the progression.

Solution. The third term is

$a + 2d$ $\qquad a + 2d = 23$

The sixth term is $a + 5d$ $\qquad \underline{a + 5d = 47}$

Subtracting $\qquad\qquad\qquad -3d = -24$

Solving for d $\qquad\qquad\quad d = 8$

To solve for a we substitute 8 for
d in
$$23 = a + 2d$$
$$23 = a + 16$$
$$a = 7$$

The first three terms of the progression are 7, 15, and 23.   Answer

EXERCISES: Determining an arithmetic progression when any two terms are given

1. The sixth term of an arithmetic progression is 16, and the third term is 7. Find the first three terms of the progression.

2. If the fifth and eighth terms of an arithmetic progression are respectively -31 and -49, find the first term.

3. If the seventh and fourth terms of an arithmetic progression are respectively $\frac{87}{7}$ and $\frac{45}{7}$, find the common difference.

4. Find the first term and the common difference of an arithmetic progression if the sixteenth term is $-9\frac{2}{5}$ and the eighth term is $-4\frac{3}{5}$.

5. The seventh term of an arithmetic progression is 3 and the fifteenth is 6.2. Find the first two terms.

6. The twenty-first term of an arithmetic progression is -15 and the fifth term is -19.8. Find the thirtieth term.

7. Find the terms of an arithmetic progression if the third and sixth terms are $\frac{4}{3}$ and $\frac{13}{6}$, respectively.

Arithmetic means.   The terms included between any two nonconsecutive terms of an arithmetic progression are called *arithmetic means*. For example, in the progression 2, 5, 8, 11, 14, 17, 20, the arithmetic means between 2 and 20 are 5, 8, 11, 14, and 17. In the same progression the arithmetic means between 8 and 17 are 11 and 14.

In the arithmetic progression x, m, y, the term m is the arithmetic mean between x and y. To evaluate m in terms of x and y, we know from our definition of an arithmetic progression that

Second term − first term = third term − second term

Substituting $m \quad - \quad x \quad = \quad y \quad - \quad m$

Solving for m $2m = x + y$

$$m = \frac{x + y}{2}$$

The arithmetic mean (A.M.) between two numbers, x and y, is expressed by the formula

$$\boxed{\text{A.M.} = \frac{x + y}{2}}$$

The arithmetic mean between two numbers is the average of those numbers.

ILLUSTRATIVE EXAMPLES: Finding arithmetic means

1. Insert six arithmetic means between 6 and 34.

Solution. Since we are given two terms and wish to insert 6 means between them, we have a total of 8 terms, namely, 6, ——, ——, ——, ——, ——, ——, 34.

Hence $n = 8$, $a = 6$, and $l = 34$

Applying the formula $l = a + (n - 1)d$

Substituting $34 = 6 + (8 - 1)d$

Solving for d $34 - 6 = 7d$

$$d = 4$$

Adding 4 to the first term, 6, and then adding 4 to each successive term, we get 10, 14, 18, 22, 26, 30, which are the six arithmetic means.

2. Find the arithmetic mean between $-\frac{1}{4}$ and $\frac{1}{3}$.

Solution. We apply the formula for the arithmetic mean between two numbers.

$$\text{A.M.} = \frac{x + y}{2}$$

Substituting $\text{A.M.} = \dfrac{-\frac{1}{4} + \frac{1}{3}}{2}$

Simplifying $\text{A.M.} = \dfrac{\frac{-3 + 4}{12}}{2}$

$$\text{A.M.} = \frac{1}{24} \qquad \text{Answer}$$

E X E R C I S E S : Finding arithmetic means

1. Insert two arithmetic means between 2 and 14.

2. Find the arithmetic mean between 0.5 and 0.8.

3. Insert three arithmetic means between -9 and 15.

4. Find the arithmetic mean between $\dfrac{\sqrt{x}+\sqrt{y}}{2}$ and $\dfrac{\sqrt{x}-\sqrt{y}}{2}$.

5. Insert four arithmetic means between $-\frac{5}{6}$ and $\frac{5}{6}$.

6. Insert three arithmetic means between $\frac{7}{12}$ and $-\frac{13}{12}$.

7. If there are nineteen arithmetic means between 6 and 106, find the tenth arithmetic mean of these nineteen.

8. If there are fourteen arithmetic means between 10 and 70, find the seventh arithmetic mean of these fourteen.

9. Insert three arithmetic means between $a + \dfrac{b}{2}$ and $\dfrac{2a+5b}{2}$.

10. Insert three arithmetic means between $\dfrac{x-y}{3}$ and $\dfrac{5x-y}{3}$.

11. Find the arithmetic mean between $(p+q)$ and $(p-q)$.

12. Find the arithmetic mean between $\dfrac{a+b}{a-b}$ and $\dfrac{a-b}{a+b}$.

Arithmetic series.   The indicated sum of the terms of an arithmetic progression is an arithmetic series.   Thus, $1 + 3 + 5 + \cdots$ is an arithmetic series.

The formula for the sum of the terms in an arithmetic series.   Let us represent the sum of the terms in an arithmetic series by S. We next indicate the sum of n terms beginning with the first term a and ending with the last term l. We again write the sum beginning with the last term l and ending with the first term a. The addition of these two identities is shown below.

$$
\begin{aligned}
S &= \quad a \;\;+ (a+d) + (a+2d) + \cdots + (l-2d) + (l-d) + \quad l \\
S &= \quad l \;\;+ (l-d) + (l-2d) + \cdots + (a+2d) + (a+d) + \quad a \\
\hline
2S &= (a+l) + (a+l) + (a+l) \;\; + \cdots + (a+l) \;\; + (a+l) + (a+l)
\end{aligned}
$$

Since there are n terms in the series, there are n sums of $(a+l)$.
Therefore $2S = n(a+l)$.

$$\boxed{\,S = \frac{n}{2}(a+l)\,}$$

We previously learned that $l = a + (n-1)d$.

Substituting this value for l in the formula $S = \frac{n}{2}(a+l)$, we have

$$S = \frac{n}{2}[a + a + (n-1)d]$$

Simplifying

$$\boxed{S = \frac{n}{2}[2a + (n-1)\,d]}$$

ILLUSTRATIVE EXAMPLES: Finding the sums of arithmetic series

1. Find the sum of an arithmetic series if the first term is 100, the last term 10, and the number of terms, 90.

Solution. We are given $a = 100$, $l = 10$, and $n = 90$.

Applying the formula $\qquad\qquad\qquad S = \frac{n}{2}(a + l)$

Substituting $\qquad\qquad\qquad\qquad S = \frac{90}{2}(100 + 10)$

$$S = 4950 \quad \text{Answer}$$

2. The first term of an arithmetic series is -16 and the common difference is $\frac{1}{2}$. Find the sum of the first thirteen terms of the series.

Solution. We are given $a = -16$, $d = \frac{1}{2}$, and $n = 13$

Applying the formula $\quad S = \frac{n}{2}[2a + (n-1)d]$

Substituting $\qquad\qquad\quad S = \frac{13}{2}[2(-16) + (13-1)\tfrac{1}{2}]$

Simplifying $\qquad\qquad\quad S = \frac{13}{2}[-32 + 6]$

$$S = \frac{13}{2}(-26)$$

$$S = -169 \quad \text{Answer}$$

EXERCISES: Applying the formulas for the sum of an arithmetic series

1. If $a = 2$, $d = 5$, and $n = 20$, find S.

2. If $a = 10$, $l = -12$, and $n = 12$, find S.

3. Find the sum of the first nine terms of the series $3 + 11 + 19 + \cdots$

4. Find the sum of the first seven terms of the series $\frac{1}{4} + \frac{1}{2} + \frac{3}{4} + \cdots$

5. Find the sum of all the odd integers from 1 to 99 inclusive.

6. Find the sum of all the integers exactly divisible by 4 from 1 to 100 inclusive.

7. If $S = 39$, $a = \frac{1}{2}$, $l = 6$, find n.

8. If $S = 22.8$, $a = -0.6$, $n = 19$, find d.

9. If $S = 77$, $d = \frac{1}{6}$, $n = 33$, find a.

10. If $S = 21\frac{2}{3}$, $a = \frac{2}{3}$, $n = 10$, find l.

ILLUSTRATIVE EXAMPLES: Applying arithmetic progressions to problems

1. The sum of three consecutive terms in an arithmetic series is 24, and the third term is seven times the first. Find the progression.

Solution. Since we may begin or end a progression at any term, we shall begin with the term represented by $a - d$. Therefore, let the progression be $a - d$, a, $a + d$, $\cdots$ As we shall demonstrate below, we can eliminate one unknown in the first equation. From the statement of the problem we get the equation

$$(a - d) + a + (a + d) = 24$$

Simplifying $3a = 24$

Solving for a $a = 8$

Also from the statement of the problem we get the second equation

$$a + d = 7(a - d)$$

Removing parentheses $a + d = 7a - 7d$

Simplifying $8d = 6a$

Solving for d in terms of a $d = \frac{3}{4}a$

Substituting 8 for a $d = \frac{3}{4}(8)$ or $d = 6$

The progression is 2, 8, 14, $\cdots$ Answer

2. If the numbers $x - 3$, $2x + 1$, and $4x$ are in arithmetic progression, find the value of x and write the first three terms of the progression.

Solution. In an arithmetic progression we know

            Second term $-$ first term $=$ third term $-$ second term

Substituting $(2x + 1) \;\; - (x - 3) \;\; = 4x - (2x + 1)$

Simplifying $2x + 1 \;\; - x + 3 \;\; = 4x - 2x - 1$

Solving for x $x + 4 \;\; = 2x - 1$

                                $x \;\; = 5$

Given progression $x - 3$, $2x + 1$, $4x$, $\cdots$

Substituting $x = 5$ in the progression $5 - 3$, $10 + 1$, 20, $\cdots$

The three terms of the arithmetic progression are 2, 11, 20, $\cdots$ Answer

Gauss solves a problem. A most interesting story is told of the boy Karl Friedrich Gauss (1777–1855) who later became one of the greatest mathematicians of all time. When nine years old, he entered his first arithmetic class under a teacher named Buttner. As their first assignment Karl and his classmates were required to add a column of one hundred numbers of five and six digits each. To save himself a lot of work Buttner wrote on the board numbers which were in arithmetic progression. He therefore knew the sum immediately by applying the formula, $S = \frac{n}{2}(a + l)$. Young Karl, who had never seen an arithmetic progression, recognized what Buttner was doing. As soon as Buttner had written the last number, Karl computed the sum mentally and wrote the figure on his slate. Then, as required by school discipline, he placed the slate face downward on the table in front of his teacher, saying respectfully in his southwest German dialect, "Ligget se" (Da liegt sie), "There it lies." Karl returned to his seat, folded his hands, and waited for his classmates to find the sum, a task which most finished an hour later. Buttner was astonished to find that only Gauss had the correct answer. Recognizing that he had a genius before him, Buttner purchased out of his own meagre savings an arithmetic for Karl, which the boy promptly mastered. At this Buttner shook his head saying, "I can do nothing more for him" and turned young Gauss over to superior teachers. Gauss' climb to fame had begun.

EXERCISES: Applying arithmetic progressions to problems

1. The sum of three numbers in arithmetic series is 138, and twice the first number exceeds the third by 19. Find the numbers.

2. The sum of four numbers in arithmetic series is −56, and the sum of the first and second terms exceeds three times the fourth by 1. Find the numbers.

3. There are three numbers in arithmetic progression. Three times the second number exceeds twice the third number by 2. The sum of the three numbers equals the tenth term of the arithmetic progression − 18, − 14, − 10, ⋯. Find the three numbers.

4. The sum of four terms in arithmetic series is 2.4, and the ratio of the first term to the fourth is 1 to 4. Find the numbers.

5. If $x + 3$, $3x + 9$, and $10x$ form an arithmetic progression, find x and state the progression.

6. The first three terms of an arithmetic progression are $5x$, x, and x^2. Find x and the progression.

7. On her birthday a girl was offered a $500 government bond for her future education or a bank in which her father agreed to deposit one cent the first day, two cents the second, three cents the third, and so on up to and including 365 days. The girl chose the bond. Did she gain or lose by her choice and by how much?

8. A man selected four numbers that were in arithmetic progression. The product of the first and last was 45, and the product of the second and third was 77. What numbers did he select?

9. A man bought a house for $12,000 with no down payment required and with the understanding that he should pay $600 annually plus the interest at 3% on the debt at that time. At the end of the first year he paid $960. How much did he have to pay at the end of the second year? at the end of the third year? Under these conditions how many years were required to pay for the house? What was the total amount of interest paid?

10. A boy bought a second-hand automobile for $120 and agreed to pay for it at the rate of $4 a month and 6% annual interest on the debt at that time, payable and computed each month. How much did the boy pay at the end of the first month? at the end of the second? In how many months did he pay off the debt? What was the total of interest payments?

11. Two arithmetic progressions whose first terms are respectively − 1 and 3 have the same common difference. The ratio of the sums of the first six terms of the respective progressions in the same order is $\frac{23}{31}$. Find the first two terms of each progression.

12. There are many games in which articles such as potatoes, oranges, peanuts, and cups of water are placed at equal distances apart and the player must return these articles one by one to a fixed place. There are usually other added restrictions, such as carrying the potato on a spoon, the peanut on a knife, the water without spilling, and so on. They are all based on an arithmetic progression. How far would a player travel if, starting at a goal line, he was required to gather ten potatoes, one at a time, and return them to the basket at the goal line if the potatoes were arranged in a line at intervals of 5 ft.?

Geometric progressions.   A geometric progression is a sequence of numbers in which *each term* after the first is found by *multiplying* the *preceding term* by the *same number*. This number is called the *common ratio* and is usually represented by the letter r.

The following are geometric progressions.

$$2, 4, 8, \cdots \qquad\qquad\qquad r = 2$$
$$+ \tfrac{1}{3}, -\tfrac{1}{12}, +\tfrac{1}{48}, \cdots \qquad r = -\tfrac{1}{4}$$
$$\sqrt{5}, 5, 5\sqrt{5}, \cdots \qquad\qquad r = \sqrt{5}$$
$$-0.2, -0.6, -1.8, \cdots \qquad r = 3$$
$$\frac{1}{\sqrt{x}}, \frac{\sqrt{y}}{x}, \frac{y}{x\sqrt{x}}, \cdots \qquad r = \sqrt{\frac{y}{x}}$$

Notice that in each sequence the second term divided by the first term is equal to the third term divided by the second term. In fact, throughout the progression the ratio of any two consecutive terms remains the same. Conversely, if the ratio of every two consecutive terms in a sequence is the same, the sequence is a geometric progression.

O R A L   E X E R C I S E S : Recognizing geometric progressions

State whether or not each sequence is a geometric progression. If it is, give the value of the common ratio.

1. $3, 6, 12, \cdots$

2. $18, 6, 2, \cdots$

3. $8, 10, 12, \cdots$

4. $a, 2a, 3a, \cdots$

5. $x, x^2, x^3, \cdots$

6. $1, \tfrac{1}{2}, \tfrac{1}{4}, \cdots$

7. $a, abc, ab^2c^2, \cdots$

8. $-8, -4, -2, \cdots$

9. $a, ab, b, \cdots$

10. $-4, 12, -36, \cdots$

E X E R C I S E S : Recognizing geometric progressions

In ex. 1–10 state whether or not each sequence is a geometric progression. If it is, give the value of the common ratio.

1. $\tfrac{1}{25}, \tfrac{1}{5}, 1, \cdots$

2. $\sqrt{7}, \sqrt{21}, 3\sqrt{7}, \cdots$

3. $4\tfrac{1}{3}, 8\tfrac{1}{3}, 12\tfrac{1}{3}, \cdots$

4. $\dfrac{\sqrt{a}}{b}, \dfrac{a}{b}, \dfrac{a\sqrt{a}}{b}, \cdots$

5. $0.1, 0.001, 0.00001, \cdots$

6. $1.01, 1.011, 1.0111 \cdots$

7. $\dfrac{\sqrt{a}}{\sqrt{b}}, \dfrac{a}{b}, \dfrac{a\sqrt{a}}{b\sqrt{b}}, \cdots$

8. $\dfrac{a}{\sqrt{b}}, \dfrac{2a}{\sqrt{b}}, \dfrac{3a}{\sqrt{b}}, \cdots$

9. $\dfrac{\sqrt{x}}{\sqrt{y}}, 1, \dfrac{\sqrt{y}}{\sqrt{x}}, \cdots$

10. $\dfrac{1}{\sqrt{c}+\sqrt{d}}, \dfrac{1}{c-d}, \dfrac{1}{(c-d)(\sqrt{c}-\sqrt{d})}, \cdots$

11. The sequence $2, \underline{\quad}, \underline{\quad}, -\tfrac{1}{4}, \tfrac{1}{8}, \underline{\quad}$ is a geometric progression. State the ratio, and the second, third, and sixth terms.

12. If the sequence ——, ——, $\sqrt{7}$, ——, —— is a geometric progression and the ratio is $\sqrt{2}$, find the first, second, fourth, and fifth terms.

13. In the geometric progression $\dfrac{2}{\sqrt{3}}$, ——, $\dfrac{\sqrt{3}}{2}$, what is the missing term?

14. The sequence ——, -0.3, ——, -0.012, -0.0024 is a geometric progression. Find the ratio and the first and third terms.

The formula for the last term of a geometric progression. Let us represent the first term of a geometric progression by a; the common ratio by r; the number of terms by n.

No. of the term	1	2	3	4	$\cdots$
A geometric progression	a	ar	ar^2	ar^3	$\cdots$

Notice that each term consists of a multiplied by a power of r. Also notice that the exponent of r is always one less than the number of the term. Hence the exponent of r in the nth term is $(n-1)$. If we call the nth term the last term and represent it by l, we have

$$l = ar^{n-1}$$

ILLUSTRATIVE EXAMPLES: Applying the formula $l = ar^{n-1}$

1. Find the fifth term in the progression 6, 12, 24, $\cdots$

> *Solution.* In this progression, $a = 6$; $r = \frac{12}{6}$ or 2; $n = 5$.
>
> Applying the formula $\qquad\qquad l = ar^{n-1}$
>
> Substituting $\qquad\qquad\qquad l = (6)(2)^4$
>
> $\qquad\qquad\qquad\qquad\qquad l = (6)(16)$
>
> $\qquad\qquad\qquad\qquad\qquad l = 96 \quad$ Answer

2. In a geometric progression $a = -\frac{1}{3}$, $l = -\frac{1}{96}$, $n = 6$. Find r.

> *Solution.*
>
> Applying the formula $\qquad\qquad l = ar^{n-1}$
>
> Substituting $\qquad\qquad -\frac{1}{96} = (-\frac{1}{3})r^5$
>
> Dividing both members by $(-\frac{1}{3})$ $\qquad \frac{1}{32} = r^5$
>
> Finding the real
> fifth root $\qquad\qquad\qquad\qquad r = \sqrt[5]{\frac{1}{32}}$
>
> $\qquad\qquad\qquad\qquad\qquad r = \frac{1}{2} \quad$ Answer

3. The seventh term of a geometric progression is $\frac{1}{32}$, and the fourth term is $-\frac{1}{4}$. Find the common ratio and the fifth term.

Solution. Applying the formula $l = ar^{n-1}$ and substituting for each given term.

Seventh term	$\frac{1}{32} = ar^6$
Fourth term	$-\frac{1}{4} = ar^3$
Dividing	$\dfrac{\frac{1}{32}}{-\frac{1}{4}} = \dfrac{ar^6}{ar^3}$
Simplifying	$-\frac{1}{8} = r^3$
Solving for the real value of r	$r = -\frac{1}{2}$

To find the fifth term we multiply the fourth term by r. Thus $(-\frac{1}{2})(-\frac{1}{4}) = \frac{1}{8}$ the fifth term.

E X E R C I S E S : Applying the formula $l = ar^{n-1}$

The following table of powers of 2 and 3 will prove helpful in solving problems in geometric progressions.

Table of powers of 2 and 3

Power	1st	2d	3d	4th	5th	6th	7th	8th
	2	4	8	16	32	64	128	256
	3	9	27	81	243	729	2187	6561

1. Find the ninth term in the progression $2, 4, 8, \cdots$

2. Find the seventh term in the progression $3, 6, 12, \cdots$

3. Find the last term in the progression $-2, -6, -18, \cdots$ if $n = 7$.

4. Find the eighth term in the progression $\frac{1}{2}, \frac{1}{4}, \frac{1}{8}, \cdots$

5. Find the last term in the progression $6, -12, 24, \cdots$ if $n = 8$.

6. Find the sixth term in the progression $\frac{1}{3}, 1, 3, \cdots$

7. Find the last term in the progression $4a, 2, \frac{1}{a}, \cdots$ if $n = 9$.

8. Find the seventh term in the progression $-\frac{x}{3}, -\frac{x^2}{9}, -\frac{x^3}{27}, \cdots$

9. In a geometric progression $a = 5x$, $l = 320x^7$, $n = 7$; find r.

10. If $l = \frac{1}{625}$, $r = \frac{1}{5}$, $n = 4$, in a geometric progression, find a.

11. If $l = \frac{243}{2x^4}$, $r = \frac{3}{x}$, $a = \frac{x}{2}$, in a geometric progression, find n.

12. If the sixth term of a geometric progression is $243\,pm^5n^{10}$ and the fourth term is $27\,pm^3n^6$, find the common ratio and the seventh term.

13. If the seventh term of a geometric progression is $8x^3\sqrt{3x}$ and the fifth term is $4x^2\sqrt{3x}$, find the common ratio and the sixth term.

14. If the sum of the first and fourth terms of a geometric equation equals $4\frac{1}{2}$ and the sum of the second and third terms equals 3, find the common ratio and the first term. Hint: $\dfrac{a + ar^3}{ar + ar^2} = \dfrac{4\frac{1}{2}}{3}$. Factor, divide, and solve the resulting equation.

15. If the sum of the second and sixth terms of a geometric progression is $25\frac{1}{2}$ and the sum of the third and seventh terms is $12\frac{3}{4}$, find the common ratio and the first term.

Geometric means. The terms included between any two nonconsecutive terms of a geometric progression are called *geometric means*. Let x, m, and y be consecutive terms of a geometric progression. In a geometric progression we know that: The second term divided by the first term equals the third term divided by the second term.

From the progression	$\dfrac{m}{x} = \dfrac{y}{m}$
Clearing of fractions	$m^2 = xy$
Solving for m	$m = \pm\sqrt{xy}$

In symbol form the geometric mean (G.M.) between two numbers, x and y, is expressed by the formula

$$\boxed{\text{G.M. } = \pm\sqrt{xy}}$$

The geometric mean between two numbers is the mean proportional between those numbers.

I L L U S T R A T I V E   E X A M P L E S : Finding geometric means

1. Insert three geometric means between -8 and $-\frac{128}{81}$.

Solution. Since we are given 2 terms and we are inserting 3 means, we have a total of 5 terms, namely -8, _____, _____, _____, $-\frac{128}{81}$.

We are given	$n = 5$, $a = -8$, and $l = -\frac{128}{81}$
Applying the formula	$l = ar^{n-1}$
Substituting	$-\frac{128}{81} = (-8)(r)^4$
Dividing by (-8)	$\frac{16}{81} = r^4$
Finding the two real values of r	$r = \pm\frac{2}{3}$

Because r can be either positive or negative, we get two sets of means. When $r = +\frac{2}{3}$, we multiply (-8) by $\frac{2}{3}$ to get the next term and then multiply each term by $\frac{2}{3}$ to get the next successive term.

Thus $(-8)(\frac{2}{3}) = -\frac{16}{3}$; $(-\frac{16}{3})(\frac{2}{3}) = -\frac{32}{9}$; $(-\frac{32}{9})(\frac{2}{3}) = -\frac{64}{27}$

Therefore $-\frac{16}{3}, -\frac{32}{9}, -\frac{64}{27}$ Answer

Similarly when $r = -\frac{2}{3}$, we get $+\frac{16}{3}, -\frac{32}{9}, +\frac{64}{27}$ Answer

2. Find the mean proportional between $\frac{2}{9}$ and $\frac{1}{8}$.

Solution. Applying the formula   G.M. $= \pm \sqrt{xy}$

Substituting   G.M. $= \pm \sqrt{\frac{2}{9} \cdot \frac{1}{8}}$

$= \pm \sqrt{\frac{1}{36}}$

$= \pm \frac{1}{6}$ Answer

E X E R C I S E S : Finding geometric means

1. Insert two geometric means between 2 and 16.

2. Insert three geometric means between 3 and 48.

3. Insert four geometric means between 1 and 243.

4. If the fifth term of a geometric progression is $-\frac{1}{567}$ and the first term is $-\frac{1}{7}$, insert three geometric means between them.

5. Insert three geometric means between 0.01 and 6.25.

6. Find the mean proportional between $\dfrac{27x}{16}$ and $\dfrac{3x^3}{4}$.

7. Find the geometric mean between $\sqrt{3a}$ and $3a\sqrt{3a}$.

8. Find the mean proportional between $\dfrac{9a^3}{11}$ and $\dfrac{11}{4a}$.

9. What is the mean proportional between m and n?

10. If two geometric means are inserted between p and q, express in terms of p and q the common ratio.

Geometric Series.   The indicated sum of the terms of a geometric progression is a geometric series. Thus, $2 + 6 + 18 + \cdots$ is a geometric series.

The formula for the sum of a geometric series.   Let us represent the sum of the terms of a geometric series by S. We first indicate the sum of n terms. Then we multiply both members of this identity by r. The two series are:

$$S = a + ar + ar^2 + ar^3 + \cdots + ar^{n-1}$$
$$Sr = \qquad ar + ar^2 + ar^3 + \cdots + ar^{n-1} + ar^n$$

Subtracting
$$S - Sr = a \qquad\qquad\qquad\qquad\qquad\qquad - ar^n$$
$$S - Sr = a - ar^n$$
$$S(1 - r) = a - ar^n$$

$$S = \frac{a - ar^n}{1 - r}$$

This formula may also be expressed in the forms

$$S = \frac{ar^n - a}{r - 1} \qquad \text{or} \qquad S = \frac{a(r^n - 1)}{r - 1}$$

Notice that in each formula for S, the r's in the numerator are directly over the r's in the denominators. This is an aid in remembering the formula. Since $l = ar^{n-1}$, then $rl = ar^n$. We may substitute rl for ar^n in

$$S = \frac{ar^n - a}{r - 1} \text{ to get} \qquad S = \frac{rl - a}{r - 1}$$

ILLUSTRATIVE EXAMPLES: Finding the sum of geometric series

1. Find the sum of the terms of the geometric series $5 + 10 + 20 + \cdots$ to seven terms.

Solution. We are given $a = 5, n = 7$, and $r = \frac{10}{5}$ or 2

Applying the formula
$$S = \frac{a(r^n - 1)}{r - 1}$$

Substituting
$$S = \frac{5(2^7 - 1)}{2 - 1}$$

Simplifying
$$S = \frac{5(128 - 1)}{1}$$

$$S = 635 \quad \text{Answer}$$

2. Find the sum of a geometric series when $a = 2$, $l = 1458$, and $r = 3$.

Solution.

Applying the formula
$$S = \frac{rl - a}{r - 1}$$

Substituting $\qquad S = \dfrac{(3)(1458) - 2}{3 - 1}$

Simplifying $\qquad S = \dfrac{4374 - 2}{2}$

$$S = 2186 \quad \text{Answer}$$

EXERCISES: Applying the formula for the sum of a geometric series

1. Find the sum of the first six terms of the series $8 + 24 + 72 + \cdots$

2. In a geometric series $a = 10$, $l = 1280$, and $n = 8$. Find the sum.

3. If $l = 1408$, $r = 2$, $n = 8$, find the sum of the geometric series.

4. In the series $\frac{2}{3} + \frac{2}{9} + \frac{2}{27} + \cdots$ find the sum of seven terms.

5. In a geometric series $r = 5$, $a = -2$, and $l = -6250$. Find the sum.

6. If, in a geometric series, $a = -3$, $r = -2$, and $n = 7$, find the sum.

7. In the series $\sqrt{27} + \sqrt{3} + \dfrac{\sqrt{3}}{3} + \cdots$ find the sum of the first four terms.

8. If $l = \frac{81}{256}$, $n = 4$, $r = \frac{3}{4}$ in a geometric series, find the sum.

9. In the geometric series $\sqrt{2} + \dfrac{\sqrt{2}}{2} + \dfrac{\sqrt{2}}{4} + \cdots$ find the sum of the first five terms.

10. The sum of a geometric series is 682, the last term 512, and the common ratio 4. Find the first term.

ILLUSTRATIVE EXAMPLE: Determining a geometric progression

Find the value of x in the geometric progression $x + 4$, $3x + 3$, $8x - 4$

Solution. From our definition of a geometric progression we know

$$\frac{\text{Second term}}{\text{First term}} = \frac{\text{Third term}}{\text{Second term}}$$

Substituting from the given progression $\qquad \dfrac{3x + 3}{x + 4} = \dfrac{8x - 4}{3x + 3}$

Clearing of fractions $\qquad (3x + 3)(3x + 3) = (x + 4)(8x - 4)$

Multiplying $\qquad 9x^2 + 18x + 9 = 8x^2 + 28x - 16$

Solving for x
$$x^2 - 10x + 25 = 0$$
$$(x - 5)^2 = 0$$
$$x = 5 \quad \text{Answer}$$

E X E R C I S E S : Determining geometric progressions

Find the value of x in each of the following geometric progressions.

1. $x - 2, 2x + 2, 9x + 3, \cdots$

2. $\dfrac{x}{2}, x^3, \dfrac{x}{8}, \cdots$

3. $2x - 2, x + 2, x - 2, \cdots$

4. $x^2, 2x, \dfrac{2x}{5}, \cdots$

5. $x - 2, 2x + 4, 7x + 2, \cdots$

An infinite series.   A series that contains an unlimited number of terms is known as an infinite series. If a series contains a fixed number of terms, it is a finite series. We have already derived a formula for the sum of a finite geometric series. It is also possible to derive a formula for the sum of an infinite geometric series, if the common ratio is numerically less than one.

Sum of an infinite geometric series.   For an infinite series we cannot use directly the formula $S = \dfrac{a - ar^n}{1 - r}$ which we have already learned for the sum of a geometric series, because this formula contains n. In an infinite series, n does not have a definite value. However, if r is numerically less than one (that is, a proper fraction), then r^n becomes numerically smaller as n increases. For example, if $r = \frac{1}{2}$, then $r^n = \frac{1}{1024}$ when $n = 10$, and $r^n = \dfrac{1}{2^{100}}$ when $n = 100$. As n increases without limit, r^n approaches zero as a limit.

When r^n approaches zero as a limit, the product ar^n must also approach zero as a limit.

If ar^n approaches zero as a limit, then $a - ar^n$ must approach the value a as a limit.

If $a - ar^n$ approaches a as a limit, then the fraction $\dfrac{a - ar^n}{1 - r}$ must approach $\dfrac{a}{1 - r}$ as a limit. That is, the sum S must approach $\dfrac{a}{1 - r}$ as a limit.

> The formula for the sum of the terms of an infinite geometric series when the common ratio is numerically less than one **is**
>
> $$S_\infty = \frac{a}{1 - r}$$

ILLUSTRATIVE EXAMPLE: Finding the sum of an infinite geometric series

Find the sum to infinity of the series $24 + 12 + 6 + \cdots$

Solution. In the series $24 + 12 + 6 + \cdots$, $a = 24$ and $r = \frac{1}{2}$. This is an infinite geometric series, with the common ratio numerically less than one.

Applying the
formula $\qquad S_\infty = \dfrac{a}{1 - r}$

Substituting $\qquad S_\infty = \dfrac{24}{1 - \frac{1}{2}}$

$$S_\infty = \frac{24}{\frac{1}{2}}$$

$$S_\infty = 48 \quad \text{Answer}$$

Linear demonstration of an infinite geometric series. It is often difficult for a student to visualize a finite sum (that is, a definite number for a sum) when there is no limit to the number of terms in the series. In the infinite series $1 + \frac{1}{2} + \frac{1}{4} + \frac{1}{8} + \cdots$, by using the formula $S_\infty = \dfrac{a}{1 - r}$, we find the sum to be 2. Below is a line made up of segments, which are equal, in inches, to terms in this series: $AB = 1$; $BC = \frac{1}{2}$; $CD = \frac{1}{4}$; $DE = \frac{1}{8}$, etc.

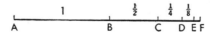

Notice that each time we mark off the length of another term in the series, its length is equal to one-half the remaining portion of the line. Thus you can see that as you add more terms, the sum becomes closer to the total length of the line, which is 2 in. For convenience, then, we say that the sum of an unlimited number of terms in this series is 2.

E X E R C I S E S : Applying the formula for the sum of an infinite geometric series

In ex. 1–12 find the sum of the terms of each of the infinite series.

1. $6 + 3 + \frac{3}{2} + \cdots$

2. $3 + \frac{3}{2} + \frac{3}{4} + \cdots$

3. $8 + 2 + \frac{1}{2} + \cdots$

4. $6 + \frac{6}{5} + \frac{6}{25} + \cdots$

5. $9 + 6 + 4 + \cdots$

6. $-\frac{1}{2} - \frac{1}{4} - \frac{1}{8} - \cdots$

7. $0.1 + 0.01 + 0.001 + \cdots$

8. $\sqrt{5} + \frac{\sqrt{5}}{5} + \frac{\sqrt{5}}{25} + \cdots$

9. $-2 - \frac{1}{4} - \frac{1}{32} - \cdots$

10. $1 - \frac{1}{2} + \frac{1}{4} - \cdots$

11. $8 + 6 + 4\frac{1}{2} + \cdots$

12. $\frac{1}{9} + \frac{1}{27} + \frac{1}{81} + \cdots$

13. The sum of an infinite number of terms of a geometric series is 4, and the ratio of the sum of the third and fourth terms to the sum of the first and second terms is 1 to 4. Find the series.

14. The sum to infinity of a geometric series is $\frac{27}{2}$, and the second term is 3. Find the series.

15. If the first term of a geometric series of an infinite number of terms is 18 and the sum to infinity is 24, find the series.

16. The sum of an infinite number of terms of a geometric series is 12, and the ratio of the sum of the second and third terms to the sum of the first and second terms is 1 to 2. Find the series.

I L L U S T R A T I V E   E X A M P L E S : Converting repeating decimals to common fractions

Express each of the following repeating decimals as a common fraction or a mixed number.

a) 0.4444···   *b)* 0.576576···   *c)* 3.242121···

Solution. *a)* The repeating decimal 0.4444 is equal to

$$0.4 + .04 + .004 + \cdots$$

This is an infinite geometric series in which $a = 0.4$ and $r = \dfrac{.04}{0.4} = 0.1$.

Applying the formula $S_\infty = \dfrac{a}{1 - r}$

and substituting $S_\infty = \dfrac{0.4}{1 - 0.1}$

Simplifying $S_\infty = \dfrac{0.4}{0.9}$ or $\dfrac{4}{9}$

Therefore $0.4444\cdots = \frac{4}{9}$ Answer

b) The repeating decimal $0.576576\cdots$ is equal to

$$0.576 + 0.000576 + 0.000000576 + \cdots$$

In this infinite geometric series $a = 0.576$ and $r = \dfrac{0.000576}{0.576}$ or $.001$

Applying the formula $S_\infty = \dfrac{a}{1-r}$

Substituting $S_\infty = \dfrac{0.576}{1-.001}$

Simplifying $S_\infty = \dfrac{0.576}{0.999}$ or $\frac{64}{111}$

Therefore $0.576576\cdots = \frac{64}{111}$ Answer

c) In the repeating decimal $3.242121\cdots$, only the digits 21 repeat.

$$3.242121\cdots = 3.24 + (.0021 + .000021 + .00000021 + \cdots)$$

The infinite geometric series here has $a = .0021$ and $r = .01$.

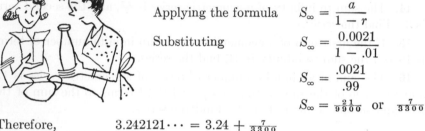

Applying the formula $S_\infty = \dfrac{a}{1-r}$

Substituting $S_\infty = \dfrac{0.0021}{1-.01}$

$S_\infty = \dfrac{.0021}{.99}$

$S_\infty = \frac{21}{9900}$ or $\frac{7}{3300}$

Therefore, $3.242121\cdots = 3.24 + \frac{7}{3300}$

$$= 3\frac{24}{100} + \frac{7}{3300}$$

$$= 3\frac{799}{3300}   \text{Answer}$$

Note: Another method for converting repeating decimals to common fractions can be found on page 170.

E X E R C I S E S : Converting repeating decimals to common fractions

In ex. 1–9 express each repeating decimal as a common fraction.

1. $0.3333\cdots$ **4.** $0.242424\cdots$ **7.** $0.123123\cdots$
2. $0.5555\cdots$ **5.** $0.323232\cdots$ **8.** $0.908908\cdots$
3. $0.8888\cdots$ **6.** $0.484848\cdots$ **9.** $0.4353535\cdots$

In ex. 10–12 express each repeating decimal as a mixed number.

10. $1.222\cdots$ **11.** $3.646464\cdots$ **12.** $6.132525\cdots$

E X E R C I S E S : Problems in arithmetic and geometric progressions

1. In order to build up a fund for his son, a father deposited a cent a day in the child's bank for the first year of the boy's life, two cents a day for the second year, three cents a day for the third year, and so on. How much was deposited by the end of the son's twenty-first year? Assume 365 days in every year. Hint: Form a series of 21 terms.

2. What number must I add to each of 10, 4, and 1 to form a geometric progression? What is the progression?

3. Three numbers are in the continued ratio 5:4:3. If 25 is added to the first, 1 subtracted from the second, and 7 subtracted from the third, the resulting numbers are in geometric progression. Find the original numbers.

4. Three numbers are in the continued ratio 2:3:5. If 11 is added to the first number, 6 added to the second, and 1 subtracted from the third, the resulting numbers are in arithmetic progression. Find the original numbers. Hint: Second term − first term = third term − second term.

5. If the first and fourth terms of a geometric progression are 3 and 192 respectively, find the fifth term.

6. The product of three numbers in geometric progression is 64 and their sum is 21. Find the numbers. Hint: Let the numbers be $\frac{a}{r}$, a, ar.

7. The sum of three numbers in a geometric series is 35. If the first number is multiplied by 2, the second by $2\frac{1}{2}$, and the third by 2, the resulting numbers are in arithmetic progression. Find the original numbers.

8. Of four numbers the first three form an arithmetic progression and the last three form a geometric progression. If the sum of the arithmetic series is 3 and the sum of the four numbers is 52, find the numbers. Hint: Let the numbers be $x - y$, x, $x + y$, and w.

9. In the adjacent figure, triangle ABC is equilateral with each side equal to 6 in. The sides are divided respectively into two equal parts by the points D, E, and F, forming a second equilateral triangle with each side equal to 3 in. In like manner, the sides of equilateral triangle GHK are formed with each side equal to $1\frac{1}{2}$ in. If this process of forming new triangles were continued indefinitely, what would be the sum of the perimeters of all the triangles?

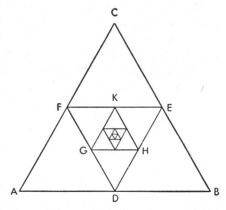

10. In the adjacent figure, the diameter of the large circle is 12 in., and the diameter of each succeeding circle is half the diameter of the next larger circle. If the process of forming new circles is continued indefinitely, find the total area in terms of π of all the circles, assuming that each is constructed separately. The formula for the area of a circle is $A = \pi r^2$.

11. An army jeep left its base at 12 noon for a destination 300 mi. distant across a flat terrain. The jeep's average rate during the first hour was 40 mph; during the second hour, 45 mph; during the third hour, 50 mph; and so on. At 1:40 o'clock a helicopter, traveling at a uniform rate of 75 mph, set out to overtake the jeep. At what time did the helicopter reach the jeep?

Hint:		T	R	D
	Jeep	n	A.P. = 40,45,50···	$S = \dfrac{n}{2}[2\,a + (n-1)d]$
	Helicopter	$(n - \frac{5}{3})$	75	

12. A man bought an automobile for $2400 and for the first year his local taxes were computed on the full value of the car. Each year thereafter he was allowed to take off 25% of the car's value (during the preceding year) and his taxes were computed on the depreciated value. If the tax rate was 2.5¢ on a dollar, how much were the man's taxes for the fourth year? Hint: In the G.P., $r = \frac{3}{4}$.

13. From modern chemical research the rate at which certain elements are constantly disintegrating has been determined. The half life of uranium is 4.498 billion years; that is to say, for any given amount of uranium, only half of it will be left after 4.498 billion years, and only half of that which then remains will be left in 4.498 billion years more, and so on. According to Joliot-Curie, the half life of an isotope of chlorine (Cl_{34}) is 40 min. What fraction of a sample will be left after 4 hr.? Hint: The G.P. is $\frac{1}{2}, \frac{1}{4}, \frac{1}{8} \cdots$

14. According to Fermi the half life of an isotope of oxygen (O_{19}) is 40 sec. What fraction of a sample will disintegrate in 2 min.?

15. A rubber ball was thrown to a height of 60 ft. and on each rebound rose three fourths of its previous height. How far did the ball travel before coming to rest? Hint: Apply $S_\infty = \dfrac{a}{1-r}$.

16. A man left an estate of $100,000 with the stipulation that his wife should receive half the estate ; his son, half of the remainder ; his daughter half the second remainder, and so on, in similar succession to his grand-daughter, his brother, his nephew. What was then left should go to his niece. How much did the niece receive?

17. Magdeburg hemispheres are frequently used to demonstrate the pressure of the atmosphere. The air between the hemispheres is exhausted by means of a pump. At each stroke of the pump one third of the air in the sphere at the time is removed. How much of the air will remain after the sixth stroke?

CHAPTER REVIEW EXERCISES

1. In the progression 10, 5, $2\frac{1}{2}$ $\cdots$ what is the number of the term which is equal to $\frac{5}{32}$?

2. In the progression $-\frac{1}{2}$, $-\frac{1}{4}$, 0 $\cdots$ what is the number of the term which is equal to $2\frac{1}{2}$?

3. Find the sum of the odd integers beginning with 1 and ending with 99.

4. Find the arithmetic mean between 206 and 834.

5. Find the geometric mean between $5x^2y$ and $20y^3$.

6. Insert three arithmetic means between -10 and -4.

7. Insert four geometric means between -1 and -1024.

8. If the sixth term of an arithmetic progression is 4.2 and the ninth term is 6, find the first term.

9. If the third term of a geometric progression is 8 and the sixth term is $\frac{64}{27}$, find the progression.

10. The sum of five numbers in arithmetic series is 60 and the second term is $10\frac{1}{2}$. Find the numbers.

11. If the sum of three numbers in an arithmetic series is 3 and the sum of their squares is 3.32, find the numbers.

12. If $x+3$, $x-3$, and $x-7$ in that order form a geometric progression, find x and the progression.

13. Express the repeating decimal $0.787878 \cdots$ as a common fraction.

14. Three numbers whose sum is 6 are in an arithmetic progression. If the first is multiplied by 2, the second by 3, and the third by $-\frac{3}{2}$, the resulting numbers are in geometric progression. Find the original numbers.

15. The difference between two numbers is 15, and the arithmetic mean exceeds the positive geometric mean by $\frac{5}{2}$. Find the numbers.

16. Due to friction a swinging pendulum is brought gradually to rest. In studying the swing of a pendulum bob, a student found that the first swing was 24 cm. and that the length of each succeeding swing was $\frac{9}{10}$ of the preceding swing. Through what distance did the bob pass over during the fourth swing? Through what distance did the bob pass before coming to rest?

CUMULATIVE REVIEW EXERCISES

1. Determine the slope and y intercept of the line whose equation is $2x - 3y = 15$.

2. Using synthetic division, perform the following: $(y^3 - 7y^2 - 6y + 72) \div (y - 4)$.

3. Factor $x^3 + 2x^2 + 2x + 1$.

4. Divide $(6\sqrt{105} + 18\sqrt{40} - 45\sqrt{12})$ by $3\sqrt{15}$.

5. Find by the graph method the respective values of x and y in the system of equations: $3x + y = 2$
$$5x + 2y = 1$$

6. Without solving the equation, determine the sum, the product, and the nature of the roots of $2x^2 - 3x = 4$.

7. Form a quadratic equation whose roots are $\dfrac{2 \pm \sqrt{3}}{3}$.

8. In the equation $4x^2 + 6x - 2cx + 1 = 0$ for what values of c will the roots be equal?

9. Solve for x: $\dfrac{2x + 2}{x^2 - x} + \dfrac{x - 2}{x^2 + x} + \dfrac{3x}{1 - x} = -3$

10. How many quarts of pure water must be evaporated from an 18 qt. solution that contains 10% acid in order to make a solution of 15% acid?

11. Solve for x: $3x = \sqrt{x + 3} + 1$

12. Find by formula the seventh term of the progression $\frac{2}{3}, \frac{1}{3}, \frac{1}{6} \cdots$

13. The sum of three numbers in a geometric series is 52. If the first is multiplied by 24, the second by 48, and the third by 72, the resulting numbers are in arithmetic progression. Find the three original numbers.

14. In his study of the planet Mars, Kepler discovered that the square of the number of years it requires a planet to revolve about the sun varies directly as the cube of the average distance of the planet from the sun. If we consider earth's distance as 1 unit and Jupiter's 5.2 units, how long does it take Jupiter to revolve about the sun? State your answer to the nearest tenth of a year.

15. From the graph of $y = 2x^2 - 3x - 5$ estimate the roots of the equation $2x^2 - 3x - 5 = 0$.

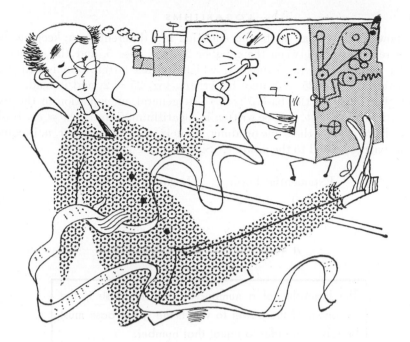

CHAPTER 15

Logarithms

The need of logarithms. The increasing complexity of our modern world demands that we find methods of doing routine jobs with greater ease. Ordinary processes of arithmetic are not sufficient for doing the tedious computations which are required in the sciences, in engineering, and in the business world. As a result of this need men have developed ideas, mechanical devices, and electronic computers, which help us do mathematical operations rapidly and accurately. One such time-saving invention is the method of logarithms.

Meaning of a logarithm. A logarithm is essentially an exponent. To develop this idea, let us take a specific example of a number expressed in exponential form such as $25 = 5^2$. This equation states that the number 25 is equal to the base 5 raised to

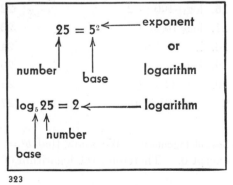

the power 2. We can write this equation in a different form, keeping the same relationship between the number 25, the base 5, and the exponent 2, but emphasizing the exponent, which in this latter form is called a logarithm. Thus $25 = 5^2$ may be written $\log_5 25 = 2$, and is read, "the logarithm of 25 to the base 5 is 2." In general, an equation in the exponential form $n = b^e$ can be written in logarithmic form $\log_b n = e$. Both forms have exactly the same meaning, namely, that the number, n, is equal to the base, b, raised to the power e. Similarly, we know

Exponential Form	Logarithmic Form
$100 = 10^2$	$\log_{10} 100 = 2$
$64 = 2^6$	$\log_2 64 = 6$
$625 = 5^4$	$\log_5 625 = 4$
$n = b^e$	$\log_b n = e$

> The logarithm of a number to a given base is the exponent of the power to which the given base must be raised in order to equal that number.

E X E R C I S E S : Logarithmic and exponential equations

In ex. 1–15 write each equation in logarithmic notation.

1. $1000 = 10^3$

2. $32 = 2^5$

3. $3^3 = 27$

4. $10^5 = 100,000$

5. $M = N^r$

6. $r^5 = t$

7. $8^{\frac{1}{3}} = 2$

8. $3 = 81^{\frac{1}{4}}$

9. $100 = 1000^{\frac{2}{3}}$

10. $\frac{1}{16} = 2^{-4}$

11. $2^7 = 128$

12. $1 = a^0$

13. $b^0 = 1$

14. $10^{-3} = .001$

15. $.1 = 10^{-1}$

In ex. 16–27 write each equation in exponential notation.

16. $\log_{10} 100 = 2$

17. $\log_2 16 = 4$

18. $\log_b 1 = 0$

19. $\log_3 27 = 3$

20. $\log_4 32 = \frac{5}{2}$

21. $\log_{10} 100,000 = 5$

22. $\log_b b = 1$

23. $\log_{25} \frac{1}{5} = -\frac{1}{2}$

24. $\log_8 4 = \frac{2}{3}$

25. $\log_4 256 = 4$

26. $\log_a n = c$

27. $\log_{10} .01 = -2$

Special logarithms. We know that $b^0 = 1$, where b represents any number except 0. Therefore, the logarithm of 1 to any base is zero.

$$\boxed{\log_b 1 = 0}$$

We know that $b^1 = b$, that is, any quantity raised to the first power equals itself. Therefore the logarithm of any number to a base equal to the given number is 1.

$$\boxed{\log_b b = 1}$$

ILLUSTRATIVE EXAMPLES: Solving simple equations

1. Determine the value of x in the equation: $\log_2 64 = x$

Solution. Given equation $\qquad \log_2 64 = x$

Changing to exponential form $\qquad 2^x = 64$

Expressing 64 as 2^6 $\qquad 2^x = 2^6$

Since the bases of the equalities are the same, their exponents will be equal. Thus $\qquad x = 6$ Answer

2. Determine the value of x in the equation:
$$\log_3 x = -2$$

Solution. Given equation $\qquad \log_3 x = -2$

Changing to exponential form $\qquad 3^{-2} = x$

Simplifying 3^{-2} $\qquad x = \dfrac{1}{3^2}$

Solving for x $\qquad x = \tfrac{1}{9}$ Answer

EXERCISES: Solving simple logarithmic equations

Determine the value of x in each of the following equations:

1. $\log_{10} 100 = x$
2. $x = \log_3 27$
3. $\log_{10} x = 3$
4. $\log_5 x = 2$
5. $\log_x 4 = 2$
6. $\log_2 x = 1$
7. $x = \log_6 1$

8. $\log_x 1000 = 3$
9. $\log_{10} x = 0$
10. $\log_x 1 = 5$
11. $\log_2 x = 4$
12. $\log_8 8 = x$
13. $\log_x 625 = 4$
14. $\log_x 5 = 1$

15. $x = \log_5 125$
16. $\log_2 \tfrac{1}{2} = x$
17. $\log_x .01 = -2$
18. $\log_9 x = \tfrac{1}{2}$
19. $\log_{10} \tfrac{1}{100} = x$
20. $\log_{27} x = \tfrac{2}{3}$
21. $\log_x 27 = \tfrac{3}{2}$

Common logarithms. We may use as the base of a system of logarithms any positive number except 1. However, since our number system is based upon the number 10, it has been found that a system of logarithms with the number 10 as a base is best suited for computational purposes.

Logarithms with 10 as a base are called *common logarithms*. Since common logarithms are so widely used for computational purposes, we usually omit the base 10 in expressions written in logarithmic form. For example, $\log_{10} 625$ is written log 625. Similarly $\log_{10} n = x$ is written log $n = x$.

Every positive number can be written as an exact or as an approximate power of 10. Let us examine a table of integral powers of 10, together with the corresponding logarithmic forms.

Table of Powers of Ten	Logarithmic Form
$10^4 = 10,000$	$\log 10,000 = 4$
$10^3 = 1000$	$\log 1000 = 3$
$10^2 = 100$	$\log 100 = 2$
$10^1 = 10$	$\log 10 = 1$
$10^0 = 1$	$\log 1 = 0$
$10^{-1} = 0.1$	$\log 0.1 = -1$
$10^{-2} = 0.01$	$\log 0.01 = -2$
$10^{-3} = 0.001$	$\log 0.001 = -3$

From this table we observe:

> The logarithm of 1 is zero.
> The logarithm of a number greater than 1 is positive.
> The logarithm of a number less than 1 is negative.

Logarithms of numbers which are not integral powers of 10. Studying the above table, select any number between 1 and 10, such as 7. We observe that the logarithm of 7 is greater than 0 and less than 1. Therefore the logarithm of 7 must be a positive decimal.

> The logarithm of any number between 1 and 10 is a positive decimal.

Again studying the above table, select a number between 10 and 100, such as 35. We observe that the logarithm of 35 is greater than 1 and is less than 2. Therefore the logarithm of 35 must be the whole number 1 and a positive decimal.

> The logarithm of any number between 10 and 100
> is the whole number 1 and a positive decimal.

From these illustrations we can readily see that the *logarithm* of every positive number *consists of two parts*, an *integral part* and a *decimal part*. The integral part of the logarithm is called the *characteristic* and may be equal to 0, a positive integer, or a negative integer. The decimal part of the logarithm is called the *mantissa*. For example

$$\log 752 = 2.\overset{\frown}{8762} \quad \underset{\text{mantissa}}{\text{characteristic}}$$

Similarly, in $\log 17 = 1.2304$, the characteristic of the logarithm is 1 and the mantissa is .2304. Also, in $\log 6 = 0.7782$, the characteristic is 0; the mantissa is .7782. Again in $\log 100 = 2.0000$, the characteristic is 2; the mantissa is .0000.

Characteristic of the logarithm of a number.   In order to determine by inspection the characteristic of the logarithm of a number, we must review what is meant by standard position in a number. Standard position in a number is the position to the right of the first nonzero digit of a number. In the following numbers the caret ($\wedge$) indicates standard position:

$$3485 \qquad 34.85 \qquad .03485 \qquad 3.485$$
$$\wedge \qquad\quad \wedge \qquad\quad\quad \wedge \qquad\quad \wedge$$

Writing a number in standard form, we have:

$$3.485 = 3.485 \times 10^0$$
$$34.85 = 3.485 \times 10^1$$
$$348.5 = 3.485 \times 10^2$$
$$0.3485 = 3.485 \times 10^{-1}$$
$$0.03485 = 3.485 \times 10^{-2}$$

Each one of these numbers consists of a factor whose value lies between 1 and 10 and a second factor expressed as an integral power of 10. From page 326 we know the characteristic of the logarithm of the first factor is 0 and the characteristic of the logarithm of the second factor is the exponent of the power of 10. Hence by inspection:

The characteristic of the logarithm of 3.485 or 3.485×10^0 is 0

The characteristic of the logarithm of 34.85 or 3.485×10^1 is 1

The characteristic of the logarithm of 348.5 or 3.485×10^2 is 2

The characteristic of the logarithm of 0.3485 or 3.485×10^{-1} is -1

The characteristic of the logarithm of 0.03485 or 3.485×10^{-2} is -2

From these illustrations we can state a rule for determining by inspection the characteristic of a logarithm of a number.

When the *decimal point* is in *standard position*, the *characteristic* of the logarithm of the number is *zero*.

When the decimal point is *n places* to the *right* of standard position, the *characteristic* of the logarithm of the number is + *n*.

When the *decimal point* is *n places* to the *left* of standard position, the *characteristic* of the logarithm of the number is − *n*.

I L L U S T R A T I V E   E X A M P L E S : Finding the characteristic of the logarithm of a number

Determine the characteristic of the logarithm of each of the following numbers:

1. 876.5

Solution. Given number   876.5

Since the decimal point is two places to the right of standard position, the characteristic of the logarithm of the number is + 2.

2. .6345

Solution. Given number   .6345

The decimal point is one place to the left of standard position. Therefore, the characteristic of the logarithm of the number is − 1.

3. 9.6

Solution. Given number   9.6

The decimal point is in standard position. Therefore, the characteristic of the logarithm of the number is 0.

4. 6954

Solution. Given number   6954

The decimal point is three places to the right of standard position. Therefore, the characteristic of the logarithm of the number is + 3.

ORAL EXERCISES: Finding the characteristic of the logarithm of a number

Determine the characteristic of the logarithm of each of the following numbers:

1. 7.654	**5.** 83.13	**9.** 12.325	**13.** .0006
2. 631.09	**6.** 9610	**10.** 7	**14.** 333.3
3. 597	**7.** .02578	**11.** 70	**15.** .9002
4. .125	**8.** 2.11	**12.** 19,000	**16.** 1.01

ILLUSTRATIVE EXAMPLES: Placing the decimal point in a number when the characteristic of its logarithm is known

In each of the following numbers place the decimal point in proper position:

1. 2345   Characteristic of the logarithm is 0.

> *Solution.* Since the characteristic is 0, the decimal point must be placed in *standard position.* Thus, we have   2.345   Answer

2. 90324   Characteristic of the logarithm is 3.

> *Solution.* Since the characteristic is 3, the decimal point must be placed *three places* to the *right* of standard position. Therefore, we have   9032.4   Answer

3. 187   Characteristic of the logarithm is − 2.

> *Solution.* The characteristic is − 2. Hence, the decimal point must be placed *two places* to the *left* of standard position. We obtain   .0187   Answer

ORAL EXERCISES: Placing the decimal point in a number when the characteristic of its logarithm is known

In each of the following nnmbers state where the decimal point should be placed:

	Number	Characteristic of its Logarithm
1.	963	0
2.	238	1
3.	7100	3
4.	6154	0
5.	35	− 1
6.	762	− 3

7.	1013	2
8.	70	0
9.	23	− 2
10.	70	1
11.	3	4
12.	1342	2
13.	1342	− 1
14.	65	3
15.	65	− 3
16.	107	0

Invention of logarithms. Logarithms were invented by John Napier, a Scotsman, in the early part of the seventeenth century. Napier spent over twenty years working on his theory before publishing his results. His invention, unlike most new ideas and devices, was based upon no previous work. It was an isolated result of his own thinking and did not follow any line of mathematical thought known at that time.

Henry Briggs, an English mathematician and a contemporary of Napier, suggested a system of logarithms to the base 10. It is to Briggs that we are indebted for our common system of logarithms. The word *characteristic* as used in the theory of logarithms first occurred in Briggs' work published in 1624.

Mantissas of logarithms.   As you already know, the mantissa of the logarithm of a number is the decimal part of the logarithm. Although the characteristic of a logarithm of a number can be determined by inspection, the mantissa must be taken from a table. (Originally, the mantissas in the table were calculated by applying mathematics beyond the scope of this text.) Although the table contains only the mantissas of the logarithms of numbers between 0 and 10, from it can be found the mantissa of the logarithm of any number. To illustrate, let us write in standard form the different numbers 3.24, 32.4, 324, 0.324, and 0.0324.

$$3.24 = 3.24 \times 10^0$$
$$\wedge$$

$$32.4 = 3.24 \times 10^1$$
$$\wedge$$

$$324 = 3.24 \times 10^2$$
$$\overset{}{\wedge}$$

$$0.324 = 3.24 \times 10^{-1}$$
$$\overset{}{\wedge}$$

$$0.0324 = 3.24 \times 10^{-2}$$
$$\overset{}{\wedge}$$

You will notice that each of these numbers consists of the same digits arranged in the same order. Each is expressed as the product of two factors, one of which is a number greater than 1 and less than 10 and the other an integral power of 10. As we previously learned the logarithm of the second factor is an integer and the logarithm of the first factor is a decimal fraction. Therefore, the mantissa of the logarithm of the numbers 3.24; of 32.4; of 324; of 0.324; of 0.0324, etc., is the mantissa of the logarithm of 3.24. Similarly, the mantissa of the logarithm of the numbers 0.0289, 2.89, 28.9, 289 is the mantissa of the logarithm of 2.89.

> The mantissa of the logarithm of any number is the mantissa of the factor number between 1 and 10 when the given number is expressed in standard form.

How to use the table of mantissas. On pages 487–488 is a four-place table of mantissas of the logarithms of numbers containing three digits or less. You will notice that there are no decimal points either in the numbers or in the mantissas. In practice this omission has proved helpful in finding mantissas, but you must always keep in mind that a mantissa is a decimal fraction. The first two digits of any number are found under the No. column, while the third digit is found at the top of one of the columns at the right.

To find the mantissa of the logarithm of 324, we first find 32 under the column headed No., and then proceed to the right to the number in the column headed 4 to find the mantissa .5105. Thus the mantissa of log 324 is .5105. As you previously learned, the mantissa of log 32.4; of log 3.24; of log .324; etc., are the same, that is, .5105.

Finding the logarithm of a number. To find the logarithm of a number:

1. Determine the characteristic by inspection.
2. Find the mantissa in the table of mantissas (pp. 487–488).

ILLUSTRATIVE EXAMPLES: Finding the logarithm of a number

1. Find the logarithm of 24.6.

> *Solution.* Writing the number 24.6 with the caret in standard position.   24.6.
> ^
>
> Since the decimal point is one place to the right of standard position: the characteristic is 1. The mantissa (from p. 487) is .3909.
>
> Hence   log 24.6 = 1.3909   Answer

2. Find the logarithm of 7.61.

> *Solution.* Since the decimal point is in standard position, the characteristic is 0. The mantissa (p. 488) is .8814.
>
> Hence   log 7.61 = 0.8814   Answer

3. Find the logarithm of 0.0653.

> *Solution.* Writing the number 0.0653 with the caret in standard position: 0.0653.
> ^
>
> Since the decimal point is two places to the left of standard position, the characteristic is − 2. The mantissa is .8149.
>
> Hence   log 0.0653 = − 2 + .8149
>
> More frequently the characteristic − 2 is written 0 − 2 or 8 − 10.
>
> Thus   log 0.0653 = 0.8149 − 2
> or   log 0.0653 = 8.8149 − 10   Answer

EXERCISES: Finding the logarithm of a number

Write the logarithm of each of the following numbers:

1. 6.53	**6.** 8	**11.** .563	**16.** 3.14
2. 1.84	**7.** 346	**12.** .0627	**17.** .00052
3. 4.78	**8.** 75	**13.** .00276	**18.** .02
4. 30.7	**9.** 54,000	**14.** 80.6	**19.** 1000
5. 500	**10.** 4.9	**15.** .24	**20.** 3.01

The logarithmic curve.   The graph in the figure below represents $y = \log_{10} x$. Numbers are represented on the x axis, and the logarithms of the numbers are represented on the y axis.

x	y
0	no value
0.5	$- 0.301$
1	0
2	0.301
4	0.602
6	0.778
8	0.903
10	1.

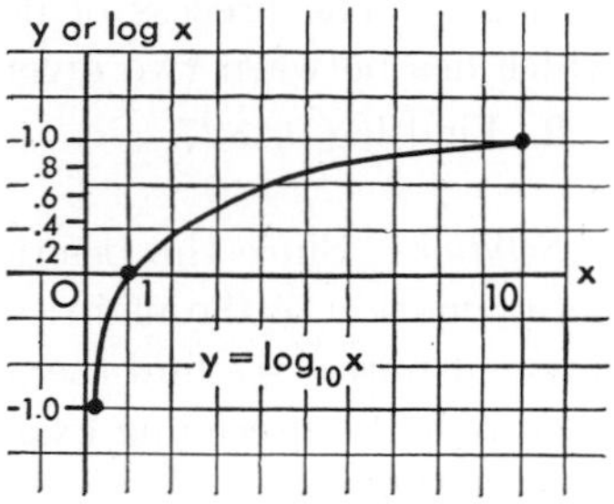

This graph shows more clearly the following facts:

1. Negative numbers do not have common logarithms.
2. Positive numbers less than 1 have negative logarithms.
3. Positive numbers greater than 1 have positive logarithms.

I L L U S T R A T I V E   E X A M P L E S : Finding the logarithm of a number whose mantissa does not appear in the table

1. Find log 21.34.

Solution. While the mantissa of log 2134 does not appear in the table, it does lie between two mantissas which do appear there. In the adjacent diagram observe that as the number increases from 2130 to 2140 the mantissa of the logarithm increases from 3284 to 3304, that is 20 units. Since the number 2134 is $\frac{4}{10}$ of the way from the number 2130 to the number 2140, we reason that the mantissa of log 2134 must be approximately $\frac{4}{10}$ of the way from 3284 to 3304. From the diagram we see that

Number	Mantissa
2140	3304
2134	?
2130	3284

$$\frac{4}{10} = \frac{c}{20}$$
$$10c = 80$$
$$c = 8$$

$$\text{mantissa of log 2134} = 3284 + c$$

The value of c, obtained by a proportion, is **8** (see diagram). Substituting 8 for c, we have

$$\text{mantissa of log 2134} = 3284 + 8$$
$$= 3292$$

Determining the characteristic by inspection and writing the mantissa in decimal form, .3292, we have the complete logarithm. Thus

$$\log 21.34 = 1.3292 \quad \text{Answer}$$

Note : The process of determining a value (in this case a mantissa) which lies between two given values is called *interpolation*.

2. Find log 0.1827.

Solution. Since the position of the decimal point plays no part in the determination of the mantissa, we may ignore it now. We find the mantissa as we did in the preceding example. We observe that

Number	Mantissa
1830	2625
1827	?
1820	2601

mantissa of log 1827 = 2601 + c

The value of c, determined by a proportion, is **17**. Substituting 17 for c we have

$$\frac{7}{10} = \frac{c}{24}$$
$$10c = 168$$
$$c = \mathbf{16.8} \text{ or } \mathbf{17}$$

$$\text{mantissa of } \log 1827 = 2601 + 17$$
$$= 2618$$

Determining the characteristic by inspection and writing the mantissa in decimal form, .2618, we have

$$\log 0.8827 = 0.2618 - 1 \quad \text{or}$$
$$\log 0.8827 = 9.2618 - 10 \quad \text{Answer}$$

E X E R C I S E S : Finding the logarithm of a number when the mantissa does not appear in the table

Find the logarithm of each of the following numbers :

1. 4625	9. .07035	17. .05692
2. 4242	10. .001035	18. 900.2
3. 4477	11. 2.167	19. 2635
4. 45.29	12. 87,280	20. .7692
5. 5.655	13. .2141	21. 1.048
6. 708.5	14. 2.643	22. 1025
7. 8.652	15. 6.187	23. .3333
8. .8758	16. 946,400	24. .1666

Finding a number whose logarithm is known. A number which corresponds to a given logarithm is called an *antilogarithm*.

ILLUSTRATIVE EXAMPLES: Finding antilogarithms

1. If log $n = 9.5587 - 10$, determine n.

Solution. In the given logarithm the characteristic is $9 - 10$ or -1; the mantissa is .5587. In the table on pages 487–488 we find that the mantissa 5587 is opposite 36 and in the "2" column. Hence, the digits corresponding to the mantissa are 362. The characteristic, -1, indicates that the decimal point should be located one place to the left of standard position. We write the solution as follows:

$$\text{Given} \quad \log n = 9.5587 - 10$$
$$\text{Then} \qquad n = .362 \quad \text{Answer}$$

2. If log $n = 2.7129$, determine n.

Solution. Since we do not find the mantissa in the table, we shall use interpolation to find the fourth digit in our answer. The mantissa, 7129, is greater than 7126 and less than 7135, two consecutive mantissas appearing in the table. In our diagram we write the mantissas 7126 and 7135 together with the numbers which correspond to them. We also insert the given mantissa, 7129, between the mantissas 7126 and 7135. Ob-

Number	Mantissa
5170	7135
?	7129
5160	7126

$$\frac{c}{10} = \frac{3}{9}$$
$$9c = 30$$
$$c = 3 \quad \text{Nearest integer}$$

serve that we write zeros after the numbers 516 and 517, since the desired number shall contain four digits. The value of c, obtained from a proportion, is 3. From the diagram we see that

$$n = 5160 + c$$
$$n = 5160 + 3$$

The sequence of digits for n is therefore 5163. Since the characteristic is 2, the decimal point is located two places to the right of standard position. We write our solution:

$$\text{Given} \qquad \log n = 2.7129$$
$$n = 516.3 \quad \text{Answer}$$

EXERCISES: Finding antilogarithms

Find the number whose logarithm is:

1. 0.7419

2. 1.9533

3. 2.1303

4. 1.3365

5. $8.6803 - 10$

6. 2.4771

7. 4.9031

8. $7.2601 - 10$

9. 0.5888

10. $9.9542 - 10$

11. 2.6508

12. 1.9356

13. 0.7455	**19.** 9.8529 − 10	**25.** 5.6032
14. 1.3251	**20.** 3.7408	**26.** 8.3770 − 10
15. 0.3422	**21.** 7.0342 − 10	**27.** 1.1122
16. 3.9215	**22.** 1.4260	**28.** 3.8505
17. 4.8004	**23.** 9.8764 − 10	**29.** 0.7464
18. 8.2889 − 10	**24.** 2.7054	**30.** 2.5726

Finding a product by logarithms. The logarithm of the product of two numbers equals the sum of the logarithms of the numbers; that is,

$$\log_b mn = \log_b m + \log_b n$$

Proof:

Let $\log_b m = x$, then $\qquad m = b^x$
Let $\log_b n = y$, then $\qquad n = b^y$
Multiplying $\qquad\qquad mn = b^{x+y}$
Expressing in logarithmic form $\log_b mn = x + y$
Substituting for x and y $\quad \log_b mn = \log_b m + \log_b n$

ILLUSTRATIVE EXAMPLES: Finding a product by logarithms

1. Find by logarithms: 146×53

Solution. Let

$P = $ the indicated product $\quad P = 146 \times 53$
Expressing as a logarithm of a product $\quad \log P = \log 146 + \log 53$
Finding log 146 $\quad \log 146 = 2.1644$
Finding log 53 $\quad \underline{\log 53 \ = 1.7243}$
Adding $\quad \log P \ = 3.8887$
Finding the antilogarithm $\quad P \ = 7740$ Answer

The product of 146×53 is 7738. Computations by logarithms give *approximate* results. Greater accuracy can be obtained by use of tables more extensive than the table used in this course.

2. Find by logarithms: $(.0354)(- 9.135)$.

Solution. Negative numbers do not have common logarithms. In this example we compute as if the numbers are positive and then prefix the minus sign to the product.

Let $P =$ the indicated product $\qquad\qquad P = (.0354)(9.135)$

Expressing as a logarithm of a product $\qquad \log P = \log .0354 + \log 9.135$

Finding $\log .0354$ $\qquad\qquad\qquad\qquad \log .0354 = 8.5490 - 10$

Finding $\log 9.135$ $\qquad\qquad\qquad\quad \underline{\log 9.135 = 0.9607}$

Adding $\qquad\qquad\qquad\qquad\qquad\qquad \log P = 9.5097 - 10$

Finding the antilogarithm $\qquad\qquad\qquad P = .3234$

Solving for $(- P)$, we obtain $\qquad\quad (- P) = - .3234$ Answer

EXERCISES: Finding a product by logarithms

Find each of the following products by logarithms:

1. 1.21×66.6
2. 4.8×1.15
3. 22.8×31.6
4. 24.3×65
5. 13.4×89
6. 35×69.9
7. 470×2.12
8. $5.37 \times (- 7.53)$
9. 80.1×29.4
10. $.76 \times 295$
11. $(- 91) \times 9.52$
12. $.384 \times 8.5$
13. $.0254 \times 746$
14. $537.9 \times .0062$
15. $77.8 \times .5122$
16. $.894 \times .925$
17. $35,000 \times .01352$
18. $27.1 \times 3.7 \times 6.04$
19. $.0568 \times .2113 \times 79,000$
20. $(- .3332) \times (12) \times (- 6.455)$

Finding a quotient by logarithms. The logarithm of the quotient of two numbers equals the logarithm of the dividend minus the logarithm of the divisor; that is,

$$\log_b \frac{m}{n} = \log_b m - \log_b n$$

Proof: Let $\log_b m = x$, then $\qquad\qquad m = b^x$

Let $\log_b n = y$, then $\qquad\qquad n = b^y$

Dividing $\qquad\qquad\qquad\qquad\qquad \frac{m}{n} = b^{x-y}$

Expressing in logarithmic form $\log_b \frac{m}{n} = x - y$

Substituting for x and y $\qquad \log_b \frac{m}{n} = \log_b m - \log_b n$

ILLUSTRATIVE EXAMPLES: Finding a quotient by logarithms

1. Find by logarithms: $4468 \div 21.5$.

Solution. Let $Q =$ the indicated quotient $\quad Q = 4468 \div 21.5$

Expressing as a logarithm of a quotient $\quad \log Q = \log 4468 - \log 21.5$

Finding log 4468 $\qquad \log 4468 = 3.6501$

Finding log 21.5 $\qquad \underline{\log 21.5 = 1.3324}$

Subtracting $\qquad\qquad\qquad \log Q = 2.3177$

Finding the antilogarithm $\qquad\qquad Q = 207.8 \quad$ Answer

2. Find by logarithms: $34.5 \div 429$

Solution. Let $Q =$ the quotient $\qquad Q = 34.5 \div 429$

Expressing as a logarithm of a quotient $\quad \log Q = \log 34.5 - \log 429$

Finding log 34.5 $\qquad\qquad \log 34.5 = 11.5378 - 10$

Finding log 429 $\qquad\qquad \underline{\log 429 = 2.6325}$

Subtracting $\qquad\qquad\qquad \log Q = 8.9053 - 10$

Finding the antilogarithm $\qquad\qquad Q = .0804 \quad$ Answer

Observe that log 34.5 is written $11.5378 - 10$ rather than 1.5378. The characteristic $11 - 10$ is equivalent to the characteristic 1, and its use enables us to subtract log 429 from log 34.5. We thereby avoid a negative mantissa.

EXERCISES: Finding a quotient by logarithms

Find each quotient by logarithms:

1.	$815 \div 33$	**5.**	$4790 \div 72.1$	**13.**	$\dfrac{6823}{31.87}$
2.	$621 \div 260$	**6.**	$87 \div 2.75$		
3.	$67.8 \div 2.14$	**7.**	$.787 \div 2.18$	**14.**	$\dfrac{3080}{562.5}$
4.	$2560 \div 8.14$	**8.**	$.089 \div 3.14$		
		9.	$27.3 \div 865$	**15.**	$\dfrac{217}{46{,}320}$
		10.	$5.61 \div 9.2$		
		11.	$\dfrac{1.2}{51.7}$	**16.**	$\dfrac{63{,}270}{1581}$
		12.	$\dfrac{.754}{.0858}$	**17.**	$\dfrac{14.79}{392.5}$

Finding powers and roots by logarithms. The logarithm of a power of a number equals the logarithm of the number multiplied by the exponent of the power; that is,

$$\log_b m^p = p \log_b m$$

Proof: Let $\log_b m = x$, then $\qquad\qquad m = b^x$

Raising both members to p power $\qquad m^p = b^{px}$

Expressing in logarithmic form $\qquad \log_b m^p = px$

. Substituting for x $\qquad\qquad\qquad \log_b m^p = p \log_b m$

The logarithm of a root of a number is equal to the logarithm of the number divided by the index of the root; that is,

$$\log_b \sqrt[r]{m} = \frac{\log_b m}{r} \text{ or } \frac{1}{r} \log_b m$$

Proof: Let $\log_b m = x$, then $\qquad\qquad m = b^x$

Taking rth root of both members $\qquad \sqrt[r]{m} = b^{\frac{x}{r}}$

Expressing in logarithmic form $\qquad \log_b \sqrt[r]{m} = \frac{x}{r}$

Substituting for x $\qquad\qquad\qquad \log_b \sqrt[r]{m} = \frac{\log_b m}{r}$

ILLUSTRATIVE EXAMPLES: Evaluating powers and roots by logarithms

1. Evaluate by logarithms: 2.21^5

Solution. Let R represent the
indicated power of the number $\qquad\qquad R = 2.21^5$

Expressing as a logarithm of a power $\quad \log R = 5 \log 2.21$

Finding log 2.21 $\qquad\qquad\qquad \log 2.21 = 0.3444$

Substituting $\qquad\qquad\qquad\qquad \log R = 5(0.3444)$

Multiplying by 5 $\qquad\qquad\qquad \log R = 1.7220$

Finding the antilogarithm $\qquad\qquad R = 52.73 \quad$ Answer

2. Evaluate by logarithms: $(.342)^4$

Solution. Let R represent the
indicated power of the number $\qquad\qquad R = (.342)^4$

Expressing as a logarithm of a power $\quad \log R = 4 \log .342$

Finding log .342 $\log .342 = 9.5340 - 10$

Multiplying by 4
$$\begin{array}{r} 4 \\ \hline \log R = 38.1360 - 40 \end{array}$$

Finding the antilogarithm $R = .01368$ Answer

Observe that the characteristic $38 - 40$ is equivalent to the characteristic -2.

3. Evaluate by logarithms: $\sqrt[3]{.7265}$

    Solution. Let R represent the indicated root of the number $R = \sqrt[3]{.7265}$

    Writing $\sqrt[3]{.7265}$ in exponential form $R = .7265^{\frac{1}{3}}$

    Expressing as a logarithm of a root $\log R = \frac{1}{3} \log .7265$

    Finding log .7265 and substituting $\log R = \frac{1}{3} (9.8612 - 10)$

    Writing the characteristic $9 - 10$ as $29 - 30$ $\log R = \frac{1}{3} (29.8612 - 30)$

    Multiplying by $\frac{1}{3}$ $\log R = 9.9537 - 10$

    Finding the antilogarithm $R = .8988$ Answer

Observe that log .7265 is expressed as $29.8612 - 30$ rather than as $9.8612 - 10$ since $\frac{1}{3}$ multiplied by the negative part of the characteristic must give an integer.

E X E R C I S E S :   Finding powers and roots by logarithms

Evaluate each of the following by logarithms:

1. 29^2		**13.** $\sqrt{8.41}$	
2. 9.1^3		**14.** $\sqrt{48,400}$	
3. 47.2^2		**15.** $\sqrt[4]{922}$	
4. $.419^2$		**16.** $\sqrt[3]{3.02}$	
5. 3.14^4		**17.** $\sqrt{6450}$	
6. $.52^6$		**18.** $\sqrt[5]{-571}$	
7. 7.23^5		**19.** $\sqrt[9]{29.75}$	
8. 1.04^{10}		**20.** $\sqrt{.2704}$	
9. $(-28.55)^3$		**21.** $\sqrt{.6947}$	
10. 1.01^{20}		**22.** $\sqrt[3]{.567}$	
11. $.893^6$		**23.** $\sqrt[5]{.0227}$	
12. 1.025^8		**24.** $\sqrt[3]{.0812}$	

Performing a combination of operations by logarithms.   The first step in solving problems involving the use of logarithms consists of writing the logarithm of the indicated operations in expanded form.   Consider the formula from physics

$$T = \pi\sqrt{\frac{l}{g}}$$

We assume that the values of π, l, and g are known and that we wish to compute the values of T by logarithms.   Since the logarithm of the product of two numbers is equal to the sum of the logarithms of the numbers, we may write:

$$\log T = \log \pi + \log \sqrt{\frac{l}{g}}$$

Expressing the second term as a logarithm of a root

$$\log T = \log \pi + \tfrac{1}{2} \log \frac{l}{g}$$

Expressing the second term as a logarithm of a quotient

$$\log T = \log \pi + \tfrac{1}{2} (\log l - \log g)$$

E X E R C I S E S : Using logarithms in a combination of operations

Give the logarithm of both members of each equation, writing the logarithm of the right member in expanded form.

1. $K = rs$
2. $V = lwh$
3. $C = 2\pi r$
4. $I = PRT$
5. $r = \dfrac{d}{t}$
6. $A = \dfrac{bh}{2}$
7. $A = s^2$
8. $S = 2\pi rh$
9. $A = \pi r^2$

10. $S = 4\pi r^2$
11. $F = \dfrac{Cx}{D}$
12. $S = \dfrac{kwd}{l}$
13. $N = a\sqrt{b}$
14. $a = \dfrac{x}{by}$
15. $S = \tfrac{1}{2}gt^2$

16. $a = \dfrac{\pi r^2 E}{180}$
17. $R = y^3\sqrt{x}$
18. $t = \sqrt{\dfrac{2S}{g}}$
19. $N = \sqrt[3]{\dfrac{ab}{c}}$
20. $c = \dfrac{A^4}{\sqrt[3]{w}}$

I L L U S T R A T I V E   E X A M P L E S : Performing a combination of operations by logarithms

1. Evaluate by logarithms: $\sqrt{\dfrac{38.2 \times 7.18}{34}}$

Solution.   Let $R =$ the result obtained by performing the indicated operations. $R = \sqrt{\dfrac{38.2 \times 7.18}{34}}$

Expressing in logarithmic
form
$$\log R = \tfrac{1}{2}(\log 38.2 + \log 7.18 - \log 34)$$

Outlining the solution first
and then adding the log-
arithms

$$\log 38.2 = 1.5821$$
$$\log 7.18 = \underline{0.8561}$$
$$2.4382$$
$$\log 34 = \underline{1.5315}$$

Subtracting 0.9067

Multiplying by $\tfrac{1}{2}$ $\log R = 0.4534$

Finding the antilogarithm $R = 2.841$ Answer

It is good practice to estimate the answer by rounding off numbers and performing the processes mentally. This estimate can serve as a check for gross errors in computations. Thus

$$\sqrt{\frac{38.2 \times 7.18}{34}} \text{ or } \sqrt{\frac{4\cancel{0} \times 7}{3\cancel{0}}} \text{ or } \sqrt{\tfrac{28}{3}} \text{ or } \sqrt{9} = 3 \text{ approximately}$$

2. Evaluate by logarithms: $\dfrac{4.69^3}{.86}$

Solution. Let $R =$ the result obtained by performing the indicated
operations
$$R = \frac{4.69^3}{.86}$$

Expressing in logarithmic form $\log R = 3 \log 4.69 - \log .86$

Outlining the solution and
finding the logarithms

$$\log 4.69 = \quad 0.6712$$
$$3 \log 4.69 = \quad 2.0136$$

Writing   the   characteristic
12–10

$$3 \log 4.69 = 12.0136 - 10$$
$$\log .86 = \underline{9.9345 - 10}$$

Subtracting $\log R = \quad 2.0791$

Finding the antilogarithm $R = 120$ Answer

E X E R C I S E S :   Performing a combination of operations by logarithms

Evaluate each of the following by logarithms:

1. $\dfrac{64.1 \times 23}{54.8}$

2. $\dfrac{2.53 \times .0084}{.006}$

3. $\dfrac{436}{5.21 \times 73.8}$

4. $\dfrac{.778}{5 \times .662}$

5. 1850×1.02^{10}

6. $.325\sqrt{152}$

7. $\sqrt{73.8 \times 3.14}$

8. $\dfrac{5.23^2}{.97}$

9. $\dfrac{(-71.6) \times 0.236}{22.62 \times (-1.4)}$

10. $\sqrt{\dfrac{28.23}{.625}}$

11. 657.5×1.06^4

12. $\left(\dfrac{25.5}{3.21}\right)^3$

13. $-\dfrac{8526}{6.1^3}$

14. $\sqrt[3]{\dfrac{4.25 \times 69}{671}}$

15. $\dfrac{\sqrt{85,000}}{3.247 \times 12.7}$

16. $\dfrac{32.08 \times 5.5^2}{2}$

17. $2.15^3 \times \sqrt{.3016}$

18. $\sqrt{\dfrac{6700}{.739 \times 41}}$

19. $\dfrac{.32 \times 795}{98.3 \times 1.02^3}$

20. $\dfrac{\sqrt{5,446,000}}{2.11^2}$

Evaluating formulas by logarithms.   In solving problems by the use of formulas, we may use logarithms to advantage when the operations involved are multiplication, division, raising to a power, and extracting a root.

I L L U S T R A T I V E   E X A M P L E : Evaluating a formula by logarithms

Using the formula, $V = \dfrac{\pi r^2 h}{3}$, determine the volume of a cone, if its altitude is 6.85 in. and the radius of its base is 4.2 in.   (Let $\pi = 3.14$.)

Solution. Given formula $V = \dfrac{\pi r^2 h}{3}$

Substituting 3.14 for π, 4.2 for r, and 6.85 for h $V = \dfrac{3.14 \times 4.2^2 \times 6.85}{3}$

Expressing in logarithmic form $\log V = \log 3.14 + 2 \log 4.2 + \log 6.85 - \log 3$

Outlining the solution $\log 3.14 = 0.4969$

$\log 4.2 = 0.6232$, $2 \log 4.2 = 1.2464$

$\log 6.85 = \underline{0.8357}$

Adding $\log \text{numerator} = 2.5790$

$\log 3 = \underline{0.4771}$

Subtracting $\log V = 2.1019$

$V = 126.4$ Answer

E X E R C I S E S : Evaluating formulas by logarithms

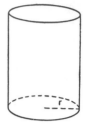

1. The lateral area of a cylinder is determined by the formula $S = 2\pi rh$. Find the lateral area of the cylinder whose height is 12.5 in. and the radius of whose base is 2.9 in. (Let $\pi = 3.14$.)

2. Solve the formula $A = \pi r^2$ for r. Using the resulting formula, determine the radius of the circle whose area is 555.5 sq. in. (Let $\pi = 3.14$.)

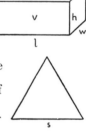

3. The volume of a rectangular-shaped box is 264.6 cu. in. If its length is 8.14 in. and its width is 6.45 in., determine its height.

4. A formula for finding the area of an equilateral triangle is $A = \dfrac{s^2\sqrt{3}}{4}$. Determine (to the nearest tenth) the area of an equilateral triangle if s, the length of each side, is 8.2 in.

5. The surface area of a sphere is determined by the formula $S = 4\pi r^2$. Find the surface area of the sphere of radius 4.5 in. (Let $\pi = 3.14$.)

6. The distance a freely falling body travels in a given time is determined by the formula $S = 16.1t^2$, where S is expressed in feet and t is expressed in seconds. Determine S to the nearest foot when $t = 6.5$ sec.

7. Using the formula $I = Prt$, determine the rate of interest at which $5621 must be invested in order to earn $3513 in 12.5 years.

8. The formula $t = \pi\sqrt{\dfrac{l}{g}}$, used in physics, describes the relationship between the length of a pendulum and the time of its swing. The letter g, representing the force of gravity, equals 32.2. Determine t to the nearest tenth of a second if $l = 1.4$ ft. (Let $\pi = 3.14$.)

9. The formula for the volume of a sphere is $V = \frac{4}{3}\pi r^3$. Determine the volume of a sphere of radius 5.4 in. (Let $\pi = 3.14$.)

10. The formula for computing the area of a triangle whose sides are known is $A = \sqrt{s(s-a)(s-b)(s-c)}$, where a, b, and c represent the three sides of the triangle, and s represents the semiperimeter. Determine the area of the triangle whose sides are 23.2 in., 18.5 in., and 16.3 in.

Doings of Dimbo. In one of Dimbo's early driving lessons he mistakenly pushed the reverse button when he actually wanted to go forward.

Find Dimbo's error in his solution of the following problem.

Find by using logarithms the value of: $(3.64)(-14.93)$

Dimbo's solution:

log 3.64 =	0.5611
or	10.5611–10
log (–14.93) =	–1.1741
log product =	9.3870–10
product =	0.2438 Answer

Exponential and logarithmic equations. An *exponential equation* is an equation in which the *unknown appears in an exponent*. The following are exponential equations:

$$5^{2x} = 871; \qquad 10^{x-1} = 718; \qquad b^{2x} = n$$

A *logarithmic equation* is an equation in which *appears the logarithm of the unknown*. An example of a logarithmic equation is

$$\log x + \log (x - 1) = 0.3010$$

ILLUSTRATIVE EXAMPLE: Solving an exponential equation

Solve for x: $5^{2x} = 871$

    Solution. Given example $5^{2x} = 871$

    Taking the logarithm of
    both sides $2x \log 5 = \log 871$

    Solving for $2x$ $2x = \dfrac{\log 871}{\log 5}$

Substituting the values of
the logarithms

$$2x = \frac{2.9400}{0.6990}$$

Dividing 2.9400 by 0.6990 $\quad 2x = 4.206$

$$x = 2.103 \quad \text{Answer}$$

The operation, $2.9400 \div 0.6990$, may be accomplished either by use of logarithms or by long division.

Notice that $\dfrac{\log 871}{\log 5}$ is a *quotient of logarithms*. It is not a logarithm of a quotient. The logarithm of 871 must be divided by the logarithm of 5.

ILLUSTRATIVE EXAMPLE: Solving a logarithmic equation

Solve for x: $\log x + \log (x - 1) = 0.3010$

Solution. Given example $\qquad \log x + \log (x - 1) = 0.3010$

Expressing $\log x + \log (x - 1)$ as the
logarithm of a product $\qquad\qquad \log x(x - 1) = 0.3010$

Finding the antilogarithm $\qquad\qquad\qquad x(x - 1) = 2$

Solving for x $\qquad\qquad\qquad\qquad\qquad x^2 - x = 2$

$$x^2 - x - 2 = 0$$

$$(x + 1)(x - 2) = 0$$

$$x + 1 = 0 \qquad x - 2 = 0$$

$$x = -1 \qquad x = 2 \quad \text{Answer}$$

Check. 2 is a root since it satisfies the original equation.

-1 cannot be a root because when substituted in the equation, it becomes necessary to determine the common logarithm of a negative number, which does not exist.

EXERCISES: Solving exponential equations and logarithmic equations

Solve each of the following exponential equations:

1. $2^x = 128$
2. $3^{2x} = 81$
3. $10^{x-1} = 1000$
4. $5^x = \frac{1}{125}$
5. $7^x = 58$

6. $3^x = 60$
7. $2^{-x} = 19$
8. $6^{x-1} = 97$
9. $4.3^{x+1} = 20.4$
10. $164 = 5^{2x}$

11. $1.52^x = 2.19$
12. $2.7 = 6.72^x$
13. $3^{2x-1} = 2^{x+1}$
14. $10^x = 17^{x-1}$
15. $5^{x+1} = 3^{2x}$

Solve each of the following logarithmic equations:

16. $\log_2 x - \log_4 16 = \log_3 27$
17. $\log x + \log 20 = 2$
18. $\log 10x = 3 - \log x$

19. $1 - \log 2x = \log (x + 0.5)$
20. $\log \frac{1}{9}x + \log \frac{1}{4}x = 0$
21. $\log_8 x + \log_8 (x - 3) = \frac{2}{3}$

Compound interest.   Logarithms are particularly useful in performing the computations required when money is invested at compound interest. Banks, Federal Savings and Loan Associations and other similar institutions use compound interest tables, the construction of which is based on logarithms. While the use of such tables is not included in a course in intermediate algebra, we shall observe how logarithms may be used directly in solving compound interest problems.

The income from a given principal at simple interest is the same each year. In a compound interest investment, the interest earned at the end of a period of time, one year for example, is added to the principal, and this sum becomes the new principal which earns interest during the next period of time. For example:

Suppose we invest $1.00 at 6% interest compounded annually. The amount at the end of the first year is $1.00 + (1.00)(.06)$ or $(1.00)(1.06)$ $= 1.06$ or $(1.06)^1$; the amount at the end of the second year is $(1.06)(1.06)$ $= (1.06)^2$; in like manner, the amount at the end of the third year is $(1.06)^3$: the amount at the end of the nth year is $(1.06)^n$.

Similarly, if P dollars were invested under the above conditions the amount at the end of the nth year would be $P(1.06)^n$.

Similarly, if P dollars are invested for n years at r per cent, compounded annually, we may determine the amount, A, by the compound interest formula

$$A = P(1 + r)^n$$

If interest is compounded semiannually, then the number of interest periods is doubled and can be represented by $2n$. Also, since r represents the yearly or annual rate of interest, the rate per "six months period" will be represented by $\frac{r}{2}$ per cent. Therefore, when interest is compounded semiannually, the compound interest formula becomes

$$A = P\left(1 + \frac{r}{2}\right)^{2n}$$

Likewise, when interest is compounded *quarterly*, the compound interest formula becomes

$$A = P\left(1 + \frac{r}{4}\right)^{4n}$$

ILLUSTRATIVE EXAMPLES: Solving compound interest problems by logarithms

1. Find the amount of $1470 invested for 7 years at 5% compounded semiannually.

Solution. The formula is $A = P\left(1 + \frac{r}{2}\right)^{2n}$

Substituting 1470 for P, .05 for r, and 7 for n

$$A = 1470\left(1 + \frac{.05}{2}\right)^{2\cdot7}$$

Simplifying $\qquad\qquad A = 1470(1.025)^{14}$

Expressing in logarithmic form $\qquad \log A = \log 1470 + 14 \log 1.025$

Substituting the values of the logarithms and combining

$$\log A = 3.1673 + 14(0.0107)$$
$$\log A = 3.1673 + 0.1498$$
$$\log A = 3.3171$$

Finding the antilog $\qquad\qquad A = \$2075 \quad$ Answer

2. Mr. Williams estimates that he will need \$6000 ten years hence in order to send his son to college. If money is worth 5% compounded annually, how much must Mr. Williams invest now in order that the necessary \$6000 will be available when needed?

Solution. The formula is $\qquad\qquad A = P(1 + r)^n$

Substituting 6000 for A, .05 for r, and 10 for n

$$6000 = P(1 + .05)^{10}$$

Solving for P $\qquad\qquad\qquad P = \dfrac{6000}{(1.05)^{10}}$

Expressing in logarithmic form $\qquad \log P = \log 6000 - 10 \log 1.05$

$$\log P = 3.7782 - 10(0.0212)$$

Completing the solution $\qquad \log P = 3.7782 - 0.2120$
$$\log P = 3.5662$$
$$P = \$3683 \quad \text{Answer}$$

3. Ned invests \$755 at 3% compounded annually. In approximately how many years will his investment be worth \$900?

Solution. The formula is $\qquad\qquad A = P(1 + r)^n$

Substituting 900 for A, 755 for P, and .03 for r

$$900 = 755(1.03)^n$$

Dividing each side by 755 $\qquad \tfrac{900}{755} = (1.03)^n$

Taking the logarithm of both sides $\qquad \log 900 - \log 755 = n \log 1.03$

Solving for n $\qquad\qquad\qquad n = \dfrac{\log 900 - \log 755}{\log 1.03}$

Completing the solution $\qquad\qquad n = \dfrac{2.9542 - 2.8779}{0.0128}$

$$n = \dfrac{0.0763}{0.0128}$$
$$n = 6 \text{ approximately} \quad \text{Answer}$$

E X E R C I S E S : Solving compound interest problems by logarithms

In exercises 1–6 find the amount of :

1. $650 invested for 8 years at 3% compounded annually.

2. $925 invested for 12 years at 2% compounded annually.

3. $1500 invested for 5 years at 6% compounded semiannually.

4. $2135 invested for 4 years at 5% compounded semiannually.

5. $1340 invested for 5 years at 4% compounded quarterly.

6. $1000 invested for 2 years at 8% compounded quarterly.

7. What sum of money invested at 5% compounded annually will amount to $2500 in 6 years?

8. What sum of money invested at 4% compounded semiannually will amount to $3650 in 10 years?

9. What sum of money invested at 4% compounded quarterly will amount to $4670 in 10 years?

10. In how many years will $2960 amount to $5000 at 6% compounded annually?

11. In approximately how many years will $3000 amount to $3960 at 4% compounded semiannually?

12. Six years ago Mr. Jones deposited $100 in a savings account for Bill's graduation trip. If the rate of interest was 4% compounded semi-annually, how much money does Bill now have for his trip?

13. If I anticipate needing $3000 for a new automobile 4 years hence, how much should I invest now at 5% compounded semiannually?

14. At the time of John's birth his father invested $1400 for him. If the money is earning 5% compounded annually, what will be the value of John's investment when he becomes twenty-one years of age?

15. Mr. Smith deposits $1750 in a Federal Savings and Loan account. What will his investment be worth at the end of 7 years if the interest rate is 4% compounded semiannually?

16. Mr. Brown borrowed $720 from Mr. Jones 10 years ago with interest at 8% compounded quarterly. How much does Mr. Brown owe Mr. Jones?

17. In how many years will any sum of money double itself if invested at 6% compounded annually?

18. Suppose one of your ancestors had invested $10 in the year 1776 and you have just inherited the principal and interest. If the investment has earned 4% interest compounded semiannually, what is the amount of your inheritance?

The slide rule.   A slide rule is a mechanical logarithm table. The rule described here is an inexpensive 10-in. graduated rule. On the body of the rule are the scales A and D. The movable part of the rule, called

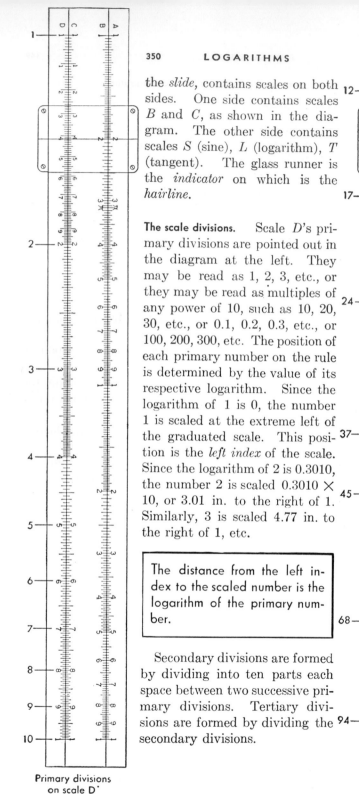

the *slide*, contains scales on both sides. One side contains scales *B* and *C*, as shown in the diagram. The other side contains scales *S* (sine), *L* (logarithm), *T* (tangent). The glass runner is the *indicator* on which is the *hairline*.

The scale divisions. Scale *D*'s primary divisions are pointed out in the diagram at the left. They may be read as 1, 2, 3, etc., or they may be read as multiples of any power of 10, such as 10, 20, 30, etc., or 0.1, 0.2, 0.3, etc., or 100, 200, 300, etc. The position of each primary number on the rule is determined by the value of its respective logarithm. Since the logarithm of 1 is 0, the number 1 is scaled at the extreme left of the graduated scale. This position is the *left index* of the scale. Since the logarithm of 2 is 0.3010, the number 2 is scaled 0.3010 × 10, or 3.01 in. to the right of 1. Similarly, 3 is scaled 4.77 in. to the right of 1, etc.

> The distance from the left index to the scaled number is the logarithm of the primary number.

Secondary divisions are formed by dividing into ten parts each space between two successive primary divisions. Tertiary divisions are formed by dividing the secondary divisions.

Primary divisions
on scale D

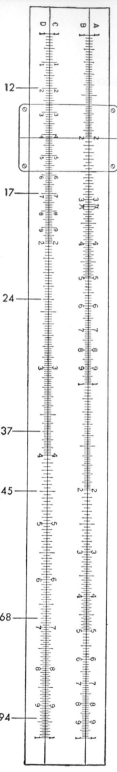

Reading the slide rule.   As previously illustrated, numbers containing a single digit are located at the primary divisions. Two-digit numbers are located at the secondary divisions with the first digit, reading from left to right, the primary division, and the second digit, the secondary division. The respective positions on the rule of two-digit numbers are illustrated in the figure at the right of the opposite page.

Three-digit numbers are located at the tertiary divisions or at points between tertiary divisions. The position on the rule of the three-digit number 478 is illustrated in the figure below.

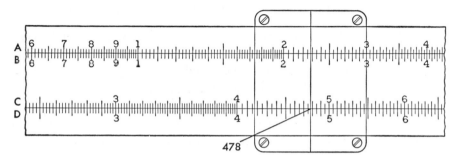

Scales A, B, and C.   Scale C is identical to scale D. Scale B consists of two identical halves, each similar to scale D but only half as long. Scale A is identical to scale B.

Finding squares by slide rule.   We can square a number with the aid of a slide rule, using scales A and D. The slide itself may be removed for the purpose of finding squares and square roots.

In order to square a number, place the indicator in a position so that the hairline falls on the number on scale D. Without moving the indicator, we can read the square of that number on scale A. The operator himself must determine the correct number of digits or the location of the decimal point in the square. The slide rule does not indicate the number of digits in the answer. This operation is the equivalent of doubling the logarithm of the given number, which operation is necessary in the process of squaring a number by using logarithms.

Finding square roots by slide rule.   The operation for finding square roots by slide rule is the reverse of the process of finding squares. If the number is greater than 1 and contains an odd number of digits to the left of the decimal, the left half of scale A is used. If the number is greater than 1 and contains an even number of digits to the left of the decimal, the right half of scale A is used. Similarly, if the number is less than 1, and the number of zeros immediately following the decimal point is odd, then the left half of scale A is used. If the number of zeros is even, the right half of scale A is used.

The hairline is placed on the number on scale A in accordance with the directions in the above paragraph. The hairline is not moved from this position, and the square root of the given number can be read on scale D. The operator himself must determine the correct number of digits, or the location of the decimal point in the square root. This operation is the equivalent of dividing the logarithm of the given number by 2, an operation which is necessary in finding square roots by using logarithms.

I L L U S T R A T I V E E X A M P L E S : Squares and square roots by slide rule

1. Find the square of 522 by using a slide rule.

    Solution. Without using the slide, we place the hairline on 522 on scale D.

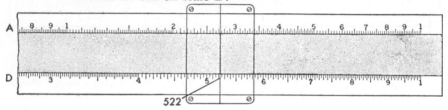

On scale A we read 272. Since the square of 522 must have 6 digits, we know the answer is approximately 272,000.

2. Find the square root of 2810 by using a slide rule.

    Solution. The number 2810 contains an even number of digits to the left of the decimal point. Therefore, we place the hairline on 281 on the right half of scale A.

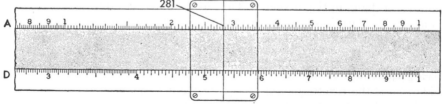

On scale D we read 53. Since the square root of 2810 must have 2 digits to the left of the decimal, we know the answer is approximately 53.0.

Multiplication by slide rule.   In the process of multiplying two numbers by using logarithms, it is necessary to add the logarithms of the two numbers.   Similarly, in multiplying two numbers with a slide rule we add the lengths of the logarithms of the two numbers.   First we measure off the length of the logarithms of one number on one scale (D).   Then the length of

the logarithm of the second number is measured off on scale C.   Their combined lengths are read on the first scale.   This is shown in the illustrative example.   In actual practice it is simpler to deal with the multiplication of two factors as terms of a proportion.

I L L U S T R A T I V E   E X A M P L E : Multiplication by slide rule

Multiply 18 by 26.

   Solution.   We let $18 \times 26 = x$.   Stated as a proportion: $\frac{1}{18} = \frac{26}{x}$.   Using the rule, we move the hairline to 18 on D.   We draw the slide so that the left index of C is over 18 on D.   We move the hairline to 26 on C.   Under 26 on C we read 468 on D.   The answer is 468.

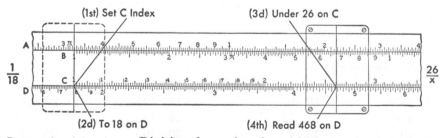

Division by slide rule.   Division by using logarithms involves the subtraction of the logarithm of the divisor from the logarithm of the dividend. Similarly, in division by slide rule we subtract the length of the logarithm of the divisor from the length of the logarithm of the dividend.   First we measure off the length of the logarithm of the divisor on one scale (D).   Then the length of the logarithm of the divisor is measured off on scale C.   Their difference is then read off on the first scale.   This is shown in the illustrative example.   In actual practice it is simpler to deal with the division of two numbers as terms of a proportion.

ILLUSTRATIVE EXAMPLE: Division by slide rule

Divide 875 by 35.

    Solution. Let $875 \div 35 = x$. Stated as a proportion: $\dfrac{1}{x} = \dfrac{35}{875}$. Using the slide rule, we move the hairline to 875 on D. We draw the slide so that 35 on C is over 875 on D. Under the left index on C we read 25 on D.   The answer is 25.

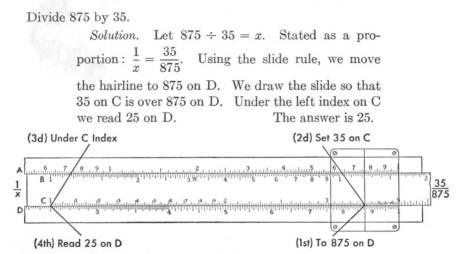

(3d) Under C Index   (2d) Set 35 on C

(4th) Read 25 on D   (1st) To 875 on D

Widespread use of the slide rule. The slide rule can be used for solving problems which involve multiplication, division, squares, square roots, cubes, cube roots, and proportion. While the accuracy of a slide rule is limited to three or four digits, results are adequate for many calculations. The slide rule is used widely by scientists, engineers, and business men.

    A thorough understanding of the use of a slide rule can be obtained only by actually working with one. Slide rules, with directions for their use, are available at prices affordable by most secondary school students.

EXERCISES: Use of slide rule

    In ex. 1–32, using a slide rule, move the hairline to each of the following numbers on scale D.

1. 10	**9.** 5500	**17.** 115	**25.** 25.2
2. 15	**10.** 640	**18.** 125	**26.** 364
3. 180	**11.** 72	**19.** 135	**27.** 4.55
4. 20	**12.** 8	**20.** 105	**28.** 575
5. 25	**13.** 0.85	**21.** 142	**29.** 6.85
6. 31	**14.** 0.0088	**22.** 154	**30.** 705
7. 360	**15.** 0.90	**23.** 1.66	**31.** 835
8. 400	**16.** 0.095	**24.** 178	**32.** 90.5

    In ex. 33–40, using a slide rule, move the hairline to approximately each of the following numbers on scale D.

33. 233	**35.** 412	**37.** 642	**39.** 834
34. 345	**36.** 566	**38.** 728	**40.** 957

In ex. 41–52, using a slide rule, find the square of each number given.

41. 4	**44.** 0.7	**47.** 92	**50.** 1.5
42. 11	**45.** 3.1	**48.** 65	**51.** 61
43. 60	**46.** 190	**49.** 35	**52.** 41

In ex. 53–64, using a slide rule, find the square root of each number.

53. 36	**56.** 400	**59.** 2.89	**62.** 1560
54. 900	**57.** 40	**60.** 6400	**63.** 950
55. 169	**58.** 324	**61.** 19.6	**64.** 8550

In ex. 65–76, using a slide rule, multiply each of the following as indicated.

65. 2×3	**68.** 6×5 (use right index)	**71.** 9×7
66. 3×3	**69.** 4×7 (use right index)	**72.** 9×9
67. 2×4	**70.** 5×8 (use right index)	**73.** 4×25

74. 6×75
75. 12×30
76. 22×15

In ex. 77–88, using a slide rule, divide each of the following as indicated.

77. $6 \div 3$	**80.** $12 \div 3$	**83.** $55 \div 11$	**86.** $88 \div 11$
78. $8 \div 4$	**81.** $24 \div 8$	**84.** $64 \div 8$	**87.** $120 \div 15$
79. $4 \div 2$	**82.** $36 \div 9$	**85.** $72 \div 9$	**88.** $225 \div 25$

Mathematical vocabulary. The student should know the meanings of the following mathematical expressions and should be able to spell them.

absolute inequality	discriminant
antilogarithm	ellipse
arithmetic mean	exponential equation
arithmetic progression	focus of ellipse
axis of symmetry	focus of hyperbola
branches of a hyperbola	focus of parabola
character of roots	geometric mean
characteristic of a logarithm	geometric progression
common logarithms	hyperbola
complete quadratic equation	imaginary number
completing the square	incomplete quadratic equation
compound interest	inequality
conditional inequality	infinite series
conic section	interpolation
conjugate axis of hyperbola	irrational
degree of an equation	literal equation
directrix of parabola	logarithm

logarithmic equation
major axis of ellipse
mantissa
mean proportional
minor axis of ellipse
nappe
nature of roots
parabola
progression
quadratic equation

quadratic function
rational number
real number
sequence
series
transverse axis of hyperbola
trinomial square
turning point
vertex of parabola
vertices of hyperbola

CHAPTER REVIEW EXERCISES

In ex. 1–3 determine the value of x.

1. $x = \log_2 16$ **2.** $\log_{16} x = \frac{1}{2}$ **3.** $\log_x .25 = -2$

If $\log 2 = 0.3010$ and $\log 3 = 0.4771$ find the value of each exercise in ex. 4–7.

4. $\log 4$ **5.** $\log 9$ **6.** $\log 6$ **7.** $\log 1.5$

Use logarithms to evaluate each exercise in ex. 8–13.

8. $(.76)(23.4)$ **10.** $\sqrt[5]{91.2}$ **12.** $\dfrac{(37.8)(2.51)}{139}$

9. $\dfrac{32.6}{.87}$ **11.** $(.889)^3$ **13.** $\sqrt{\dfrac{1.11}{(78.3)(0.0081)}}$

14. Solve for x: $7^x = 193$

15. What is the amount of $3440 invested for 4 years at 3% compounded annually?

16. What sum of money must I invest now at 4% interest compounded semiannually in order to have $5000 in 10 years?

17. Using the formula $V = \pi r^2 h$, determine the volume of a cylinder if its height equals 32.5 ft. and the radius of its base equals 7.2 ft. (Let $\pi = 3.14$.)

18. Without the use of tables, determine the value of $\log_6 9 + \log_6 4$.

CUMULATIVE REVIEW EXERCISES

1. Remove symbols of grouping and simplify:
$$8(a - 2b) - [b + \{-3a - 2(b - 3a) + 5a\}]$$

2. Solve for x and y:
$$\begin{cases} \dfrac{2}{x} + \dfrac{1}{3y} = \dfrac{5}{6} \\ \dfrac{4}{3x} - \dfrac{2}{y} = -\dfrac{5}{9} \end{cases}$$

3. Factor: *a*) $14x^2 - 53x + 14$ *b*) $a^3 + \frac{8}{27}b^3$

          c) $16a^2 - (2a + b)^2$

4. Combine into a single fraction:

$$\frac{a}{(a - b)(a - c)} - \frac{b}{(c - b)(a - b)} - \frac{c}{(b - c)(c - a)}$$

5. Simplify: $\dfrac{2x - 11 + \dfrac{5}{x}}{1 - 2x}$

6. Solve for *x*: $\dfrac{x}{x^2 - 3x + 2} + \dfrac{x + 2}{x^2 - 2x} = \dfrac{2x + 3}{x^2 - x}$

7. Simplify: $\dfrac{17}{3 - 5i}$

8. Find the square roots of $-7 + 24i$.

9. Simplify: $\dfrac{2x^0 y + 36^{\frac{1}{2}}}{8^{\frac{2}{3}} + y - (3x)^0}$

10. Solve the quadratic equation $3x^2 + 4x - 2 = 0$.

11. Solve and check: $2 + \sqrt{5x - 1} = \sqrt{x - 1}$

12. Determine the quadratic equation whose roots are $\pm\, i\,\sqrt{3}$.

13. Solve for *x* and *y*: $\begin{cases} 2x - y = 5 \\ x^2 + xy = 2 \end{cases}$

14. Name the graph of each of the following equations:

          a) $2x^2 - y^2 = 15$ *b*) $2x^2 + y^2 = 15$ *c*) $2x + y^2 = 15$

15. Find the value of $a + b + c$ if $4^a = 2$; $4^b = 1$; $4^c = 0.25$

16. Thomas is *x* years old now. Express algebraically, "Three years ago four times Thomas's age was 8 more than twice what his age will be 5 yr. hence."

17. Write an equation expressing the relationship between *x* and *y* if Mr. Bruce earns *y* dollars per month, spends *x* dollars per month, and saves \$850 per year.

18. If James can walk *x* miles in 5 hr., how far can he walk in *y* hours?

19. The area of a certain triangle is 20 sq. in. Its altitude is 3 in. less than its base. Find the base and altitude of the triangle.

20. The numerator of a certain fraction is 3 less than the denominator. If the numerator is tripled and the denominator increased by 5, the resulting fraction will have a value of $\frac{7}{5}$. Determine the original fraction.

CHAPTER 16

Trigonometry of the Right Triangle

Trigonometry is a word derived from two Greek words that mean "triangle measuring." It is the science that enables us, by measuring certain parts of a triangle, to obtain the measurements of the other parts without actually measuring them directly. Let us review some basic facts about angles and triangles.

A review of angles and triangles. An angle (symbol $\angle$) is measured in degrees and in subdivisions of a degree.

A degree (symbol °) is $\frac{1}{90}$ of a right angle; that is, a right angle (symbol rt. $\angle$) contains 90°.

A degree is divided into 60 equal parts called minutes (symbol ').

An acute angle is greater than 0° and less than 90°.

The sum of the angles of a triangle (symbol $\triangle$) is equal to 180°.

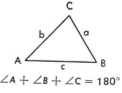

$$\angle A + \angle B + \angle C = 180°$$

Each side of a triangle may be labeled with a small letter which corresponds to the capital letter of the angle opposite that side.

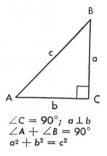

$\angle C = 90°;\ a \perp b$
$\angle A + \angle B = 90°$
$a^2 + b^2 = c^2$

A right triangle has one right angle and two acute angles. The sum of the acute angles equals 90°. In rt. $\triangle\ ABC$, side c opposite rt. $\angle\ C$ is called the hypotenuse of the right triangle. Sides a and b are called the legs of the right triangle. The sides of the right angle are perpendicular (symbol $\perp$) to each other.

In a right triangle the square of the hypotenuse is equal to the sum of the squares of the two legs. This statement is the Law of Pythagoras.

Two triangles are similar if the angles of one are equal respectively to the angles of the other.

Two right triangles are similar if an acute angle of one right triangle equals an acute angle of the other right triangle.

Corresponding sides of similar triangles are proportional.

Trigonometric functions. In the adjacent figure, since $\angle\ A$ is an angle of each of the rt. $\triangle$'s ABC, ADE, and AFG, the right triangles are similar. The corresponding sides of these similar right triangles are proportional. Thus,

$$\frac{BC}{AB} = \frac{DE}{AD} = \frac{FG}{AF}$$

Observe that in each right triangle the numerator of each ratio is the leg opposite $\angle\ A$; the denominator of each ratio is the hypotenuse.

Triangle	Ratio		
ABC	$\dfrac{BC}{AB}$	or	$\dfrac{\text{leg opposite } \angle\ A}{\text{hypotenuse}}$
ADE	$\dfrac{DE}{AD}$	or	$\dfrac{\text{leg opposite } \angle\ A}{\text{hypotenuse}}$
AFG	$\dfrac{FG}{AF}$	or	$\dfrac{\text{leg opposite } \angle\ A}{\text{hypotenuse}}$

In trigonometry we call the ratio, $\dfrac{\text{leg opposite } \angle\ A}{\text{hypotenuse}}$, the "sine of $\angle\ A$," (abbreviation sin A).

The sine of an acute angle of a right triangle is the ratio of the leg opposite the acute angle to the hypotenuse.

The value of the sine is a function of the angle. That means that the value of the sine is always the same for any given angle, regardless of the triangle in which the ratio is measured.

In the adjacent figure, since the corresponding sides of the similar rt. $\triangle$'s ABC, ADE, and AFG are proportional, then

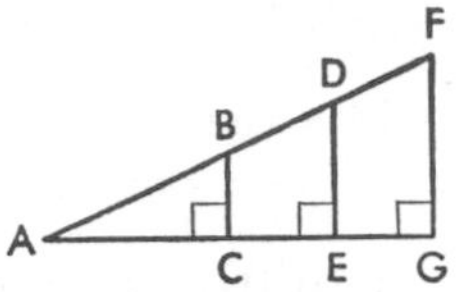

$$\frac{AC}{AB} = \frac{AE}{AD} = \frac{AG}{AF}$$

Observe that in each right triangle the numerator of each ratio is the leg adjacent to $\angle A$; the denominator of each ratio is the hypotenuse.

Triangle	Ratio	
ABC	$\dfrac{AC}{AB}$ or	$\dfrac{\text{leg adjacent to } \angle A}{\text{hypotenuse}}$
ADE	$\dfrac{AE}{AD}$ or	$\dfrac{\text{leg adjacent to } \angle A}{\text{hypotenuse}}$
AFG	$\dfrac{AG}{AF}$ or	$\dfrac{\text{leg adjacent to } \angle A}{\text{hypotenuse}}$

We call the ratio, $\dfrac{\text{leg adjacent to } \angle A}{\text{hypotenuse}}$, the "cosine of $\angle A$" (abbreviation $\cos A$).

The cosine of an acute angle of a right triangle is the ratio of the leg adjacent to the acute angle to the hypotenuse.

The value of the cosine is a function of the angle.

In the above figure, since the corresponding sides of the similar rt. $\triangle$'s ABC, ADE, and AFG are proportional, so

$$\frac{BC}{AC} = \frac{DE}{AE} = \frac{FG}{AG}$$

In each triangle the numerator of each ratio is the leg opposite ∠ A; the denominator of each ratio is the leg adjacent to ∠ A.

Triangle			Ratio
ABC	$\dfrac{BC}{AC}$	or	$\dfrac{\text{leg opposite } \angle A}{\text{leg adjacent to } \angle A}$
ADE	$\dfrac{DE}{AE}$	or	$\dfrac{\text{leg opposite } \angle A}{\text{leg adjacent to } \angle A}$
AFG	$\dfrac{FG}{AG}$	or	$\dfrac{\text{leg opposite } \angle A}{\text{leg adjacent to } \angle A}$

We call this ratio, $\dfrac{\text{leg opposite } \angle A}{\text{leg adjacent to } \angle A}$, the "tangent of ∠ A" (abbreviation tan A).

> The tangent of an acute angle of a right triangle is the ratio of the leg opposite the acute angle to the leg adjacent to the acute angle.

The value of the tangent is a function of the angle.

The cotangent (abbreviation ctn or cot) of an angle is the reciprocal of the tangent of the angle, that is,

$$\text{ctn } A = \frac{1}{\tan A}$$

> The cotangent of the acute angle of a right triangle is the ratio of the leg adjacent to the acute angle to the leg opposite the acute angle.

Summary. In rt. △ ABC, with ∠ C the rt. ∠:

$$\sin A = \frac{a}{c} \qquad\qquad \sin B = \frac{b}{c}$$

$$\cos A = \frac{b}{c} \qquad\qquad \cos B = \frac{a}{c}$$

$$\tan A = \frac{a}{b} \qquad\qquad \tan B = \frac{b}{a}$$

$$\text{ctn } A = \frac{b}{a} \qquad\qquad \text{ctn } B = \frac{a}{b}$$

In your study of elementary algebra you may have learned the name of the mythical Indian chief, **SOH-CAH-TOA**, as an aid in remembering the definitions of the sine, cosine, and tangent. The Sine is the Opposite leg divided by the Hypotenuse (**SOH**). The Cosine is the Adjacent leg divided by the **H**ypotenuse (**CAH**). The Tangent is the Opposite leg divided by the Adjacent leg (**TOA**). The definition of the cotangent is remembered as the reciprocal of the tangent.

ILLUSTRATIVE EXAMPLE: Evaluating trigonometric functions

In rt. $\triangle ABC$, $a = 2$ and $b = 3$; find the hypotenuse c; and write the values of four trigonometric functions of $\angle A$; of $\angle B$.

Solution. To find c we use the Law of Pythagoras.

In any right triangle
$$c^2 = a^2 + b^2$$
Substituting 2 for a and 3 for b
$$c^2 = 4 + 9$$
$$c^2 = 13$$
$$c = \pm \sqrt{13}$$

Since the side of a $\triangle$ cannot be negative $c = \sqrt{13}$ Answer

Referring to the figure, we write the functions of $\angle A$ and $\angle B$.

$\sin A = \dfrac{\text{opp. leg}}{\text{hyp.}} = \dfrac{2}{\sqrt{13}} = \dfrac{2\sqrt{13}}{13}$ $\sin B = \dfrac{\text{opp. leg}}{\text{hyp.}} = \dfrac{3}{\sqrt{13}} = \dfrac{3\sqrt{13}}{13}$

$\cos A = \dfrac{\text{adj. leg}}{\text{hyp.}} = \dfrac{3}{\sqrt{13}} = \dfrac{3\sqrt{13}}{13}$ $\cos B = \dfrac{\text{adj. leg}}{\text{hyp.}} = \dfrac{2}{\sqrt{13}} = \dfrac{2\sqrt{13}}{13}$

$\tan A = \dfrac{\text{opp. leg}}{\text{adj. leg}} = \dfrac{2}{3}$ $\tan B = \dfrac{\text{opp. leg}}{\text{adj. leg}} = \dfrac{3}{2}$

$\operatorname{ctn} A = \dfrac{\text{adj. leg}}{\text{opp. leg}} = \dfrac{3}{2}$ $\operatorname{ctn} B = \dfrac{\text{adj. leg}}{\text{opp. leg}} = \dfrac{2}{3}$

ORAL EXERCISES: Trigonometric functions

1. Refer to rt. $\triangle ABC$ in the adjacent figure.
     a) Give the values of four trigonometric functions of $\angle A$.
     b) If $\angle A = 20°$, how many degrees in $\angle B$?

2. Refer to rt. $\triangle DEF$ on the next page.
     a) Give the values of four trigonometric functions of $\angle D$.
     b) Give the values of four trigonometric functions of $\angle E$.

c) What is the relationship between the trigonometric
    functions of ∠ D and the respective trigonometric
    functions of ∠ E?
d) What is the relationship between ∠ D and ∠ E?
e) How many degrees in ∠ D?   In ∠ E?

3. Refer to the right triangle in the adjacent figure.
    a) Give the values of four trigonometric functions of
        ∠ x in terms of s, r, and t.
    b) Give the values of four trigonometric functions of
        ∠ y in terms of s, r, and t.
    c) How many degrees in ∠ z?
    d) How many degrees in the sum of ∠ x + ∠ y + ∠ z?

4. Refer to the right triangle in the adjacent figure.
    a) Give the values of four trigonometric functions of
        ∠ 1 in terms of m, n, and p.
    b) Give the values of four trigonometric functions of
        ∠ 2 in terms of m, n, and p.
    c) How many degrees in the sum of ∠ 1 and ∠ 2?

E X E R C I S E S : Evaluating trigonometric functions

1. In rt. △ ABC, a = 8 in., b = 15 in., and
c = 17 in.   Sketch the triangle.   Write the value
of four trigonometric functions of ∠ A and of ∠ B.

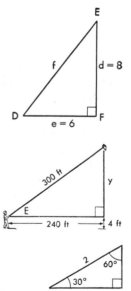

2. In rt. △DEF, d = 8 and e = 6.   Find the
length of the hypotenuse f.   Write the values of
four trigonometric functions of ∠ D.

3. While flying his kite Bob let out 300 ft. of
string. If the distance from Bob to a point directly
beneath the kite is 240 ft., use the adjacent figure
to determine the distance y.   How high is the kite
above the ground?   Write the values of four trigonometric functions of ∠ E.

4. In a 30°–60° right triangle the leg opposite the
30° angle equals one half the hypotenuse.   Determine the unknown sides of the adjacent triangle
and find the values of four trigonometric functions
of 30°.

5. Triangle ABC is an equilateral triangle.   Line BD divides $\angle\, B$ into two equal angles.   From plane geometry we know that BD bisects AC and $BD \perp AC$.   How large is each of the following angles: $\angle\, A$, $\angle\, ABC$, $\angle\, ABD$, $\angle\, CBD$, $\angle\, ADB$, $\angle\, CDB$?   If $AB = 2$ in., how long is AC? AD? BD?   What is the value of cos 60°?   tan 60°? sin 60°?   ctn 60°?

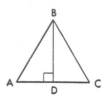

Solving right triangles.   To solve a right triangle means to find the parts of the right triangle whose values are not known.

There are six parts of a right triangle: three sides and three angles. One angle is a right angle.   If two other parts, including at least one side, are known, the triangle is fixed in size and shape; and we can solve for the remaining parts of the triangle.

Tables of values of trigonometric functions.   There is no angle greater than 90° in a right triangle.   To solve right triangles, then, we are interested in the values of the trigonometric functions of acute angles.   In order to find the values of the functions of all acute angles, we use a table of values which has been prepared for us by methods beyond the scope of this course. Such a table is found on pages **489–491.**   This table gives to four decimal places the values of four of the trigonometric functions of angles at 10′-intervals from 0° to 90°.   Angles from 0° to 45° are read in the left column while each trigonometric function is indicated at the top of the page. Angles from 45° to 90° are read in the right column while each trigonometric function is indicated at the bottom of the page.

In studying this table notice that:

1. The sine of 0° is 0.   The sine increases in value as the angle increases in size.   The sine of 90° is 1.

2. The cosine of 0° is 1.   The cosine decreases in value as the angle increases in size.   The cosine of 90° is 0.

3. The tangent of 0° is 0.   The tangent increases in value as the angle increases in size.   The tangent of 45° is 1; the tangent of an angle less than 45° is less than 1, and the tangent of an angle greater than 45° is greater than 1.

4. The tangent of 90° has no finite value and cannot be expressed as a number.   The cotangent of 0° has no finite value and cannot be expressed as a number.   The cotangent decreases in value as the angle increases in size.   The cotangent of 45° is 1; the cotangent of an angle less than 45° is greater than 1, and the cotangent of an angle greater than 45° is less than 1.   The cotangent of 90° is 0.

ILLUSTRATIVE EXAMPLES: Using the table of values of the trigonometric functions

1. Using the table on pages 489–491, find the respective values of sin 39° 20′, cos 39° 20′, and tan 39° 20′.

Solution. Since the angle 39° 20′ is less than 45°, we use the column headed "Angle" at the left of the page and look for the indicated functions at the top of the page. The first column at the left of the table is headed "Angle." In this column find the given angle 39° 20′. Move horizontally to the right to the column headed "Sin" at the top of the page and find .6338.

Hence   sin 39° 20′ = .6338   Answer

Again move horizontally to the right from 39° 20′ to the column headed "Cos" and find .7735.

Hence   cos 39° 20′ = .7735   Answer

Similarly   tan 39° 20′ = .8195   Answer

2. Using the table on pages 489–491, find the respective values of tan 47° 10′ and ctn 47° 10′.

Solution. Since the angle 47° 10′ is larger than 45°, we use the column headed "Angle" at the right of the page to find the given angle 47° 10′. Moving horizontally to the left to the "Tan" column (indicated at the bottom of the page), we find the indicated function 1.0786.

Hence   tan 47° 10′ = 1.0786   Answer

Similarly   ctn 47° 10′ = .9271   Answer

3. If tan A = .6371, determine ∠ A.

Solution. We look for .6371 in the Tangent columns (there are two). We find this value in the column headed "Tan" at the top of the page. Moving horizontally to the "Angle" column at the left of the page we read 32° 30′. We write the solution as follows:

$$\tan A = .6371$$
$$\angle A = 32° 30′ \quad \text{Answer}$$

4. If cos B = .3638, determine ∠ B.

Solution. We look for .3638 in the "Cos" columns (there are two). We find this value in the column indicated "Cos" at the bottom of the page. Hence, we move horizontally to the right and read in the "Angle" column, 68° 40′. We write the solution as follows:

$$\cos B = .3638$$
$$\angle B = 68° 40′ \quad \text{Answer}$$

E X E R C I S E S : Using the table of values of trigonometric functions of angles

Using the table on pages 489–491, find the value of each of the following:

1. $\sin 13° 10′$
2. $\tan 0° 40′$
3. $\cos 23° 30′$
4. $\cos 23° 40′$
5. $\tan 45°$

6. $\operatorname{ctn} 30° 20′$
7. $\sin 75° 30′$
8. $\tan 52° 10′$
9. $\operatorname{ctn} 5° 30′$
10. $\sin 2°$

11. $\tan 29° 50′$
12. $\cos 60°$
13. $\sin 44° 50′$
14. $\operatorname{ctn} 68° 10′$
15. $\cos 84° 20′$

Using the table on pages 489–491, find the number of degrees and minutes in each angle:

16. $\tan X = .4279$
17. $\cos A = .0640$
18. $\sin Y = .5000$
19. $\operatorname{ctn} B = .2370$
20. $\cos B = .9272$

21. $\tan B = .0612$
22. $\operatorname{ctn} A = 1.3848$
23. $\sin A = .8526$
24. $\cos X = .4094$
25. $\tan A = .7860$

26. $\sin X = .7585$
27. $\tan Y = 1.0058$
28. $\operatorname{ctn} X = 1.0000$
29. $\sin B = .9465$
30. $\cos Y = .7071$

Regiomontanus and trigonometry. Much of trigonometry in its present form originated with John Müller (1436–1476), a German mathematician, commonly known as Regiomontanus. By dividing the radius of a circle into very small parts he was able to work out a much more accurate table of sines than had hitherto been available. Regiomontanus constructed the first table of tangents. He also published a treatise on trigonometry containing solutions of plane and spherical triangles.

The sextant.   The sextant is an instrument used by the navigator on board ship or plane for measuring the altitude of the sun, the moon, a planet, or a star. By comparing true actual observations with the computed observations based on navigation tables, the navigator is able to "fix" his position on the sea or in the air.

Measuring angles.   We have all seen engineers using transits in surveying or for laying down guide lines for construction work. Before measuring an angle, the engineer adjusts the transit until it is in horizontal position on its tripod stand.   When the transit is at A as illustrated in the adjacent figure the line AH is horizontal. To measure the angle of elevation of point E from A, with E, A, H in a vertical plane, the engineer rotates the telescopic eyepiece of the transit upward until he sights on E.   The line AE is called the *line of sight* and $\angle HAE$ is the *angle of elevation* of E from A.   The number of degrees in $\angle HAE$ is read on the vertical arc of the transit. Similarly, when the engineer is at E the line EH' is horizontal. To measure the angle of depression of point A from E, the engineer rotates the telescopic eyepiece downward until he sights on A.   The line EA is called the *line of sight* and $\angle H'EA$ is the *angle of depression* of A from E. The angle of elevation equals the angle of depression.

To measure an angle between two points in a horizontal plane, the engineer sights on one point and then rotates the transit horizontally on its lower plate until the second point is in line of sight.   The number of degrees in the angle subtended by the two points is read on the horizontal arc of the transit.

ILLUSTRATIVE EXAMPLES: Solving right triangles

1. From the top of a lighthouse 210 ft. above sea level the angle of depression of a ship at sea is $10° 20'$.   How far is the ship from the base of the lighthouse?

Solution.   Let d represent the distance from the ship to the base of the lighthouse.   Since the angle of depression is $10° 20'$, $\angle r$ of the right triangle will also equal $10° 20'$.   We know the length of the leg opposite $\angle r$.   Since we wish to find d, the leg adjacent to $\angle r$, we use the cotangent ratio.

Thus

$$\text{ctn } r = \frac{\text{leg adjacent to } \angle r}{\text{leg opposite } \angle r}$$

Substituting $10° 20'$ for $\angle r$ and substituting 210 in the denominator

$$\text{ctn } 10° 20' = \frac{d}{210}$$

Finding the value of ctn $10° 20'$ in the table on pages 489–491

$$5.4845 = \frac{d}{210}$$

Solving for d

$$d = 1152 \text{ ft.} \quad \text{Answer}$$

The tangent ratio could have been used in solving this problem. For example, $\tan r = \dfrac{210}{d}$, and therefore $d = \dfrac{210}{\tan r}$.

2. In rt. $\triangle ABC$, $b = 216$ and $\angle B = 70° 50'$. Find c.

  Solution. We select a function of the known angle, B, which involves the known side b and the unknown side c. Thus,

$$\sin B = \frac{b}{c}$$

  Substituting the given values

$$\sin 70° 50' = \frac{216}{c}$$

  Substituting the value of $\sin 70° 50'$ from the table

$$.9446 = \frac{216}{c}$$

  Solving for c

$$c = \frac{216}{.9446}$$

$$c = 228.7 \quad \text{Answer}$$

3. In rt. $\triangle ABC$, $b = 2109$ and $c = 3000$. Find $\angle A$ and $\angle B$.

  Solution. To find $\angle A$, we select the function of $\angle A$ which involves the known sides b and c.

  Thus

$$\cos A = \frac{b}{c}$$

  Substituting 2109 for b and 3000 for c

$$\cos A = \frac{2109}{3000}$$

  Dividing 2109 by 3000

$$\cos A = .7030$$

  In the "Cos" column on page **491** we find .7030. Then $\angle A = 45° 20' \quad$ Answer
  To find $\angle B$, we use the fact that the sum of two acute angles of a right triangle equals 90°.

  Thus $\angle A + \angle B = 89° 60'$
  Substituting 45° 20' $\underline{\angle A \qquad\qquad = 45° 20'}$
  for $\angle A$ and subtracting $\angle B = 44° 40' \quad$ Answer

EXERCISES: Solving right triangles

1. In the adjacent figure with the data given as indicated
   a) solve for y.
   b) determine the value of the unknown acute angle.

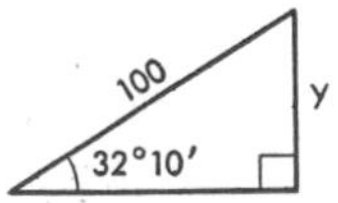

2. In the adjacent figure with the data given as indicated
  a) solve for y
  b) determine the value of the unknown acute angle.

47° 30′
60
y

880.2
28° 20′

3. In the adjacent figure with the data given as indicated
  a) determine the value of the unknown acute angle
  b) solve for c.

c
a
?

4. In $\triangle ABC$ below with the data given as indicated
  a) find $\angle B$
  b) find $\angle A$.

5. In the second triangle at the right with the data given as indicated
  a) find $\angle r$
  b) find $\angle s$.

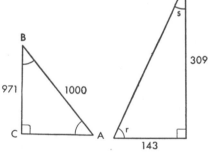

B
971
1000
C
A
143

s
309
r

6. In rt. $\triangle ABC$ if $\angle A = 56° 40′$ and $c = 200$, solve for the remaining parts of the triangle.

7. A ladder 30 ft. in length rests against the side of a building. If the ladder makes an angle of 74° with the ground, how high upon the wall does the top of the ladder rest? (Find answer to nearest tenth of a foot.)

8. From the top of a lookout tower the angle of depression of a small fire is 6° 10′. If the height of the tower is 100 ft., how far from the base of the tower is the fire?

9. When the angle of elevation of the sun is 55° 20′, a flagpole casts a shadow 30 ft. in length. Determine the height of the flagpole.

10. In a certain department store the distance between two floors is 20.6 ft. If the angle of inclination of the escalator is 31°, determine the distance (to the nearest tenth of a foot) a person would travel in riding the escalator from one floor to the other.

Number magic.   Try a little magic on your friends.

Have a friend write a number of several digits. Suppose he writes 8243. Thus

8243

Now ask him to write the same digits but in a different order. Suppose he writes 2384. Thus

2384

Ask him to find the difference between the numbers. He does so and obtains 5859.

5859

Next, ask him to circle one of the digits, not a zero. Suppose he does and obtains

5 ⑧ 5 9

You, of course, are not observing your friend's work. However, you can determine which digit he circled. Ask him to give you the sum of the remaining digits.

$5 + 5 + 9$

He states that this sum is 19.

19

Add the digits until the sum of the digits is less than 9.

$1 + 9 = 10$
$1 + 0 = 1$

Subtract this last sum (in this case, 1) from 9. The difference will be the number your friend circled.

$9 - 1 = \mathbf{8}$

Interpolation.   In the table of trigonometric functions on pages 489–491 angles are given at ten minute (10′) intervals. To find a function of some angle, for example 25° 37′, which does not appear in the table, we must use *interpolation*. The process of interpolation is illustrated in the two examples which follow.

ILLUSTRATIVE EXAMPLES: Finding the functions of angles which do not appear in the table

1. Find sin 25° 37′.

Solution.   While the angle 25° 37′ does not appear in the table, it must lie between the angles 25° 30′ and 25° 40′, which do appear in the table. In the adjacent diagram observe that as the angle increases from 25° 30′ to 25° 40′, the sine value increases from .4305 to .4331; that is, the sine increases by .0026.

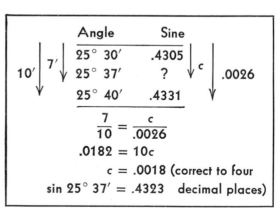

	Angle	Sine
	25° 30′	.4305
	25° 37′	?
	25° 40′	.4331

$$\frac{7}{10} = \frac{c}{.0026}$$

$$.0182 = 10c$$

$$c = .0018 \text{ (correct to four}$$

$$\sin 25° 37′ = .4323 \quad \text{decimal places)}$$

Since $25° 37'$ is $\frac{7}{10}$ of the way from $25° 30'$ to $25° 40'$, we reason that $\sin 25° 37'$ is approximately $\frac{7}{10}$ of the way from .4305 to .4331.
From the diagram we observe that

$$\sin 25° 37' = .4305 + c$$

The value of c, obtained by a proportion, is .0018 (see diagram). Substituting .0018 for c, we obtain

$$\sin 25° 37' = .4305 + .0018$$
$$\sin 25° 37' = .4323 \quad \text{Answer}$$

2. Find $\cos 50° 23'$.

Solution. The angle $50° 23'$ comes between the angles $50° 20'$ and $50° 30'$. We find $\cos 50° 20'$ and $\cos 50° 30'$. Observe that as the angle *increases* from $50° 20'$ to $50° 30'$, the cosine *decreases* from .6383 to .6361; that is, the cosine decreases by .0022. From the diagram we observe that

$$\cos 50° 23' = .6383 - c$$

Angle	Cosine
50° 20'	.6383
50° 23'	?
50° 30'	.6361

$$\frac{3}{10} = \frac{c}{.0022}$$
$$.0066 = 10\,c$$
$$c = .0007 \text{ (correct to four}$$
$$\cos 50° 23' = .6376 \quad \text{decimal places)}$$

The value of c, obtained by a proportion, is .0007 (see diagram). Substituting .0007 for c, we obtain

$$\cos 50° 23' = .6383 - .0007$$
$$\cos 50° 23' = .6376 \quad \text{Answer}$$

E X E R C I S E S : Using interpolation to find the values of trigonometric functions of angles

Find the value of each of the following:

1. $\sin 26° 25'$
2. $\sin 70° 43'$
3. $\tan 45° 55'$
4. $\tan 6° 12'$
5. $\cos 11° 8'$
6. $\cos 61° 14'$
7. $\operatorname{ctn} 54° 55'$
8. $\operatorname{ctn} 38° 3'$
9. $\sin 23° 23'$
10. $\tan 65° 35'$
11. $\cos 30° 5'$
12. $\cos 65° 33'$
13. $\operatorname{ctn} 42° 48'$
14. $\sin 10° 1'$
15. $\tan 73° 21'$

Finding the angle which corresponds to a given value of a function. When the value of a trigonometric function appears in the table, the corresponding angle can be found immediately. When the value of a trigonometric function does not appear in the table, the corresponding angle is found by interpolation.

ILLUSTRATIVE EXAMPLES: Finding the angle which corresponds to a given value of a trigonometric function

1. If tan A = .5906, find $\angle A$.

Solution. In the table on pages 489–491 the value .5906 does not appear in the "Tan" columns. We observe that this given value does lie between two successive values, .5890 and .5930, which do appear in the "Tan" column. We write the tangent values .5890, .5906, and .5930, together with their corresponding angles. From the diagram

$$\angle A = 30° 30' + c'$$

Angle	Tangent
30° 30'	.5890
A	.5906
30° 40'	.5930

$10'$ $\quad c'$ $\quad$ .0016 $\quad$ .0040

or

$$\frac{c}{10} = \frac{.0016}{.0040}$$

$$\frac{c}{10} = \frac{16}{40}$$

$$40c = 160$$

$$c = 4'$$

Hence $\angle A = 30° 34'$

The value of c, found by a proportion, is $4'$ (see diagram).

Substituting $4'$ for c, we have, $\quad \angle A = 30° 30' + 4'$

$$\angle A = 30° 34' \quad \text{Answer}$$

2. If cos B = .6762, find $\angle B$.

Solution. The cosine value, .6762, does not appear in the table. We write .6762 together with the successive values in the "Cos" column between which this given value lies. We also write the angles which correspond to these cosine values. Notice that although the cosine is *decreasing*, the angle is *increasing*. From the diagram

$$\angle B = 47° 20' + c'$$

Angle	Cosine
47° 20'	.6777
B	.6762
47° 30'	.6756

$10'$ $\quad c'$ $\quad$ 15 $\quad$ 21

$$\frac{c}{10} = \frac{15}{21}$$

$$21c = 150$$

$$c = 7' \text{ (to the nearest minute)}$$

Hence $\angle B = 47° 27'$

The value of c, found by a proportion, is $7'$ (see diagram).
Substituting 7 for c, we have $\angle B = 47° 20' + 7'$
$$\angle B = 47° 27' \quad \text{Answer}$$

E X E R C I S E S : Finding the angle which corresponds to a given value of a function

In each of the following determine the unknown angle:

1. $\tan A = .8026$
2. $\tan B = 1.3789$
3. $\sin A = .7224$
4. $\sin A = .3220$
5. $\cos x = .8877$

6. $\text{ctn } x = 1.5627$
7. $\sin y = .9186$
8. $\cos B = .2591$
9. $\cos A = .5332$
10. $\cos A = .6971$

11. $\tan B = .1685$
12. $\text{ctn } B = 3.6761$
13. $\sin A = .2153$
14. $\tan B = .5373$
15. $\sin A = .7386$

I L L U S T R A T I V E   E X A M P L E : Solving a right triangle

In rt. $\triangle ABC$, $b = 80$ and $\angle B = 22° 23'$. Find $\angle A$ and a.

Solution. In rt. $\triangle ABC$, $\angle A + \angle B = 90°$.

Substituting $22° 23'$ for $\angle B$,
$$\angle A + 22° 23' = 90°$$
Then $\qquad \angle A = 67° 37' \quad$ Answer

To find a we may use any one of the following:

$$\tan B = \frac{b}{a}; \quad \text{ctn } B = \frac{a}{b}; \quad \tan A = \frac{a}{b}; \quad \text{ctn } A = \frac{b}{a}$$

Computations are easier when the unknown is the numerator of the ratio. Therefore, we select

$$\text{ctn } B = \frac{a}{b} \text{ or } \tan A = \frac{a}{b}$$

A mistake in determining $\angle A$ in the first part of this example would cause this solution to be in error if the relationship $\tan A = \frac{a}{b}$ were used. There-

fore, we select $\qquad\qquad\qquad \text{ctn } B = \frac{a}{b}$

Substituting the given values $\qquad\qquad \text{ctn } 22° 23' = \frac{a}{80}$

Finding in the table the value of $\text{ctn } 22° 23'$ $\qquad 2.4282 = \frac{a}{80}$

Solving for a $\qquad\qquad\qquad\qquad\qquad\qquad a = 194.3 \quad$ Answer

E X E R C I S E S : Solving right triangles

1. In rt. $\triangle ABC$, $c = 1200$, $\angle A = 38° 15'$. Find a.
2. In rt. $\triangle ABC$, $a = 1000$, $\angle A = 49° 22'$. Find b.
3. In rt. $\triangle ABC$, $a = 60$, $\angle B = 58° 17'$. Find c.
4. In rt. $\triangle ABC$, $a = 300$, $b = 400$. Find $\angle A$ and $\angle B$.

5. A 30-ft. ladder is placed against a building so that the foot of the ladder is 10 ft. from the building. Assuming that the ground is level, determine to the nearest minute the angle which the ladder makes with the building.

6. A man in a boat (assume the man to be 5 ft. above the surface of the water) determines the angle of elevation of the top of a lighthouse to be $11° 14'$. If the top of the lighthouse is 100 ft. above the water, find the horizontal distance from the man to the lighthouse.

7. Joe is flying a kite. If he has let out 200 ft. of string and the angle of elevation of the kite is $44° 23'$, how high is the kite above the ground? Assume that Joe is holding his end of the string 4 ft. above the ground.

8. A ship sails 24 mi. in a direction $32° 35'$ west of north. How far north has it sailed? See diagram.

Doings of Dimbo. Dimbo will not reach Big Town because he was not attentive. He is traveling in the wrong direction. Have you ever made the error that Dimbo made in this example? Find his mistake.

Find the value of $\cos 32° 14'$.

Dimbo's solution

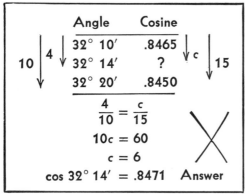

		Angle	Cosine		
		32° 10′	.8465		
10	4	32° 14′	?	c	15
		32° 20′	.8450		

$$\frac{4}{10} = \frac{c}{15}$$

$$10c = 60$$

$$c = 6$$

$$\cos 32° 14' = .8471 \quad \text{Answer}$$

The logarithms of trigonometric functions. In many cases the tedious arithmetical computations required in solving a right triangle can be avoided by use of logarithms.

On pages 492–494 there is a table of logarithms of the trigonometric functions. In this table are found complete logarithms — characteristics, as well as mantissas. The characteristics, 7, 8, and 9, mean $7 - 10$, $8 - 10$, and $9 - 10$ respectively. For example:

the table reads $\log \sin 70° 50' = 9.9752$

which means $\log \sin 70° 50' = 9.9752 - 10$

We read this table in much the same manner that we read the table of values of trigonometric functions.

Observe that we can find $\log \sin 70° 50'$ by first finding the value of $\sin 70° 50'$ ($\sin 70° 50' = .9446$) in the table of values of trigonometric functions and then finding the logarithm of this value ($\log .9446 = 9.9752 - 10$). This new table on pages 492–494 enables us to find the logarithms of trigonometric functions by using one table instead of two.

ILLUSTRATIVE EXAMPLES: Using the table of logarithms of trigonometric functions

1. Find log cos 44° 14′.

Solution. To find log cos 44° 14′, we must interpolate. We proceed in the same manner as before.

Angle	Log Cosine
44° 10′	9.8557–10
44° 14′	?
44° 20′	9.8545–10

$$\frac{4}{10} = \frac{c}{12}$$
$$10c = 48$$
$$c = 4.8 \quad \text{or} \quad 5$$
$$\log \cos 44° 14' = 9.8552 - 10$$

2. If log tan $A = 0.3096$, find ∠ A.

Solution. To find ∠ A, we must interpolate. We proceed in the same manner as before.

Angle	Log Tangent
63° 50′	0.3086
A	0.3096
64° 00′	0.3118

$$\frac{c}{10} = \frac{10}{32}$$
$$32c = 100$$
$$c = 3$$
$$\angle A = 63° 53'$$

E X E R C I S E S :   Using the table of logarithms of trigonometric functions

Using the table on pages 492–494, find each of the following:

1. log sin 20° 40′
2. log tan 53° 10′
3. log ctn 37° 50′
4. log cos 71°
5. log ctn 65° 30′

6. log tan 41° 32′
7. log cos 24° 17′
8. log sin 53° 51′
9. log tan 68° 45′
10. log ctn 35° 13′

In each of the following find the value of the angle to the nearest minute:

11. log sin $x = 9.1157 - 10$
12. log cos $B = 9.1157 - 10$
13. log tan $A = 9.9443 - 10$
14. log ctn $y = 7.9409 - 10$
15. log tan $B = 0.0101$

16. log sin $A = 9.5026 - 10$
17. log tan $B = 1.3215$
18. log cos $x = 9.9720 - 10$
19. log ctn $y = 9.7267 - 10$
20. log sin $B = 9.8047 - 10$

Solving right triangles by use of logarithms.   Let us observe how logarithms may be used in finding certain unknown parts of a right triangle.

I L L U S T R A T I V E   E X A M P L E : Solving a right triangle by use of logarithms

In rt. $\triangle ABC$, $b = 216$ and $\angle B = 70°\ 50'$. Determine the remaining parts of the triangle.

Solution. The remaining parts are $\angle A$, a, and c.

To find $\angle A$:

$\angle A = 90° - 70°\ 50' = 19°\ 10'$ Answer

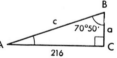

To find a and c: In solving for a and c it is best to outline the solutions completely before referring to the tables. The solutions should then be completed simultaneously.

$\text{ctn } 70°50' = \dfrac{a}{216}$	$\sin 70°\ 50' = \dfrac{216}{c}$
$a = 216 \text{ ctn } 70°\ 50'$	$c = \dfrac{216}{\sin 70°\ 50'}$
$\log a = \log 216 + \log \text{ctn } 70°\ 50'$	$\log c = \log 216 - \log \sin 70°\ 50'$

Outline

$\log 216 =$	$\log 216 =$
$\log \text{ctn } 70°\ 50' = \underline{\quad\quad}$	$\log \sin 70°\ 50' = \underline{\quad\quad}$
Adding $\log a =$	Subtracting $\log c =$
$a =$	$c =$

Completed Outline

$\log 216 =$ 2.3345	$\log 216 = 12.3345 - 10$
$+ \log \operatorname{ctn} 70° 50' =$ $9.5411 - 10$	$- \log \sin 70° 50' =$ $9.9752 - 10$
$\log a = 11.8756 - 10$	$\log c =$ 2.3593
$a = 75.1$ Answer	$c = 228.7$ Answer

E X E R C I S E S : Solving right triangles **by** use of logarithms

Ex. 1–8 refer to rt. $\triangle ABC$, where $\angle C$ is the right angle. By the use of logarithms, determine the parts of each triangle that are not given.

1. $c = 24.5$ $\angle A = 43° 20'$ 5. $a = 47.4$ $b = 55.4$
2. $a = 12.6$ $\angle A = 25° 10'$ 6. $b = 344.7$ $c = 722.3$
3. $b = 31$ $\angle A = 60° 40'$ 7. $a = 1025$ $\angle B = 54° 12'$
4. $c = 6.72$ $\angle B = 36° 5'$ 8. $b = .7528$ $\angle B = 63° 37'$

9. An observer standing 135 ft. from the base of a building finds that the angle of elevation of the top is 53° 35'. How high is the building?

10. An observer on the beach finds that the angle of elevation of an airship flying offshore is 32°. If the altitude of the airship is known to be 1300 ft., how far (horizontally) from shore is the airship?

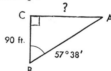

11. Two points, A and C, are on opposite sides of a ravine. If the distance CB along one side of the ravine, perpendicular to AC, is 90 ft. and if $\angle ABC$ is 57° 38′, find the distance CA across the ravine.

12. Determine each angle (to the nearest 10′) of an isosceles triangle if the base is 16 in. in length and if each of the equal sides is 11 in. long.

13. In rt. $\triangle ABC$, $c = 7.54$ in. and $\angle A = 58° 46'$. Find the area of the triangle.

14. In the adjacent $\triangle MNP$, $\angle M = 33° 20'$, $\angle N = 49° 30'$, and $n = 35.2$ in. Find the area of the triangle.

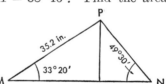

15. The horizontal distance between two buildings is 190 ft. From a window of one building the angle of elevation of the top of the second building is found to be 30° 18′, and the angle of depression of the base of the second building is found to be 13° 2′. Assuming that the ground is level, determine the height of the second building.

Solution of an oblique triangle.   A triangle which has no two sides perpendicular is called an oblique triangle. If two angles and one side of an oblique triangle are known, the remaining parts of the triangle can be found by using the *law of sines:*

> In any triangle the sides are directly proportional to the sines of the opposite angles.

Algebraically this law may be expressed:

$$\frac{a}{\sin A} = \frac{b}{\sin B} = \frac{c}{\sin C}$$

Proof of the law of sines.   In $\triangle ABC$ draw the altitude h from B to AC. In rt. $\triangle ABD$

$$\frac{h}{c} = \sin A \text{ ; or } h = c \sin A$$

In rt. $\triangle CBD$

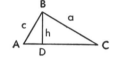

$$\frac{h}{a} = \sin C \text{ ; or } h = a \sin C$$

Therefore, $a \sin C = c \sin A$

Dividing each member of this equation by $\sin C \sin A$, we obtain

$$\frac{a \sin C}{\sin C \sin A} = \frac{c \sin A}{\sin C \sin A}$$

$$\frac{a}{\sin A} = \frac{c}{\sin C}$$

Similarly, by drawing the altitude from A to BC, it can be proven that

$$\frac{b}{\sin B} = \frac{c}{\sin C}$$

Therefore, $\dfrac{a}{\sin A} = \dfrac{b}{\sin B} = \dfrac{c}{\sin C}$

Although this law is true for any triangle, we shall restrict its use in this book to acute triangles (where all of the angles are acute). This law can be used also to solve acute triangles when given two sides and an angle opposite one of them.

ILLUSTRATIVE   EXAMPLE: Use of the law of sines

In $\triangle ABC$, $a = 23.85$, $c = 31.73$, $\angle C = 58° 20'$. Find the remaining parts of the triangle.

Solution. The remaining parts of the triangle are $\angle A$, $\angle B$, and b.

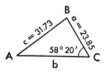

To find $\angle A$:

We select the formula which involves $\angle A$ and the three known

parts of the triangle. $\dfrac{a}{\sin A} = \dfrac{c}{\sin C}$

Substituting the known values
$$\frac{23.85}{\sin A} = \frac{31.73}{\sin 58° 20'}$$

Solving for sin A
$$\sin A = \frac{23.85 \sin 58° 20'}{31.73}$$

Expressing in logarithmic form
$$\log \sin A = \log 23.85 + \log \sin 58° 20' - \log 31.73$$

$$
\begin{aligned}
\log 23.85 &= 1.3775 \\
\log \sin 58° 20' &= 9.9300 - 10 \\
(\text{log numerator}) &= \overline{11.3075} - 10 \\
\log 31.73 & \quad\ 1.5015 \\
\log \sin A &= \overline{9.8060} - 10 \\
A &= 39° 46' \quad \text{Answer}
\end{aligned}
$$

To find $\angle B$:
$$\angle A + \angle B + \angle C = 180°$$
$$39° 46' + \angle B + 58° 20' = 180°$$
$$\angle B = 81° 54' \quad \text{Answer}$$

To find b: We select
$$\frac{b}{\sin B} = \frac{c}{\sin C}$$

Substituting
$$\frac{b}{\sin 81° 54'} = \frac{31.73}{\sin 58° 20'}$$

Solving for b
$$b = \frac{31.73 \sin 81° 54'}{\sin 58° 20'}$$

Expressing in logarithmic form
$$\log b = \log 31.73 + \log \sin 81° 54' - \log \sin 58° 20'$$

$$
\begin{aligned}
\log 31.73 &= 1.5015 \\
\log \sin 81° 54' &= 9.9957 - 10 \\
(\text{log numerator}) &= \overline{11.4972} - 10 \\
\log \sin 58° 20' &= 9.9300 - 10 \\
\log b &= \overline{1.5672} \\
b &= 36.92 \quad \text{Answer}
\end{aligned}
$$

Check: Gross errors can sometimes be detected by close scrutiny of the answers. The larger side must be opposite the larger angle, etc.

EXERCISES: Using the law of sines

Ex. 1–6 refer to $\triangle ABC$. By the use of logarithms, determine the parts of each triangle that are not given.

1. $a = 425$, $b = 526$, and $\angle A = 50°$

2. $b = 2.44$, $\angle B = 38° 10'$, and $\angle C = 74° 20'$

3. $a = 59.7$, $c = 70.3$, and $\angle C = 67° 40'$

4. $a = 75.37$, $\angle A = 77° 34'$, and $\angle B = 54° 48'$

5. $b = 5424$, $c = 5090$, and $\angle B = 62° 25'$

6. $c = 437.9$, $\angle A = 62° 33'$, and $\angle B = 49° 27'$

7. A surveyor is unable to measure the distance AB with his steel tape because of marshy terrain. To determine AB he first lays off a base line AD. After determining $\angle A$ with his transit, he measures a distance AC along the base line. He then measures $\angle C$. If $\angle A = 58°$, $AC = 530$ ft., and $\angle C = 74°$, how far is it from point A to point B?

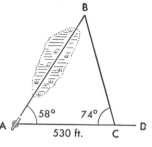

8. A man at point B wishes to determine the height of a tree (CD) which stands on the opposite bank of a stream (BC). He finds that at point B the angle of elevation of the top of the tree is 37°. After moving 75 ft. directly away from the tree, he finds that at point A the angle of elevation of the top of the tree is 29°. How high is the tree?

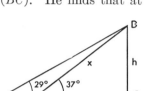

Hint: In $\triangle ABD$ determine log x by the law of sines. Then, in rt. $\triangle BCD$ find h.

CHAPTER REVIEW EXERCISES

1. In rt. $\triangle ABC$, $\angle A = 38° 42'$. Find $\angle B$.

2. Using the table of trigonometric functions, find

    a) tan 49° 14'   *b)* cos 28° 47'   *c)* ctn 66° 12'

3. Using the table of trigonometric functions, find $\angle A$ in each of the following:

    a) sin A = .7435   *b)* cos A = .5120   *c)* tan A = .4782

4. Using the table of logarithms of trigonometric functions, find

    a) log sin 37° 23'   *b)* log tan 47° 57'   *c)* log ctn 19° 24'

5. Using the table of logarithms of trigonometric functions, find $\angle A$ in each of the following:

    a) log tan A = 9.6637 − 10   *b)* log cos A = 9.8265 − 10

6. In rt. $\triangle ABC$, $c = 200$ and $\angle B = 42° 37'$. Find b.

7. In rt. $\triangle ABC$, $b = 130$ and $\angle A = 27° 22'$. Find a.

8. In rt. $\triangle ABC$, $a = 752$ and $\angle A = 44° 15'$. Find c.

9. In rt. $\triangle ABC$, $b = 400$ and $\angle B = 35° 46'$. Find a.

10. At a certain time the shadow along level ground of a 125 ft. tree is 100 ft. in length. Determine the angle of elevation of the sun at that time.

11. An engineer is designing an approach to a bridge which is 25 ft. above the level roadway. If the angle of rise is to be 4°, how far (horizontally) from the end of the bridge must he begin the project?

12. Each of the two equal sides of an isosceles triangle is 7.6 in. and the angle included between them equals 70°. Find, to the nearest tenth of an inch, the third side of the triangle.

13. Find angle B in $\triangle ABC$ if $a=48, b=41, \angle A =44°$.

14. A surveyor wished to find the distance AC across the river. See adjacent diagram. With his transit at C he measured $\angle ACB - 66° 21'$. Then he measured the distance $CB = 101.5$ ft. With the transit at B he measured $\angle ABC = 71° 42'$. How wide is the river (AC)?

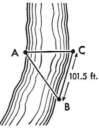

101.5 ft.

CUMULATIVE REVIEW EXERCISES

1. Subtract $6x^2 - 10x - 11$ from unity; subtract $-3x^2 + 5x$ from zero. Then add one half of the first difference to the second difference.

2. Using synthetic division, determine the partial quotient and the remainder when $2x^3 - 3x + 8$ is divided by $x + 2$.

3. Solve for x: $4(x - 5)(2x + 1) - (2x + 3)^2 = 4x^2 - 45$

4. Solve the formula $A = p + prt$ for p. In the resulting formula find the value of p when $A = \$6000$, $r = 4\%$, and $t = 5$ yr.

5. Factor: $m^2 - 4t^2 - r^2 + 4rt$.

6. Factor: $2b - ac - 2ab + c$.

7. Perform the indicated operation: $\dfrac{x^4 - 16}{32 - 4x^3} \div \dfrac{2x^2 + 3x - 2}{2x^3 + 4x^2 + 8x}$

8. Solve for x: $\dfrac{3x + 4}{8} - \dfrac{4x - 1}{3} = \dfrac{5 - 3x}{4}$

9. Name the methods which you can use to solve the following system of equations. Using one of these methods, determine the respective values of x and y.

$$5x + 7y = 9$$
$$3x - 4y = -11$$

10. Combine into a single radical: $\sqrt{12} - 2\sqrt{\dfrac{1}{3}} - \dfrac{5}{2\sqrt{3}}$

11. Simplify: $3^{\frac{5}{3}} \div \sqrt{3}$

12. Simplify : $\dfrac{16^{\frac{1}{2}} - 4^0}{27^{\frac{2}{3}}}$

13. Determine the value of the discriminant and the nature of the roots of each of the following quadratic equations :

      a) $x^2 - 4x = -4$ *b)* $2x^2 - 3x + 5 = 0$ *c)* $3x^2 = 1 - 4x$

14. Solve by the quadratic formula. Express the answer correct to two decimal places. $2x^2 + 3x - 3 = 0$

15. Solve and check : $\sqrt{3x - 5} = x - 1$

16. One leg of a right triangle is 24 in. in length. The hypotenuse is 6 in. more than twice the other leg. Determine the unknown sides of the triangle.

CHAPTER 17   *Binomial Theorem*

Powers of (a + b).   If we were to multiply the binomial $(a + b)$ by itself repeatedly, we would obtain the following polynomials as its powers.

$$(a + b)^0 = 1$$
$$(a + b)^1 = a + b$$
$$(a + b)^2 = a^2 + 2ab + b^2$$
$$(a + b)^3 = a^3 + 3a^2b + 3ab^2 + b^3$$
$$(a + b)^4 = a^4 + 4a^3b + 6a^2b^2 + 4ab^3 + b^4$$
$$(a + b)^5 = a^5 + 5a^4b + 10a^3b^2 + 10a^2b^3 + 5ab^4 + b^5$$

After a careful study of all these expansions of this binomial, we can arrive at the rules that would enable us to write out any integral power of the binomial without performing the actual multiplication. These rules make up the *binomial theorem.*

Binomial theorem.   To expand a general binomial $(a + b)$ to the nth power, the rules are as follows:

  1. The first term is a^n.

2. In each succeeding term (except the last) a appears as a factor, always raised to a power one less than in the preceding term.

3. In the second term b appears as a factor. In each succeeding term b appears as a factor, always raised to a power one greater than in the preceding term.

4. The numerical coefficient of the second term is n.

5. The numerical coefficient of any term is obtained by multiplying the coefficient of the preceding term by the exponent of a in that term and by dividing this product by the number of that term.

6. The number of terms in the expansion is $n + 1$ when n is a positive integer.

These rules may be expressed by the following formula:

$$(a+b)^n = a^n + \frac{n}{1}a^{n-1}b + \frac{n(n-1)}{1\cdot 2}a^{n-2}b^2 + \frac{n(n-1)(n-2)}{1\cdot 2\cdot 3}a^{n-3}b^3 + \cdots + b^n$$

The three dots used in this formula preceding the last term have a meaning similar to those used in progressions. They are a kind of mathematical *et cetera*. They take the place of an indefinite number of terms, all of which are obtained in a manner similar to the way the previous terms were obtained. The number of terms that are missing depends upon the numerical value of n.

ILLUSTRATIVE EXAMPLES: Expanding binomials raised to a power

1. Expand: $(x + y)^4$

Solution. To expand $(x + y)^4$, we use the formula given above.

$$x^4 + \frac{4}{1}x^3y + \frac{4\cdot 3}{1\cdot 2}x^2y^2 + \frac{4\cdot 3\cdot 2}{1\cdot 2\cdot 3}xy^3 + \frac{4\cdot 3\cdot 2\cdot 1}{1\cdot 2\cdot 3\cdot 4}y^4$$

Simplifying, we have $\qquad x^4 + 4x^3y + 6x^2y^2 + 4xy^3 + y^4$. Answer

2. Expand: $(m - n)^5$

Solution. $(m - n)^5 = m^5 + 5\,m^4(-n) + \frac{5\cdot 4}{2}m^3(-n)^2$

$$+ \frac{5\cdot 4\cdot 3}{1\cdot 2\cdot 3}m^2(-n)^3 + \frac{5\cdot 4\cdot 3\cdot 2}{1\cdot 2\cdot 3\cdot 4}m(-n)^4 + \frac{5\cdot 4\cdot 3\cdot 2\cdot 1}{1\cdot 2\cdot 3\cdot 4\cdot 5}(-n)^5$$

Simplifying, we have

$$m^5 - 5m^4n + 10m^3n^2 - 10m^2n^3 + 5mn^4 - n^5. \quad \text{Answer}$$

Notice : When the two terms of the binomial are in the form $(a - b)^n$ with n a positive integer, the signs of the terms in the expansion alternate, beginning with a plus sign.

E X E R C I S E S : Expanding binomials raised to a power

Expand :

1. $(x + y)^3$
2. $(m + n)^4$
3. $(a + b)^5$
4. $(x - y)^4$

5. $(a - b)^5$
6. $(x + y)^7$
7. $(x - y)^6$
8. $(a - b)^7$

Write expansions of the following binomials to the first four terms only :

9. $(x + a)^{12}$
10. $(m + p)^{16}$

11. $(m - n)^{10}$
12. $(a - b)^{20}$

Proof of the binomial theorem.   Comparing the binomial formula with the expansions shown in the first paragraph of this chapter, we see that the binomial formula is correct for binomials raised to any power up to the fifth. To check the formula for all powers which are integral values of n would be an impossibility. If we can prove that the binomial formula is true when the binomial is raised to the nth power, n being a positive integer, and that it is also true when the binomial is raised to the next higher power $(n + 1)$, then we have proved it true when the binomial is raised to any integral power.

Let us assume that

$$(a + b)^n = a^n + na^{n-1}b + \frac{n(n - 1)}{1 \cdot 2} a^{n-2}b^2 + \frac{n(n - 1)(n - 2)}{1 \cdot 2 \cdot 3} a^{n-3}b^3 + \cdots$$

If both sides are multiplied by $a + b$, the result is

$$(a + b)^{n+1} = a^{n+1} + na^n b + \frac{n(n - 1)}{1 \cdot 2}a^{n-1}b^2 + \frac{n(n - 1)(n - 2)}{1 \cdot 2 \cdot 3}a^{n-2}b^3 + \cdots$$

$$+ a^n b + \quad\quad na^{n-1}b^2 + \quad\quad \frac{n(n - 1)}{1 \cdot 2}a^{n-2}b^3 + \cdots$$

Collecting like terms

$$(a + b)^{n+1} = a^{n+1} + (n + 1)a^n b + \frac{(n + 1)n}{1 \cdot 2}a^{n-1}b^2$$

$$+ \frac{(n + 1)n(n - 1)}{1 \cdot 2 \cdot 3}a^{n-2}b^3 + \cdots$$

In examining this formula, we find that it is identical with the binomial formula except that $n + 1$ replaces n. Since we know that the binomial formula is true for $n = 5$ (p. 383), we know now that it is also true for $n + 1$, that is, the 6th power of the binomial.

If the binomial formula is true for the 6th power of the binomial, we can let $n = 6$. Then it must be true for $n + 1$, or the 7th power of the binomial. In this way we can see that the binomial formula is true for all positive integral values of n.

This method of proof of a theorem is known as mathematical induction. This method of *mathematical induction* consists in proving a theorem true for one certain integer and then proving that, if it is true for any integer, than it is also true for the next higher integer.

I L L U S T R A T I V E   E X A M P L E S : Applying the binomial theorem

1. Expand $\left(x + \dfrac{y}{2}\right)^4$.

Solution.

$$\left(x + \frac{y}{2}\right)^4 = x^4 + 4x^3\left(\frac{y}{2}\right) + \frac{4\cdot 3}{1\cdot 2}x^2\left(\frac{y}{2}\right)^2 + \frac{4\cdot 3\cdot 2}{1\cdot 2\cdot 3}x\left(\frac{y}{2}\right)^3 + \frac{4\cdot 3\cdot 2\cdot 1}{1\cdot 2\cdot 3\cdot 4}\left(\frac{y}{2}\right)^4$$

$$= x^4 + 2x^3y + \tfrac{3}{2}x^2y^2 + \tfrac{1}{2}xy^3 + \tfrac{1}{16}y^4 \quad \text{Answer}$$

2. Write the first four terms of $(a - 2b)^{10}$.

Solution. $(a - 2b)^{10} = a^{10} + 10a^9(-2b) + \dfrac{10\cdot 9}{1\cdot 2}a^8(-2b)^2$

$$+ \frac{10\cdot 9\cdot 8}{1\cdot 2\cdot 3}a^7(-2b)^3 + \cdots$$

$$= a^{10} - 20a^9b + 180a^8b^2 - 960a^7b^3 + \cdots \quad \text{Answer}$$

E X E R C I S E S : Applying the binomial theorem

Expand :

1. $\left(a + \dfrac{b}{2}\right)^5$

2. $(2x + y)^4$

3. $(a + 2b)^5$

4. $\left(\dfrac{x}{2} - y\right)^4$

5. $\left(y + \dfrac{z}{3}\right)^5$

6. $\left(\dfrac{x}{2} - \dfrac{y}{3}\right)^4$

7. $(2x - y)^5$

8. $(2a - 3b)^4$

9. $\left(4x - \dfrac{y}{2}\right)^4$

10. $\left(2m - \dfrac{n}{3}\right)^5$

Write the first three terms of :

11. $\left(\dfrac{a}{2} - 4b\right)^{12}$

12. $\left(x - \dfrac{2y}{3}\right)^{15}$

Write the first four terms of :

13. $\left(\dfrac{x}{2} - 2y\right)^{10}$

14. $\left(a + \dfrac{b}{3}\right)^{12}$

ILLUSTRATIVE EXAMPLE : Further use of the binomial theorem

Write the first four terms of $(x^{\frac{1}{2}} - y^{\frac{2}{3}})^6$

$Solution.$ $(x^{\frac{1}{2}} - y^{\frac{2}{3}})^6 = (x^{\frac{1}{2}})^6 + 6(x^{\frac{1}{2}})^5(-y^{\frac{2}{3}}) + \dfrac{6\cdot5}{2}(x^{\frac{1}{2}})^4(-y^{\frac{2}{3}})^2$

$$+ \dfrac{6\cdot5\cdot4}{2\cdot3}(x^{\frac{1}{2}})^3(-y^{\frac{2}{3}})^3 + \cdots$$

$$= x^3 - 6x^{\frac{5}{2}}y^{\frac{2}{3}} + 15x^2y^{\frac{4}{3}} - 20x^{\frac{3}{2}}y^2 + \cdots \quad \text{Answer}$$

Notice: The exponents of x form an arithmetic progression:
$$3, \tfrac{5}{2}, 2, \tfrac{3}{2}, \cdots$$
The exponents of y also form an arithmetic progression:
$$0, \tfrac{2}{3}, \tfrac{4}{3}, 2, \cdots$$
Errors can often be quickly detected if, when the simplification is completed, a check is made of the exponents of the literal quantities to find if they form an arithmetic progression.

EXERCISES : Further use of the binomial theorem

Expand :

1. $(x^{\frac{1}{2}} + y)^4$
2. $(x - y^{\frac{1}{3}})^5$
3. $(a^{\frac{2}{3}} + b^{\frac{1}{2}})^4$

4. $(x^2 - y)^6$
5. $(x^3 + y^{\frac{1}{2}})^5$
6. $(2a^{\frac{1}{3}} - 3b^2)^4$

Write the first three terms of:

7. $(a^{\frac{2}{3}} + b^{\frac{2}{3}})^{12}$
8. $(2a^{\frac{1}{2}} - 3b^{\frac{3}{2}})^6$
9. $(a^{\frac{5}{3}} + 4x^{\frac{3}{2}})^{10}$
10. $(m^{\frac{7}{2}} - \frac{2}{3}n^4)^{16}$

11. $(x^{-1} + y^{-1})^5$
12. $(2a^{-3} + b^{-2})^6$
13. $(x^{-\frac{1}{2}} - y^{-\frac{1}{3}})^{12}$
14. $(x^{-\frac{2}{3}} + \frac{3}{2}y^{-\frac{1}{2}})^{15}$

Factorial notation.   The symbol 4! is read "4 factorial." It represents the product of all the integers from 1 to 4. That is, $4! = 1\cdot2\cdot3\cdot4$ or 24.

Likewise, $6! = 1\cdot2\cdot3\cdot4\cdot5\cdot6$ or 720.

Similarly, $n! = 1\cdot2\cdot3\cdots n$ (n factors).

ILLUSTRATIVE EXAMPLE : Using factorial notation

Evaluate: $\dfrac{3!5!}{4!}.$

$Solution.$ $\dfrac{3!5!}{4!} = \dfrac{1\cdot2\cdot3\cdot1\cdot2\cdot3\cdot4\cdot5}{1\cdot2\cdot3\cdot4}$

$$= 30 \quad \text{Answer}$$

EXERCISES: Using factorial notation

Evaluate:

1. $5!$

2. $(4!)(3!)$

3. $\dfrac{6!}{5!}$

4. $\dfrac{8!}{4!4!}$

5. $\dfrac{9!}{7!3!}$

6. $\dfrac{(n-1)!}{n!}$

7. $\dfrac{(n+1)!}{2 \cdot n!}$

The binomial formula written with factorial notation

$$(a+b)^n = a^n + \frac{n}{1!}a^{n-1}b + \frac{n(n-1)}{2!}a^{n-2}b^2 + \frac{n(n-1)(n-2)}{3!}a^{n-3}b^3 + \cdots$$

Pascal's triangle. By studying the expansions of the binomial $a+b$ in the opening paragraph of this chapter (p. 383), we find the numerical coefficients form the following triangle:

```
              1
           1     1
        1     2     1
     1     3     3     1
  1     4     6     4     1
1     5    10    10     5     1
```

More rows can be added for powers of $a+b$ above the fifth. Any number in the triangle is the sum of the two numbers in the row above it, one to the left and one to the right. The next row would be:

$$1 \quad 6 \quad 15 \quad 20 \quad 15 \quad 6 \quad 1$$

Can you add still another row?

Notice that the numbers appearing in each of the first five rows represent a power of 11: $11^0 = 1$; $11^1 = 11$; $11^2 = 121$; $11^3 = 1331$; $11^4 = 14{,}641$.

The triangle is known as *Pascal's triangle,* named for its discoverer, Blaise Pascal, a French mathematician who lived 300 years ago.

Some students prefer to use Pascal's triangle in writing the expansion of a binomial raised to a power. Others prefer to use the method explained in the preceding paragraphs.

The general term. To find any required term in an expansion we may use the formula:

$$rth \ term = \frac{n(n-1)(n-2)\cdots(n-r+2)}{(r-1)!}a^{n-r+1}b^{r-1}$$

In this formula r represents the number of the term in the expansion of $(a + b)^n$.

Notice that $r - 1$ occurs twice in the formula. It occurs as the largest factor in the denominator of the coefficient. It is also the exponent of b. This number, $r - 1$, which is one less than the number of the term, is usually considered the key for finding the whole term. This is demonstrated in the following example.

I L L U S T R A T I V E   E X A M P L E S : Finding a particular term

1. Find the sixth term of $\left(2x - \dfrac{1}{y}\right)^9$.

Solution. In finding the sixth term, the key number is 5, which is one less than the number of the term.

$$\frac{?}{1 \cdot 2 \cdot 3 \cdot 4 \cdot 5}(2x)^? \left(-\frac{1}{y}\right)^5$$

The denominator of the coefficient is $(r - 1)!$, or 5! in this problem. The exponent of the second term of the binomial is also 5. Thus, $-\dfrac{1}{y}$ is raised to the fifth power. The numerator of the coefficient has the same number of factors as the denominator. The first factor is n, in this problem, 9.

The coefficient is $\dfrac{9 \cdot 8 \cdot 7 \cdot 6 \cdot 5}{1 \cdot 2 \cdot 3 \cdot 4 \cdot 5}$.

Since the sum of the exponents of $2x$ and $-\dfrac{1}{y}$ must be equal to the power of the binomial, in this case 9, and since the exponent of $\dfrac{1}{y}$ is 5, then the exponent of $2x$ must be $(9 - 5)$ or 4.

$$\frac{9 \cdot 8 \cdot 7 \cdot 6 \cdot 5}{1 \cdot 2 \cdot 3 \cdot 4 \cdot 5}(2x)^4 \left(-\frac{1}{y}\right)^5$$

Simplifying $\qquad 126(16x^4)\left(-\dfrac{1}{y^5}\right) = -2016\dfrac{x^4}{y^5}$ Answer

2. Find the fourth term of $\left(3x^{\frac{1}{2}} - \dfrac{1}{y^{\frac{1}{3}}}\right)^7$.

Solution. Key number is 3.

$$\frac{7 \cdot 6 \cdot 5}{1 \cdot 2 \cdot 3}(3x^{\frac{1}{2}})^4 \left(-\frac{1}{y^{\frac{1}{3}}}\right)^3$$

Simplifying $\qquad 35(81x^2)\left(-\dfrac{1}{y}\right)$ or $\dfrac{-2835x^2}{y}$ Answer

E X E R C I S E S : Finding a particular term

Find :

1. The third term of $(x + y)^5$.
2. The fourth term of $(n - p)^7$.
3. The fifth term of $(2a - b)^6$.
4. The fourth term of $\left(2x + \dfrac{y}{2}\right)^6$.
5. The sixth term of $(a^2 - b)^9$.
6. The fifth term of $(a^{\frac{1}{2}} + b)^7$.
7. The fourth term of $(2m - n^{\frac{1}{2}})^8$.
8. The sixth term of $\left(x - \dfrac{2}{y}\right)^9$.
9. The eleventh term of $(x^2 - y^{\frac{1}{3}})^{13}$.
10. The twelfth term of $(2a^{\frac{1}{3}} + b^{\frac{2}{5}})^{13}$.
11. The seventh term of $(2x^{\frac{3}{2}} - y^{\frac{1}{2}})^{10}$.
12. The third term of $(x^{\frac{1}{3}} - 2y^{\frac{1}{4}})^8$.
13. The middle term of $(x^2 - 2a)^8$.

Hint : If there are nine terms in the expansion, the fifth term is the middle term.

14. The middle term of $(a^{\frac{3}{4}} + 2b^{\frac{1}{4}})^6$.
15. The middle term of $(3m^2 + n^2)^{10}$.
16. The middle terms of $(2r^{\frac{1}{3}} + s^{\frac{1}{2}})^7$.

Hint : If there are eight terms in the expansion, the fourth and the fifth terms are the middle terms.

17. The middle terms of $(3x^{\frac{2}{3}} - 2y^{\frac{4}{5}})^5$.
18. The middle term of $\left(\dfrac{1}{\sqrt{x}} + \dfrac{2}{\sqrt[3]{x}}\right)^8$

Hint : Convert the radicals to exponential form.

I L L U S T R A T I V E   E X A M P L E S : Finding special terms in binomial expansions

1. Find the term that contains x^3 in the expansion of $(2x - y)^7$.

Solution. In order to write the term that contains x^3 in the expansion of $(2x - y)^7$, it is necessary first to determine which term this is. In the first term of the expansion $(2x)^7$, the exponent of x is 7. In the second term of the expansion $- 7(2x)^6y$, the exponent of x is 6. Knowing the exponents of x in the terms of the expansion form an arithmetic progression, we can write that progression: 7, 6, 5, $\cdots$. Since we are interested in finding which term contains x^3, we must determine which term in this

progression is 3. The fifth term is 3. Therefore, the fifth term of the expansion of $(2x - y)^7$
is the required term.

The key number is 4. The fifth term is

$$\frac{7 \cdot 6 \cdot 5 \cdot 4}{1 \cdot 2 \cdot 3 \cdot 4}(2x)^3(-y)^4$$

Simplifying $\quad\quad 35(2x)^3(-y)^4$

$$280\,x^3y^4 \quad \text{Answer}$$

2. Find the term that contains $\dfrac{1}{y}$ in the expansion of $\left(2y^{\frac{2}{5}} + \dfrac{1}{y^{\frac{3}{5}}}\right)^5$.

Solution. In the first term $(2y^{\frac{2}{5}})^5$ the exponent of y is 2.

The second term is $\quad\quad 5(2y^{\frac{2}{5}})^4\left(\dfrac{1}{y^{\frac{3}{5}}}\right)$

Simplifying $\quad\quad 5 \cdot 2^4 \dfrac{y^{\frac{8}{5}}}{y^{\frac{3}{5}}} \quad$ or $\quad 80y$

The exponent of y in the second term is 1. The arithmetic progression
formed by the exponents of y in the terms of the expansion is 2, 1, 0, $\cdots$.
Since we are interested in finding which term in the given expansion con-
tains $\dfrac{1}{y}$ or y^{-1}, we find the number of the term in the progression 2, 1, 0, $\cdots$
which is equal to -1. The fourth term in this progression is -1. There-
fore, the required term in the expansion of $\left(2y^{\frac{2}{5}} + \dfrac{1}{y^{\frac{3}{5}}}\right)^5$ is the fourth term.

Key number is 3. The fourth term is $\dfrac{5 \cdot 4 \cdot 3}{1 \cdot 2 \cdot 3}(2y^{\frac{2}{5}})^2\left(\dfrac{1}{y^{\frac{3}{5}}}\right)^3$

Simplifying $\quad\quad 40\dfrac{y^{\frac{4}{5}}}{y^{\frac{9}{5}}}$

$$\dfrac{40}{y} \quad \text{Answer}$$

EXERCISES: Finding special terms

Find the term that contains:

1. x^3 in $(2x + 3y)^8$.

2. $x^{\frac{5}{2}}$ in $(1 + x^{\frac{1}{2}})^9$.

3. y^6 in $(x - 2y)^7$.

4. x in $(x^{\frac{1}{3}} - 2)^6$.

5. $x^{\frac{7}{2}}$ in $(2\sqrt{x} + y)^{11}$.

6. $y^{\frac{3}{5}}$ in $(x - y^{\frac{3}{5}})^8$.

Hint: Find the term that contains x^0.

7. $x^{\frac{1}{4}}$ in $\left(x + \dfrac{1}{x^{\frac{1}{4}}}\right)^9$.

8. $y^{\frac{1}{2}}$ in $\left(y^{\frac{1}{2}} - \dfrac{3}{y^{\frac{3}{2}}}\right)^{13}$.

9. x in $\left(x^{\frac{1}{5}}y - \dfrac{2}{x^{\frac{2}{5}}y}\right)^{14}$.

10. No x in $\left(x^{\frac{2}{3}} + \dfrac{3}{x^{\frac{1}{3}}}\right)^9$.

When _n_ is a fraction or a negative number.   Even if the power of the binomial has a negative exponent or a fractional exponent, the binomial theorem still applies. However, it is true only if the numerical value of _a_ is greater than the numerical value of _b_. Of course, the number of terms cannot be one greater than _n_, if _n_ is negative or fractional. In such cases there is no last term. The expansion contains an unlimited number of terms.

To prove the binomial theorem true for these special exponents is beyond the scope of this text. We shall accept it as true and shall apply it to the solution of the problems in the exercises that follow.

I L L U S T R A T I V E   E X A M P L E S : Expanding binomials with fractional or negative exponents

1. Write the first four terms of $(a^2 - b)^{\frac{1}{2}}$

Solution. $(a^2 - b)^{\frac{1}{2}} = (a^2)^{\frac{1}{2}} + \frac{1}{2}(a^2)^{-\frac{1}{2}}(-b) + \frac{\frac{1}{2}(-\frac{1}{2})}{1\cdot 2}(a^2)^{-\frac{3}{2}}(-b)^2$

$+ \frac{(\frac{1}{2})(-\frac{1}{2})(-\frac{3}{2})}{1\cdot 2\cdot 3}(a^2)^{-\frac{5}{2}}(-b)^3 + \cdots$

$$(a^2 - b)^{\frac{1}{2}} = a - \frac{a^{-1}b}{2} - \frac{a^{-3}b^2}{8} - \frac{a^{-5}b^3}{16} - \cdots$$

$$(a^2 - b)^{\frac{1}{2}} = a - \frac{b}{2a} - \frac{b^2}{8a^3} - \frac{b^3}{16a^5} - \cdots \quad \text{Answer}$$

2. Write the first five terms of $(a^{\frac{2}{3}} + 2b^{\frac{1}{2}})^{-3}$

Solution. $(a^{\frac{2}{3}} + 2b^{\frac{1}{2}})^{-3} = (a^{\frac{2}{3}})^{-3} - 3(a^{\frac{2}{3}})^{-4}(2b^{\frac{1}{2}}) + \frac{(-3)(-4)}{2}(a^{\frac{2}{3}})^{-5}(2b^{\frac{1}{2}})^2$

$+ \frac{(-3)(-4)(-5)}{1\cdot 2\cdot 3}(a^{\frac{2}{3}})^{-6}(2b^{\frac{1}{2}})^3 + \frac{(-3)(-4)(-5)(-6)}{1\cdot 2\cdot 3\cdot 4}(a^{\frac{2}{3}})^{-7}(2b^{\frac{1}{2}})^4 + \cdots$

$(a^{\frac{2}{3}} + 2b^{\frac{1}{2}})^{-3} = a^{-2} - 6a^{-\frac{8}{3}}b^{\frac{1}{2}} + 24a^{-\frac{10}{3}}b - 80a^{-4}b^{\frac{3}{2}} + 240a^{-\frac{14}{3}}b^2 - \cdots$

$(a^{\frac{2}{3}} + 2b^{\frac{1}{2}})^{-3} = \frac{1}{a^2} - \frac{6b^{\frac{1}{2}}}{a^{\frac{8}{3}}} + \frac{24b}{a^{\frac{10}{3}}} - \frac{80b^{\frac{3}{2}}}{a^4} + \frac{240b^2}{a^{\frac{14}{3}}} - \cdots \quad \text{Answer}$

E X E R C I S E S : Expanding binomials with fractional or negative exponents

Write the first four terms of :

1. $(x + y)^{\frac{1}{2}}$	**5.** $(1 + x)^{-4}$	**9.** $(a^2 - b)^{\frac{2}{3}}$
2. $(1 - a)^{-1}$	**6.** $(x - 1)^{\frac{1}{2}}$	**10.** $(x^{\frac{1}{2}} - y^{\frac{1}{3}})^{-2}$
3. $(1 + x)^{-\frac{1}{2}}$	**7.** $(1 - x)^{-2}$	**11.** $(\sqrt{x} - y)^{-3}$
4. $(a - b)^{\frac{2}{3}}$	**8.** $(a + b)^{-2}$	**12.** $(\sqrt[3]{x} + \sqrt{y})^{\frac{7}{5}}$

Find:

13. The sixth term of $(1 + 2x)^{\frac{1}{2}}$ **15.** The fifth term of $(2a - 3b)^{-1}$

14. The seventh term of $(r - 1)^{-3}$ **16.** The tenth term of $(1 + 3a^2)^{\frac{7}{3}}$

Numerical approximation by the binomial theorem.   The binomial theorem can be used to find the value, to any degree of accuracy, of the roots or the powers of numbers. The importance of the binomial formula in more advanced mathematics is the best reason for using it in solving problems in the following exercise. Although the values of the roots and the powers could be found more easily by logarithms, the exercises are included for the purpose of giving the student drill in the very important topic of the binomial formula.

ILLUSTRATIVE   EXAMPLES: Using the binomial formula for numerical approximation

1. Find to the nearest tenth: $\sqrt[3]{30}$.

Solution. To convert $\sqrt[3]{30}$ into a binomial expansion, we change the root to a power, $30^{\frac{1}{3}}$. Then we change the number 30 into the binomial $(27 + 3)$. The choice of 27 and 3 was made because 27 is the cube nearest to 30.

$$\sqrt[3]{30} = (27 + 3)^{\frac{1}{3}}$$

Using the binomial formula,

$$\sqrt[3]{30} = (27 + 3)^{\frac{1}{3}} = 27^{\frac{1}{3}} + \tfrac{1}{3}(27)^{-\frac{2}{3}}(3) + \frac{\tfrac{1}{3}(-\tfrac{2}{3})}{2}(27)^{-\frac{5}{3}}(3)^2 + \cdots$$

$$\sqrt[3]{30} = 3 + \tfrac{1}{9} - \tfrac{1}{243} + \cdots$$

The student can see, through careful study, that terms beyond the third term will be numerically smaller than the third term. He can see, too, that the signs will alternate. Therefore, to find the value of the $\sqrt[3]{30}$ to the nearest tenth, it is unnecessary to go beyond the second term. Converting the fractions to decimals

$$\sqrt[3]{30} = 3 + 0.111 - .004 + \cdots$$
$$= 3.1 \text{ to the nearest tenth} \quad \text{Answer}$$

2. Find to the nearest hundredth: $(1.05)^6$.

Solution. Using the binomial formula

$$(1.05)^6 = (1 + .05)^6$$
$$= 1^6 + 6 \cdot 1^5(.05) + \frac{6 \cdot 5}{1 \cdot 2} \cdot 1^4(.05)^2 + \frac{6 \cdot 5 \cdot 4}{1 \cdot 2 \cdot 3} \cdot 1^3(.05)^3 + \cdots$$
$$= 1 + .30 + .0375 + .0025 + \cdots$$

Every term beyond the fourth will be less than .001. Therefore, finding 1.05^6 to the nearest hundredth, we obtain

$$1.05^6 = 1.34 \quad \text{Answer}$$

E X E R C I S E S :   Using the binomial formula for numerical approximations

Find the value of the following to the nearest tenth:

1. $\sqrt[3]{9}$ 3. $\sqrt[4]{17}$ 5. $34^{\frac{1}{2}}$

2. $\sqrt{26}$ 4. $\sqrt[5]{31}$ 6. $125^{\frac{1}{3}}$

Find the value of the following to the nearest hundredth:

7. $(1.01)^6$ 9. $(0.99)^3$ 11. $(2.01)^7$

8. $(1.02)^5$ 10. $(3.02)^4$ 12. $(0.98)^5$

Find the exact value of the following, by using the binomial formula:

13. $(1.05)^3$ 15. $(1.01)^5$ 17. $(1.03)^4$

14. $(1.02)^5$ 16. $(1.04)^4$ 18. $(1.025)^3$

Find to the nearest tenth the value of the following, using the binomial formula:

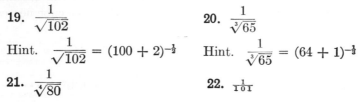

19. $\dfrac{1}{\sqrt{102}}$ 20. $\dfrac{1}{\sqrt[3]{65}}$

Hint. $\dfrac{1}{\sqrt{102}} = (100 + 2)^{-\frac{1}{2}}$ Hint. $\dfrac{1}{\sqrt[3]{65}} = (64 + 1)^{-\frac{1}{3}}$

21. $\dfrac{1}{\sqrt[4]{80}}$ 22. $\frac{1}{101}$

The Binomial Theorem.
Euclid (300 B.C.) knew how to expand $(a+b)^2$. The Arabs and Hindus used the expansion $(a + b)^2$ and $(a + b)^3$. The French mathematician Vieta (1540–1603) used the expansion $(a + b)^4$. Pascal (1623–1662) constructed the arithmetic (Pascal) triangle which had been known to the Arabs and Chinese for centuries. The Binomial Theorem, as we know it now, was first stated by Sir Isaac Newton in 1676. The proof of the theorem was given by Solvemini (1742), by Euler (1774), and by Abel (1825) for integral exponents, for fractional exponents, and for complex exponents, respectively.

CHAPTER REVIEW EXERCISES

In each exercise express the final answer in simplified form.

1. Expand $(x - y)^5$.

2. Expand $(2a + b)^4$.

3. Expand $\left(m - \dfrac{n}{2}\right)^5$.

4. Write the first four terms of the expansion of $\left(\dfrac{x}{3} - 2y\right)^{12}$.

5. Write the first four terms of the expansion of $(x^{\frac{1}{2}} + 2y^{\frac{2}{3}})^{10}$.

6. Write the first five terms of the expansion of $(2x^{-1} + y^{-1})^{11}$.

7. Evaluate:

$$a)\ \frac{7!}{5!} \qquad b)\ \frac{6!3!}{5!4!} \qquad c)\ \frac{9!}{5!4!} \qquad d)\ \frac{2\cdot n!}{(n-1)!}$$

8. Find the sixth term of $(2a - b^{\frac{1}{2}})^8$.

9. Find the eleventh term of $\left(m^2 + \dfrac{n}{2}\right)^{13}$.

10. Find the middle term of $(2x^{-\frac{1}{2}} + y^{\frac{2}{3}})^8$.

11. Find the term that contains x^3 in $\left(x^2 + \dfrac{3}{x}\right)^9$.

12. Write the first five terms of $(x + y)^{-1}$.

13. Using the binomial formula, find the exact value of $(1.01)^4$.

14. Using the binomial formula, find to the nearest tenth the value of $\sqrt[4]{79}$.

CUMULATIVE REVIEW EXERCISES

1. Factor: $24x^2 - 5x - 36$.

2. Solve for x in terms of a: $\dfrac{3x - a}{2} - 3a = 1 + \dfrac{ax - 3a}{3a}$

3. Solve graphically:

$$2x + 5y = -16$$
$$x = 3y + 14$$

4. If $3x = 4y$, what is the value of the ratio $y : x$?

5. Divide $2x + 5x^{\frac{2}{3}}y^{\frac{1}{3}} + 5x^{\frac{1}{3}}y^{\frac{2}{3}} + 2y$ by $x^{\frac{1}{3}} + y^{\frac{1}{3}}$.

6. Simplify: $\dfrac{3\sqrt{5} - 5\sqrt{3}}{\sqrt{5} + \sqrt{3}}$

7. Identify the graphs of the following equations:

a) $2y - x^2 = 4$ d) $3x^2 = 13 - 3y^2$

b) $y = \dfrac{-7}{x}$ e) $5x^2 - 4y^2 = 3$

                       f) $4x^2 + 3y^2 = 12$

c) $2y - 2x = 5$

8. Solve for x and y:

$$x + y^2 = 13$$
$$x^2 + y^2 = 25$$

9. Using logarithms, solve for x: $3^{x+2} = 17$

10. Find the value of $\dfrac{4!\,6!}{3!\,5!}$

11. Find the eighth term of $(2x^{\frac{1}{2}} - y^{\frac{1}{3}})^9$.

12. The length of a certain rectangle is three times as long as the width. If a line is drawn from the midpoint of a long side to a vertex of the other long side, find the acute angle that this line makes with a short side of the rectangle.

13. If the sum of the first four terms of a geometric series is four times the sum of the first two terms, what is the common ratio?

14. A hiker planned to walk the last 7 mi. back to camp to arrive in time for dinner. After he walked 1 mi., he learned that his watch was $\frac{1}{2}$ hr. slow, and consequently he was $\frac{1}{2}$ hr. behind schedule. In order to arrive at camp on time, he increased his rate of walking 1 mph. What was his original rate?

15. Solve the following system of equations for y by use of determinants:

$$1.2x + 0.4z = 1$$
$$2.1x - 3.3y = 1$$
$$1.3x + 0.6z = 1$$

16. Estimate the roots of $x^2 - 3x - 3 = 0$ from the graph of $y = x^2 - 3x - 3$.

CHAPTER 18

Permutations, Combinations, and Probability

A fundamental principle.   Let us consider the following problem. Suppose there are three roads connecting town A and town B and two roads connecting town B and town C. How many different ways can a man travel from town A to town C by way of town B?

The man can go from town A to town B in any of three different ways; he can go from town B to town C in any of two ways. Therefore he may make the trip from A to B to C in $3 \cdot 2$, or 6 different ways. We can readily list these six different routes, referring to the map, as:

$$a, p \qquad b, p \qquad c, p$$
$$a, q \qquad b, q \qquad c, q$$

In the above example we have used the fundamental principle:

> If an act can be performed in x different ways, and if after this act has been performed in any one of these ways, a second act can be performed in y different ways, then the total number of ways of performing the two acts in succession is xy.

This principle can be extended to include any number of different acts.

ILLUSTRATIVE EXAMPLES: Applying the fundamental principle

1. In buying Christmas gifts, a girl wishes to buy a book for her brother and a book for her sister. If the store's book shelf contains 7 different books for boys and 5 different books for girls, in how many ways can the girl make her purchases?

Solution. We apply the fundamental principle. The girl can buy a boy's book in 7 different ways. Then she can buy a girl's book in 5 different ways. The total number of ways of making the purchase is

$$7 \cdot 5 \text{ or } 35. \quad \text{Answer}$$

2. How many two-digit numbers can be formed using only the odd digits (1, 3, 5, 7, 9)?

Solution. In selecting the digits of the two-digit number, we are applying the fundamental principle. The first digit of the two-digit number (the tens digit) may be selected in any one of five ways; any one of the five digits may be selected. The second digit of the two-digit number (the units digit) may also be selected in any one of five ways. The number of two-digit numbers that can be formed is, therefore,

$$5 \cdot 5 \text{ or } 25. \quad \text{Answer}$$

3. How many three-digit, even numbers can be formed from the digits 1, 4, 5, 8, 9 if no digit may be repeated?

Solution. In selecting the three digits, we are applying the fundamental principle for 3 acts. The answer will be in the form of three factors. We write three blanks

$$(\quad)(\quad)(\quad)$$

which are to be filled by the number of ways in which each of the three acts may be performed. Since the problem requires an even number, we begin by considering the units digit first. We have only 2 even digits to choose from; therefore, we have *two* choices for the units place.   ( )( )(2)

After we have used either the 4 or 8 as the units digit, we have four digits left, since we may not repeat the digit which we have already used. Therefore the tens digit may be chosen in *four* ways.   ( )(4)(2)

After the units digit and the tens digit have both been selected, there remain *three* digits which may be chosen for the hundreds digit. Thus the number of three-digit, even numbers that can be formed from the given digits is   (3)(4)(2)

$$3 \cdot 4 \cdot 2 \text{ or } 24. \quad \text{Answer}$$

O R A L   E X E R C I S E S : Applying the fundamental principle

1. A boys' dormitory has six windows. In how many different ways may a boy enter by one window and leave by a different one?

2. In the sophomore class of our school there are four candidates for president and three candidates for vice president. In how many different ways may the two offices be filled?

3. A girl has five skirts and four sweaters. In how many different costumes may she appear?

4. How many different two-digit numbers can be formed using the digits 1, 2, 3, and 4, if the digits may be repeated?

5. A soda fountain offers 12 different kinds of soft drinks and 10 different kinds of sandwiches. How many different luncheon combinations of a soft drink and a sandwich are possible?

6. An English teacher asked each student to write a book report on 1 novel and on 1 biography. If the list of acceptable books consisted of 12 novels and 6 biographies, how many different combinations of a novel and a biography could the student choose?

7. If any combination of a vowel and a consonant makes a syllable, how many two-letter syllables can be formed from 6 different consonants and 3 different vowels? (Remember that the vowel may come first or last.)

8. An automobile manufacturer uses 10 different basic colors for the body of the car and 8 different contrasting colors for the trim. How many different color combinations can be offered in a two-color car?

E X E R C I S E S : Applying the fundamental principle

1. Ten dogs are entered in a children's pet show. In how many different ways may the judge award first, second, and third prizes?

2. On a certain baseball team all of the starting positions are fixed except the battery (the pitcher and the catcher). If there are four pitchers and three catchers, how many different starting teams are possible?

3. How many different two-digit numbers can be formed using the digits 1, 2, 3, 4, and 5, if no digit may be repeated? How many of these numbers are divisible by 2?

4. If six sprinters enter a hundred-yard dash, in how many different ways may first, second, and third places be won?

5. A dinner menu lists four different appetizers, three different soups, ten different entrees, and eight different desserts. How many different complete dinners can be ordered?

6. A man has a quarter, a half dollar, and a dime which he gives to three children. If each child receives a coin, in how many different ways may he distribute the coins? If a child may receive more than one coin, in how many ways may the coins be distributed?

7. How many numbers of three different digits can be made using the digits 1, 3, 5, 7, and 9? How many of these numbers are greater than 300? How many are greater than 370?

8. A certain state uses five symbols on each license plate. If each of the first two symbols is one of the twenty-six letters of the alphabet, and if the last three symbols are each one of the ten numerical digits, how many different plates can be made?

Permutations.   A permutation is an arrangement of a number of things in a definite order. Thus the letters *abc* and the letters *bac* are different permutations of the first three letters of the alphabet.

Permutation of *n* things, taken all at a time.   Let us consider all the possible different permutations of the three letters *a*, *b*, and *c*. By the principle that was stated on page 398, when the letters are arranged in a row, there are three choices for the first position. After the first position has been filled, only two letters remain; therefore, there are two choices for the second position. Finally, after the first two positions have been filled, one letter remains. The number of possible different permutations of the three letters is, therefore, $3 \cdot 2 \cdot 1$ or 6, or in factorial notation, 3!. This is an example of the number of permutations of three things, taken all at a time. It is sometimes indicated as $_3P_3$, where the first 3 indicates the number of things being arranged (here, the three letters a, b, c), and the second 3 indicates the number of things used in each arrangement. The number of permutations of four things taken all at a time is indicated as $_4P_4$; and it is equal to 4!. In general,

> The number of permutations of *n* things, taken all at a time, is $_nP_n$, and is equal to *n*!

I L L U S T R A T I V E   E X A M P L E : Permutation of *n* things, taken all at a time

How many six-letter arrangements can be made from the letters a, c, d, e, k, r, if none of the letters is repeated?

Solution. If all 6 of the given letters are to be used to make each arrangement, then we find the number of permutations of 6 things, taken all at a time. The formula is $_nP_n$.

$$_6P_6 = 6!$$
$$= 6 \cdot 5 \cdot 4 \cdot 3 \cdot 2 \cdot 1$$
$$= 720 \quad \text{Answer}$$

E X E R C I S E S : Permutation of *n* things, taken all at a time

1. What is the value of $_5P_5$?

2. In how many ways may 6 boys be arranged in a straight line?

3. How many different arrangements can be made using all of the letters of the word TRACK?

4. How many different arrangements can be made using all of the letters of the word HOCKEY? How many of these begin with H and end in Y?

5. In how many different ways may 7 boys be arranged in a straight line?

6. In how many different ways may 8 girls be arranged in a straight line if one particular girl is to be at the head of the line and another particular girl is to be at the foot of the line?

7. How many different arrangements can be made using all of the letters of the word DIMBO?

8. How many numbers between 1000 and 2000 can be made with the digits 1, 2, 3, and 4?

Permutations of *n* things, taken some at a time.   Let us consider the number of different three-letter permutations of the five letters a, b, c, d, and e with no letter repeated. Here we have five choices for the first position, four for the second position, and three for the third position. Thus the number of different three-letter arrangements is $5 \cdot 4 \cdot 3$, or 60. This is an example of the number of permutations of 5 things, taken 3 at a time; it is indicated by the notation $_5P_3$. The number of permutations of 7 things, taken 4 at a time, is indicated as $_7P_4$. In general,

---

The number of permutations of *n* things, taken *r* at a time, is indicated as $_nP_r$. It is equal to $n(n-1)$ $(n-2)...$ for *r* factors.

I L L U S T R A T I V E   E X A M P L E : Permutation of *n* things, taken some at a time

Four ladies enter a room in which there are 6 chairs. In how many ways may the ladies be seated?

Solution. Here we have 6 chairs, to be used 4 at a time. This is a number of permutations of 6 things, taken 4 at a time. The formula is

$$_nP_r = n(n-1)(n-2) \cdots \text{ for } r \text{ factors}$$
$$_6P_4 = 6 \cdot 5 \cdot 4 \cdot 3 \text{ (4 factors)}$$
$$= 360 \quad \text{Answer}$$

E X E R C I S E S : Permutations of *n* things, taken some at a time

1. What is the value of $_6P_3$?

2. What is the value of $_7P_6$?

3. What is the number of permutations of 7 things, taken 3 at a time?

4. How many different arrangements consisting of 3 different letters can be made from the word MUSIC?

5. Three mice are placed in a box having 5 outlets. In how many ways can the mice leave the box, if all three mice use a different exit?

6. How many numbers of three digits can be made from the nine digits 1, 2, 3, $\cdots$, 9, if no digit is repeated?

7. At Pumpkin Corners 4 persons boarded a train of 7 cars. If no 2 persons entered the same car, in how many ways could these persons be arranged on the train?

8. How many four-digit numbers can be made from the five digits 1, 2, 3, 4, 5? How many of these numbers end in 5?

9. How many five-digit numbers can be made from the digits 1, 2, 3, 4, 5, 6? How many of these numbers are even?

10. How many arrangements of four letters can be made from the word PLENTY? How many of these start with P?

The number of permutations of *n* things some of which are alike.   Let us consider the permutations that can be formed by the letters a, a, a, b, c. Here we have five things to be arranged, but three of them are alike. Suppose that we label the three a's with subscripts so that we can distinguish among them and consider the five given letters to be a_1, a_2, a_3, b, c. Let us keep the b and c in the fourth and fifth positions respectively and then write all possible permutations of the three a's. We are able to write these permutations in 3!, or 6, different ways, as illustrated in the column below :

a_1 a_2 a_3 b c

a_1 a_3 a_2 b c

a_2 a_1 a_3 b c Dropping the subscripts, these 3! permutations

a_2 a_3 a_1 b c all become the permutation

a_3 a_1 a_2 b c a a a b c

a_3 a_2 a_1 b c

Thus for each permutation of the letters a a a b c, there are 3! permutations of a_1 a_2 a_3 b c. Since the number of permutations of the five letters is 5!, then the number of permutations of five letters, three of which are alike, is $\frac{5!}{3!}$. By similar reasoning, the number of permutations of n things of which p are alike is $\frac{n!}{p!}$. This reasoning can be continued with the result that the number of permutations of n things, of which p are alike and q others are alike, is $\frac{n!}{p!q!}$.

The number of permutations of n things of which p are alike, q are alike, etc., is

$$\frac{n!}{p!q!\cdots}$$

I L L U S T R A T I V E   E X A M P L E S : Permutations of things, some of which are alike

1. How many different permutations can be made using all of the letters of the word EXERCISES?

Solution. There are 9 letters in the word EXERCISES, of which 3 are E's and 2 are S's; hence we can form $\frac{9!}{3!\,2!}$ different permutations.

$$\frac{9!}{3!\,2!} = \frac{9\cdot8\cdot7\cdot6\cdot5\cdot\overset{2}{\cancel{4}}\cdot\cancel{3}\cdot\cancel{2}\cdot\cancel{1}}{\cancel{3}\cdot\cancel{2}\cdot\cancel{1}\cdot\cancel{2}\cdot1} = 30{,}240 \quad \text{Answer}$$

EXERCISES : Permutations of things, some of which are alike

1. How many different permutations can be made using all of the letters of the word

  a) ALGEBRA? *b*) BASEBALL? *c*) TEETH? *d*) ANNUAL?

2. How many different permutations can be made using all of the letters of the word

  a) DECEMBER?   *c*) TALLAHASSEE?

  b) CINCINNATI?   *d*) TENNESSEE?

3. How many different five-digit numbers can be made using all of the five digits 2, 2, 3, 3, 3?

4. A child has 6 red blocks and 4 blue blocks. In how many different ways can the child arrange the ten blocks in a straight line?

5. If the expression $x^4y^3z^2$ were written without the use of exponents, in how many different ways could the letters be arranged?

Circular permutations.   Suppose we arrange four persons *A*, *B*, *C*, and *D* around a circular table. If we start with *A* in the north position and place the others in clockwise order, we have the arrangement

If we move everyone to the right one, two, or three places respectively, we have the arrangements

These four arrangements are identical, however, as far as the four persons are concerned. For any individual, the persons opposite him, to his right, and to his left are the same in each arrangement; so what appears to be four arrangements is actually only one.

Suppose that *A* is seated at the table first. It is immaterial where he sits, in the north, east, south, or west seat; so we consider that *A* can be seated in only one way. After *A* has been seated, there are three choices for *B*, two for *C*, and finally one for *D*. In other words, the *four persons may be arranged in* 3! *different ways around the table.* This gives us the principle :

> If we have *n* different things to arrange in a circle, they can be arranged in (*n* − 1)! different ways.

ILLUSTRATIVE EXAMPLE: Circular permutations

In how many different ways may 7 different colored plants be arranged in a circular flower bed?

> *Solution.* The 7 plants may be arranged in a circle in 6! different ways;
> $$6! = 6 \cdot 5 \cdot 4 \cdot 3 \cdot 2 \cdot 1 = 720 \quad \text{Answer}$$

EXERCISES: Circular permutations

1. In how many different ways may 5 children form a circle?

2. In how many different ways may 6 women be seated at a circular luncheon table?

3. In how many ways may a child arrange 7 toy houses around his circular model railroad track?

4. In how many different ways may 4 boys and 4 girls be seated at a round table?

5. In how many different ways may 4 boys and 4 girls be seated at a round table if the boys and girls alternate?

Combinations. A *combination* of things is a group of those things without regard to order. Thus the letters *a, b, c* and the letters *b, a, c* are the same combination of letters, although they are different permutations of the letters. If we have three different things, such as the first three letters of the alphabet, these things can be arranged in 3! ways, but they form only a single combination. Thus *the number of combinations of three things taken three at a time*, abbreviated $_3C_3$, multiplied by 3! is equal to $_3P_3$, which is the number of permutations of those three things taken three at a time. That is,

$$_3C_3 \cdot 3! = {_3P_3}, \text{ or } {_3C_3} = \frac{_3P_3}{3!}.$$

Suppose we wish to find the number of combinations of the five letters *a, b, c, d, e* taken four at a time. The five possible combinations are:

> *bcde* (omitting letter *a*)
> *acde* (omitting letter *b*)
> *abde* (omitting letter *c*)
> *abce* (omitting letter *d*)
> *abcd* (omitting letter *e*)

If *we represent the number of combinations of five things taken four at a time* as $_5C_4$, then each of these combinations can be written in 4! different ways.

Therefore

$$_5C_4 \cdot 4! = {_5P_4}$$

Solving for $_5C_4$

$$_5C_4 = \frac{_5P_4}{4!}$$

$$= \frac{5 \cdot 4 \cdot 3 \cdot 2}{1 \cdot 2 \cdot 3 \cdot 4}$$

$$= 5$$

In general, the number of combinations of n things taken r at a time, multiplied by $r!$ equals the number of permutations of those n things taken r at a time, that is

$$_nC_r \cdot r! = {_nP_r}$$

Solving for $_nC_r$

$$_nC_r = \frac{_nP_r}{r!}$$

This gives us the principle :

The number of combinations of n things taken r at a time, $_nC_r$, is $\dfrac{_nP_r}{r!}$

ILLUSTRATIVE EXAMPLES: Combination of n things taken some at a time

1. A committee of three is to be chosen from a group of 10 persons. How many different committees are possible?

Solution. In this problem we are interested in the number of different groups of three persons that can be selected. We are not concerned with the arrangement of the group. In other words, we are to find the number of different combinations of 10 things, taken 3 at a time.

$$_{10}C_3 = \frac{_{10}P_3}{3!}$$

$$= \frac{10 \cdot 9 \cdot 8}{1 \cdot 2 \cdot 3}$$

$$= 120 \quad \text{Answer}$$

2. A committee of 3 is to be chosen from a group of 10 club members. If the committee must include the president, in how many ways can the committee be formed?

Solution. Since the president must be on the committee, there remain only 2 positions to be filled on the committee. Because the president is one of the 10 members, there remain only 9 members from whom these 2 positions may be filled. The number of ways of selecting 2 things out of 9 is

$$_9C_2 = \frac{_9P_2}{2!}$$

$$= \frac{9 \cdot 8}{1 \cdot 2}$$

$$= 36 \quad \text{Answer}$$

E X E R C I S E S : Combinations of *n* things, taken some at a time

1. Evaluate $_{12}C_5$.

2. Find the number of combinations of 12 things taken 4 at a time.

3. How many different committees of 3 persons each can be formed from a group of 8 persons?

4. How many different committees of 5 members each can be formed from a club of 10 members if a particular man M is to be on the committee?

5. In how many ways can Mrs. Waters invite 5 children from among Jane's 12 classmates for a party, if she wishes to exclude Henry?

6. The basketball squad of 15 members (including the manager) is traveling to an "away" game. In how many ways may the coach select 5 boys to ride in his car, if he wants to include the captain but exclude the manager?

7. If 8 points are marked in a plane, no 3 of which are in a straight line, how many different triangles can be formed using these points as vertices?

8. If 9 points are marked in a plane, no 3 of which are in a straight line, how many different quadrilaterals can be formed using these points as vertices?

9. If there are 8 teams in a baseball league, how many games must be scheduled so that each team plays every other team?

10. Mr. Ward wishes to invite four of his office co-workers to join him on a fishing party. If 9 other men work in his office, in how many ways can he do this, if he wishes to include Mr. Higgins and Mr. Gilford, but to exclude Mr. Simmons?

Equal combinations.   Whenever we select a combination of r things from a group of n things, there is left a combination of $n - r$ things. That is, if we select a combination of 3 things from a group of 5 things, there remains a combination of 2 things. This means that $_5C_3 = {}_5C_2$. This leads us to the general principle:

> The number of combinations of n things taken r at a time is equal to the number of combinations of n things taken $(n - r)$ at a time.
> $$_nC_r = {}_nC_{n-r}$$

ILLUSTRATIVE EXAMPLE: Equal combinations

In how many ways may a bat boy select 10 baseball bats to take out for practice from a group of 12 bats?

> *Solution.* We wish to find the number of combinations of 12 things taken 10 at a time. This is $_{12}C_{10}$. Since $_nC_r = {}_nC_{n-r}$, then $_{12}C_{10} = {}_{12}C_2$
>
> $$= \frac{12 \cdot 11}{1 \cdot 2}$$
>
> $$= 66 \quad \text{Answer}$$

Note that the problem could have been asked: In how many ways may a bat boy select 2 baseball bats from a group of 12 bats to be left in the supply room?

EXERCISES: Using the formula $_nC_r = {}_nC_{n-r}$

1. Evaluate $_{40}C_{38}$.

2. Find the number of combinations of 50 things taken 47 at a time.

3. On an examination paper 10 questions are given of which any 8 are to be answered. In how many different ways may the 8 questions be chosen?

4. If $_nC_{20} = {}_nC_5$, find n.

5. If $_{16}C_r = {}_{16}C_4$, find r.

6. If $_nC_{12} = {}_nC_3$, find the value of $_nC_2$.

7. If $_{14}C_r = {}_{14}C_{r+4}$, find $_rC_3$.

ILLUSTRATIVE EXAMPLE: Applying the fundamental principle to combinations

From a committee of 12 Republicans and 10 Democrats a subcommittee is to be formed consisting of 3 Republicans and 2 Democrats. How many different subcommittees can be formed?

Solution. First we select the Republicans. We want 3 Republicans selected from a group of 12. This can be done in $_{12}C_3$ ways.

$$_{12}C_3 = \frac{12 \cdot 11 \cdot 10}{1 \cdot 2 \cdot 3} \quad \text{or} \quad 220$$

Then we select the Democrats. We want 2 Democrats selected from a group of 10. This can be done in $_{10}C_2$ ways.

$$_{10}C_2 = \frac{10 \cdot 9}{1 \cdot 2} \quad \text{or} \quad 45$$

We apply the fundamental principle. Since there are 220 ways to select the Republicans and 45 ways to select the Democrats, the total number of ways to form the subcommittee is

$$220 \cdot 45$$
$$= 9900 \quad \text{Answer}$$

E X E R C I S E S : Applying the fundamental principle to combinations

1. A class consists of 24 boys and 18 girls. How many different committees can be formed consisting of 3 boys and 2 girls?

2. From a committee of 8 Democrats and 6 Republicans, a subcommittee is to be formed consisting of 2 Democrats and 1 Republican. How many different subcommittees can be formed?

3. In electing the student council, 3 boys are to be elected from 6 nominees and 2 girls from 5 nominees. How many different councils are possible?

4. Mrs. Wood wished to invite 3 boys and 4 girls from Jim's class for his party. If Jim's classmates included 9 boys and 8 girls, in how many ways could she make the selection?

5. A committee of the Parent-Teachers Association consisted of 3 mothers, 4 fathers, and 5 teachers. In how many ways can a subcommittee be chosen from this group consisting of 2 mothers, 2 fathers, and 3 teachers?

6. Chuck wished to select 3 girls and 2 boys from among his classmates to go with him on a swimming party. His classmates included 12 girls and 11 boys. If he wanted to include Mary, but not Bob, in how many ways could he form his party?

Permutations and combinations. As you have already seen in your work in this chapter, each problem is solved by applying basic principles rather than by formulas. The miscellaneous problems which follow may involve either permutations or combinations, or both. The formulas which have been developed will help you to express in simple form the arithmetic which is to be done, but they cannot be used as a substitute for thinking. For each problem decide first whether it is a problem of arrangement (permutation), of selection (combination), or of both.

ILLUSTRATIVE EXAMPLE: Permutation and combination

From the vowels a, e, i and the consonants b, c, d, f, g how many arrangements of five different letters, consisting of two different vowels and three different consonants can be made?

Solution. This problem involves both permutation and combination. We must first select the different groups consisting of two different vowels and three different consonants, and then we must arrange each group. The number of different pairs of vowels that can be chosen from the three given vowels is $_3C_2$. The number of different trios of consonants that can be selected from the five given consonants is $_5C_3$. Thus, the number of different combinations of two vowels and three consonants is

$$(_3C_2)(_5C_3) ;$$

but each of these combinations of five different things can be arranged in 5! different ways. Hence the solution is:

$$(_3C_2)(_5C_3)5! = \frac{3 \cdot 2}{1 \cdot 2} \cdot \frac{5 \cdot 4 \cdot 3}{1 \cdot 2 \cdot 3} \cdot 5 \cdot 4 \cdot 3 \cdot 2 \cdot 1 = 3600 \quad \text{Answer}$$

EXERCISES: Permutations and combinations

1. From the letters of the word BOATING how many arrangements can be formed consisting of 2 vowels and 2 consonants?

2. From the letters of the word DIALOGUE how many arrangements of 5 letters consisting of 3 vowels and 2 consonants can be formed if each word begins with A and ends with E?

3. From 8 different kinds of flower plants how many different arrangements of the plants around a circular pool are possible if there is room for only 5 plants at a time?

4. From the letters of the word HEROICAL how many arrangements of 6 letters consisting of 3 vowels and 3 consonants can be formed if the vowels and the consonants alternate?

5. From the letters of the word ASCERTAIN how many arrangements of 6 letters consisting of 3 vowels and 3 consonants can be formed if each word begins and ends with A?

6. How many integers less than 300 can be formed from the digits 1, 2, 3, 4, 5, if no digit is repeated?

7. From the letters of the word ERUPTION how many arrangements of 5 letters consisting of 2 vowels and 3 consonants can be formed if the middle letter of each word is P?

8. From the letters of the word FALLACIOUS how many words of 7 letters consisting of 3 vowels and 4 consonants can be formed if the first letter of each word is L and the middle letter of each word is A?

9. Solve for n: $_nP_2 = {}_{n+1}C_3$

10. How many different arrangements consisting of 6 letters can be formed from the letters of the word AVENUE?

11. Solve for n: $_nP_2 = \frac{21}{5} \cdot {}_5C_3$

12. How many different arrangements consisting of 8 letters can be formed from the letters of the word PARALLEL?

13. Solve for n: $_9P_n = 120 \, {}_9C_n$

14. How many even integers greater than 300 and less than 500 can be made from the digits 1, 2, 3, 4, 5?

Doings of Dimbo. This time Dimbo used a sledgehammer to kill a fly! What is the best way to do the problem, and what is the correct answer?

A drawer contains six yellow socks and six green socks, all of the same size. If a boy reaches into the drawer without looking, how many socks must he take out in order to be sure that he will have two that match?

Dimbo's solution

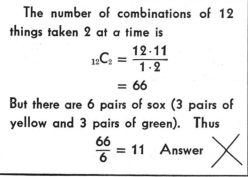

The number of combinations of 12 things taken 2 at a time is

$$_{12}C_2 = \frac{12 \cdot 11}{1 \cdot 2}$$

$$= 66$$

But there are 6 pairs of sox (3 pairs of yellow and 3 pairs of green). Thus

$$\frac{66}{6} = 11 \quad \text{Answer}$$

Probability.   If n is the number of equally likely ways in which an event *can happen*, and if m is the number of equally likely ways in which that event *cannot happen*, then the *probability* that the event will happen is the ratio of the number of ways in which the event can happen, n, to the total number of ways, $n + m$.

$$\text{Probability} = \frac{\text{no. of favorable ways}}{\text{total no. of ways}} = \frac{n}{n + m}$$

If it is a certainty that an event will happen, the probability of its happening is equal to 1. That is, probability $= \dfrac{n}{n + m} = \dfrac{n}{n + 0} = 1.$

The probability that an event will not happen is the ratio of the number of ways in which the event cannot happen, m, to the total number of ways, $m + n$. That is, the probability that an event will not happen is $\dfrac{m}{n + m}$.

Since an event will happen or will not happen, and if the probability of an event's happening is $\dfrac{n}{n + m}$, then the probability that it will not happen is

$1 - \dfrac{n}{n + m}$, which when simplified equals $\dfrac{m}{n + m}$.

If it is a certainty that an event will not occur, then the probability of its happening is 0. That is, $\dfrac{m}{m + n} = \dfrac{m}{m + 0} = 1,$ therefore

$\dfrac{m}{n + m} = 1 - 1 = 0.$

Another name for probability is *chance*.

I L L U S T R A T I V E   E X A M P L E : Probability

There are 7 red marbles and 3 blue marbles in a bag. If one marble is drawn from the bag, what is the probability (chance) that the marble is red? What is the chance that the marble is blue?

> *Solution.* Of a total of 10 marbles, 7 are red.
>
> Therefore the probability (chance) that a red marble is drawn is $\frac{7}{10}$.
>
> Similarly, the probability (chance) that a blue marble is drawn is $\frac{3}{10}$.

O R A L   E X E R C I S E S : Simple probability

1. What is the probability that a tossed coin will land heads up?

2. What is the probability that a thrown die will land with the 6 up? (*Die* is the singular of *dice*.)

3. If a bag contains only 5 black balls, what is the probability that the first ball drawn from the bag will be black?

4. If a purse contains 43 cents, what is the probability that a coin drawn from the purse is a half dollar?

5. What is the chance of drawing a red ball from a box containing only 2 red balls and 5 white balls?

6. If a bettor knows nothing about the relative merits of the 8 horses in a race, what is the probability that he can pick the winner?

7. If your chance of passing an algebra test is $\frac{4}{5}$, what is your chance of failing the test?

8. What is the probability that the next snow storm in Caribou, Maine, will occur on a Tuesday?

9. What is the chance of throwing a number greater than 3 with an ordinary die?

10. If a league of 10 professional basketball teams is organized, what is the probability that the team representing Fort Wayne in the league will not win the championship in the first season?

Odds.   Probability, or chance, is often expressed in the form of odds in favor of an event, or of odds against the event. If the probability of an event's happening is $\frac{n}{n+m}$, then the probability against its happening is $\frac{m}{n+m}$.

The odds in favor of an event happening are the ratio of the probability of the event happening to the probability of the event not happening,

that is, $\dfrac{\dfrac{n}{n+m}}{\dfrac{m}{n+m}} = \dfrac{n}{m}.$

Therefore

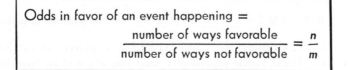

Odds in favor of an event happening =
$$\frac{\text{number of ways favorable}}{\text{number of ways not favorable}} = \frac{n}{m}$$

Similarly

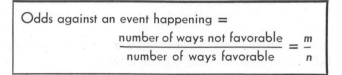

$$\text{Odds against an event happening} =$$
$$\frac{\text{number of ways not favorable}}{\text{number of ways favorable}} = \frac{m}{n}$$

Conversely

If the odds in favor of an event are $\dfrac{n}{m}$, then the chance

of the event happening is $\dfrac{n}{n + m}$ and the chance of

the event not happening is $\dfrac{m}{n + m}$.

ORAL EXERCISES: Odds

If a bag contains only 2 white balls and 3 red balls:

1. What is the chance of drawing a white ball?
2. What is the chance of drawing a red ball?
3. What are the odds in favor of drawing a white ball?
4. What are the odds against drawing a white ball?
5. What are the odds in favor of drawing a red ball?

If the chance of an event is $\frac{2}{5}$:

6. What are the odds in favor of its happening?
7. What are the odds against its happening?
8. What is the probability that it will not occur?

If the odds against an event are $\frac{6}{5}$:

9. What are the odds in favor of the event?
10. What is the chance that it will occur?

ILLUSTRATIVE EXAMPLES: Solving problems of probability

1. The letters forming the word APPLE are placed at random in a straight line. What is the probability that the P's will be together?

Solution.

$$\text{Probability} = \frac{\text{no. of favorable ways}}{\text{total no. of ways}}$$

To find the "no. of favorable ways," we find the number of ways of arranging the five letters with the P's together. If we think of the P's as tied together, we may treat them as a single letter. Then we have only 4 letters to permute.

$$\text{No. of favorable ways} = 4! \text{ or } 24$$

To find the "total no. of ways," we find the number of ways of arranging 5 letters, two of which are alike.

$$\text{Total no. of ways} = \frac{5!}{2!} \quad \text{or} \quad 60$$

$$\text{Probability} = \tfrac{24}{60} \quad \text{or} \quad \tfrac{2}{5} \quad \text{Answer}$$

2. From a pile of 7 cards consisting of 3 aces and 4 kings, a man draws 3 cards at random. What are the odds in favor of these cards being all kings?

Solution. Before we find the odds in favor of an event, we must first find the probability in favor of the event and the probability against the event. The number of ways of drawing 3 kings from 4 kings is $_4C_3$. The total number of ways of drawing 3 cards from 7 cards is $_7C_3$.

$$\text{Probability} = \frac{\text{no. of favorable ways}}{\text{total no. of ways}} = \frac{_4C_3}{_7C_3} = \frac{\dfrac{4\cdot3\cdot2}{1\cdot2\cdot3}}{\dfrac{7\cdot6\cdot5}{1\cdot2\cdot3}} = \frac{4}{35}$$

Probability in favor: $\tfrac{4}{35}$

Probability against drawing 3 kings: $1 - \tfrac{4}{35} = \tfrac{31}{35}$

The odds in favor of drawing 3 kings is: $\dfrac{\tfrac{4}{35}}{\tfrac{31}{35}}$ or $\tfrac{4}{31}$ **Answer**

EXERCISES: Solving problems of simple probability

1. In a game of chance at a fair a boy threw a hoop over a numbered cane. If the canes were numbered from 1 to 100 inclusively, what is the probability the hoop landed on an even number?

2. If there are 12 boys in a class of 21 boys and girls, what is the chance that the president of the class will be a girl?

3. Six persons, including A and B, are seated at random on a bench. What is the probability that A is seated at the left end of the bench and that B is seated at the right end?

4. A bag contains 15 balls, of which 6 are white. If 3 balls are drawn, what is the probability they will all be white?

5. From the bag mentioned in ex. 4, if 3 balls are drawn, what is the probability that none will be white?

6. If the letters of the word CASSIDY are arranged at random, what are the odds against the two S's appearing together?

7. John's class is composed of 10 boys and 14 girls. If a committee of 2 boys and 1 girl is appointed, what is the probability that John will be on the committee?

8. A Senate committee contained 3 Republicans and 4 Democrats. The Senate was composed of 50 Democrats and 46 Republicans. What is the chance that the senior senator from Georgia, a Democrat, was on that committee?

9. Four cards are drawn from a pack of 52. What is the chance that the cards are the four aces?

10. Compare the probability of throwing more than 4 on one die with the probability of throwing more than 8 on two dice.

11. A bridge deck contains 52 cards, of which there are 13 of each suit. What is the probability that a hand of 13 cards would all be of the same suit?

CHAPTER REVIEW EXERCISES

1. Evaluate: *a)* 6!   *b)* $\dfrac{8!}{6!}$ *c)* $_6P_3$ *d)* $_{10}C_7$

2. How many different arrangements of 5 letters each can be made, using the letters of the word STUDENT, if each arrangement must end in T?

3. If there are no ties, in how many different ways can the eight teams in the American League finish a season?

4. How many different signals can be given with five flags of different color if all of the flags are displayed together, one above the other?

5. From 46 Republican Senators in the United States Senate how many committees of 3 can be appointed if the Republican "minority leader" is to be one of the members of the committee?

6. A book dealer has 6 copies of a history book, 5 copies of an English book, and 4 copies of a science book. In how many different ways can he arrange these 15 books on a shelf?

7. After a coach has decided on the 9 men who are to a start a baseball game, how many different batting orders are possible if the pitcher is to bat in the ninth position?

8. From 4 teachers and 12 students, how many different committees can be formed consisting of 3 teachers and 5 students?

9. From 5 vowels and 10 consonants, how many different arrangements can be formed consisting of 3 vowels and 3 consonants?

10. In how many different ways can 5 white balls, 3 red balls, and 4 green balls be arranged in a straight line?

11. From a group of 12 men, how many different committees of 4 can be formed which will include a particular man A and exclude a particular man B?

12. Find the value of n if $_nP_4 = 6 \cdot {}_nP_2$.

13. How many numbers less than 300, each containing three different digits, can be made with the digits 1, 2, 3, 4, 5?

14. In how many different ways may the letters of the word CHOATE be arranged so that the vowels and consonants alternate?

15. If $_nP_4 = 20(_{n-1}C_2)$ find the value of n.

16. How many three-letter arrangements can be made using the letters of the word OCEAN that include C, but not N?

17. In the decimal system, we use the ten digits 0, 1, 2, $\cdots$, 9. In the duodecimal system, we use 12 digits, 0, 1, 2, $\cdots$, 9, and two other characters, say t and e. How many more three-digit numbers can be formed in the duodecimal system than in the decimal system?

18. From our alphabet of 21 consonants and 5 vowels, how many different arrangements of 5 different letters can be made consisting of 3 consonants and 2 vowels?

19. From a group of 8 boys, 4 boys are selected. What is the chance that a particular boy, B, will be selected?

20. From a group of 7 girls, 3 girls are selected and arranged in a straight line. What is the chance that a particular girl, G, will stand at the front of the line? What are the odds that she will not be at the front of the line?

21. From a group of 10 students, a committee of 3 is to be selected. What are the odds that a certain student, S, will be selected? What are the odds that he will not be selected?

22. If I select 3 cards from a pack of 52 playing cards, what is the chance that I select a king, queen, and jack of the same suit?

CUMULATIVE REVIEW EXERCISES

1. Solve for x: $x^2 = -2\frac{1}{2}x$.

2. For what value of k will the graph of the equation $y = 6x^2 - 5k$ pass through the origin?

3. Simplify: $\left(\dfrac{x^2 x^0}{x^{-1}}\right)^{\frac{1}{3}}$

4. How many terms are there in the expansion of $(2x - 3y)^{15}$?

5. In the progression 84, 80, 76, $\cdots$ by how much does the 100th term exceed the 103rd term?

6. Solve for x: $\sqrt[3]{x^2 + 6x} = 3$.

7. Find the value of $\log_4 4\frac{1}{2} - \log_{\frac{1}{2}} 4$.

8. Find the geometric mean between $\sqrt{27}$ and $\sqrt{48}$.

9. If the graph of the equation $y = ax^2 + c$ passes through the points $(-1, 5)$ and $(2, 11)$ find the value of a and c.

10. For what value of x does the fraction $\dfrac{x - 4}{x + 1}$ have no meaning?

11. A mountain lake is to be used as a reservoir for a village's water supply. The altitude of the lake is 600 ft. higher than the altitude of the village. The lake and the village storage tank are 3300 ft. apart in a straight line. At what angle of elevation should the tunnel for the pipe be started from the village so that it will come out at the level of the lake?

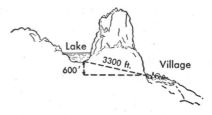

12. The cube of a planet's distance from the sun varies as the square of the time of the planet's revolution. The earth is $91\frac{1}{4}$ million miles from the sun, and Venus is 66 million miles from the sun. Assuming the time of the earth's revolution to be 365 days, find the time of Venus's revolution to the nearest tenth of a day, by using logarithms.

13. In the following system of equations solve for x by determinants:

$$2x + 3y - 5z = 18$$
$$\tfrac{1}{2}x - y + z = -\tfrac{7}{6}$$
$$3x - 2y + \tfrac{2}{3}z = \tfrac{19}{3}$$

14. *a)* Plot the graph of $y = 3 - 2x$.

b) Plot the graph of $y = x^2 - 4x$, using the same axes as in (*a*).

c) Obtain from the figure the values of x and y that satisfy both equations.

15. A farmer bought two herds of cattle for $2400 each. One herd contained 12 head less than the second but cost $10 more per head. How many head of cattle were in the smaller herd?

16. The circumference of the rear wheel of a wagon is 1 ft. more than the circumference of the front wheel. The rear wheel makes 10 less revolutions than the front wheel in traveling a distance of 720 ft. How many feet are there in the circumference of the rear wheel?

17. Solve for the remaining parts of the acute oblique triangle ABC, if $a = 51$, $b = 49.3$, and $\angle A = 65° 20'$.

CHAPTER 19 *Introduction to Analytic Geometry and Statistics*

Analytic geometry.   Analytic geometry is the branch of mathematics which combines algebra and geometry by means of a system of coordinates. You have already had some experience with analytic geometry, although not under that name, in your work with algebraic graphs. In this chapter we shall take up some of the applications of analytic geometry to the straight line and the circle.

Distance between two points.   In the adjacent figure $P(x_1, y_1)$ and $Q(x_2, y_2)$ represent any two points in the coordinate system. The right triangle has been completed in which the hypotenuse is PQ and

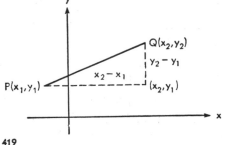

the legs are parallel to the coordinate axes. The coordinates of the vertex at the right angle would then be (x_2, y_1). The legs of the right triangle must be $(y_2 - y_1)$ and $(x_2 - x_1)$. According to the Pythagorean theorem,

$$PQ = \sqrt{(x_2 - x_1)^2 + (y_2 - y_1)^2}$$

This gives us a formula.

The distance between two points (x_1, y_1) and (x_2, y_2) is $d = \sqrt{(x_2 - x_1)^2 + (y_2 - y_1)^2}$

This formula applies to any pair of points, regardless of the quadrants in which they are located. Furthermore, the coordinates of either point may be considered to be (x_1, y_1) or (x_2, y_2).

ILLUSTRATIVE EXAMPLE: Distance between two points

Find the distance between the points $(-2, 7)$ and $(5, -3)$.

Solution. Considering the point $(-2, 7)$ to be the point (x_1, y_1) and the point $(5, -3)$ to be the point (x_2, y_2), we have:

$$d = \sqrt{(x_2 - x_1)^2 + (y_2 - y_1)^2}$$

Substituting
$$d = \sqrt{(5 - [-2])^2 + (-3 - 7)^2}$$
$$= \sqrt{49 + 100}$$
$$= \sqrt{149} \quad \text{Answer}$$

The same answer is obtained if we consider the point $(5, -3)$ to be (x_1, y_1) and the point $(-2, 7)$ to be (x_2, y_2). As an exercise the student may wish to substitute these values in the formula to see if he can obtain the same answer.

EXERCISES: Distance between two points

In exercises 1–6, find the distance between each of the following pairs of points:

1. $(5, 3)$ and $(2, 7)$ 4. $(3, -7)$ and $(5, -2)$
2. $(6, 5)$ and $(-9, -3)$ 5. $(-6, 4)$ and $(0, 0)$
3. $(0, -3)$ and $(-3, 0)$ 6. (a, a) and $(5a, 4a)$

7. Find the lengths of the three sides of a triangle whose vertices are $(-2, 3), (-2, -1),$ and $(4, -1)$.

8. Prove that the triangle whose vertices are $(-2, 4)$, $(4, 3)$, and $(-3, -2)$ is isosceles. (Hint: show that two of the sides are equal.)

9. Prove that the trapezoid whose vertices are $(-8, 2)$, $(4, 2)$, $(-1, 14)$, $(-3, 14)$ is isosceles (i.e., show that the nonparallel sides are equal).

10. Prove that the quadrilateral whose four vertices are $(-3, -2)$, $(-1, 2)$, $(3, 3)$, $(1, -1)$ is a parallelogram (i.e., show that the opposite sides are equal).

The standard equation of a circle.   The standard equation of a circle is derived from the formula for the distance between two points. In the adjacent figure the radius of the circle is r, the coordinates of the center of the circle are (h, k), and the coordinates of any point on the circle are (x, y). Applying the distance formula

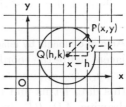

$$(x - h)^2 + (y - k)^2 = r^2$$

This is the standard equation of a circle the coordinates of whose center are (h, k) and whose radius is r.

ILLUSTRATIVE EXAMPLES: Applying the standard equation of a circle

1. Find the equation of a circle the coordinates of whose center are $(2, -3)$ and whose radius is 7.

Solution. Apply the formula $(x - h)^2 + (y - k)^2 = r^2$

Substitute 2 for h, -3 for k,
and 7 for r $(x - 2)^2 + (y + 3)^2 = 49$

Simplifying $x^2 - 4x + y^2 + 6y - 36 = 0$

2. The equation of a circle is $x^2 + 12x + y^2 - 20y = 8$.   Find the radius and the coordinates of its center.

Solution. To write the equation $x^2 + 12x + y^2 - 20y = 8$ in the form of a standard equation of a circle, it is necessary to make the left member the sum of two trinomial squares. Adding 36 and 100 to each member we have

$$x^2 + 12x + 36 + y^2 - 20y + 100 = 8 + 36 + 100$$

Factoring $(x + 6)^2 \quad + (y - 10)^2 \quad = 12^2$

Thus the radius equals 12 and the coordinates of the center are $(-6, 10)$.

EXERCISES: The standard equation of a circle

In ex. 1–3 write the equation of a circle when given:

1. The coordinates of the center $(-3, -5)$; radius $= 6$.

2. The coordinates of the center $(6, -\frac{1}{2})$; radius $= \sqrt{10}$

3. The coordinates of the center $\left(\dfrac{m}{2}, -\dfrac{n}{3}\right)$; radius $= r$

In ex. 4, 5 find the coordinates of the center of the circle and the radius when the equation of the circle is given as follows:

4. $x^2 + 14x + y^2 - 16y + 13 = 0$

5. $x^2 + y^2 - 24x + 20y - 5 = 0$

Area of a triangle by using determinants. In the adjacent figure the coordinates of the vertices are (x_1, y_1), (x_2, y_2), and (x_3, y_3), respectively. With this data let us find the area of $\triangle ABC$. By drawing AD, BE, and CF, each perpendicular to the x-axis, we have $\triangle ABC =$ trapezoid $DABE +$ trapezoid $EBCF -$ trapezoid $DACF$. Applying the formula that the area of a trapezoid equals one half the sum of its bases times its altitude, we have

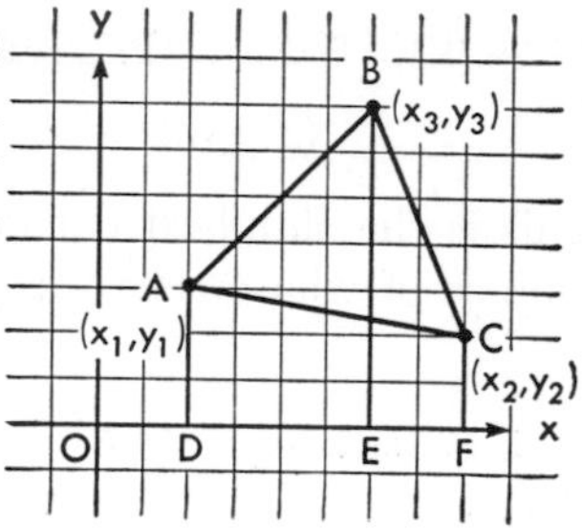

$$\triangle ABC = \frac{y_1 + y_3}{2}(x_3 - x_1) + \frac{y_3 + y_2}{2}(x_2 - x_3) - \frac{y_1 + y_2}{2}(x_2 - x_1)$$

$$\triangle ABC = \tfrac{1}{2}(x_3 y_1 + x_3 y_3 - x_1 y_1 - x_1 y_3 + x_2 y_3 + x_2 y_2 - x_3 y_3 - x_3 y_2$$
$$- x_2 y_1 - x_2 y_2 + x_1 y_1 + x_1 y_2)$$

$$\triangle ABC = \tfrac{1}{2}(x_1 y_2 + x_3 y_1 + x_2 y_3 - x_3 y_2 - x_2 y_1 - x_1 y_3)$$

From the above we can say that the formula for the area of a triangle when given the coordinates of the respective vertices is

$$A = \tfrac{1}{2} \begin{vmatrix} x_1 & y_1 & 1 \\ x_2 & y_2 & 1 \\ x_3 & y_3 & 1 \end{vmatrix}$$

Since the coordinates of the vertices of the triangle are arbitrarily designated (x_1, y_1), (x_2, y_2), and (x_3, y_3) respectively, the sign of the developed determinant may be either positive or negative. However, regardless of the sign of the developed determinant, the sign of the area of the triangle is always expressed in positive units.

ILLUSTRATIVE EXAMPLE: Area of a triangle

Find the area of a triangle, the coordinates of whose vertices are $(2, 5)$, $(6, 3)$, and $(8, 4)$ respectively.

Solution. Let $(x_1, y_1) = (2, 5)$; $(x_2, y_2) = (6, 3)$; $(x_3, y_3) = (8, 4)$
Substituting in the formula given on page 422

$$A = \tfrac{1}{2} \begin{vmatrix} 2 & 5 & 1 \\ 6 & 3 & 1 \\ 8 & 4 & 1 \end{vmatrix}$$

Developing the determinant $A = \tfrac{1}{2}(6 + 40 + 24 - 24 - 30 - 8)$
$A = 4$ sq. units   Answer

EXERCISES: Area of a triangle

In ex. 1–8 find the area of each of the triangles when given the coordinates of each vertex.

1. A $(2, 4)$, B $(3, 8)$, C $(9, 5)$
2. A $(- 2, 5)$, B $(- 8, 4)$, C $(- 6, 7)$
3. A $(- 5, - 2)$, B $(- 7, - 6)$, C $(- 12, - 1)$
4. A $(8, - 1)$, B $(5, - 4)$, C $(9, - 6)$
5. A $(0, 4)$, B $(7, 0)$, C $(- 4, - 6)$
6. A $(- 3, 2)$, B $(0, - 8)$, C $(0, 5)$
7. A $(- 4, 0)$, B $(- 6, - 3)$, C $(2, 0)$
8. A $(0, 0)$, B $(0, - 9)$, C $(8, 0)$
9. Find the area of square $ABCD$ when given A $(12, 0)$, B $(0, 12)$, C $(12, 24)$, D $(24, 12)$.

10. Find the area of quadrilateral $ABCD$ when given A $(8, 1)$, B $(- 1, 10)$, C $(- 2, - 2)$, D $(3, - 5)$.

The equation of a line through two points.   The adjacent figure shows the line drawn through the two points (x_1, y_1) and (x_2, y_2). To write the equation of this line, we consider any point on the line as a general point $P(x, y)$. Applying the formula for slope (page 116), the slope of the line through (x_1, y_1) and (x, y) is

$$m = \frac{y - y_1}{x - x_1}$$

Similarly, the slope of the line through the points (x_1, y_1) and (x_2, y_2) is

$$m = \frac{y_2 - y_1}{x_2 - x_1}$$

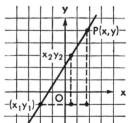

Since m, in each case, represents the slope of the same line, we have an equation of a line through two given points:

$$\frac{y - y_1}{x - x_1} = \frac{y_2 - y_1}{x_2 - x_1}$$

This equation is the *two-point form* of an equation of a straight line.

In the special case of a line parallel to the y axis, this equation cannot be applied since the denominator of the fraction in the right member is zero. We write the equation of such a line as was shown on page 114. Thus the equation of the line passing through the points $(5, 7)$ and $(5, -2)$ is $x = 5$. Similarly, the equation of a line passing through the points $(3, 7)$ and $(-6, 7)$ is $y = 7$.

The equation of a line having a given slope and passing through a given point. Let the given point be (x_1, y_1) and the slope be m.

From our definition of a slope $\quad \dfrac{y - y_1}{x - x_1} = m$

$$(y - y_1) = m(x - x_1)$$

This equation is the *point-slope form* of an equation of a straight line.

The equation of a line in intercept form. If the x intercept of the line is a, and the y intercept of the line is b, then the line passes through the two points $(a, 0)$ and $(0, b)$. We write the equation of the line through these two points.

Applying the formula $\qquad \dfrac{y - y_1}{x - x_1} = \dfrac{y_2 - y_1}{x_2 - x_1}$

We consider $(a, 0)$ and $(0, b)$ as the two given points $\qquad \dfrac{y - 0}{x - a} = \dfrac{b - 0}{0 - a}$

Clearing of fractions $\qquad -ay = bx - ab$

$$bx + ay = ab$$

Dividing both members by ab $\qquad \dfrac{bx}{ab} + \dfrac{ay}{ab} = \dfrac{ab}{ab}$

Simplifying $\qquad \dfrac{x}{a} + \dfrac{y}{b} = 1$

I L L U S T R A T I V E   E X A M P L E S : Writing the equation of a line

1. Write the equation of a line passing through the points $(-4, -3)$ and $(2, 5)$.

> *Solution.* Write the two-point form of an equation
> of a straight line $\dfrac{y - y_1}{x - x_1} = \dfrac{y_2 - y_1}{x_2 - x_1}$
>
> Substituting $\dfrac{y - (-3)}{x - (-4)} = \dfrac{5 - (-3)}{2 - (-4)}$
>
> $$\dfrac{y + 3}{x + 4} = \dfrac{4}{3}$$
>
> Clearing of fractions $3y + 9 = 4x + 16$
>
> $$4x - 3y = -7 \quad \text{Answer}$$

2. Write the equation of the line passing through the point $(2, -3)$ with a slope of $-\frac{1}{2}$.

> *Solution.* Write the point-slope form of an equation of a straight line $y - y_1 = m(x - x_1)$
>
> Substituting $y + 3 = -\frac{1}{2}(x - 2)$
>
> Clearing of fractions $-2y - 6 = x - 2$
>
> $$x + 2y = -4 \quad \text{Answer}$$

3. Write the equation of the line whose x intercept is 4 and whose y intercept is -3.

> *Solution.* We write the intercept form of the equation of a straight line $\dfrac{x}{a} + \dfrac{y}{b} = 1$
>
> Substituting $\dfrac{x}{4} + \dfrac{y}{-3} = 1$
>
> Clearing of fractions $3x - 4y = 12 \quad \text{Answer}$

E X E R C I S E S : Writing the equation of a straight line

In ex. 1–4, write the equation of the line passing through the given pairs of points.

1. $(-5, 3)$ and $(1, 10)$ **3.** $(-2, -3)$ and $(-4, -5)$

2. $(1, -3)$ and $(3, 0)$ **4.** $(10, -5)$ and $(7, -8)$

5. Write the equation of the line passing through the point $(-1, 3)$ and the point of intersection of the lines whose equations are $2x + y = 7$ and $x - 3y = 7$.

In ex. 6–9, write the equation of the line passing through the given point and having the given slope.

6. $(-3, 4)$; $m = 2$ **8.** $(10, -5)$; $m = -5$

7. $(-1, -4)$; $m = \frac{1}{2}$ **9.** $(0, -9)$; $m = \frac{5}{3}$

10. A line passes through the point $(-4, 1)$ with a slope of 3. Find the point at which this line intersects the line whose equation is $x - 2y = -1$.

In ex. 11–14, write the equation of the line having the given intercepts.

11. x intercept   3, y intercept   5
12. x intercept   1, y intercept   6
13. x intercept $1\frac{1}{2}$, y intercept $-2\frac{1}{2}$
14. x intercept $-7\frac{1}{3}$, y intercept $-2\frac{2}{3}$

15. The x and y intercepts of a line are -6 and 8, respectively. Find the point at which this line intersects the line passing through the point $(-6, -3)$ having a slope of $\frac{1}{3}$.

Parameters. If we use $y = mx + b$ as a standard form for a linear equation, the constants m and b are called parameters. In this form of the linear equation the parameters m and b represent the slope and the y intercept of the line respectively. There is a direct relationship between the geometrical fact that a straight line is determined by two geometrical conditions and the algebraic fact that a linear equation has two parameters.

If we consider the equation $\dfrac{x}{a} + \dfrac{y}{b} = 1$ as a standard form of a linear equation, the parameters a and b represent the x intercept and the y intercept of the line respectively.

The general form of a linear equation $Ax + By = C$, although appearing to have three parameters, A, B, and C, has only two. These can be determined by dividing the general equation $Ax + By = C$ by A, B, or C. If we divide the general equation by B, we obtain

$$\frac{A}{B}x + y = \frac{C}{B}$$

Solving for y $$y = -\frac{A}{B}x + \frac{C}{B}$$

If we let $m = -\dfrac{A}{B}$ and $b = \dfrac{C}{B}$, we obtain the slope-intercept form of the line's equation

$$y = mx + b$$

If we divide the general equation $Ax + By = C$ by C, we obtain

$$\frac{A}{C}x + \frac{B}{C}y = 1$$

If we let $a = \dfrac{C}{A}$ and $b = \dfrac{C}{B}$, we obtain the *intercept* form of the line's equation

$$\frac{x}{a} + \frac{y}{b} = 1$$

Determining parameters.   If we are given two points, we can find the equation of the line that passes through these points by finding the parameters m and b.   Two geometric conditions are sufficient to determine a line. These two geometric conditions also give us two algebraic equations that can be solved simultaneously to find the two parameters of the standard equation $y = mx + b$.

ILLUSTRATIVE EXAMPLE: Determining parameters of a linear equation

Using parameters m and b, find the equation of the line that passes through the points $(-2, -5)$ and $(1, -3)$.

Solution.   Let us use the standard form $y = mx + b$

If the line passes through $(-2, -5)$, then $x = -2$ and $y = -5$ are a pair of values that satisfy the equation of the line passing through this point.

Substituting these values in the standard form $-5 = -2m + b$

Similarly, if the line passes through $(1, -3)$ $-3 = m + b$

We solve these two equations simultaneously to find m and b.

$$
\begin{aligned}
-5 &= -2m + b \\
-3 &= m + b \\
\hline
\end{aligned}
$$

Subtracting

$$-2 = -3m$$
$$m = \tfrac{2}{3}$$

Substituting $m = \tfrac{2}{3}$ in $-3 = m + b$

$$-3 = \tfrac{2}{3} + b$$
$$b = -\tfrac{11}{3}$$

Therefore, the equation of the line passing
through $(-2, -5)$ and $(1, -3)$ is $\qquad y = \frac{2}{3}x - \frac{11}{3}$

Simplifying $\qquad\qquad\qquad\qquad\qquad\qquad 3y = 2x - 11$

$$2x - 3y = 11 \quad \text{Answer}$$

EXERCISES: Writing linear equations when given two conditions

In ex. 1–4, using parameters m and b, write the equation of the line
passing through each of the given pair of points.

1. $(-5, 3)$ and $(1, 10)$ $\qquad\qquad$ **3.** $(-2, -3)$ and $(-4, -5)$

2. $(1, -3)$ and $(3, 0)$ $\qquad\qquad$ **4.** $(10, -5)$ and $(7, -8)$

In ex. 5–8, using parameters m and b, write the equation of the line
passing through the given point and having the given slope.

5. $(-3, 4)$; $m = 2$ $\qquad\qquad$ **7.** $(10, -5)$; $m = -5$

6. $(-1, -4)$; $m = \frac{1}{2}$ $\qquad\qquad$ **8.** $(0, -9)$; $m = \frac{5}{3}$

In ex. 9–12 write the equation of the line which has the given slope and
the given y intercept.

9. $m = 2$; $b = 7$ $\qquad\qquad$ **11.** $m = \frac{1}{2}$; $b = -\frac{7}{2}$

10. $m = -\frac{1}{4}$; $b = -5$ $\qquad\qquad$ **12.** $m = 0$; $b = -8$

In ex. 13–16 find the slope (m) and the y intercept (b) of the graph of
each equation.

13. $3x - y = 8$ $\qquad\qquad$ **15.** $7x - 6y + 4 = 0$

14. $6x + 3y = -2$ $\qquad\qquad$ **16.** $8 - 5y = 9x$

17. For what value of k will the equation $3x + ky = 4$ have a slope
of 1?

18. Write the equation of the line whose y intercept is the same as the
y intercept of the line $x - 2y = 12$, but whose slope is 1 greater than the
slope of the line $x - 2y = 12$.

19. Given the line whose equation is $2x - 3y + 6 = 0$, write the
equation of the line whose y intercept is the negative of that of the given
line, and whose slope is the negative reciprocal of that of the given line.

Meaning of "statistics." Statistics is the science that deals with the collection and tabulation of numerical data and the methods of analyzing
such data. In its many departments the United States Government uses
statistics involving a wide variety of data. Statistical methods are used

by businessmen for analyzing sales and production figures; by public opinion polls applying the statistical technique of sampling; and by educators and psychologists in scoring and interpreting mental tests. In recent years engineers have found that statistical methods play an important role in the development of new electronic devices. Today statistics occupy a permanent position in the family circle of mathematics.

Forming an equation from experimental data.   Engineers and other scientists often wish to write the equation that relates the variables in a given experiment. This equation may represent a straight line, a parabola or other conic section, a cubic (third-degree equation), or it may be an equation higher than the third degree. Usually the experimenter will graph the data that he has obtained during the course of an experiment, and, from the graph, he will decide what degree the equation should be.

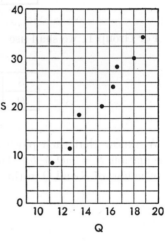

In most experiments there are errors in measurement. These errors, usually small in a well-conducted study, will cause the plotted data to vary somewhat from the graph of a simple equation. In the adjacent diagram the experimental readings of two variables, S and Q, have been plotted. Although these plotted points do not lie in a straight line, it is possible to draw a line that would come very close to all these points. The equation of this line would represent for the experimenter the relationship of the two variables, S and Q.

Fitting data to a straight line.   To form the equation of the line that fits the data shown in the above diagram we may use the standard equation $y = mx + b$. It is then necessary only to find the two parameters m and b in the equation $S = mQ + b$. The variables are S and Q. The *method of averages*, which uses all of the given data, is applied to find these two parameters. This method is demonstrated in the following illustrative example.

ILLUSTRATIVE EXAMPLE: Fitting data to a straight line

Find the equation of the straight line in variables S and Q that fits the following experimental data:

S	8	11	18	20	24	28	30	34
Q	11.2	12.7	13.5	15.3	16.2	16.6	18.0	18.9

Solution. It is necessary to find the two parameters m and b in the equation $S = mQ + b$. This requires two simultaneous equations. For this reason we divide the data as nearly as possible into two equal groups. For Group I we shall use

S	8	11	18	20
Q	11.2	12.7	13.5	15.3

For Group II we shall use

S	24	28	30	34
Q	16.2	16.6	18.0	18.9

We know that each plotted point should approximately fit the required equation $S = mQ + b$. Therefore, for Group I, we substitute the pairs of values of S and Q in this equation

$$8 = 11.2\,m + b$$
$$11 = 12.7\,m + b$$
$$18 = 13.5\,m + b$$
$$20 = 15.3\,m + b$$

We add these equations $\quad\quad 57 = 52.7\,m + 4b$

Divide by 4 (the number of equations) $\quad\quad 14.25 = 13.18\,m + b$ (Equation 1)

This is one of the two simultaneous equations necessary.

We proceed in the same manner for the data of Group II.

$$24 = 16.2\,m + b$$
$$28 = 16.6\,m + b$$
$$30 = 18.0\,m + b$$
$$34 = 18.9\,m + b$$

Adding $\quad\quad 116 = 69.7\,m + 4b$

Dividing by 4 $\quad\quad 29 = 17.43\,m + b$ (Equation 2)

This is the second of the two simultaneous equations.

Equation 2 $29 \ \ = 17.43\,m + b$

Equation 1 $14.25 = 13.18\,m + b$

Subtracting $14.75 = \ \ 4.25\,m$

$$m = \frac{14.75}{4.25} \quad \text{or approx. } 3.47$$

Substituting 3.47 for m in $29 = 17.43\,m + b$

$29 = 60.48 + b$

$b = -31.48$

The required equation is $S = 3.47Q - 31.48$ Answer

The figure below shows the graph of this equation, along with the points determined by the experimental data.

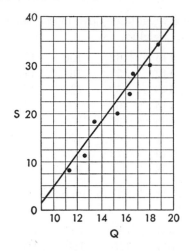

EXERCISES: Fitting data to a straight line

In each of the following exercises find the equation of the straight line that fits the following experimental data. Plot the equation on a system of coordinates.

1.

R	2	3	4	5	6	7	8	9
S	3.7	6.4	7.6	10.3	12.2	13.8	16.7	17.3

2.

P	1	3	5	8	10	15	18	20	22	25
Q	− 6	− 3.8	− 2.4	1.4	2.8	8.0	10.6	12.8	15.6	18.0

3.

x	10.0	12.9	17.0	20.1	22.1	25.4	27.5	30.0
y	4.6	6.6	9.4	11.4	13.2	15.8	18.2	20.8

Ordering of data. After a set of measurements has been found, the numbers should be arranged in some kind of order, preferably according to size, either in increasing or in decreasing order. From the ordered data one can easily find the *median*. The median is that point above which half of the measurements lie and below which half of the measurements lie.

ILLUSTRATIVE EXAMPLE: Ordering data; finding the median

Arrange the following weights of boys in the same school in increasing order. Find the median weight.

145	146	162	150	131	150
180	142	151	164	117	129
140	146	152	141	177	138
120	176	161	136	153	155
166	126	133	156	148	132
143	121	133	147	154	164
171	149	172	128	147	143
154	158	157	169	155	174

Solution. Arranged in increasing order, these weights are:

117	133	143	150	155	166
120	133	145	150	156	169
121	136	146	151	157	171
126	138	146	152	158	172
128	140	147	153	161	174
129	141	147	154	162	176
131	142	148	154	164	177
132	143	149	155	164	180

Since there are 48 measurements, the median is that weight midway between the twenty-fourth and the twenty-fifth measurements. These two measurements are 149 and 150, regardless of the end from which the counting is done. Midway between 149 and 150 is 149.5.

The median is 149.5   **Answer**

Finding quartiles. Quartiles are those points in a list of ordered data that divide the data into four equal parts. The value of the measurement at the point below which $\frac{1}{4}$ of the data lie is called the *first quartile*, sometimes symbolized Q_1. The second quartile is equivalent to the median. The *third quartile* is the value of the measurement at the point below which $\frac{3}{4}$ of the data lie.

ILLUSTRATIVE EXAMPLE: Finding quartiles

Find the first and third quartiles of the data given in the preceding illustrative example on p. 432.

> *Solution.* Since there are 48 measurements, one fourth of the data includes 12 measurements. The first quartile is halfway between the twelfth and the thirteenth measurements.
> The 12th reading is 138.
> The 13th reading is 140.
> The first quartile, therefore, is $Q_1 = 139$ Answer

The third quartile is halfway between the thirty-sixth and the thirty-seventh measurements.
The 36th measurement is 158.
The 37th measurement is 161.
Therefore, the third quartile is $Q_3 = 159.5$ Answer

EXERCISES: Ordering data; finding median and quartiles

In each of the following exercises arrange the data in increasing order and find the median, the first quartile, and the third quartile of the data.

1. In a factory manufacturing sterling silver goods, a sampling of weekly wages expressed in dollars paid to workmen in different departments was as follows: 80, 81.50, 82.20, 83.60, 76.40, 60, 90.50, 108, 50.75, 70.80, 84.40, 78.20, 64, 110, 58.25, 75, 104, 66, 94, 55.

2. The following scores were made in a final examination by students of one algebra class:

82	66	100	70	77	76
96	52	50	81	91	68
47	86	75	73	74	69
52	94	78	83	70	65
72	51	59	74	80	81

3. In the June physical examination the heights in inches of the boys in the twelfth grade of a certain school were measured as follows:

72	65	76	69.5	64.5
73	68.5	69.5	71.5	60
70.5	67.5	68.5	72	61.5
64	69	61.5	74.5	67.5
66.5	71	66.5	71.5	66.5
62.5	72.5	63.5	69.5	65
74.5	74.5	65.5	62	67.5

Frequency distributions. After a set of measurements has been ordered, the next step is to organize the measures systematically into groups or classes. The most commonly used arrangement of statistical data is called a *frequency distribution*. The following illustrative example demonstrates the method of making a frequency distribution.

ILLUSTRATIVE EXAMPLE: Making a frequency distribution

Make a frequency distribution of the following 49 algebra test scores:

63	60	73	93	58	59	65
68	73	74	87	74	63	67
76	87	62	79	84	71	77
69	97	62	67	75	79	73
49	92	84	89	80	80	72
59	70	83	60	66	75	71
69	70	85	52	56	76	73

Solution. We prepare a sheet with headings *Scores, Tabulation,* and *Frequency.*

The highest score is 97; the lowest score is 49. The difference of these scores, 48, is the range of the scores. We then determine the approximate number of intervals or groups that we consider convenient for the distribution and divide the range by that number. Suppose we use 15 intervals. The quotient $\frac{48}{15}$ (or 3.2) suggests that we use a stretch of 3, the nearest integer, for each interval.

The top interval, to be recorded under *Scores*, is 96–98. This range will include the highest score 97. The lower limit of this interval was chosen as 96, because it is divisible by 3, the range of each interval.

The remaining intervals are then recorded in the column under *Scores*. The lowest interval is 48–50, which will include the lowest score 49 in the distribution.

Then each of the 49 test scores, from an ordered list or an unordered list, is tabulated with a tally mark in its appropriate interval. When all scores have been tallied, the total in each interval is recorded in the corresponding row in the column labeled *Frequency*. This completes the frequency distribution.

Scores	Tabulation	Frequency
96–98	/	1
93–95	/	1
90–92	/	1
87–89	///	3
84–86	///	3
81–83	/	1
78–80	////	4
75–77	////	5
72–74	//// //	7
69–71	//// /	6
66–68	////	4
63–65	///	3
60–62	////	4
57–59	///	3
54–56	/	1
51–53	/	1
48–50	/	1
	Total	49

E X E R C I S E S : Making frequency distributions

In each of the following exercises make a frequency distribution of the given data. In each case use approximately 12 intervals.

1. The following measurements are shoe sizes for a group of male college freshmen:

$8\frac{1}{2}$	12	7	$9\frac{1}{2}$	8	$9\frac{1}{2}$
10	$8\frac{1}{2}$	$9\frac{1}{2}$	11	8	10
$10\frac{1}{2}$	6	$9\frac{1}{2}$	$6\frac{1}{2}$	7	$11\frac{1}{2}$
$7\frac{1}{2}$	$8\frac{1}{2}$	$9\frac{1}{2}$	$10\frac{1}{2}$	$11\frac{1}{2}$	$9\frac{1}{2}$
11	9	10	12	10	8
11	9	$12\frac{1}{2}$	$8\frac{1}{2}$	10	$7\frac{1}{2}$
10	$11\frac{1}{2}$	$7\frac{1}{2}$	$10\frac{1}{2}$	9	10
$10\frac{1}{2}$	12	$11\frac{1}{2}$	11	9	$10\frac{1}{2}$

2. The following scores are algebra examination grades for a certain high school:

72	68	65	87	82	78	61
97	55	92	88	80	91	66
66	79	83	94	55	76	69
71	75	75	77	82	60	80
72	69	65	60	84	90	86
66	90	84	86	57	68	74
75	81	72	69	73	79	77

3. Use the data in exercise 3 on page 433, representing the heights in inches of the boys in the twelfth grade of a certain school.

Frequency polygon. Many questions about a frequency distribution can be answered immediately if the distribution is presented in graphic form. The simplest form of graphical representation of a frequency distribution is the *histogram*, sometimes called a bar graph. Another type commonly used is the *frequency polygon*.

Score	f
7	1
6	3
5	6
4	7
3	8
2	6
1	2
0	1

Frequency Distribution

Histogram

Frequency Polygon

I L L U S T R A T I V E   E X A M P L E : Constructing a frequency polygon

Construct a frequency polygon for the following frequency distribution.

Algebra Grade	Midpoint of Interval	f
95–99	97	2
90–94	92	3
85–89	87	5
80–84	82	7
75–79	77	8
70–74	72	6
65–69	67	4
60–64	62	2
55–59	57	1
50–54	52	1

Solution. First we determine the midpoint of each interval. The top interval includes the grades 95, 96, 97, 98, 99. The midpoint is 97. This midpoint, along with the midpoints for all the other intervals, has already been indicated in a column adjacent to the frequency distribution. On the horizontal coordinate axis we indicate the algebra grades, including the

entire range from 50 to 99. On the vertical coordinate axis we indicate frequency;
that is, in this exercise, the number of
students receiving a certain score. Since
the largest frequency for any interval is
8, the vertical axis must be laid off to include 8 units. Then we plot the points
whose coordinates are the respective
mid-algebraic grade of each interval and
the number of frequency. We connect

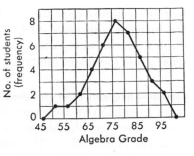

them in order with straight lines. The polygon is closed at each end by
drawing a line from the end points to the horizontal axis at the midpoint
of the next outlying interval. (In this case the outlying intervals would
be 45–49 and 100–104, with midpoints 47 and 102.)

EXERCISES: Constructing a frequency polygon

1. Construct a frequency polygon for the data given in ex. 1 on page 435.
2. Construct a frequency polygon for the data given in ex. 2 on page 435.
3. Construct a frequency polygon for the data given in ex. 2 on page 433.

Cumulative frequency. The cumulative frequency for any interval in a
frequency distribution is the sum of the frequencies in that given interval
and the frequencies in all the lower intervals. This is shown in the following:

Algebra Grade	f	Cumulative Frequency
95–99	2	39
90–94	3	37
85–89	5	34
80–84	7	29
75–79	8	22
70–74	6	14
65–69	4	8
60–64	2	4
55–59	1	2
50–54	1	1

As an example, notice the cumulative frequency for the interval 75–79; it is 22. This
number 22 is the sum of the frequencies in
this interval and the frequencies in all the lower
intervals. The column of cumulative frequency

may be recorded most readily by starting at the lowest interval. Then the frequency for each interval is merely added to the cumulative frequency of the next lower interval. This sum is the cumulative frequency for the given interval.

Cumulative frequency curve (or ogive). Because it is superior for certain purposes a cumulative frequency curve (sometimes called an *ogive*) is often used rather than the histogram or frequency polygon to represent a distribution graphically. The cumulative frequency curve is constructed in a manner very similar to the method used for constructing the frequency polygon.

ILLUSTRATIVE EXAMPLE: Constructing a cumulative frequency curve

Construct a cumulative frequency curve (an ogive) for the distribution given on page 437.

Solution. The axes are prepared in the same manner as those for the frequency polygon. However, on the vertical coordinate axis we now indicate cumulative frequency. Since the largest value of the cumulative frequency in our distribution is 39, this axis must be laid off to include 39 units.

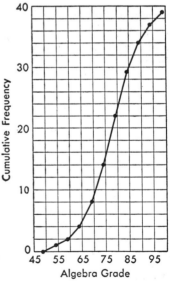

The value of the cumulative frequency for each interval is plotted directly above the *upper limit* of the algebra grade for that interval. That is, above a grade of 54 is plotted a cumulative frequency of 1. Above a grade of 59 is plotted a cumulative frequency of 2, etc. The points are connected in order with straight lines. The curve is closed at the bottom by joining the end point to the horizontal axis at a point that represents the upper limit of the interval below the first interval of the distribution. This point would fall at a position where the algebra grade is 49.

Finding quartiles from a cumulative frequency curve. We can readily determine the median and the first and third quartiles from a cumulative frequency curve. To find the median it is necessary only to draw a horizontal line through the midpoint of the vertical axis, if we consider the length of the vertical axis to be equal to the total frequency of the distribution. From the intersection of this horizontal line and the cumulative frequency curve a vertical line is drawn. The reading of the point at which this vertical line intersects the horizontal axis is the value of the median. Similar methods can be used to find the first and third quartiles.

ILLUSTRATIVE EXAMPLE: Finding quartiles from an ogive

Find the median and the first and third quartiles from the ogive shown in the illustrative example on p. 438.

Solution. The vertical axis is 39 units in length. To find the *median,* we draw a horizontal line through the point on the vertical axis that reads $\frac{1}{2}$ of 39, or $19\frac{1}{2}$. Upon locating the intersection of this line and the curve, we draw a vertical line through the intersection. This vertical line intersects the horizontal axis at a point reading 77.4. The median is 77.4.   Answer

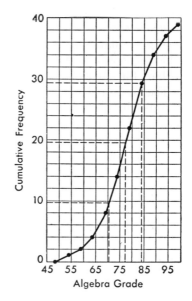

To find the first quartile, Q_1, we draw a horizontal line through the point on the vertical axis that reads $\frac{1}{4}$ of 39, or $9\frac{3}{4}$. Through the intersection of this line and the curve we draw a vertical line. This vertical line intersects the horizontal axis at a point reading 70.5. Therefore, $Q_1 = 70.5$ Answer

To find the third quartile, Q_3, we draw a horizontal line through the point on the vertical axis that reads $\frac{3}{4}$ of 39, or $29\frac{1}{4}$. Through the intersection of this line and the curve we draw a vertical line. This vertical line intersects the horizontal axis at a point reading 84.3. Therefore, $Q_3 = 84.3$.   Answer

EXERCISES: Finding quartiles from an ogive

1. Construct a cumulative frequency curve (or ogive) for the data given in ex. 1 on page 435. From this ogive determine the median and the first and third quartiles.

2. Construct a cumulative frequency curve (or ogive) for the data given in ex. 2 on page 435. From this ogive determine the median and the first and third quartiles.

3. Construct a cumulative frequency curve (or ogive) for the data given in ex. 2 on page 433. From this ogive determine the median and the first and third quartiles.

Central tendency and variability. If it is desired to give an indication of the measurements in a distribution by a single number, then a measure of *central tendency* should be used. To compare the salaries of the teachers in one school with the salaries of the teachers in another school we should first obtain some measure of the central tendency of the distributions of salaries in each respective school. One of the common measures used to indicate the central tendency of a distribution is the median. We can compare the median of teachers' salaries in School A with the median of teachers' salaries in School B. This will give us some indication as to which school pays its teachers more. It will not give us an indication as to how the salaries vary within each school.

The median alone can describe only one of the important characteristics of a distribution. It is often very important to know how compactly the measures are distributed about this central point, or how far they are scattered from it. Several methods can be used to describe this variability of the scores in a distribution. For example, we have already mentioned the *range* of scores, that is, the difference between the highest and lowest scores on a distribution. This gives some indication of the variability.

Another measure of variability is the *semi-interquartile range*. This is one half the difference between the first and third quartiles. This could be represented symbolically as $\dfrac{Q_3 - Q_1}{2}$. This is a better measure of variability than the range, because its value depends upon more scores than does the value of the range.

A better and more commonly used measure of variability is *average deviation*. The reliability of the average deviation as a measure of variability is due to the fact that the average deviation depends upon the value of every score in the distribution.

Average deviation. As its name implies, the average deviation is an average of the numerical deviation of each score from the median of the scores.

$$\text{Average deviation} = \frac{\text{sum of deviations (disregarding sign)}}{\text{number of measurements}}$$

$$\text{A.D.} = \frac{\Sigma \, |d|}{N}$$

where Σ represents "the sum of";
           $|d|$, the absolute value of the
           deviation (or difference) of
           each score from the median;
           N, the total frequency.

The greater the value of the average deviation the farther the scores in the distribution are scattered from the median.

ILLUSTRATIVE EXAMPLE: Finding the average deviation

Determine the average deviation from the median of the following scores: 0, 3, 2, 5, 8, 4, 4, 6, 5, 2, 5, 7, 4, 1, 3, 7, 8, 1, 5, 4.

Solution. We order the data:

0, 1, 1, 2, 2, 3, 3, 4, 4, 4, 4, 5, 5, 5, 5, 6, 7, 7, 8, 8

N = the total frequency = 20 scores

The median is halfway between the tenth and eleventh scores. Since the tenth score is 4 and the eleventh score is also 4, the median is 4. We determine the difference between each score and the median, regardless of sign. In the same order as the ordered scores above, the deviations (or differences) are: 4, 3, 3, 2, 2, 1, 1, 0, 0, 0, 0, 1, 1, 1, 1, 2, 3, 3, 4, 4.

The sum of these differences, $\Sigma |d| = 36$

The average deviation, $$\text{A.D.} = \frac{\Sigma |d|}{N}$$

$$\text{A.D.} = \tfrac{36}{20}$$
$$\text{A.D.} = 1.8 \quad \text{Answer}$$

EXERCISES: Finding measures of variability

In the following exercises compute the average deviation from the median for each of the given sets of data.

1. The monthly salaries (in dollars) in a certain office: 140, 140, 180, 200, 200, 240, 260, 280, 340, 340, 340, 400, 440.

2. The ages at time of marriage of the girls in one college class: 25, 28, 22, 22, 19, 26, 23, 20, 19, 30, 27, 21, 22, 25, 23, 22, 23, 24, 25, 24.

3. The time (in minutes) required for the students in one class to complete a certain algebra assignment:

42	35	46	38	39	35
40	44	41	42	37	43
39	40	39	45	44	37
48	42	39	33	43	42
34	42	37	42	41	38
33	43	37	38	31	41

Mathematics vocabulary

The student should be familiar with the following words or expressions. He should know their meanings, and he should be able to spell them.

angle of depression	interpolation
angle of elevation	median
average deviation	method of averages
central tendency	odds
chance	ogive
circular permutation	parameter
combination	permutation
cosine	probability
cotangent	quartile
cubic	range
cumulative frequency	semi-interquartile range
determinant	sine
element of a determinant	statistics
first quartile	tangent
frequency distribution	third quartile
frequency polygon	variability
histogram	

CHAPTER REVIEW EXERCISES

1. Find the distance between the points $(3, -9)$ and $(5, 2)$.

2. Write the equation of the line passing through the points $(-4, 1)$ and $(3, 6)$.

3. Write the equation of the line passing through the point $(-3, 1)$ with a slope of $-\frac{1}{2}$.

4. Write the equation of the line whose x intercept is 2 and whose y intercept is -3.

5. Find the x intercept and the y intercept of the line whose equation is $2x - 3y = 6$.

6. Show that the points $(-3, 2)$, $(6, 5)$, and $(3, -1)$ are the vertices of an isosceles triangle.

7. Find the area of the triangle whose vertices are $(-3, 2)$, $(6, 5)$, and $(3, -1)$.

Exercises 8–15 refer to the following scores which were obtained on an algebra test:

20	30	30	28	16	29	28	31	23	34
27	28	30	31	21	31	21	31	32	29
23	24	28	35	22	29	25	29	23	32

25	26	28	33	31	27	27	38	34	30
26	31	29	31	22	26	32	18	32	31
28	19	30	37	33	24	20	36	29	22

8. Order the data.

9. Find the median.

10. Make a frequency distribution.

11. What is the range?

12. Make a frequency polygon.

13. Make an ogive.

14. Compute the semi-interquartile range.

15. Find the average deviation.

CUMULATIVE REVIEW EXERCISES

1. Factor completely: $60\,ab - 80 + 20\,a^2 + 45\,b^2$

2. Simplify: $\dfrac{\dfrac{3x+y}{2x} + \dfrac{x-2y}{3y}}{\dfrac{x^2 - y^2}{24\,xy}}$

3. Solve for x and y: $\begin{cases} \dfrac{3}{2x} + \dfrac{2}{3y} = -\dfrac{5}{6} \\[2mm] \dfrac{2}{5x} - \dfrac{3}{y} = -\dfrac{17}{5} \end{cases}$

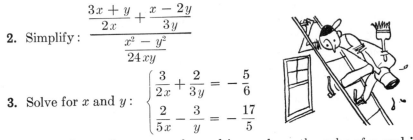

4. If x varies as the square of y and inversely as the cube of z, and if $x = 9$ when $y = 6$ and $z = 4$, what does x equal when $y = 3$ and $z = 3$?

5. Simplify: $\left(\dfrac{2x^{\frac{1}{2}}y^0z^{\frac{3}{2}}}{54\,x^5y^3}\right)^{-\frac{2}{3}}$

6. Solve graphically, expressing the roots to the nearest tenth:
$$x^2 - 3x = 3$$

7. Solve by completing the square: $px^2 + qx + r = 0$.

8. Find the common ratio in a geometric series if the sum of the terms to infinity equals $\dfrac{-32}{3}$ and the first term is -16.

9. Evaluate by logarithms:
$$\sqrt[3]{\dfrac{131.4 \times 367}{(6.951)^2}}$$

10. A ladder, leaning against a building, makes an angle of $68°\,23'$ with the ground when its foot is placed 4.32 ft. from the building. What angle would this ladder make with the ground if its foot were placed 2.75 ft. from the building?

11. Find, if one exists, the term that contains x^2 in the expansion of $(2x^{\frac{1}{2}} - y^{\frac{1}{2}})^{14}$.

12. If three balls are drawn from a bag containing 4 red balls, 3 white balls, and 2 black balls, what is the probability that the three balls are all red?

13. Evaluate the determinant:
$$\begin{vmatrix} 2 & 4 & 6 \\ -1 & 8 & -3 \\ -3 & 2 & -9 \end{vmatrix}$$

14. The list below gives the annual precipitation (in inches) for the state of Kansas, during the period 1888–1937, as reported by the U. S. Weather Bureau. What was the median precipitation for one year? Make a frequency distribution, using any conveniently sized interval.

1888	23	1898	32	1908	32	1918	28	1928	33
1889	29	1899	26	1909	31	1919	26	1929	28
1890	21	1900	28	1910	20	1920	27	1930	27
1891	31	1901	21	1911	25	1921	24	1931	26
1892	29	1902	34	1912	27	1922	29	1932	24
1893	20	1903	31	1913	23	1923	32	1933	22
1894	21	1904	31	1914	26	1924	24	1934	20
1895	28	1905	31	1915	41	1925	25	1935	28
1896	29	1906	29	1916	24	1926	25	1936	18
1897	24	1907	26	1917	20	1927	32	1937	21

CHAPTER 20

Review Exercises and Examinations

Directions. Each problem is followed by five choices, one of which is the correct answer. By working each problem, find the correct answer, and put its letter after the number of the problem on your paper.

1. When simplified, $\dfrac{3x^2 + 3xy}{x^2 - xy}$ equals

a) 0 b) 6 c) $\dfrac{3x + y}{x - y}$ d) $\dfrac{3(x + y)}{x - y}$ e) $\dfrac{2x(x + y)}{x - y}$

2. When simplified, $3c\sqrt{8x^3}$ equals

a) $6cx\sqrt{2x}$ b) $6cx^2\sqrt{2x}$ c) $12c\sqrt{x^3}$ d) $12cx\sqrt{x}$ e) $24cx\sqrt{x}$

3. Solve for x: $x^2 - a^2 = 0$

a) $a, 2a$ b) $a, -a$ c) $-1, a$ d) $-a, 1$ e) $a, 2$

4. What is the sum to infinity of $2 + \frac{2}{3} + \frac{2}{9} + \cdots$?

a) $\frac{4}{3}$ b) $2\frac{8}{9}$ c) 3 d) 6 e) Unlimited

5. What is the value of $\log_5 5$?

a) 0 b) 1 c) 5 d) 25 e) 3125

6. What is the value of the discriminant in $3x^2 - 5x + 2 = 0$?

a) -1 b) $\frac{2}{3}$ c) 1 d) $\frac{5}{3}$ e) 49

7. The graph of which of the following equations passes through the origin?

a) $x - 3 = 0$ b) $x + 2y = 0$ c) $2x + y = 2$

d) $x + y = 1$ e) $x - 3y = 5$

8. What is the numerical value of $4!$?

a) 1 b) 4 c) 16 d) 24 e) 64

9. What determinant placed in the numerator of the fraction $\dfrac{?}{\begin{vmatrix} 3 & 2 \\ 7 & -9 \end{vmatrix}}$ would make the fraction equal to the value of x in the solution of the system of equations

$$3x + 2y = 5$$
$$7x - 9y = 1$$

a) $\begin{vmatrix} 3 & -2 \\ 7 & 9 \end{vmatrix}$ b) $\begin{vmatrix} 3 & 5 \\ 7 & 1 \end{vmatrix}$ c) $\begin{vmatrix} 3 & -5 \\ 7 & -1 \end{vmatrix}$ d) $\begin{vmatrix} 5 & 2 \\ 1 & -9 \end{vmatrix}$ e) $\begin{vmatrix} 5 & 3 \\ 1 & 7 \end{vmatrix}$

10. If two coins are tossed, what is the chance that one is heads and one is tails?

a) 0 b) $\frac{1}{8}$ c) $\frac{1}{4}$ d) $\frac{1}{2}$ e) 1

11. What is the median in the following set of measurements?

0, 1, 1, 2, 2, 2, 3, 4, 4, 5, 5, 5, 5, 6, 7, 7, 8

a) 3 b) 3.5 c) 4 d) 4.5 e) 5

12. What is the slope of the line that passes through the points $(-1, 3)$ and $(6, -2)$?

a) $-\frac{5}{7}$ b) $-\frac{1}{7}$ c) $\frac{1}{5}$ d) 1 e) $\frac{7}{5}$

13. Add and simplify: $\dfrac{3x}{x^2 - xy} + \dfrac{4}{x}$

a) $\dfrac{3x + 4}{x(x^2 - xy)}$ b) $\dfrac{3x^2 - 4y}{x^2 - xy}$ c) $\dfrac{7x - 4y}{x(x - y)}$ d) $7x^2 - 4xy$

e) $3x + 4x^2 - 4xy$

14. One of the factors of $12x^2 - 8x - 15$ is

a) $2x + 3$ b) $3x - 5$ c) $3x + 5$ d) $4x + 3$ e) $6x + 5$

15. When simplified, $\sqrt[3]{\frac{1}{9}}$ equals

a) $\frac{1}{3}$ b) $\frac{1}{3}\sqrt[3]{3}$ c) $\frac{1}{3}\sqrt{3}$ d) $3\sqrt[6]{3}$ e) $3\sqrt[3]{3}$

16. The value of $(\frac{1}{2})^{-2}$ is

a) $\dfrac{\sqrt{2}}{2}$ b) $\sqrt{2}$ c) 2   d) 4   e) none of these

17. Find the third term of $(x - 2y)^8$.

a) $-112x^5y^3$ b) $56x^4y^2$ c) $56x^5y^3$ d) $60x^6y^2$ e) $112x^6y^2$

18. What is the seventh term of the progression 24, 12, 6, $\cdots$?

a) -48 b) -18 c) 0   d) $\frac{3}{16}$ e) $\frac{3}{8}$

19. Expressed as a single logarithm, $\log a + \log b$ equals

a) $\log (a + b)$ b) $\log ab$ c) $\log \dfrac{a}{b}$ d) $\log_a b$ e) $\log a_b$

20. What is the product of the roots of the equation $rx^2 + sx + t = 0$?

a) $s^2 - 4rt$ b) $\dfrac{-s}{r}$ c) $\dfrac{t}{r}$ d) $\dfrac{r}{s}$ e) $-\dfrac{r}{t}$

21. The graph of which of the following equations is not a straight line?

a) $x + y = 3$ b) $2x = 5 - y$ c) $6x - 3 = 2y$

d) $xy = 4$ e) $x = 7$

22. Solve simultaneously : $5x - 2y = 0$
$$7x - y = 9a$$

x is equal to

a) 2   b) 5   c) $2a$ d) $5a$ e) none of these

23. In right triangle ABC the ratio of sin A to cos A equals

a) 0   b) 1   c) tan A d) ctn A e) none of these

24. If an airplane takes off from an airport, climbing at an angle of $3° 45'$, how far must it fly until it is over a town 9979 yd. from the airport?

a) 1000 yd.   b) 2000 yd.   c) 9979 yd.   d) 10,000 yd.

e) 1 mi.

25. In how many ways can the letters of the word ATLANTA be arranged?

a) 24   b) 420   c) 1540   d) 4620   e) 9240

26. When simplified $\dfrac{3}{x + 1} - \dfrac{2}{x^2 - 1}$ equals

a) $\dfrac{3x^2 - 2x - 5}{(x^2 - 1)(x + 1)}$ b) $\dfrac{3x^2 - 2x - 5}{x^2 - 1}$ c) $\dfrac{x - 5}{x^2 - 1}$

d) $\dfrac{3x - 5}{x^2 - 1}$ e) $\dfrac{3x - 5}{x - 1}$

27. When simplified, $\sqrt{\frac{3}{16}}$ equals

a) $\dfrac{\sqrt{3}}{4}$ b) $\dfrac{\sqrt{48}}{16}$ c) $\frac{3}{4}$ d) $\frac{9}{4}$ e) $4\sqrt{3}$

28. When simplified, $\sqrt{4^3 + 8^2}$ equals

   a) $2\sqrt{7}$ b) $8\sqrt{2}$ c) $12\sqrt{2}$ d) 16   e) 24

29. Multiply x^2 by $x^{\frac{3}{2}}$.

   a) $x^{\frac{5}{2}}$ b) x^3 c) $x^{\frac{7}{2}}$ d) x^6 e) none of these

30. Solve for x: $x^2 + ax - bx - ab = 0$

   a) $-a, b$ b) $a, -b$ c) a, b d) $\dfrac{ab}{a-b}$ e) $\dfrac{ab}{a-b-1}$

31. What is the equation whose roots are $2 \pm \sqrt{-1}$?

   a) $x^2 - 2x - 3 = 0$ c) $x^2 - 4x + 3 = 0$

   b) $x^2 - 4x - 3 = 0$ d) $x^2 - 4x + 5 = 0$

                 e) none of these

32. Which of the following equations represents a hyperbola that does not cross either the x axis or the y axis?

   a) $3x^2 - y^2 = 6$ b) $y^2 = 7 + x^2$ c) $xy = 5$

   d) $x^2 - 7 = y^2$ e) $5y^2 - 2x^2 = 1$

33. Which of the following expressions represents the speed of a stream's current if a boat goes g mph. downstream and r mph. upstream?

   a) $g - r$ b) $g + r$ c) $\dfrac{g+r}{2}$ d) $\dfrac{g-r}{2}$ e) $\dfrac{gr}{2}$

34. The factors of $x^3 - x - y + y^3$ are

   a) $(x + y)(x^2 - xy + y^2 - 1)$ d) $(x + y)^2(x^2 - xy + y^2)$

   b) $(x + y)(x^2 - 2xy + y^2 - 1)$ e) $(x + y)(x - y)^2$

   c) $(x + y)(x^2 - xy + y^2)$

35. When $5 + \sqrt{3}$ is divided by $5 - \sqrt{3}$, the quotient is

   a) 0   b) 1   c) $\frac{14}{11}$ d) $\dfrac{14 + 5\sqrt{3}}{11}$ e) $28 + 10\sqrt{3}$

36. When simplified, $(a^2b^3)^{\frac{1}{2}}$ equals

   a) $(ab)^3$ b) $ab^{\frac{3}{2}}$ c) $a^{\frac{1}{2}}b^2$ d) $a^{\frac{3}{2}}b^{\frac{5}{2}}$ e) $a^{\frac{5}{2}}b^{\frac{7}{2}}$

37. Which of the following equations would enable you to find the width (x) of a rectangle, if the perimeter of the rectangle is 94, and the length is 3 more than the width?

   a) $x + x + 3x + 3x = 94$

   b) $x + (x + 3) = 94$

   c) $x(x + 3) = 94$

   d) $2x + 2(x + 3) = 94$

   e) $2x(x + 3) = 94$

38. Given the two formulas $m = kd^2$ and $p = \dfrac{kd}{2}$. If $d = 4$ and $p = 12$, then m equals

   a) $\frac{3}{8}$ *b)* $\frac{8}{3}$ *c)* 48   *d)* 96   *e)* none of these

39. The intensity of light on a screen is inversely proportional to the square of the distance from its source. If the intensity of light on a screen is satisfactory at a distance of 20 ft., then if the distance is changed to 40 ft., the intensity of the light to be satisfactory should be

   a) doubled   *b)* tripled   *c)* increased fourfold
    d) increased twentyfold   *e)* none of these

40. If $f(x) = x^3 + x^2 - k$ and $f(x)$ equals zero when $x = -1$, then

   a) $x - 1$ is a factor of $f(x)$ *d)* $k = 1$
   b) $x + 1$ is a factor of $f(x)$ *e)* none of these
   c) $k = -1$

R E V I E W E X E R C I S E S : Multiple-choice test II

Directions. Each problem is followed by five choices, one of which is the correct answer. By working each problem, find the correct answer, and put its letter after the number of the problem on your paper.

1. When simplified, $\sqrt{\frac{1}{3}}$ equals

   a) $\frac{1}{9}$ *b)* $\frac{1}{9}\sqrt{3}$ *c)* $\frac{1}{3}\sqrt{3}$ *d)* $\sqrt{3}$ *e)* 3

2. In right triangle ABC with the right angle at C, the ratio of b to c is equal to

   a) $\cos A$ *b)* $\cos B$ *c)* $\sin A$ *d)* $\tan A$ *e)* $\tan B$

3. The value of 2^{-4} is

   a) $\sqrt[4]{2}$ *b)* $\frac{1}{16}$ *c)* $\frac{1}{8}$ *d)* 8   *e)* 32

4. When simplified, $\dfrac{(x-y)^2}{x^2 - y^2}$ equals

   a) 1   *b)* $\dfrac{1}{x+y}$ *c)* $\dfrac{2}{x+y}$ *d)* $\dfrac{x-y}{x+y}$ *e)* $-2xy - 1$

5. Change the repeating decimal $0.4444\cdots$ to a common fraction.

   a) $\frac{4}{11}$ *b)* $\frac{2}{5}$ *c)* $\frac{4}{9}$ *d)* $\frac{44}{9}$ *e)* none of these

6. What is the nature of the roots of $x^2 - 3x - 4 = 0$?

   a) real, rational, equal   *d)* real, irrational, unequal
   b) real, rational, unequal   *e)* imaginary
   c) real, irrational, equal

7. Which of the following points lies on the line whose equation is $x + 2y = 5$?

   a) $(0, 0)$ *b)* $(3, 2)$ *c)* $(1, 2)$ *d)* $(10, -5)$ *e)* $(0, 5)$

8. Solve simultaneously :

$$x + y = 11$$
$$x - y = 3$$

x is equal to

a) $- 7$ b) $- 4$ c) 4 d) 8 e) none of these

9. Which of the following numbers is not real?

a) $- 4$ b) $\frac{2}{3}$ c) $\sqrt{3}$ d) 3 e) $\sqrt{- 11}$

10. Which of the following formulas represents the lateral surface S of a right circular cone, if the surface is equal to the product of one half the slant height (h) and the circumference of the base, whose radius is r?

a) $S = \frac{h}{2}(\pi r^2)$ b) $S = \pi h r$ c) $S = \frac{\pi h r}{2}$ d) $S = \frac{h}{2}r$ e) $S = 2hr$

11. Solve simultaneously : $x^2 + y^2 = 32$

$$x = y$$

Which of the following is a solution?

a) $x = - 4, y = 4$ d) $x = - 4\sqrt{2}, y = - 4\sqrt{2}$
b) $x = 4, y = - 4$ e) none of these
c) $x = 4\sqrt{2}, y = 4\sqrt{2}$

12. What are the values of x at the two points where the parabola $y = x^2 - 5x + 6$ crosses the x axis?

a) $- 2$ and $- 3$ d) 0 and 3
b) 0 and 2 e) $- 1$ and 6
c) 2 and 3

13. What is the equation whose roots are 0 and $- 2$?

a) $y + 2 = 0$ d) $y^2 - 2 = 0$
b) $y^2 + 2y = 0$ e) $y^2 + 2 = 0$
c) $y^2 - 2y = 0$

14. What is the sixty-third term of $2, \frac{9}{4}, \frac{5}{2}, \cdots$?

a) $15\frac{3}{4}$ b) $17\frac{1}{2}$ c) $17\frac{3}{4}$ d) 31 e) none of these

15. What is the middle term of $\left(x - \frac{1}{x}\right)^{10}$?

a) $- 126$ b) 126 c) $- 252$ d) $252x^5$ e) none of these

16. Solve for y : $y^2 - 4y = 0$

a) $0, - 4$ b) $0, 4$ c) ± 2 d) ± 4 e) none of these

17. Simplify : $x - \dfrac{1 - x}{2x - 1}$

a) $2x + 1$ b) $2x^2 - 1$ c) $2x^2$ d) $\dfrac{2x^2 - 1}{2x - 1}$ e) $\dfrac{2x^2 - 2x - 1}{2x - 1}$

18. What is the median of the following scores:

$$1, 1, 2, 2, 2, 3, 3, 3, 4, 5, 6?$$

  a) 2   *b)* 2.5   *c)* 2.9   *d)* 3   *e)* none of these

19. What is the area of the triangle whose vertices are located at the points $(0, 0)$, $(1, 2)$, and $(2, 2)$?

  a) 0   *b)* 1   *c)* 2   *d)* $3\frac{1}{2}$ *e)* 4

20. What is the value of $(.09)^{\frac{1}{2}}$?

  a) 0.0081   *b)* .03   *c)* 0.3   *d)* 0.81   *e)* $\frac{10}{3}$

21. Simplify $\sqrt[3]{16}$

  a) 2   *b)* $2\sqrt[3]{2}$ *c)* $2\sqrt{2}$ *d)* 4   *e)* $4\sqrt[3]{2}$

22. Which of the following equations will enable you to determine the number of hours (x) it will take two pipes together to fill a tank, if one pipe can fill the tank alone in 3 hr. and the other pipe can fill the tank alone in 5 hr.?

  a) $3 + 5 = x$ *b)* $5 - 3 = x$ *c)* $\frac{1}{3} - \frac{1}{5} = x$

  d) $\dfrac{1}{3} - \dfrac{1}{5} = \dfrac{1}{x}$ *e)* $\dfrac{1}{3} + \dfrac{1}{5} = \dfrac{1}{x}$

23. At what point will the two lines meet, whose equations are $x - y = 5$ and $x + y = 7$?

  a) $(2, 3)$ *b)* $(3, -2)$ *c)* $(4, 3)$ *d)* $(6, -1)$ *e)* $(6, 1)$

24. What is the value of $\log_9 27$?

  a) $\frac{2}{3}$ *b)* $\frac{3}{2}$ *c)* 2   *d)* 3   *e)* 18

25. Which of the following is a solution of the equation $x^2 - x + 1 = 0$?

  a) -1 *b)* 1   *c)* i *d)* $\dfrac{1 + i\sqrt{3}}{2}$ *e)* $\dfrac{1 - 3i}{2}$

26. Expressed with positive exponents and simplified, $\dfrac{a^2 b^{-3}}{2^{-3} m^{-1} n^2}$ equals

  a) $\dfrac{a^2 b^{\frac{1}{3}}}{2^{\frac{1}{3}} m n^2}$ *b)* $\dfrac{8 a^2 n^2}{b^3 m}$ *c)* $\dfrac{8 a^2 m}{b^3 n^2}$ *d)* $\dfrac{8\, mn^2}{a^2 b^3}$ *e)* none of these

27. When factored completely, $x^4 - 8x^2 - 9$ equals

  a) $(x^2 - 9)(x^2 + 1)$
  b) $(x + 3)(x - 3)(x^2 + 1)$
  c) $(x + 3)(x - 3)(x + 1)(x - 1)$
  d) $(x + 1)(x - 1)(x^2 + 9)$
  e) none of these

28. What is the average deviation from the median of the following set of measurements?

$$0, 1, 2, 2, 3, 3, 3, 3, 4, 5$$

  a) 0.3   *b)* 1   *c)* 1.3   *d)* 3   *e)* 5

29. How many numbers greater than 1000 can be formed with the digits 2, 3, 0, 4 if no digit is repeated?

> *a)* 3   *b)* 4   *c)* 18   *d)* 24   *e)* 256

30. A triangular piece of land ABC has a right angle at C. If $AB = 420$ yd. and $BC = 210$ yd., what is the number of degrees in angle A?

> *a)* 20   *b)* 30   *c)* 45   *d)* 60   *e)* none of these

31. Simplify $2\sqrt{3}(\sqrt{3} + \sqrt{5})$

> *a)* $18\sqrt{5}$ *b)* $6 + 2\sqrt[4]{15}$ *c)* $2\sqrt{3} + 2\sqrt{15}$ *d)* $6 + 2\sqrt{15}$ *e)* 42

32. Solve simultaneously: $\dfrac{x}{y} = 5$

$$\frac{x}{y - 200} = 10$$

x is equal to

> *a)* 20   *b)* 40   *c)* 200   *d)* 400   *e)* 2000

33. In the equation $mx^2 + 9x + 9 = 0$, if one root is twice the other root, what is the value of m?

> *a)* $-\frac{9}{2}$ *b)* -9 *c)* 2   *d)* 9   *e)* 45

34. If $\sqrt{10} = 3.162$, what is the value of $\log_{10} 3.162$?

> *a)* 0.3162   *b)* 0.4763   *c)* $\frac{1}{2}$ *d)* 2   *e)* 31.62

35. If the equation $\dfrac{x - a}{a} + \dfrac{x}{x - a} = \dfrac{7}{2}$ is solved for x, one of the solutions is

> *a)* $\frac{2}{3}a$ *b)* $3a$ *c)* $\dfrac{a + \sqrt{34 - a^2}}{2}$ *d)* $\frac{9}{2}a$ *e)* none of these

36. When a^3 is multiplied by a^{-4}, the product is

> *a)* $\dfrac{1}{a^{12}}$ *b)* $\dfrac{1}{a^7}$ *c)* $\dfrac{1}{a}$ *d)* a *e)* a^7

37. When factored completely, $1 - 6(a - b) + 9(a - b)^2$ equals

> *a)* $(1 - 3a + 3b)^2$
> *b)* $(1 - 3a - 3b)^2$
> *c)* $(1 - 3a - 3b)(1 - 3a + 3b)$
> *d)* $(1 + 3a - 3b)^2$
> *e)* none of these

38. Perform the indicated division and simplify:

$$\left(\frac{a}{b} - \frac{b}{a}\right) \div \left(\frac{a - b}{a}\right)$$

> *a)* a^2 *b)* $\dfrac{a - b}{b}$ *c)* $\dfrac{a + b}{b}$ *d)* $a - b$ *e)* $a + b$

39. Rationalize the denominator: $\dfrac{3\sqrt{5} - 2\sqrt{7}}{3\sqrt{5} + 2\sqrt{7}}$

a) $1 - 6\sqrt{35}$ b) $1 - 12\sqrt{35}$ c) $29 - 6\sqrt{35}$

d) $29 - 12\sqrt{35}$ e) $\dfrac{73 - 12\sqrt{35}}{17}$

40. What is the first quartile score as determined from the ogive below?

a) 2

b) 3

c) 3.5

d) 4

e) 6

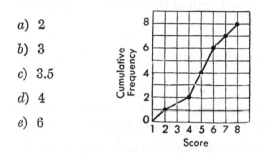

REVIEW EXERCISES: Multiple-choice test III

Directions. Each problem is followed by five choices, one of which is the correct answer. By working each problem, find the correct answer, and put its letter after the number of the problem on your paper.

1. Solve simultaneously: $x + 3y = 2$
$2x - 3y = 13$

x is equal to

a) -1 b) 1 c) $\frac{11}{2}$ d) 5 e) 11

2. What is the radius of a circle whose equation is $x^2 + y^2 = 9$?

a) $\sqrt{3}$ b) 3 c) 9 d) 81 e) none of these

3. Simplify: $\dfrac{a^2 + 8a + 16}{a^2 - 16}$

a) -1 b) $8a$ c) $8a - 1$ d) $\dfrac{a + 4}{a - 4}$ e) $\dfrac{(a + 4)^2}{(a - 4)^2}$

4. If the odds are 5 to 1 against an event, what is the chance of its happening?

a) $\frac{1}{6}$ b) $\frac{1}{5}$ c) $\frac{1}{4}$ d) $\frac{4}{5}$ e) $\frac{5}{6}$

5. Simplify: $\sqrt{\dfrac{3}{16}}$

a) $\dfrac{\sqrt{3}}{4}$ b) $\dfrac{\sqrt{48}}{16}$ c) $\frac{3}{4}$ d) $\frac{9}{4}$ e) $4\sqrt{3}$

6. Which one of the following numbers is imaginary?

a) -4 b) $\frac{2}{3}$ c) π d) $\sqrt{11}$ e) $\sqrt{-3}$

7. Which of the following expressions represents the time, in hours, that it would take to walk k mi. at s mph.?

a) ks b) $\dfrac{k}{s}$ c) $\dfrac{s}{k}$ d) $\sqrt{ks}$ e) $s-k$

8. What is the length of the longer axis of the ellipse whose equation is $x^2 + 4y^2 = 16$?

a) 2   b) 4   c) 6   d) 8   e) 16

9. If the equation $2x^2 + 3x - k = 0$ has one root equal to 5, what is the value of k?

a) -10 b) $-\frac{9}{8}$ c) $-\frac{3}{2}$ d) 10   e) 65

10. If log 2 = 0.3010 and log 3 = 0.4771, what is the value of log 6?

a) 0.1761   b) 0.7781   c) 0.9030   d) 0.9542   e) none of these

11. What is the sum to infinity of $5 + \frac{15}{11} + \frac{45}{121} + \cdots$?

a) $\frac{40}{11}$ b) $\frac{55}{8}$ c) $\frac{55}{3}$ d) $\frac{44}{2}$ e) The sum is unlimited.

12. One of the factors of $2x^2 - 5x - 3$ is

a) $x+1$ b) $x+3$ c) $2x-3$ d) $2x-1$ e) $2x+1$

13. The distance between the points $(-1, 4)$ and $(3, 2)$ is

a) $\sqrt{6}$ b) $2\sqrt{2}$ c) $2\sqrt{5}$ d) 6   e) 20

14. In how many ways can 5 persons form a ring?

a) 5   b) 20   c) 24   d) 25   e) 120

15. Solve simultaneously: $bx + ay = 2ab$
$$ax + by = a^2 + b^2$$

x is equal to

a) a b) b c) $a+b$ d) $2(a+b)$ e) none of these

16. If the graphs of the equations $x^2 + y^2 = 16$ and $x + y = 0$ are drawn, how many points of intersection will there be?

a) 0   b) 1   c) 2   d) 3   e) 4

17. For what values of m will the graph of $y = 4x^2 - mx + 9$ touch the x axis at only one point?

a) $\frac{1}{4}, \frac{9}{4}$ b) $\frac{1}{4}, 9$ c) $-4, 9$ d) $4, \frac{9}{4}$ e) $-\pm 12$

18. If $\log_{10} 6.1 = 0.7853$, what is the value of x in $10^x = 0.61$?

a) 1.7853   b) -1 c) $9.7853 - 10$ d) 7.853
e) none of these

19. What is the first term of an arithmetic progression if the sum of 22 terms is 803 and the common difference is 3?

a) 5   b) 6   c) 8   d) 10   e) none of these

20. What is the second term of the expansion of $(1 - x)^{-1}$?

  a) -1 b) $-x$ c) 1 d) $\dfrac{x}{2}$ e) x

21. What is the difference between the roots of $x^2 - 70x + 1200 = 0$?
  a) 10 b) 20 c) 40 d) 70 e) 120

22. Divide m^2 by m^0.
  a) 1 b) 2 c) m d) m^2 e) none of these

23. Multiply : $\dfrac{16x^2y^3}{9xz} \cdot \dfrac{27z^2}{8yz^2}$

  a) $\dfrac{6y^2}{z}$ b) $\dfrac{6xy^2}{z}$ c) $\dfrac{12xy}{z}$ d) $6xy^2$ e) $12xy$

24. Multiply : $\left(\dfrac{2}{x+2}\right)\left(\dfrac{1}{x} - 3\right)$

  a) $\dfrac{2(1 - 3x)}{x(x + 2)}$ b) $\dfrac{3x - 1}{x + 2}$ c) $\dfrac{1 - 3x}{x + 2}$

          d) $\dfrac{3x - 1}{x}$ e) $\dfrac{3x - 5}{x - 1}$

25. Which of the following formulas would enable you to find side b in the oblique triangle ABC, if $\angle C = 45°$, $\angle B = 60°$, $c = 4$?

  a) $\tan A = \dfrac{a}{b}$ b) $\sin B = \dfrac{b}{c}$ c) $\operatorname{ctn} B = \dfrac{a}{b}$

  d) $\dfrac{a}{\sin A} = \dfrac{b}{\sin B}$ e) $\dfrac{b}{\sin B} = \dfrac{c}{\sin C}$

26. What is the altitude of an isosceles triangle if the base is 20 ft. and one of the base angles is $40° \, 14'$?
  a) 6.46 b) 7.63 c) 8.46 d) 11.82 e) 16.92

27. From the top of a lighthouse 200 ft. high the angle of depression of a passing ship is $4°$. The distance (x) from the base of the lighthouse to the ship can be found from the equation

  a) $\sin 4° = \dfrac{x}{200}$ b) $\tan 4° = \dfrac{x}{200}$ c) $\cos 4° = \dfrac{x}{200}$

          d) $\sin 4° = \dfrac{200}{x}$ e) $\tan 4° = \dfrac{200}{x}$

28. Simplify: $\sqrt{\tfrac{3}{4}} + \sqrt{\tfrac{4}{3}} - \sqrt{\tfrac{1}{12}}$

  a) 1 b) $\sqrt{3}$ c) $\tfrac{4}{3}\sqrt{3}$ d) $6\sqrt{3}$ e) $\dfrac{\sqrt{3}}{2} + \dfrac{\sqrt{2}}{3} - \dfrac{\sqrt{12}}{12}$

29. Written with positive exponents and simplified, $3a^{-3}x^4$ equals

  a) $\dfrac{x^4}{3a^{\frac{1}{3}}}$ b) $3a^{\frac{1}{3}}x^4$ c) $\dfrac{x^4}{27a^3}$ d) $\dfrac{x^4}{3a^3}$ e) $\dfrac{3x^4}{a^3}$

30. Simplify: $\sqrt{45} \div \sqrt{15}$

a) $\dfrac{3\sqrt{5}}{\sqrt{15}}$ b) $\dfrac{\sqrt{5}}{5}$ c) $\dfrac{\sqrt{3}}{3}$ d) $\sqrt{3}$ e) $45\sqrt{5}$

31. When factored completely, $x^4 - x^3 + x - 1$ equals

a) $(x^3 + 1)(x - 1)$ b) $x^3(x - 1)^2$ c) $(x + 1)(x - 1)^3$

d) $(x - 1)(x + 1)(x^2 - x + 1)$ e) $(x - 1)^2(x^2 - x + 1)$

32. Simplify: $\left(\dfrac{4x^4y^3}{y^5x^2}\right)^{-\frac{1}{2}}$

a) $\dfrac{y}{2x}$ b) $\dfrac{y^4}{16x^4}$ c) $\dfrac{2y}{x}$ d) $\dfrac{16y^4}{x^4}$ e) none of these

33. Which of the following equations would enable you to determine the number of days (x) it would take B alone to do a job, if A and B together can do the job in 3 da. and if A can do the job alone in 10 da.?

a) $10 - 3 = x$ c) $\dfrac{10 + 3}{2} = x$

b) $10 + 3 = x$ d) $\dfrac{1}{10} + \dfrac{1}{x} = \dfrac{1}{3}$

e) $\frac{1}{3} - \frac{1}{10} = x$

34. Solve simultaneously: $\dfrac{4}{x} + \dfrac{3}{y} = 2$

$$\dfrac{8}{x} - \dfrac{3}{y} = 1$$

x is equal to

a) $\frac{1}{4}$ b) $\frac{1}{3}$ c) 3   d) 4   e) none of these

35. The product of $2\sqrt{32}$ and $3\sqrt{2}$ is

a) 13   b) $5\sqrt{34}$ c) 40   d) 48   e) none of these

36. If $i = \sqrt{-1}$, then i^{19} equals

a) -1 b) 1   c) $-i$ d) i e) none of these

37. For what value of a will the point $(2, a)$ lie on the graph of $3x + y = 2$?

a) -4 b) -2 c) 2   d) 4   e) none of these

38. The equation $7x - \dfrac{5}{x} = 2$

a) has two roots, both positive.

b) has two roots, one positive and one negative.

c) has two roots, both negative.

d) has only one root.

e) none of these.

39. If $2\sqrt{14} = 7.484$, the value of $4\sqrt{\frac{7}{2}}$ equals

a) 1.871   b) 3.742   c) 5.613   d) 7.484   e) none of these

40. $(m + n)(m - n) = m^2 - n^2$ is

a) an identity   d) a cubic equation

b) an equation of condition   e) none of these

c) a linear equation

REVIEW EXAMINATION I

Directions. Each problem is followed by five choices, one of which is the correct answer. By working each problem, find the correct answer, and put its letter after the number of the problem on your paper.

1. When reduced to its lowest terms, $\dfrac{x^2 - 4xy + 3y^2}{x^2 - 3xy}$ equals

a) $\dfrac{x - y}{x}$ b) $\dfrac{x - 3y}{x}$ c) $\dfrac{x}{x - y}$

d) $\dfrac{x}{x - 3y}$ e) none of these

2. If $K - \dfrac{R}{S} = g$, then R equals

a) $\dfrac{K}{g}$ b) $\dfrac{g}{K}$ c) $S(g - K)$

d) $S(K - g)$ e) none of these

3. Simplify: $6\sqrt{5} - \sqrt{45}$

a) 5 b) $3\sqrt{5}$ c) $9\sqrt{5}$ d) $2\sqrt{-10}$ e) none of these

4. Simplify: $(3x^{-\frac{1}{3}}y^{-\frac{1}{2}})^0(2x^{-\frac{1}{3}}y^{-\frac{1}{2}})^0$

a) 0   b) 1   c) $\dfrac{1}{6^{\frac{2}{3}}xy}$ d) $\dfrac{6}{x^{\frac{2}{3}}y}$ e) none of these

5. Which of the following is a factor of $8x^3 + 27y^3$?

a) $8x + 27y$ b) $2x - 3y$ c) $4x^2 + 12xy + 9y^2$

d) $4x^2 - 6xy + 9y^2$ e) $4x^2 + 6xy + 9y^2$

6. Combine and simplify: $\dfrac{x - 2y}{2x} - \dfrac{x + 2y}{5x}$

a) $\dfrac{3x - 14y}{10x}$ b) $\dfrac{x^2 - 4y^2}{5x^2}$ c) $\dfrac{x^2 - 4y^2}{10x^2}$

d) $\dfrac{x^2 - 4y^2}{7x^2}$ e) none of these

7. In the series $3, 1, \frac{1}{3}, \cdots$, the seventh term is

    a) $\frac{1}{243}$ *b)* $\frac{1}{81}$ *c)* $\frac{1}{54}$ *d)* $\frac{1}{27}$ *e)* none of these

8. In the series $\frac{29}{3}, 10, \frac{31}{3}, \cdots$, the twentieth term is

    a) $\frac{25}{3}$ *b)* 16 *c)* $16\frac{1}{3}$ *d)* $16\frac{2}{3}$ *e)* none of these

9. In the expansion of the binomial $(x + y)^8$, the second term is

    a) $8 + x^7y$ *b)* $8x^7y^7$ *c)* $-8x^7y$ *d)* $8x^7y$ *e)* none of these

10. The value of the determinant $\begin{vmatrix} 2 & 4 & 0 \\ 8 & 6 & 0 \\ 3 & 2 & 1 \end{vmatrix}$ is

    a) -13 *b)* -20 *c)* 20 *d)* 44 *e)* none of these

11. Simplify: $\sqrt{\dfrac{48}{64\,a^2}}$

    a) $\dfrac{\sqrt{3}}{2\,a}$ *b)* $\dfrac{\sqrt{48}}{8\,a}$ *c)* $\dfrac{2\sqrt{12}}{4\,a}$ *d)* $4a\sqrt{48}$ *e)* none of these

12. Express with positive exponents: $\dfrac{m^{-3}(n^{-1})^2}{n^2}$

    a) $\dfrac{1}{m^3}$ *b)* $\dfrac{n^4}{m^3}$ *c)* $\dfrac{1}{m^3n^4}$ *d)* $\dfrac{m^3}{n^4}$ *e)* none of these

13. Multiply: $b^{-\frac{3}{4}} \cdot b^{\frac{5}{2}}$

    a) $b^{-\frac{15}{8}}$ *b)* $b^{\frac{1}{3}}$ *c)* $b^{\frac{3}{2}}$ *d)* $b^{\frac{7}{4}}$ *e)* none of these

14. Solve simultaneously: $\quad 1.1\,m - 0.4n = 2.4$
$$3\,m + 4n = 4$$

    a) $m = \frac{1}{2}, n = 2$ *d)* $m = 2, n = -\frac{1}{2}$
    b) $m = -2, n = -\frac{1}{2}$ *e)* none of these
    c) $m = -2, n = \frac{1}{2}$

15. Given $5\,m^2 + 2\,m - 16 = 0$. Then m can have only the values

    a) $\frac{18}{5}$ and -2 *d)* -2 and $-\frac{8}{5}$
    b) $\frac{8}{5}$ and 2 *e)* none of these
    c) 2 and $-\frac{8}{5}$

16. Reduce to lowest terms: $\dfrac{ab + b + a + 1}{a + 1}$

    a) $\dfrac{a+1}{a-1}$ *b)* $\dfrac{b+1}{a-1}$ *c)* $\dfrac{a+b}{a-1}$ *d)* $b + 1$ *e)* none of these

17. What are the factors of $4\,a^2 - (b + c)^2$?

    a) $(2a - b + c)(2a + b + c)$ *d)* $(2a - b - c)(2a - b + c)$
    b) $(2a + b - c)(2a + b + c)$ *e)* $(2a - b + c)(2a + b - c)$
    c) $(2a - b - c)(2a + b + c)$

18. A 25-ft. ladder leans against a building. If the foot of the ladder is 15 ft. from the base of the building, which of the following equations will enable one to determine the angle (X) formed by the ladder and the ground?

a) $\tan X = \frac{15}{25}$ b) $\sin X = \frac{15}{25}$ c) $\cos X = \frac{15}{25}$
d) $\tan X = \frac{25}{15}$ e) $\sin X = \frac{15}{20}$

19. The expression 4.8×10^{-5} equals

a) .0000048   b) .000048   c) .00048   d) .0048
e) none of these

20. Express as a fraction having a rational denominator : $\dfrac{\sqrt{b}}{\sqrt{b} + 1}$

a) $\dfrac{b}{b - 1}$ b) $\dfrac{b}{b + 1}$ c) $\dfrac{b - \sqrt{b}}{b - 1}$ d) $\dfrac{b + \sqrt{b}}{b + 1}$ e) none of these

21. Solve simultaneously by referring to the graph :

$$dx - ey = f$$
$$- x^2 + 2x + 3 = y$$

x is approximately equal to

a) 3 or $- \frac{1}{2}$ b) $- 2$ or $- 4$ c) $3\frac{1}{2}$ or $- \frac{1}{2}$
d) $3\frac{1}{2}$ or $- 2\frac{1}{2}$ e) 3 or $- 2$

22. Solve simultaneously by referring to the graph in ex. 21 :

$$ax + by = c$$
$$dx - ey = f$$

x is approximately equal to

a) $- 2$ b) $- 1$ c) 1 d) 2 e) 2 or $- 1$

23. The expression $\log x^2 y^2$ equals

a) $(\log xy)^2$ d) $2 \log x + 2 \log y$
b) $(\log x^2)(\log y^2)$ e) none of these
c) $4 \log xy$

24. An automobile manufacturer makes 4 styles. Each style is made in 8 colors and 2 types of engine. The number of cars required for a complete display would be

a) 14   b) 16   c) 32   d) 64   e) none of these

25. If x varies inversely as the cube of y, and $x = 25$ when $y = 3$, then when $y = 5$, x equals

a) $\frac{5}{27}$ b) $5\frac{2}{5}$ c) 135   d) 175   e) none of these

26. When the system of equations $\qquad x^2 + y^2 = 9$
$$x - y - 5 = 0$$
is solved, $\quad x = \dfrac{-5 \pm \sqrt{-7}}{2}$ and $y = \dfrac{5 \pm \sqrt{-7}}{2}$.

Therefore, the graphs representing these two equations will

a) not intersect $\qquad\qquad$ d) intersect three times
b) intersect once $\qquad\qquad$ e) intersect four times
c) intersect twice

27. Which of the following expressions is equal to the value of h in the adjacent triangle where h is perpendicular to a?

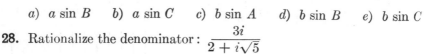

a) $a \sin B$ $\quad$ b) $a \sin C$ $\quad$ c) $b \sin A$ $\quad$ d) $b \sin B$ $\quad$ e) $b \sin C$

28. Rationalize the denominator : $\dfrac{3i}{2 + i\sqrt{5}}$

a) $\dfrac{2i - \sqrt{5}}{9}$ $\quad$ b) $\dfrac{2i - \sqrt{5}}{3}$ $\quad$ c) $\dfrac{2i + \sqrt{5}}{9}$ $\quad$ d) $\dfrac{2i + \sqrt{5}}{3}$ $\quad$ e) none of these

29. A rectangular lot is fenced on three sides and is bordered by a river on the fourth. The length of its fence is 240 ft., and the area of the lot is 7200 sq. ft. If the length of the rectangle parallels the river, what is the equation for the width (x) of the lot?

a) $7200 + 2x^2 + 240x = 0$
b) $7200 - 240x = 2x^2$
c) $7200 - 2x^2 + 240x = 0$
d) $3600 - 120x + x^2 = 0$
e) none of these

30. Right triangle ABC is drawn so that one leg is one third the hypotenuse (c), and the other leg is 2 in. less than the hypotenuse. The equation for the hypotenuse c is

a) $c^2 = \dfrac{c^2}{3} + (c - 2)^2$ $\qquad\qquad$ c) $c^2 = \dfrac{c^2}{9} + c^2 - 4$

b) $c^2 = \dfrac{c^2}{9} + (c - 2)^2$ $\qquad\qquad$ d) $c^2 = \left(\dfrac{c}{3} + c - 2\right)^2$

e) none of these

31. To reach his camp a man had to travel 150 mi. by bus and 24 mi. by canoe. If the bus went 24 mph. faster than the canoe and if it took the man 9 hr. to make the trip, the rate of the bus was

a) 20 mph. b) 30 mph. c) 34 mph. d) 40 mph. e) none of these

32. The least speed in miles per hour which an airplane must maintain to land safely is inversely proportional to the area of the wings. If an airplane with a wing area of 360 sq. ft. can land safely at 55 mph., at what speed should a plane land whose wing area is 450 ft.?

  a) 44 mph. *b)* 45 mph. *c)* 51 mph. *d)* 54 mph. *e)* 88 mph.

33. Solve simultaneously:

$$\frac{6}{x} + \frac{1}{y} = 20$$

$$\frac{3}{x} - \frac{2}{y} = 5$$

y is equal to

  a) $\frac{1}{6}$ *b)* $\frac{1}{3}$ *c)* $\frac{1}{2}$ *d)* 2 *e)* none of these

34. Solve simultaneously:

$$x^2 + y^2 = 5$$
$$x - y = 1$$

y is equal to

  a) $\frac{1 \pm \sqrt{7}}{2}$ *b)* $\frac{-1 \pm \sqrt{-7}}{2}$ *c)* $\frac{\pm \sqrt{-7}}{2}$ *d)* $-2, 1$

        e) none of these

35. An airplane, whose cruising speed is *r* miles per hour, flew for a distance of 1000 mi. in *h* hours with a tail wind of 20 mph. On the return trip, bucking a head wind of 20 mph., the plane required 2 more hours to make the trip. The pair of equations to be used to solve for *r* and *h* is

 a) $(r + 20)(h) = 1000$ *b)* $(r - 20)(h) = 1000$
   $(r - 20)(h + 2) = 1000$ $(r + 20)(h + 2) = 1000$

 c) $\dfrac{(r + 20)}{1000} = h$

   $(r - 20)(h + 2) = 1000\,h$

 d) $\dfrac{(r - 20)}{1000} = h + 2$

   $(r)(h - 2) = 1000$

 e) none of these

36. Solve simultaneously:

$$6\,r^2 + s^2 = 5\,a$$
$$3\,r^2 - s^2 = 2\,b$$

r is equal to

  a) $\pm \sqrt{a + b}$ *b)* $\pm \sqrt{7ab}$ *c)* $\pm (\sqrt{5a} + \sqrt{2b})$
  d) $\pm \frac{1}{3}\sqrt{5a + 2b}$ *e)* none of these

37. If $3^x = b$, then 3^{x+2} equals

  a) $3b^2$ *b)* b^{x+2} *c)* $b^{x+\frac{2}{x}}$ *d)* $\dfrac{x + 2}{x}$ *e)* $9b$

38. If $10^{1\cdot28} = 19.05$, then $10^{0\cdot28}$ equals

  a) 0.1905 *b)* 1.905 *c)* 190.5 *d)* 1905 *e)* none of these

39. What is the equation of a line parallel to the line whose equation is $2x - 7y = 3$ and passing through the point $(1, -3)$?

a) $2x + 7y = 3$ d) $2x + 7y = -19$

b) $7x - 2y = 3$ e) $2x - 7y = 23$

c) $7x - 2y = 13$

40. Which of the following is true about the roots of the quadratic equation $ax^2 + bx + c = 0$ if the adjacent graph represents the equation $y = ax^2 + bx + c$?

a) The roots are equal.   d) The roots are positive.

b) The roots are irrational.   e) The roots are imaginary.

c) The roots are negative.

REVIEW EXAMINATION II

Directions. Each problem is followed by five choices, one of which is the correct answer. By working each problem, find the correct answer, and put its letter after the number of the problem on your paper.

1. $\dfrac{3p}{p - q} + \dfrac{3q}{q - p}$ equals

a) $3p - 3q$ b) 3 c) $\dfrac{3}{p - q}$ d) $\dfrac{p + q}{p - q}$ e) none of these

2. $4\sqrt{-9} - 9\sqrt{-4}$ equals (if $\sqrt{-1} = i$)

a) $-6i$ b) $6i$ c) $12i$ d) $30i$ e) none of these

3. $2\sqrt{2x + 1} = 3\sqrt{x}$; then x equals

a) -2 b) -1 c) $-\frac{4}{5}$ d) $\frac{4}{5}$ e) none of these

4. In equation $2y^2 - 5y - 3 = 0$, the discriminant equals

a) 1 b) 17 c) 25 d) 49 e) none of these

5. In $2y^2 - 5y - 3 = 0$ the nature of the roots is

a) imaginary   b) real and unequal   c) irrational

        d) real and equal   e) none of these

6. Log $.0765 = 8.8837 - 10$; log $.0766 = 8.8842 - 10$. The log of $.07652$ equals

a) $8.8838 - 10$ b) $8.8839 - 10$ c) $8.8840 - 10$

d) $8.8841 - 10$ e) none of these

7. The number whose logarithm is 0.5391 is 3.46. The number whose logarithm is 0.5403 is 3.47. Then the number whose logarithm is 1.5397 is

    a) 34.65   *b)* 34.66   *c)* 34.67   *d)* 34.75   *e)* none of these

8. If x varies inversely as y, and $x = 12$ when $y = 9$, then when $x = 4$, y equals

    a) 3   *b)* 18   *c)* 27   *d)* 36   *e)* none of these

9. When factored completely, $8x^2 - 18y^2$ equals

    a) $(\sqrt{8}x - \sqrt{18}y)(\sqrt{8}x + \sqrt{18}y)$
    b) $(2\sqrt{2}x - 3\sqrt{3}y)(2\sqrt{2}x + 3\sqrt{3}y)$
    c) $2(2x - 3y)(2x + 3y)$
    d) $2(2x - 3y)^2$
    e) $(8x + 18y)(8x - 18y)$

10. Reduced to lowest terms, $\dfrac{ab - a^2}{ab(b - a)^2}$ equals

    a) $\dfrac{1}{b^2}$ *b)* $\dfrac{1}{b}$ *c)* $-\dfrac{1}{b^2}$ *d)* $-\dfrac{1}{b - a}$ *e)* $\dfrac{1}{b(b - a)}$

11. Solve for x and y in: $3x + y = 7$
                         $4x - y = 7$

    a) $x = 2$; $y = 1$ *d)* $x = 1$; $y = -3$
    b) $x = 2$; $y = -1$ *e)* $x = 3$; $y = -2$
    c) $x = 1$; $y = 4$

12. The factors of $42 - x - x^2$ are

    a) $(6 - x)(7 - x)$ *d)* $(6 + x)(7 - x)$
    b) $(6 + x)(7 + x)$ *e)* none of these
    c) $(6 - x)(7 + x)$

13. The formula for S, the sum of an infinite geometric progression, when the common ratio is numerically less than one, is

    a) $S_\infty = a + (n - 1)d$ *b)* $S_\infty = \dfrac{a}{1 - r}$ *c)* $S_\infty = \dfrac{a}{r - 1}$

    d) $S_\infty = \dfrac{ar^n - a}{r + 1}$ *e)* none of these

14. The slope of the graph of $6x - 3y = 5$ is

    a) -2 *b)* $-\frac{1}{2}$ *c)* $\frac{1}{2}$ *d)* 2   *e)* none of these

15. $3^{-2} \cdot 9 + 3^2 \cdot 9^{-1} + 3^0 - 1^x$ equals

    a) $\frac{1}{3}$ *b)* 2   *c)* 3   *d)* 9   *e)* none of these

16. In the equation $3x^2 + 2x - 5 = 0$, x equals

    a) $-1, \frac{5}{3}$ *b)* $1, \frac{3}{5}$ *c)* $-1, -\frac{5}{3}$ *d)* $1, -\frac{5}{3}$ *e)* none of these

17. The expression $\log a^2$ equals
a) $2 \log a$ d) $(\log a)(\log 2)$
b) $\log 2a$ e) none of these
c) $\log a + \log 2$

18. The product of the roots of $3y^2 + 4y + 5 = 0$ is
a) $-\frac{4}{3}$ b) $\frac{5}{4}$ c) $\frac{5}{3}$ d) 3   e) none of these

19. The graph of the equation $x^2 - y^2 = 25$ is
a) a circle   b) a hyperbola   c) an ellipse   d) a straight line
e) none of these

20. The fraction $\dfrac{\sqrt{5} - \sqrt{3}}{\sqrt{5}}$ is equal to

a) $\dfrac{\sqrt{5} + \sqrt{3}}{5}$ b) $\dfrac{5 + \sqrt{15}}{5}$ c) $1 - \sqrt{15}$ d) $\dfrac{5 - \sqrt{15}}{5}$ e) none of these

21. $4x^0 - (4x)^0$ equals
a) 0   b) $3x$ c) 3   d) $1 - 4x$ e) none of these

22. The definition of the cosine of an acute angle in a right triangle is the ratio of :
a) the adjacent leg to the hypotenuse.
b) the adjacent leg to the opposite leg.
c) the opposite leg to the hypotenuse.
d) the opposite leg to the adjacent leg.
e) the hypotenuse to the adjacent leg.

23. What is the value of $\begin{vmatrix} 1 & 2 \\ 3 & 1 \end{vmatrix}$?

a) -6 b) -5 c) -4 d) -1 e) 1

24. If three geometric means are inserted between 1 and 16, they may be
a) 2, 4, 6   d) $-2, -4, -8$
b) $-2, 4, -8$ e) none of these
c) $-2, -4, -6$

25. $\dfrac{2^{2n-1}}{4^n}$ equals

a) -2 b) $-\frac{1}{2}$ c) $-\dfrac{1}{2^n}$ d) $\frac{1}{2}$ e) 2

26. If $\sqrt{2x-7}$ is imaginary, the largest integral value of x is
a) 2   b) $3\frac{1}{2}$ c) 6   d) 7   e) none of these

27. The first three terms in the expansion of $(a - b)^9$ are
a) $a^9 - 9a^8b + 36a^7b^2$ d) $a^9 - 9a^8 + 8a^7b$
b) $a^9 + 9a^8b + 36a^7b^2$ e) none of these
c) $a^9 - 9a^8b - 36a^7b^2$

28. At a point 20 ft. from the base of a flagpole the angle of elevation of the top of the pole was 71°. If sin 71° = 0.9455, cos 71° = 0.3256, tan 71° = 2.9042, tan 19° = 0.3443, then the height of the pole in feet is approximately

       a) 19   *b)* 58   *c)* 65   *d)* 69   *e)* none of these

29. The ordinate of the point where the graph of the equation $y = 2x^2 - 3x - 9$ crosses the y axis is (do not construct the graph)

       a) $-\frac{9}{2}$ *b)* $-\frac{3}{2}$ *c)* 3   *d)* $\frac{9}{2}$ *e)* 9

30. The solutions of the equations:

$$x^2 = y + 5$$
$$y = 6x - 12$$

are

    a) $x = -1, y = 6$
        $x = -7, y = -30$

    b) $x = 1, y = -6$
        $x = 7, y = 30$

    c) $x = 6, y = -1$
        $x = 30, y = -7$

    d) $x = -6, y = 1$
        $x = -30, y = 7$

    e) none of these

31. The respective equations of the adjacent graph are

    a) $x^2 - y^2 = 25$
        $x + y = 4$

    b) $x^2 - y^2 = 25$
        $xy = 4$

    c) $x^2 - y^2 = 25$
        $xy = -4$

    d) $x^2 + y^2 = 25$
        $xy = 4$

    e) none of these

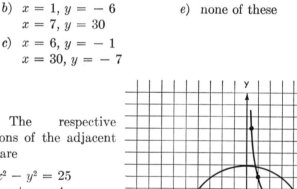

32. Three integers are in the ratio $2:5:12$. If 4 is added to the middle integer, the resulting integer is the middle term of an arithmetic progression, of which the other two integers are the first and third terms. The three integers are

    a) 2, 5, 12   *b)* 4, 10, 24   *c)* 1, 2, 6   *d)* 6, 15, 36   *e)* none of these

33. In how many ways may 3 persons be seated at a round table?

    a) 1   *b*) 2   *c*) 3   *d*) 6   *e*) 27

34. The value of the ordinate of the minimum point of the graph of the equation $y = x^2 - 5$ is

    a) $- 5$ *b*) $- \sqrt{5}$ *c*) $\sqrt{5}$ *d*) 5   *e*) none of these

35. The respective abscissas, correct to the nearest hundredth, of the points where the graph of the equation $y = 2x^2 - 4x - 5$ crosses the x axis are

    a) $2.87, - 0.13$ *d*) $2.87, - 0.87$

    b) ± 7.48 *e*) none of these

    c) ± 1.87

36. If $\log \tan 31° = 9.7788 - 10$; $\log \tan 32° = 9.7958 - 10$; $\log 4.74 = 0.6758$; $\log 4.75 = 0.6767$, then,

$$\log \frac{(47.42) \tan 31.5°}{\sqrt[3]{474.8}} \text{ equals}$$

    a) $9.5117 - 10$ *b*) 0.5711 *c*) 0.7511 *d*) 1.5171 *e*) none of these

37. In the equation $mx^2 + 3x + m = 0$, the roots are real and unequal when

    a) $m = \pm \frac{3}{2}$ *d*) $- \frac{3}{2} < m < \frac{3}{2}$

    b) $m < - \frac{3}{2}$ *e*) none of these

    c) $m > \frac{3}{2}$

38. In how many ways may the letters of the word BETTER be arranged?

    a) 16   *b*) 90   *c*) 180   *d*) 360   *e*) 720

39. Which of the following determinants has a numerical value equal to the area of a triangle whose vertices are (0, 1), (1, 4), and (3, 6)?

a) $\frac{1}{2} \begin{vmatrix} 0 & 1 & 1 \\ 1 & 4 & 1 \\ 3 & 6 & 1 \end{vmatrix}$ *d*) $\frac{1}{2} \begin{vmatrix} 0 & 1 & 1 \\ 4 & 3 & 6 \\ 1 & 1 & 1 \end{vmatrix}$

b) $\begin{vmatrix} 0 & 1 & 3 \\ 1 & 4 & 6 \\ 0 & 0 & 0 \end{vmatrix}$ *e*) $\frac{1}{2} \begin{vmatrix} 0 & 1 & 0 \\ 0 & 1 & 4 \\ 3 & 0 & 6 \end{vmatrix}$

c) $\begin{vmatrix} 0 & 1 & 1 \\ 1 & 4 & 1 \\ 3 & 6 & 1 \end{vmatrix}$

40. What is the average deviation from the median of the following set of measurements?

$$10, 12, 14, 15, 16, 16, 17, 18, 18, 20$$

    a) 1.1   *b*) 2   *c*) $2\frac{1}{5}$ *d*) 4   *e*) 16

Introduction to
Advanced Algebra

Advanced Topics in Set Theory

In *Elementary Algebra, Enlarged Edition,* you were introduced to the concept of sets, the notations used in indicating sets and elements of sets, and some work with subsets and solution sets. Before extending our discussion of sets, we shall review briefly these concepts.

Indicating sets and elements of sets. You will remember that a set is a collection of things, or objects, and that the things that belong to the set are called elements or members of the set. It is customary to indicate a set by a capital letter, and if the set consists of only a few members, to indicate the members by listing them within braces. Thus the notation $A = \{1, 2, 3, 4, 5\}$ indicates the set A whose elements are the first five natural numbers. To indicate that a particular number, for example the number 2, is a member of this set, we write $2 \in A$; to indicate that the number 7 is not a member of this set, we write $7 \notin A$.

If a set contains a great many members, it is cumbersome to list all of the members. In such cases (and in cases in which the set has an infinite number of elements) we indicate the set by description. Thus the notation $S = \{x \mid x > 5\}$ (read "The set S of all x's such that x is greater than 5") indicates the set S whose members are all numbers greater than 5.

A variable; a universal set. If we are given a set U, we use a small letter, such as x, as a placeholder for an element of the set. We call this letter a variable, and we call the set U which contains all possible replacements for the variable x, the universal set. The extent of the members of U is the domain of the variable. If we are given $U = \{1, 2, 3, \ldots, 10\}$, and we are given equation $x + 3 = 11$, we may replace the variable x in the equation by *only* the numbers 1, 2, 3, . . ., 10. The replacement of x by nine of these members gives a false statement (such as $6 + 3 = 11$); the replacement of x by the member 8 gives a true statement.

Subsets and solution sets. If all of the members of a set A are also members of a set B, then A is called a subset of B, and B is called a superset of A. Often in algebra, an equation or an inequality selects from the universal set U (usually all the real numbers) a subset for which the equation (or inequality) is true. Those elements of U that are selected by the equation or inequality form a set which is called the solution set of the equation or inequality. Since there is a one-to-one correspondence between the points on a line and the real numbers, we can represent graphically the solution set for equations and inequalities.

ILLUSTRATIVE EXAMPLES: Graphs of solution sets

In the following examples, the domain of x is the universal set U of all real numbers.

1. Draw the graph of the set $S = \{x \mid x \in U \text{ and } x^2 + x = 6\}$, read "$S$ is the set of all x's such that x is a member of the universal set U and $x^2 + x = 6$."

Solution. Solving the equation for x, we obtain $x = 2$ and $x = -3$. These are the only values of the variable for which the equation is true; hence $S = \{2, -3\}$. To graph set S, we draw a linear scale to indicate the domain of x (the universal set U of all real numbers), and on this scale we mark the points of set S which are the members of the solution set for $x^2 + x = 6$:

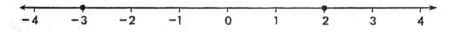

2. Draw the graph of the set $S = \{x \mid x \in U \text{ and } x^2 + 2x < 3\}$.

Solution. Solving this inequality by the method explained on page 253, we find that x can be any real number larger than -3 but smaller than 1; hence $S = \{x \mid x \in U \text{ and } -3 < x < 1\}$. To graph S, we draw a linear scale to indicate the domain of x (the universal set U of all real numbers), and on this scale we mark the open interval (it has no first element and no last element) of all the real numbers larger than -3 (but not including -3) and smaller than 1 (but not including 1):

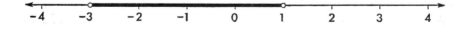

E X E R C I S E S : Sets and graphs of sets

1. If $U = \{$Mary, Jane, Alice, Anita$\}$, what is the set
$$S = \{x \mid x \in U \text{ and } x \text{ is a name beginning with } A\}?$$

2. If $U = \{1, 2, 3, 4, 5\}$, what is the set $S = \{x \mid x \in U \text{ and } x > 2\}$?

3. If U is the set of real numbers, what is the set
$$S = \{x \mid x \in U \text{ and } x^2 + 2x = 8\}?$$

Draw the graph of S.

4. If U is the set of positive integers, what is the set
$$S = \{x \mid x \in U \text{ and } x \text{ is a prime number smaller than } 10\}?$$

5. If U is the set of real numbers, what is the set

a) $A = \{x \mid x \in U \text{ and } 2x - 3 = 5\}$ *c)* $C = \{x \mid x \in U \text{ and } x^2 > 9\}$
b) $B = \{x \mid x \in U \text{ and } x > 0\}$ *d)* $D = \{x \mid x \in U \text{ and } x \leq 3\}$

(The symbol $\leq$ means "either less than or equal to".)

Union of sets.   Suppose that we have the two sets:
$$A = \{10, 11, 12, \ldots, 20\} \quad \text{and} \quad B = \{5, 6, 7, \ldots, 15\}.$$

By the union of A and B, we mean the set of all elements that are members of A or members of B or members of both A and B. That is, the union of A and B is the set $C = \{5, 6, 7, \ldots, 20\}$.

The union of sets can be represented geometrically as follows: Let us draw a rectangle to represent the universal set U. The elements of U are represented by points within the rectangle. Suppose that we now have two subsets, A and B, of U. The elements of A are represented by points within circle A and the elements of B are represented by points within circle B. The sets A and B may have no points in common, as in Figure 1; they may have some points in common, as in Figure 2; or one may be a

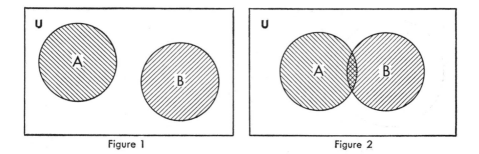

Figure 1   Figure 2

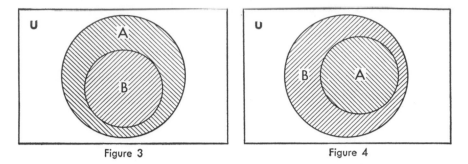

Figure 3   Figure 4

subset of the other, as in figures 3 and 4. If we indicate the *union* of A and B as the set $A \cup B$ (read "the union of A and B", or "A cup B") then the set $A \cup B$ is represented by the shaded parts in each of the four figures.

Intersection of sets.   Suppose, again, that we have the two sets:

$$A = \{10, 11, 12, \ldots, 20\} \quad \text{and} \quad B = \{5, 6, 7, \ldots, 15\}.$$

By the intersection of A and B, we mean the set of all elements that are members of both A and B. That is, the intersection of A and B is the set $D = \{10, 11, 12, 13, 14, 15\}$.

   The intersection of sets can be represented geometrically as follows: We draw a rectangle to represent the universal set U, and circles A and B to represent subsets of U. The sets A and B may have no points in common, as in Figure 5; they may have some points in common, as in Figure 6; or one may be a subset of the other, as in Figures 7 and 8. If we indicate the intersection of A and B as the set $A \cap B$ (read "the intersection of A and B," or "A cap B") then the set $A \cap B$ is represented by the shaded parts in Figures 6, 7, and 8. In Figure 5, there is no shaded part; in this case, $A \cap B$ is the null set, or empty set, designated as ϕ, which contains no members.

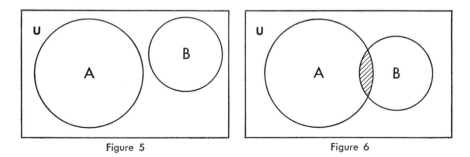

Figure 5   Figure 6

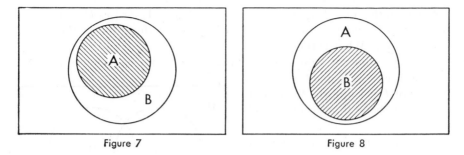

Figure 7   Figure 8

I L L U S T R A T I V E   E X A M P L E: Union and intersection of sets

In the left figure below, A, B, and C are subsets of U. Indicate the subset of U: $(A \cup B) \cap C$.

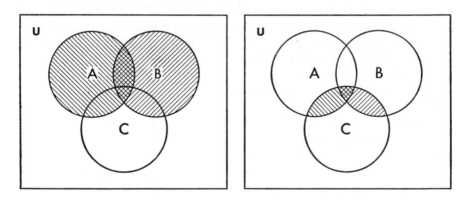

Solution. The union of A and B is shown in the left figure as all points within circle A or circle B. The intersection of this set $A \cup B$ with set C is all points within the shaded part (of the left figure) that are also points within circle C. This intersection, which is the required subset of U, $(A \cup B) \cap C$, is shown in the right figure.

E X E R C I S E S :   Union and intersection of sets

1. If $A = \{1, 2, 3, 4, 5\}$, and $B = \{4, 5, 6, 7\}$, indicate within braces the elements of the sets:

    a) $A \cup B$ *b)* $A \cap B$

2. If $A = \{x \mid x$ is an isosceles triangle$\}$ and $B = \{x \mid x$ is a right triangle$\}$, is a triangle whose angles are 45°, 45°, 90° a member of the set $A \cap B$?

3. Given the two sets: $A = \{1, 3, 5, 7, 9\}$ and $B = \{2, 4, 6, 8\}$, what are the elements of the sets   *a)* $A \cup B$,   *b)* $A \cap B$?

4. Given the sets: U is the set of real numbers; $A = \{x \mid x \in U \text{ and } x > 5\}$; $B = \{x \mid x \in U \text{ and } x < 10\}$; on a linear scale draw the graph of the subset $A \cap B$ of U. What is the subset $A \cup B$ of U?

5. In the adjacent figure, the rectangle represents the universal set U, and the circles A, B, and C represent subsets of U. Copy the figure four times and shade in each of the following sets:

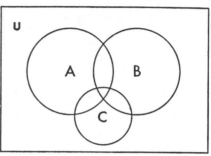

a) $A \cup B$ c) $(A \cap B) \cup C$
b) $A \cap B$ d) $(A \cup B) \cup C$

Ordered pairs of numbers.   In Chapter 6, we noted that every point on the plane of a coordinate system could be represented by a pair of numbers. Thus the point P in the adjacent figure is represented by the number pair (2, 1). The order in which the numbers are written in the parentheses is important. The point (2, 1) is not the same as the point (1, 2). We emphasize this by saying that a point is located by an *ordered* pair of numbers. Now a set can be composed of elements that are ordered pairs. Thus we can have:

$A = \{(1, 2), (-1, 6), (2, 2), (1, 7)\}$

$B = \{(3, 2), (1, 1), (1, 2), (4, 3)\}$

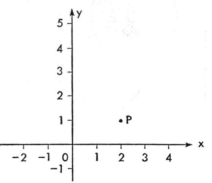

The union of these two sets, $A \cup B$, would contain all of the ordered pairs in A and all of the ordered pairs in B; the intersection of A and B, $A \cap B$, would contain the single ordered pair (1, 2), since this is the only element that the two sets have in common.

The Cartesian set.   Let us consider a universal set $U = \{1, 2, 3\}$. Using the elements 1, 2, 3, of U, we can form the following ordered pairs: (1, 1), (1, 2), (1, 3), (2, 1), (2, 2), (2, 3), (3, 1), (3, 2), and (3, 3). If U contains three numbers as elements, we can form 9 ordered pairs; in general, if U contains n numbers as elements, we can form n^2 ordered pairs. The set of ordered pairs obtained in the above manner is indicated as $U \times U$ (read "U cross U") and is called the Cartesian set of U. We can draw a graph of $U \times U$ by marking the points that represent all of the ordered pairs

on a coordinate system.   Thus if
$U = \{1, 2, 3, 4\}$, then the graph of
$U \times U$ is the sixteen points (called
a *lattice of points*) shown in the adjacent figure.   If the universal set
U is expanded to include all of the
positive integers, then the graph of
$U \times U$ consists of all of the points
in the first quadrant with integral
coordinates.   Finally, if U is the set
of all real numbers, then the graph
of $U \times U$ is the entire plane.

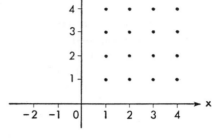

Equations in two variables.   An equation in two variables, such as $x + y$
$= 6$, is true for certain replacements of the variables x and y; that is,
the equation $x + y = 6$ selects cer-
tain ordered pairs, (x, y), from the
Cartesian set of ordered pairs $U \times U$.
For example, let us consider the
universal set $U = \{1, 2, 3, 4\}$.   The
Cartesian set, $U \times U$, consists of
the sixteen points shown in the
preceding figure.   The equation
$x + y = 6$ selects (is true for) the
elements $(2, 4)$, $(3, 3)$ and $(4, 2)$ of
$U \times U$.   In other words, given the
set $U = \{1, 2, 3, 4\}$, and the subset

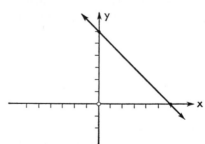

$$S = \{(x, y) \mid (x, y) \in U \times U \quad \text{and} \quad x + y = 6\}$$

(read "the set of all ordered pairs (x, y) such that (x, y) is an element of
$U \times U$ and $x + y = 6$"), then $S = \{(2, 4), (3, 3), (4, 2)\}$.   The graph of S
is shown in the above figure.

If we considered U to be the
set of all real numbers, then the
Cartesian set $U \times U$ contains all
of the points in the plane.   The
equation $x + y = 6$ selects an infinite number of ordered pairs
from $U \times U$, and the graph of
the solution set for $x + y = 6$ is
a line (of infinite length) as indicated in the adjacent figure.

ILLUSTRATIVE EXAMPLES : Inequalities in two variables

1. Given the universal set $U = \{1, 2, 3, 4, 5\}$, draw the graph of the set $R = \{(x, y) \mid (x, y) \in U \times U \text{ and } x > y\}$.

Solution. The Cartesian set, $U \times U$, is composed of the 25 points (ordered pairs) in the first quadrant that are indicated by dots (large and small) in the adjacent figure. The set S selects from the set $U \times U$ all of the points (ordered pairs) whose first coordinate, x, is greater than its second coordinate, y. These points (the graph of R) are shown by large dots in the figure.

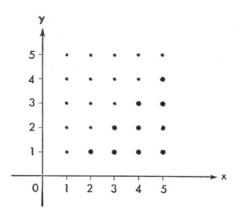

2. Given the universal set U is the set of positive real numbers, draw the graph of the set $R = \{(x, y) \mid (x, y) \in U \times U \text{ and } x > y\}$.

Solution. The Cartesian set $U \times U$ is composed of all points (ordered pairs) in the first quadrant. The set R selects from the set $U \times U$ all of the points (ordered pairs) whose first coordinate, x, is larger than its second coordinate, y. The graph of R is indicated by the portion of the plane that is shaded in the figure.

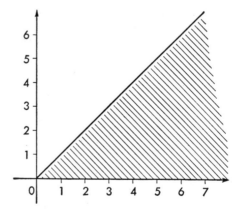

EXERCISES : Equations and inequalities in two variables

1. If $U = \{1, 2, 3, 4\}$ and $S = \{(x, y) \mid (x, y) \in U \times U \text{ and } y > x\}$, draw the graph of S.

2. If $U = \{1, 2, 3, 4\}$ and $S = \{(x, y) \mid (x, y) \in U \times U \text{ and } x = y\}$, draw the graph of S.

3. If U is the set of positive real numbers and

$$R = \{(x, y) \mid (x, y) \,\epsilon\, U \times U \quad \text{and} \quad y = x^2\},$$

draw the graph of R.

4. If U is the set of positive real numbers and

$$R = \{(x, y) \mid (x, y) \,\epsilon\, U \times U \quad \text{and} \quad x^2 + y^2 = 16\},$$

draw the graph of R.

5. If U is the set of real numbers and

$$R = \{(x, y) \mid (x, y) \,\epsilon\, U \times U \quad \text{and} \quad x < y\},$$

draw the graph of R.

Relations. Whenever we have an equation or an inequality in two variables, there is a relationship between these variables. For example, in the equation $x + y = 6$, the variables, x and y, are so related that their sum is 6. In terms of sets, the ordered pairs selected from $U \times U$ by the solution set for the equation $x + y = 6$ are ordered pairs of numbers whose sum is 6. If we speak of the set of ordered pairs that are selected from $U \times U$ by the equation as a *relation*, then the equation, itself, becomes the "rule" for determining the set of ordered pairs from $U \times U$ or the "rule" for defining the relation.

To clarify this idea, let us again consider the example in the text on page 473, where the universal set is $U = \{1, 2, 3, 4\}$ and the relation is

$$R = \{(x, y) \mid (x, y) \,\epsilon\, U \times U \text{ and } x + y = 6\}.$$

Notice that the relation *is* the set R, and that R is a subset of $U \times U$. In this example, R has, as its elements, three ordered pairs of numbers; that is,

$$R = \{(2, 4), (3, 3), (4, 2)\}.$$

The relation *is* the set of ordered pairs; the "rule" for determining the relation (for determining the ordered pairs) is $x + y = 6$.

A relation may be determined by an equation (or inequality), by a graph, or by listing the members (ordered pairs) of the relation. Thus, if $U = \{1, 2, 3, 4\}$, the relation R, above, is determined by the equation $x + y = 6$, or by the graph on the middle of page 473, or by the set, R, tabulated above.

If we are given a universal set U and a relation R, which is a set of ordered pairs (x, y) in $U \times U$, then the subset of U for which x is a placeholder is the *domain* of the relation, and the subset of U for which y is a placeholder is the *range* of the relation.

ILLUSTRATIVE EXAMPLE: Graphs of relations

If U is the set of real numbers, draw the graph of the relation that is defined by the inequality $x^2 + y^2 < 16$; state the domain and the range of the relation.

Solution. The graph of all of the ordered pairs (x, y) in $U \times U$ for which $x^2 + y^2 = 16$ is a circle whose center is at the origin and whose radius is 4 (page 266). For all points (x, y) inside this circle, the distance from the origin to (x, y) must be smaller than 4. By the Pythagorean Theorem, this distance is $\sqrt{x^2 + y^2}$; hence $\sqrt{x^2 + y^2} < 4$, and $x^2 + y^2 < 16$ for all points (x, y) inside the circle. The graph of the relation defined by this inequality is the set of all points (ordered pairs) within the circle (the shaded portion of the adjacent figure).

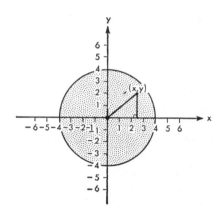

The domain of the relation is the subset of U containing all replacements of x for which the relation is defined; since x can have any value from -4 to 4 exclusive, the domain is $-4 < x < 4$. The range of the relation is the subset of U containing all replacements of y for which the relation is defined; the range is $-4 < y < 4$.

EXERCISES: Graphs of relations

If U is the set of all real numbers, draw the graph of the relation defined by each of the following; state the domain and range in each case.

1. $x = y + 1$ 3. $x^2 + y^2 > 4$ 5. $xy > 4$
2. $x > 0$ 4. $x^2 + y^2 < 9$ 6. $x^2 + 4y^2 < 36$

Functions. The word function is used by some mathematicians * to mean a special kind of relation. Since a function is a relation, it is a set of ordered pairs. Now let us see precisely what special kind of relations are functions. The left figure below shows the graph of the relation defined by the equation $x^2 + y^2 = 25$. You will notice that if x has the value

---

* The use of the word function as defined here is not universally accepted. Here it has a more restricted meaning than that generally accepted in the past.

3, there are two points on the circle whose first coordinate is 3, namely (3, 4) and (3, − 4). In other words, a line parallel to the y-axis cuts the graph of the relation twice. A function is a relation in which a line parallel to the y-axis *never* cuts the graph of the relation more than once. That is, a function is a set of ordered pairs (x, y) such that for each x there is exactly one y. From the graph of $x^2 + y^2 = 25$, we can see that this relation is not a function. The graph shown in the figure at the right below is a graph of a function.

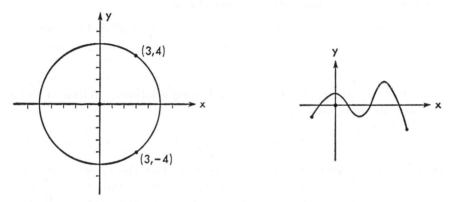

The set of ordered pairs $S = \{(1, 3), (2, 7), (1, 4), (8, 3)\}$ is not a function. The set of ordered pairs determined by the equation $x + y = 6$ is a function.

ILLUSTRATIVE EXAMPLE: The graph of a function

If U is the set of all real numbers, draw the graph of the function defined by the rule:

$$y = x \quad \text{if} \quad x \geqq 0$$
$$y = -x \quad \text{if} \quad x < 0.$$

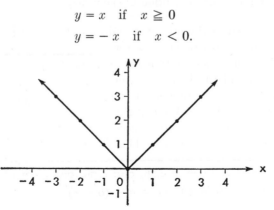

Solution. For each positive value of x, y has the same positive value (if $x = 3$, $y = 3$; if $x = \sqrt{2}$, $y = \sqrt{2}$; etc.). If $x = 0$, $y = 0$. For each negative value of x, y is the negative of x (if $x = -5$, $y = -(-5) = 5$; if $x = -\frac{1}{2}$, $y = \frac{1}{2}$; etc.). The graph of the function is shown in the figure.

This function can be indicated by the notation $y = |x|$, read "y equals the absolute value of x." Notice that $|x| = x$ if x is positive or zero, and $|x| = -x$ if x is negative.

EXERCISES : Graphs of functions and relations

In each of the following, the domain of x is the set of all real numbers.

1. Which of the following equations and inequalities define a function?

a) $x - y = 6$ c) $x > y$ e) $x = y^2$

b) $x^2 + y^2 = 9$ d) $x^2 = y$ f) $y = |x + 1|$

2. Draw the graph of each of the following relations. Which of these relations are functions?

a) $x = |y|$ c) $y > |x|$ e) $|y| - |x| = 1$

b) $|y| = |x|$ d) $|x| + |y| = 1$ f) $|x| + |y| < 1$

Closure. Let us consider the set S composed of the integers (positive whole numbers, negative whole numbers, and zero), and study some of the properties of these integers when we perform the operation of addition. We know that if we add any two integers, the result is a *unique* integer; that is, the result is exactly one and only one integer (unique) and it is an element of the original set S. If a set of elements has this property with respect to an operation (in this instance, addition), we say that the set is closed or that the set has *closure.* That is,

> Closure: If a and b are any two elements of set S, then $a + b$ is a unique element of S.

Associative Law. In arithmetic, if we add any two integers and then add this resulting integer to a third, we know that the result is the same as though we added the second and third integers and then added the resulting integer to the first (see the adjacent box). We call this property of a set of elements the *associative law* with respect to addition. That is,

$(2 + 3) + 6$	$2 + (3 + 6)$
$5 + 6$	$2 + 9$
11	11

> Associative Law: If a, b, and c are any elements of set S, then $(a + b) + c = a + (b + c)$.

Commutative Law.   In arithmetic, we know that $2 + 3$ is 5, and that $3 + 2$ is 5. In other words, the order in which two numbers are added is immaterial. We call this property of a set of elements the *commutative law* with respect to addition. That is,

> Commutative Law: If a and b are any elements of set S, then $a + b = b + a$.

Identity element.   In arithmetic, what integer can we add to 5 so that the resulting integer is 5? Of course, the integer that we must add is 0. We call 0 the identity element with respect to addition.

> Identity Element: If a is any element of set S, then there exists a unique element e of S such that
> $$a + e = e + a = a.$$

Inverse element.   In arithmetic, what integer must we add to 7 to produce the identity element e for addition (for addition, e is the element zero)? The answer, of course, is the integer -7. The element which we add is called the additive-inverse, or the inverse element with respect to addition.

> Inverse Element: For any element a of set S, there exists a unique corresponding element a' such that
> $$a + a' = a' + a = e.$$

Sets and operations.   We have seen that closure and the laws and definitions as stated above apply to the set S of all integers (positive, negative, and zero) with respect to the operation of addition. If a set S, consisting of any elements a, b, c, etc. (these elements do not even have to be numbers) and a means of "combining" any pair of elements of the set satisfy all of the above conditions, we say that this *system* is a *commutative group.**

Let us consider the same set S of all integers, but change our operation from addition to multiplication. Is this system a group? To answer this question, we must see if all of the above conditions apply:

1. We see that set S has the property of closure with respect to multiplication, since the product ab of any two integers is a unique integer.

* A system is a group if it has closure, associativity, an identity element, and an inverse element for each element. If, in addition to these, it also is commutative, it is a special (Abelian) group.

2. The associative law applies: $(ab)c = a(bc)$.

3. The commutative law applies: $ab = ba$.

4. There is an identity element e in the set such that $ae = a$ (you will recognize that the identity element with respect to multiplication is the integer 1).

5. Is there a multiplicative-inverse? The answer is "no"! For every element a of S we are required to produce an element a' of S such that $aa' = e$ (for multiplication, e is the integer 1). By what integer must we multiply the integer 7 to produce 1? The required number, $\frac{1}{7}$, is not an integer (and hence *not* an element of our set S). Thus, this system is not a group.

If we consider a set T composed of all the rational numbers and the operation of multiplication, would this system form a group? Would the set R of all real numbers form a group with respect to multiplication? Would R form a group with respect to addition? The answers to these questions are all "yes."

The structure of algebra. If you have studied geometry, you will remember that that study was based on certain *assumptions* (called postulates, or axioms) and that certain so-called primitive terms were taken as undefined. From that point on, all technical words of the subject were carefully defined, and all statements (theorems) were proved from the original assumptions. Algebraic structure is similar to this. For the algebra of real numbers, our undefined terms are a set U whose elements are a, b, c, etc. (the real numbers), and the operations are addition and multiplication. The postulates (assumptions) are the five group properties with respect to both of these operations (giving us 10 postulates) and an eleventh postulate which combines addition and multiplication. The eleventh postulate is called the *distributive law* with respect to addition and multiplication. That is,

> Distributive Law: For any elements a, b, and c of S, $a(b + c) = ab + ac$.

If a set F has these eleven postulates with respect to two operations (which can be different from the normal interpretation of addition and multiplication), we say that the system forms a *field*. If we reduce the number of postulates, or "weaken" some of them, in a field, the resulting system is called a *ring*.

With the idea of algebraic structure in your mind, you can readily see that there is an algebra of sets, in which the undefined terms are a universal set whose elements are sets, and the operations are $\cup$ and $\cap$ instead of

$+$ and $\times$. The first four postulates apply to this algebra of sets, which is called *Boolean* algebra.

EXERCISES: Groups

1. Consider the set A whose elements are all of the integers (positive, negative, and zero), and the operation of subtraction.

a) Is this a closed system?   *b*) Does the commutative law apply?
c) Is there an identity element?   *d*) Is there an inverse for each element?

2. Which of the following sets is closed for the operation of division?

a) The integers.   *b*) The positive rational numbers.   *c*) The negative rational numbers.   *d*) The rational numbers.

3. Consider the system composed of the set of the first four integral powers of $\sqrt{-1}$, $S = \{i, -1, -i, 1\}$ and the operation of multiplication.

a) Is this a closed system?   *b*) Does the associative law apply?   *c*) Does the commutative law apply?   *d*) Is there an identity element?   *e*) Is there an inverse element for each element?   *f*) Does the system form a group?

4. By means of Venn diagrams, show that "intersection" is distributive over "union"; that is, show that

$$A \cap (B \cup C) = (A \cap B) \cup (A \cap C)$$

5. By means of Venn diagrams, show that "union" is distributive over "intersection"; that is, show that

$$A \cup (B \cap C) = (A \cup B) \cap (A \cup C)$$

TABLE OF APPROXIMATE SQUARE ROOTS

N	$\sqrt{N}$	N	$\sqrt{N}$	N	$\sqrt{N}$	N	$\sqrt{N}$	N	$\sqrt{N}$
1	1.000	51	7.141	101	10.05	151	12.29	201	14.18
2	1.414	52	7.211	102	10.10	152	12.33	202	14.21
3	1.732	53	7.280	103	10.15	153	12.37	203	14.25
4	2.000	54	7.348	104	10.20	154	12.41	204	14.28
5	2.236	55	7.416	105	10.25	155	12.45	205	14.32
6	2.449	56	7.483	106	10.30	156	12.49	206	14.35
7	2.646	57	7.550	107	10.34	157	12.53	207	14.39
8	2.828	58	7.616	108	10.39	158	12.57	208	14.42
9	3.000	59	7.681	109	10.44	159	12.61	209	14.46
10	3.162	60	7.746	110	10.49	160	12.65	210	14.49
11	3.317	61	7.810	111	10.54	161	12.69	211	14.53
12	3.464	62	7.874	112	10.58	162	12.73	212	14.56
13	3.606	63	7.937	113	10.63	163	12.77	213	14.59
14	3.742	64	8.000	114	10.68	164	12.81	214	14.63
15	3.873	65	8.062	115	10.72	165	12.85	215	14.66
16	4.000	66	8.124	116	10.77	166	12.88	216	14.70
17	4.123	67	8.185	117	10.82	167	12.92	217	14.73
18	4.243	68	8.246	118	10.86	168	12.96	218	14.76
19	4.359	69	8.307	119	10.91	169	13.00	219	14.80
20	4.472	70	8.367	120	10.95	170	13.04	220	14.83
21	4.583	71	8.426	121	11.00	171	13.08	221	14.87
22	4.690	72	8.485	122	11.05	172	13.11	222	14.90
23	4.796	73	8.544	123	11.09	173	13.15	223	14.93
24	4.899	74	8.602	124	11.14	174	13.19	224	14.97
25	5.000	75	8.660	125	11.18	175	13.23	225	15.00
26	5.099	76	8.718	126	11.22	176	13.27	226	15.03
27	5.196	77	8.775	127	11.27	177	13.30	227	15.07
28	5.292	78	8.832	128	11.31	178	13.34	228	15.10
29	5.385	79	8.888	129	11.36	179	13.38	229	15.13
30	5.477	80	8.944	130	11.40	180	13.42	230	15.17
31	5.568	81	9.000	131	11.45	181	13.45	231	15.20
32	5.657	82	9.055	132	11.49	182	13.49	232	15.23
33	5.745	83	9.110	133	11.53	183	13.53	233	15.26
34	5.831	84	9.165	134	11.58	184	13.56	234	15.30
35	5.916	85	9.220	135	11.62	185	13.60	235	15.33
36	6.000	86	9.274	136	11.66	186	13.64	236	15.36
37	6.083	87	9.327	137	11.70	187	13.67	237	15.39
38	6.164	88	9.381	138	11.75	188	13.71	238	15.43
39	6.245	89	9.434	139	11.79	189	13.75	239	15.46
40	6.325	90	9.487	140	11.83	190	13.78	240	15.49
41	6.403	91	9.539	141	11.87	191	13.82	241	15.52
42	6.481	92	9.592	142	11.92	192	13.86	242	15.56
43	6.557	93	9.644	143	11.96	193	13.89	243	15.59
44	6.633	94	9.695	144	12.00	194	13.93	244	15.62
45	6.708	95	9.747	145	12.04	195	13.96	245	15.65
46	6.782	96	9.798	146	12.08	196	14.00	246	15.68
47	6.856	97	9.849	147	12.12	197	14.04	247	15.72
48	6.928	98	9.899	148	12.17	198	14.07	248	15.75
49	7.000	99	9.950	149	12.21	199	14.11	249	15.78
50	7.071	100	10.00	150	12.25	200	14.14	250	15.81

TABLE OF APPROXIMATE SQUARE ROOTS

N	$\sqrt{N}$	N	$\sqrt{N}$	N	$\sqrt{N}$	N	$\sqrt{N}$	N	$\sqrt{N}$
251	15.84	301	17.35	351	18.73	401	20.02	451	21.24
252	15.87	302	17.38	352	18.76	402	20.05	452	21.26
253	15.91	303	17.41	353	18.79	403	20.07	453	21.28
254	15.94	304	17.44	354	18.81	404	20.10	454	21.31
255	15.97	305	17.46	355	18.84	405	20.12	455	21.33
256	16.00	306	17.49	356	18.87	406	20.15	456	21.35
257	16.03	307	17.52	357	18.89	407	20.17	457	21.38
258	16.06	308	17.55	358	18.92	408	20.20	458	21.40
259	16.09	309	17.58	359	18.95	409	20.22	459	21.42
260	16.12	310	17.61	360	18.97	410	20.25	460	21.45
261	16.16	311	17.64	361	19.00	411	20.27	461	21.47
262	16.19	312	17.66	362	19.03	412	20.30	462	21.49
263	16.22	313	17.69	363	19.05	413	20.32	463	21.52
264	16.25	314	17.72	364	19.08	414	20.35	464	21.54
265	16.28	315	17.75	365	19.10	415	20.37	465	21.56
266	16.31	316	17.78	366	19.13	416	20.40	466	21.59
267	16.34	317	17.80	367	19.16	417	20.42	467	21.61
268	16.37	318	17.83	368	19.18	418	20.45	468	21.63
269	16.40	319	17.86	369	19.21	419	20.47	469	21.66
270	16.43	320	17.89	370	19.24	420	20.49	470	21.68
271	16.46	321	17.92	371	19.26	421	20.52	471	21.70
272	16.49	322	17.94	372	19.29	422	20.54	472	21.73
273	16.52	323	17.97	373	19.31	423	20.57	473	21.75
274	16.55	324	18.00	374	19.34	424	20.59	474	21.77
275	16.58	325	18.03	375	19.36	425	20.62	475	21.79
276	16.61	326	18.06	376	19.39	426	20.64	476	21.82
277	16.64	327	18.08	377	19.42	427	20.66	477	21.84
278	16.67	328	18.11	378	19.44	428	20.69	478	21.86
279	16.70	329	18.14	379	19.47	429	20.71	479	21.89
280	16.73	330	18.17	380	19.49	430	20.74	480	21.91
281	16.76	331	18.19	381	19.52	431	20.76	481	21.93
282	16.79	332	18.22	382	19.54	432	20.78	482	21.95
283	16.82	333	18.25	383	19.57	433	20.81	483	21.98
284	16.85	334	18.28	384	19.60	434	20.83	484	22.00
285	16.88	335	18.30	385	19.62	435	20.86	485	22.02
286	16.91	336	18.33	386	19.65	436	20.88	486	22.05
287	16.94	337	18.36	387	19.67	437	20.90	487	22.07
288	16.97	338	18.38	388	19.70	438	20.93	488	22.09
289	17.00	339	18.41	389	19.72	439	20.95	489	22.11
290	17.03	340	18.44	390	19.75	440	20.98	490	22.14
291	17.06	341	18.47	391	19.77	441	21.00	491	22.16
292	17.09	342	18.49	392	19.80	442	21.02	492	22.18
293	17.12	343	18.52	393	19.82	443	21.05	493	22.20
294	17.15	344	18.55	394	19.85	444	21.07	494	22.23
295	17.18	345	18.57	395	19.87	445	21.10	495	22.25
296	17.20	346	18.60	396	19.90	446	21.12	496	22.27
297	17.23	347	18.63	397	19.92	447	21.14	497	22.29
298	17.26	348	18.65	398	19.95	448	21.17	498	22.32
299	17.29	349	18.68	399	19.97	449	21.19	499	22.34
300	17.32	350	18.71	400	20.00	450	21.21	500	22.36

TABLE OF APPROXIMATE SQUARE ROOTS

N	$\sqrt{N}$	N	$\sqrt{N}$	N	$\sqrt{N}$	N	$\sqrt{N}$	N	$\sqrt{N}$
501	22.38	551	23.47	601	24.52	651	25.51	701	26.48
502	22.41	552	23.49	602	24.54	652	25.53	702	26.50
503	22.43	553	23.52	603	24.56	653	25.55	703	26.51
504	22.45	554	23.54	604	24.58	654	25.57	704	26.53
505	22.47	555	23.56	605	24.60	655	25.59	705	26.55
506	22.49	556	23.58	606	24.62	656	25.61	706	26.57
507	22.52	557	23.60	607	24.64	657	25.63	707	26.59
508	22.54	558	23.62	608	24.66	658	25.65	708	26.61
509	22.56	559	23.64	609	24.68	659	25.67	709	26.63
510	22.58	560	23.66	610	24.70	660	25.69	710	26.65
511	22.61	561	23.69	611	24.72	661	25.71	711	26.66
512	22.63	562	23.71	612	24.74	662	25.73	712	26.68
513	22.65	563	23.73	613	24.76	663	25.75	713	26.70
514	22.67	564	23.75	614	24.78	664	25.77	714	26.72
515	22.69	565	23.77	615	24.80	665	25.79	715	26.74
516	22.72	566	23.79	616	24.82	666	25.81	716	26.76
517	22.74	567	23.81	617	24.84	667	25.83	717	26.78
518	22.76	568	23.83	618	24.86	668	25.85	718	26.80
519	22.78	569	23.85	619	24.88	669	25.87	719	26.81
520	22.80	570	23.87	620	24.90	670	25.88	720	26.83
521	22.83	571	23.90	621	24.92	671	25.90	721	26.85
522	22.85	572	23.92	622	24.94	672	25.92	722	26.87
523	22.87	573	23.94	623	24.96	673	25.94	723	26.89
524	22.89	574	23.96	624	24.98	674	25.96	724	26.91
525	22.91	575	23.98	625	25.00	675	25.98	725	26.93
526	22.93	576	24.00	626	25.02	676	26.00	726	26.94
527	22.96	577	24.02	627	25.04	677	26.02	727	26.96
528	22.98	578	24.04	628	25.06	678	26.04	728	26.98
529	23.00	579	24.06	629	25.08	679	26.06	729	27.00
530	23.02	580	24.08	630	25.10	680	26.08	730	27.02
531	23.04	581	24.10	631	25.12	681	26.10	731	27.04
532	23.07	582	24.12	632	25.14	682	26.12	732	27.06
533	23.09	583	24.15	633	25.16	683	26.13	733	27.07
534	23.11	584	24.17	634	25.18	684	26.15	734	27.09
535	23.13	585	24.19	635	25.20	685	26.17	735	27.11
536	23.15	586	24.21	636	25.22	686	26.19	736	27.13
537	23.17	587	24.23	637	25.24	687	26.21	737	27.15
538	23.19	588	24.25	638	25.26	688	26.23	738	27.17
539	23.22	589	24.27	639	25.28	689	26.25	739	27.18
540	23.24	590	24.29	640	25.30	690	26.27	740	27.20
541	23.26	591	24.31	641	25.32	691	26.29	741	27.22
542	23.28	592	24.33	642	25.34	692	26.31	742	27.24
543	23.30	593	24.35	643	25.36	693	26.32	743	27.26
544	23.32	594	24.37	644	25.38	694	26.34	744	27.28
545	23.35	595	24.39	645	25.40	695	26.36	745	27.29
546	23.37	596	24.41	646	25.42	696	26.38	746	27.31
547	23.39	597	24.43	647	25.44	697	26.40	747	27.33
548	23.41	598	24.45	648	25.46	698	26.42	748	27.35
549	23.43	599	24.47	649	25.48	699	26.44	749	27.37
550	23.45	600	24.49	650	25.50	700	26.46	750	27.39

TABLE OF APPROXIMATE SQUARE ROOTS

N	$\sqrt{N}$	N	$\sqrt{N}$	N	$\sqrt{N}$	N	$\sqrt{N}$	N	$\sqrt{N}$
751	27.40	801	28.30	851	29.17	901	30.02	951	30.84
752	27.42	802	28.32	852	29.19	902	30.03	952	30.85
753	27.44	803	28.34	853	29.21	903	30.05	953	30.87
754	27.46	804	28.35	854	29.22	904	30.07	954	30.89
755	27.48	805	28.37	855	29.24	905	30.08	955	30.90
756	27.50	806	28.39	856	29.26	906	30.10	956	30.92
757	27.51	807	28.41	857	29.27	907	30.12	957	30.94
758	27.53	808	28.43	858	29.29	908	30.13	958	30.95
759	27.55	809	28.44	859	29.31	909	30.15	959	30.97
760	27.57	810	28.46	860	29.33	910	30.17	960	30.98
761	27.59	811	28.48	861	29.34	911	30.18	961	31.00
762	27.60	812	28.50	862	29.36	912	30.20	962	31.02
763	27.62	813	28.51	863	29.38	913	30.22	963	31.03
764	27.64	814	28.53	864	29.39	914	30.23	964	31.05
765	27.66	815	28.55	865	29.41	915	30.25	965	31.06
766	27.68	816	28.57	866	29.43	916	30.27	966	31.08
767	27.69	817	28.58	867	29.44	917	30.28	967	31.10
768	27.71	818	28.60	868	29.46	918	30.30	968	31.11
769	27.73	819	28.62	869	29.48	919	30.32	969	31.13
770	27.75	820	28.64	870	29.50	920	30.33	970	31.14
771	27.77	821	28.65	871	29.51	921	30.35	971	31.16
772	27.78	822	28.67	872	29.53	922	30.36	972	31.18
773	27.80	823	28.69	873	29.55	923	30.38	973	31.19
774	27.82	824	28.71	874	29.56	924	30.40	974	31.21
775	27.84	825	28.72	875	29.58	925	30.41	975	31.22
776	27.86	826	28.74	876	29.60	926	30.43	976	31.24
777	27.87	827	28.76	877	29.61	927	30.45	977	31.26
778	27.89	828	28.77	878	29.63	928	30.46	978	31.27
779	27.91	829	28.79	879	29.65	929	30.48	979	31.29
780	27.93	830	28.81	880	29.66	930	30.50	980	31.30
781	27.95	831	28.83	881	29.68	931	30.51	981	31.32
782	27.96	832	28.84	882	29.70	932	30.53	982	31.34
783	27.98	833	28.86	883	29.72	933	30.55	983	31.35
784	28.00	834	28.88	884	29.73	934	30.56	984	31.37
785	28.02	835	28.90	885	29.75	935	30.58	985	31.38
786	28.04	836	28.91	886	29.77	936	30.59	986	31.40
787	28.05	837	28.93	887	29.78	937	30.61	987	31.42
788	28.07	838	28.95	888	29.80	938	30.63	988	31.43
789	28.09	839	28.97	889	29.82	939	30.64	989	31.45
790	28.11	840	28.98	890	29.83	940	30.66	990	31.46
791	28.12	841	29.00	891	29.85	941	30.68	991	31.48
792	28.14	842	29.02	892	29.87	942	30.69	992	31.50
793	28.16	843	29.03	893	29.88	943	30.71	993	31.51
794	28.18	844	29.05	894	29.90	944	30.72	994	31.53
795	28.20	845	29.07	895	29.92	945	30.74	995	31.54
796	28.21	846	29.09	896	29.93	946	30.76	996	31.56
797	28.23	847	29.10	897	29.95	947	30.77	997	31.58
798	28.25	848	29.12	898	29.97	948	30.79	998	31.59
799	28.27	849	29.14	899	29.98	949	30.81	999	31.61
800	28.28	850	29.15	900	30.00	950	30.82	1000	31.62

No.	Squares	Cubes	Square Roots	Cube Roots	No.	Squares	Cubes	Square Roots	Cube Roots
1	1	1	1.000	1.000	51	2,601	132,651	7.141	3.708
2	4	8	1.414	1.260	52	2,704	140,608	7.211	3.733
3	9	27	1.732	1.442	53	2,809	148,877	7.280	3.756
4	16	64	2.000	1.587	54	2,916	157,464	7.348	3.780
5	25	125	2.236	1.710	55	3,025	166,375	7.416	3.803
6	36	216	2.449	1.817	56	3,136	175,616	7.483	3.826
7	49	343	2.646	1.912	57	3,249	185,193	7.550	3.849
8	64	512	2.828	2.000	58	3,364	195,112	7.616	3.871
9	81	729	3.000	2.080	59	3,481	205,379	7.681	3.893
10	100	1,000	3.162	2.154	60	3,600	216,000	7.746	3.915
11	121	1,331	3.317	2.224	61	3,721	226,981	7.810	3.936
12	144	1,728	3.464	2.289	62	3,844	238,328	7.874	3.958
13	169	2,197	3.606	2.351	63	3,969	250,047	7.937	3.979
14	196	2,744	3.741	2.410	64	4,096	262,144	8.000	4.000
15	225	3,375	3.873	2.466	65	4,225	274,625	8.062	4.020
16	256	4,096	4.000	2.520	66	4,356	287,496	8.124	4.041
17	289	4,913	4.123	2.571	67	4,489	300,763	8.185	4.062
18	324	5,832	4.243	2.621	68	4,624	314,432	8.246	4.082
19	361	6,859	4.359	2.668	69	4,761	328,509	8.307	4.102
20	400	8,000	4.472	2.714	70	4,900	343,000	8.367	4.121
21	441	9,261	4.583	2.759	71	5,041	357,911	8.426	4.141
22	484	10,648	4.690	2.802	72	5,184	373,248	8.485	4.160
23	529	12,167	4.796	2.844	73	5,329	389,017	8.544	4.179
24	576	13,824	4.899	2.884	74	5,476	405,224	8.602	4.198
25	625	15,625	5.000	2.924	75	5,625	421,875	8.660	4.217
26	676	17,576	5.099	2.962	76	5,776	438,976	8.718	4.236
27	729	19,683	5.196	3.000	77	5,929	456,533	8.775	4.254
28	784	21,952	5.292	3.037	78	6,084	474,552	8.832	4.273
29	841	24,389	5.385	3.072	79	6,241	493,039	8.888	4.291
30	900	27,000	5.477	3.107	80	6,400	512,000	8.944	4.309
31	961	29,791	5.568	3.141	81	6,561	531,441	9.000	4.327
32	1,024	32,768	5.657	3.175	82	6,724	551,368	9.055	4.344
33	1,089	35,937	5.744	3.208	83	6,889	571,787	9.110	4.362
34	1,156	39,304	5.831	3.240	84	7,056	592,704	9.165	4.380
35	1,225	42,875	5.916	3.271	85	7,225	614,125	9.220	4.397
36	1,296	46,656	6.000	3.302	86	7,396	636,056	9.274	4.414
37	1,369	50,653	6.083	3.332	87	7,569	658,503	9.327	4.431
38	1,444	54,872	6.164	3.362	88	7,744	681,472	9.381	4.448
39	1,521	59,319	6.245	3.391	89	7,921	704,969	9.434	4.465
40	1,600	64,000	6.325	3.420	90	8,100	729,000	9.487	4.481
41	1,681	68,921	6.403	3.448	91	8,281	753,571	9.539	4.498
42	1,764	74,088	6.481	3.476	92	8,464	778,688	9.592	4.514
43	1,849	79,507	6.557	3.503	93	8,649	804,357	9.644	4.531
44	1,936	85,184	6.633	3.530	94	8,836	830,584	9.695	4.547
45	2,025	91,125	6.708	3.557	95	9,025	857,375	9.747	4.563
46	2,116	97,336	6.782	3.583	96	9,216	884,736	9.798	4.579
47	2,209	103,823	6.856	3.609	97	9,409	912,673	9.849	4.595
48	2,304	110,592	6.928	3.634	98	9,604	941,192	9.899	4.610
49	2,401	117,649	7.000	3.659	99	9,801	970,299	9.950	4.626
50	2,500	125,000	7.071	3.684	100	10,000	1,000,000	10.000	4.642

No.	0	1	2	3	4	5	6	7	8	9
10	0000	0043	0086	0128	0170	0212	0253	0294	0334	0374
11	0414	0453	0492	0531	0569	0607	0645	0682	0719	0755
12	0792	0828	0864	0899	0934	0969	1004	1038	1072	1106
13	1139	1173	1206	1239	1271	1303	1335	1367	1399	1430
14	1461	1492	1523	1553	1584	1614	1644	1673	1703	1732
15	1761	1790	1818	1847	1875	1903	1931	1959	1987	2014
16	2041	2068	2095	2122	2148	2175	2201	2227	2253	2279
17	2304	2330	2355	2380	2405	2430	2455	2480	2504	2529
18	2553	2577	2601	2625	2648	2672	2695	2718	2742	2765
19	2788	2810	2833	2856	2878	2900	2923	2945	2967	2989
20	3010	3032	3054	3075	3096	3118	3139	3160	3181	3201
21	3222	3243	3263	3284	3304	3324	3345	3365	3385	3404
22	3424	3444	3464	3483	3502	3522	3541	3560	3579	3598
23	3617	3636	3655	3674	3692	3711	3729	3747	3766	3784
24	3802	3820	3838	3856	3874	3892	3909	3927	3945	3962
25	3979	3997	4014	4031	4048	4065	4082	4099	4116	4133
26	4150	4166	4183	4200	4216	4232	4249	4265	4281	4298
27	4314	4330	4346	4362	4378	4393	4409	4425	4440	4456
28	4472	4487	4502	4518	4533	4548	4564	4579	4594	4609
29	4624	4639	4654	4669	4683	4698	4713	4728	4742	4757
30	4771	4786	4800	4814	4829	4843	4857	4871	4886	4900
31	4914	4928	4942	4955	4969	4983	4997	5011	5024	5038
32	5051	5065	5079	5092	5105	5119	5132	5145	5159	5172
33	5185	5198	5211	5224	5237	5250	5263	5276	5289	5302
34	5315	5328	5340	5353	5366	5378	5391	5403	5416	5428
35	5441	5453	5465	5478	5490	5502	5514	5527	5539	5551
36	5563	5575	5587	5599	5611	5623	5635	5647	5658	5670
37	5682	5694	5705	5717	5729	5740	5752	5763	5775	5786
38	5798	5809	5821	5832	5843	5855	5866	5877	5888	5899
39	5911	5922	5933	5944	5955	5966	5977	5988	5999	6010
40	6021	6031	6042	6053	6064	6075	6085	6096	6107	6117
41	6128	6138	6149	6160	6170	6180	6191	6201	6212	6222
42	6232	6243	6253	6263	6274	6284	6294	6304	6314	6325
43	6335	6345	6355	6365	6375	6385	6395	6405	6415	6425
44	6435	6444	6454	6464	6474	6484	6493	6503	6513	6522
45	6532	6542	6551	6561	6571	6580	6590	6599	6609	6618
46	6628	6637	6646	6656	6665	6675	6684	6693	6702	6712
47	6721	6730	6739	6749	6758	6767	6776	6785	6794	6803
48	6812	6821	6830	6839	6848	6857	6866	6875	6884	6893
49	6902	6911	6920	6928	6937	6946	6955	6964	6972	6981
50	6990	6998	7007	7016	7024	7033	7042	7050	7059	7067
51	7076	7084	7093	7101	7110	7118	7126	7135	7143	7152
52	7160	7168	7177	7185	7193	7202	7210	7218	7226	7235
53	7243	7251	7259	7267	7275	7284	7292	7300	7308	7316
54	7324	7332	7340	7348	7356	7364	7372	7380	7388	7396

MANTISSAS OF LOGARITHMS OF NUMBERS

No.	0	1	2	3	4	5	6	7	8	9
55	7404	7412	7419	7427	7435	7443	7451	7459	7466	7474
56	7482	7490	7497	7505	7513	7520	7528	7536	7543	7551
57	7559	7566	7574	7582	7589	7597	7604	7612	7619	7627
58	7634	7642	7649	7657	7664	7672	7679	7686	7694	7701
59	7709	7716	7723	7731	7738	7745	7752	7760	7767	7774
60	7782	7789	7796	7803	7810	7818	7825	7832	7839	7846
61	7853	7860	7868	7875	7882	7889	7896	7903	7910	7917
62	7924	7931	7938	7945	7952	7959	7966	7973	7980	7987
63	7993	8000	8007	8014	8021	8028	8035	8041	8048	8055
64	8062	8069	8075	8082	8089	8096	8102	8109	8116	8122
65	8129	8136	8142	8149	8156	8162	8169	8176	8182	8189
66	8195	8202	8209	8215	8222	8228	8235	8241	8248	8254
67	8261	8267	8274	8280	8287	8293	8299	8306	8312	8319
68	8325	8331	8338	8344	8351	8357	8363	8370	8376	8382
69	8388	8395	8401	8407	8414	8420	8426	8432	8439	8445
70	8451	8457	8463	8470	8476	8482	8488	8494	8500	8506
71	8513	8519	8525	8531	8537	8543	8549	8555	8561	8567
72	8573	8579	8585	8591	8597	8603	8609	8615	8621	8627
73	8633	8639	8645	8651	8657	8663	8669	8675	8681	8686
74	8692	8698	8704	8710	8716	8722	8727	8733	8739	8745
75	8751	8756	8762	8768	8774	8779	8785	8791	8797	8802
76	8808	8814	8820	8825	8831	8837	8842	8848	8854	8859
77	8865	8871	8876	8882	8887	8893	8899	8904	8910	8915
78	8921	8927	8932	8938	8943	8949	8954	8960	8965	8971
79	8976	8982	8987	8993	8998	9004	9009	9015	9020	9025
80	9031	9036	9042	9047	9053	9058	9063	9069	9074	9079
81	9085	9090	9096	9101	9106	9112	9117	9122	9128	9133
82	9138	9143	9149	9154	9159	9165	9170	9175	9180	9186
83	9191	9196	9201	9206	9212	9217	9222	9227	9232	9238
84	9243	9248	9253	9258	9263	9269	9274	9279	9284	9289
85	9294	9299	9304	9309	9315	9320	9325	9330	9335	9340
86	9345	9350	9355	9360	9365	9370	9375	9380	9385	9390
87	9395	9400	9405	9410	9415	9420	9425	9430	9435	9440
88	9445	9450	9455	9460	9465	9469	9474	9479	9484	9489
89	9494	9499	9504	9509	9513	9518	9523	9528	9533	9538
90	9542	9547	9552	9557	9562	9566	9571	9576	9581	9586
91	9590	9595	9600	9605	9609	9614	9619	9624	9628	9633
92	9638	9643	9647	9652	9657	9661	9666	9671	9675	9680
93	9685	9689	9694	9699	9703	9708	9713	9717	9722	9727
94	9731	9736	9741	9745	9750	9754	9759	9763	9768	9773
95	9777	9782	9786	9791	9795	9800	9805	9809	9814	9818
96	9823	9827	9832	9836	9841	9845	9850	9854	9859	9863
97	9868	9872	9877	9881	9886	9890	9894	9899	9903	9908
98	9912	9917	9921	9926	9930	9934	9939	9943	9948	9952
99	9956	9961	9965	9969	9974	9978	9983	9987	9991	9996

VALUES OF TRIGONOMETRIC FUNCTIONS

Angle	Sin	Cos	Tan	Ctn	Angle	Angle	Sin	Cos	Tan	Ctn	Angle
0° 0′	0.0000	1.0000	0.0000	∞	90° 0′	7°30′	0.1305	0.9914	0.1317	7.5958	82°30′
10	.0029	1.0000	.0029	343.77	50′	40	.1334	.9911	.1346	7.4287	20
20	.0058	1.0000	.0058	171.89	40	50	.1363	.9907	.1376	7.2687	10
30	.0087	1.0000	.0087	114.59	30	8° 0′	.1392	.9903	.1405	7.1154	82° 0′
40	.0116	0.9999	.0116	85.940	20	10	.1421	.9899	.1435	6.9682	50
50	.0145	.9999	.0145	68.750	10	20	.1449	.9894	.1465	6.8269	40
1° 0′	.0175	.9998	.0175	57.290	89° 0′	30	.1478	.9890	.1495	6.6912	30
10	.0204	.9998	.0204	49.104	50	40	.1507	.9886	.1524	6.5606	20
20	.0233	.9997	.0233	42.964	40	50	.1536	.9881	.1554	6.4348	10
30	.0262	.9997	.0262	38.188	30	9° 0′	.1564	.9877	.1584	6.3138	81° 0′
40	.0291	.9996	.0291	34.368	20	10	.1593	.9872	.1614	6.1970	50
50	.0320	.9995	.0320	31.242	10	20	.1622	.9868	.1644	6.0844	40
2° 0′	.0349	.9994	.0349	28.636	88° 0′	30	.1650	.9863	.1673	5.9758	30
10	.0378	.9993	.0378	26.432	50	40	.1679	.9858	.1703	5.8708	20
20	.0407	.9992	.0407	24.542	40	50	.1708	.9853	.1733	5.7694	10
30	.0436	.9990	.0437	22.904	30	10° 0′	.1736	.9848	.1763	5.6713	80° 0′
40	.0465	.9989	.0466	21.470	20	10	.1765	.9843	.1793	5.5764	50
50	.0494	.9988	.0495	20.206	10	20	.1794	.9838	.1823	5.4845	40
3° 0′	.0523	.9986	.0524	19.081	87° 0′	30	.1822	.9833	.1853	5.3955	30
10	.0552	.9985	.0553	18.075	50	40	.1851	.9827	.1883	5.3093	20
20	.0581	.9983	.0582	17.169	40	50	.1880	.9822	.1914	5.2257	10
30	.0610	.9981	.0612	16.350	30	11° 0′	.1908	.9816	.1944	5.1446	79° 0′
40	.0640	.9980	.0641	15.605	20	10	.1937	.9811	.1974	5.0658	50
50	.0669	.9978	.0670	14.924	10	20	.1965	.9805	.2004	4.9894	40
4° 0′	.0698	.9976	.0699	14.301	86° 0′	30	.1994	.9799	.2035	4.9152	30
10	.0727	.9974	.0729	13.727	50	40	.2022	.9793	.2065	4.8430	20
20	.0756	.9971	.0758	13.197	40	50	.2051	.9787	.2095	4.7729	10
30	.0785	.9969	.0787	12.706	30	12° 0′	.2079	.9781	.2126	4.7046	78° 0′
40	.0814	.9967	.0816	12.251	20	10	.2108	.9775	.2156	4.6382	50
50	.0843	.9964	.0846	11.826	10	20	.2136	.9769	.2186	4.5736	40
5° 0′	.0872	.9962	.0875	11.430	85° 0′	30	.2164	.9763	.2217	4.5107	30
10	.0901	.9959	.0904	11.059	50	40	.2193	.9757	.2247	4.4494	20
20	.0929	.9957	.0934	10.712	40	50	.2221	.9750	.2278	4.3897	10
30	.0958	.9954	.0963	10.385	30	13° 0′	.2250	.9744	.2309	4.3315	77° 0′
40	.0987	.9951	.0992	10.078	20	10	.2278	.9737	.2339	4.2747	50
50	.1016	.9948	.1022	9.7882	10	20	.2306	.9730	.2370	4.2193	40
6° 0′	.1045	.9945	.1051	9.5144	84° 0′	30	.2334	.9724	.2401	4.1653	30
10	.1074	.9942	.1080	9.2553	50	40	.2363	.9717	.2432	4.1126	20
20	.1103	.9939	.1110	9.0098	40	50	.2391	.9710	.2462	4.0611	10
30	.1132	.9936	.1139	8.7769	30	14° 0′	.2419	.9703	.2493	4.0108	76° 0′
40	.1161	.9932	.1169	8.5555	20	10	.2447	.9696	.2524	3.9617	50
50	.1190	.9929	.1198	8.3450	10	20	.2476	.9689	.2555	3.9136	40
7° 0′	.1219	.9925	.1228	8.1443	83° 0′	30	.2504	.9681	.2586	3.8667	30
10	.1248	.9922	.1257	7.9530	50	40	.2532	.9674	.2617	3.8208	20
20	.1276	.9918	.1287	7.7704	40	50	.2560	.9667	.2648	3.7760	10
30	.1305	.9914	.1317	7.5958	30	15° 0′	.2588	.9659	.2679	3.7321	75° 0′
Angle	Cos	Sin	Ctn	Tan	Angle	Angle	Cos	Sin	Ctn	Tan	Angle

VALUES OF TRIGONOMETRIC FUNCTIONS

Angle	Sin	Cos	Tan	Ctn	Angle	Angle	Sin	Cos	Tan	Ctn	Angle
15° 0′	0.2588	0.9659	0.2679	3.7321	75° 0′	22°30′	0.3827	0.9239	0.4142	2.4142	67°30′
10	.2616	.9652	.2711	3.6891	50	40	.3854	.9228	.4176	2.3945	20
20	.2644	.9644	.2742	3.6470	40	50	.3881	.9216	.4210	2.3750	10
30	.2672	.9636	.2773	3.6059	30	23° 0′	.3907	.9205	.4245	2.3559	67° 0′
40	.2700	.9628	.2805	3.5656	20	10	.3934	.9194	.4279	2.3369	50
50	.2728	.9621	.2836	3.5261	10	20	.3961	.9182	.4314	2.3183	40
16° 0′	.2756	.9613	.2867	3.4874	74° 0′	30	.3987	.9171	.4348	2.2998	30
10	.2784	.9605	.2899	3.4495	50	40	.4014	.9159	.4383	2.2817	20
20	.2812	.9596	.2931	3.4124	40	50	.4041	.9147	.4417	2.2637	10
30	.2840	.9588	.2962	3.3759	30	24° 0′	.4067	.9135	.4452	2.2460	66° 0′
40	.2868	.9580	.2994	3.3402	20	10	.4094	.9124	.4487	2.2286	50
50	.2896	.9572	.3026	3.3052	10	20	.4120	.9112	.4522	2.2113	40
17° 0′	.2924	.9563	.3057	3.2709	73° 0′	30	.4147	.9100	.4557	2.1943	30
10	.2952	.9555	.3089	3.2371	50	40	.4173	.9088	.4592	2.1775	20
20	.2979	.9546	.3121	3.2041	40	50	.4200	.9075	.4628	2.1609	10
30	.3007	.9537	.3153	3.1716	30	25° 0′	.4226	.9063	.4663	2.1445	65° 0′
40	.3035	.9528	.3185	3.1397	20	10	.4253	.9051	.4699	2.1283	50
50	.3062	.9520	.3217	3.1084	10	20	.4279	.9038	.4734	2.1123	40
18° 0′	.3090	.9511	.3249	3.0777	72° 0′	30	.4305	.9026	.4770	2.0965	30
10	.3118	.9502	.3281	3.0475	50	40	.4331	.9013	.4806	2.0809	20
20	.3145	.9492	.3314	3.0178	40	50	.4358	.9001	.4841	2.0655	10
30	.3173	.9483	.3346	2.9887	30	26° 0′	.4384	.8988	.4877	2.0503	64° 0′
40	.3201	.9474	.3378	2.9600	20	10	.4410	.8975	.4913	2.0353	50
50	.3228	.9465	.3411	2.9319	10	20	.4436	.8962	.4950	2.0204	40
19° 0′	.3256	.9455	.3443	2.9042	71° 0′	30	.4462	.8949	.4986	2.0057	30
10	.3283	.9446	.3476	2.8770	50	40	.4488	.8936	.5022	1.9912	20
20	.3311	.9436	.3508	2.8502	40	50	.4514	.8923	.5059	1.9768	10
30	.3338	.9426	.3541	2.8239	30	27° 0′	.4540	.8910	.5095	1.9626	63° 0′
40	.3365	.9417	.3574	2.7980	20	10	.4566	.8897	.5132	1.9486	50
50	.3393	.9407	.3607	2.7725	10	20	.4592	.8884	.5169	1.9347	40
20° 0′	.3420	.9397	.3640	2.7475	70° 0′	30	.4617	.8870	.5206	1.9210	30
10	.3448	.9387	.3673	2.7228	50	40	.4643	.8857	.5243	1.9074	20
20	.3475	.9377	.3706	2.6985	40	50	.4669	.8843	.5280	1.8940	10
30	.3502	.9367	.3739	2.6746	30	28° 0′	.4695	.8829	.5317	1.8807	62° 0′
40	.3529	.9356	.3772	2.6511	20	10	.4720	.8816	.5354	1.8676	50
50	.3557	.9346	.3805	2.6279	10	20	.4746	.8802	.5392	1.8546	40
21° 0′	.3584	.9336	.3839	2.6051	69° 0′	30	.4772	.8788	.5430	1.8418	30
10	.3611	.9325	.3872	2.5826	50	40	.4797	.8774	.5467	1.8291	20
20	.3638	.9315	.3906	2.5605	40	50	.4823	.8760	.5505	1.8165	10
30	.3665	.9304	.3939	2.5386	30	29° 0′	.4848	.8746	.5543	1.8040	61° 0′
40	.3692	.9293	.3973	2.5172	20	10	.4874	.8732	.5581	1.7917	50
50	.3719	.9283	.4006	2.4960	10	20	.4899	.8718	.5619	1.7796	40
22° 0′	.3746	.9272	.4040	2.4751	68° 0′	30	.4924	.8704	.5658	1.7675	30
10	.3773	.9261	.4074	2.4545	50	40	.4950	.8689	.5696	1.7556	20
20	.3800	.9250	.4108	2.4342	40	50	.4975	.8675	.5735	1.7437	10
30	.3827	.9239	.4142	2.4142	30	30° 0′	.5000	.8660	.5774	1.7321	60° 0′
Angle	Cos	Sin	Ctn	Tan	Angle	Angle	Cos	Sin	Ctn	Tan	Angle

490

Angle	Sin	Cos	Tan	Ctn	Angle
30° 0'	0.5000	0.8660	0.5774	1.7321	60° 0'
10	.5025	.8646	.5812	1.7205	50
20	.5050	.8631	.5851	1.7090	40
30	.5075	.8616	.5890	1.6977	30
40	.5100	.8601	.5930	1.6864	20
50	.5125	.8587	.5969	1.6753	10
31° 0'	.5150	.8572	.6009	1.6643	59° 0'
10	.5175	.8557	.6048	1.6534	50
20	.5200	.8542	.6088	1.6426	40
30	.5225	.8526	.6128	1.6319	30
40	.5250	.8511	.6168	1.6212	20
50	.5275	.8496	.6208	1.6107	10
32° 0'	.5299	.8480	.6249	1.6003	58° 0'
10	.5324	.8465	.6289	1.5900	50
20	.5348	.8450	.6330	1.5798	40
30	.5373	.8434	.6371	1.5697	30
40	.5398	.8418	.6412	1.5597	20
50	.5422	.8403	.6453	1.5497	10
33° 0'	.5446	.8387	.6494	1.5399	57° 0'
10	.5471	.8371	.6536	1.5301	50
20	.5495	.8355	.6577	1.5204	40
30	.5519	.8339	.6619	1.5108	30
40	.5544	.8323	.6661	1.5013	20
50	.5568	.8307	.6703	1.4919	10
34° 0'	.5592	.8290	.6745	1.4826	56° 0'
10	.5616	.8274	.6787	1.4733	50
20	.5640	.8258	.6830	1.4641	40
30	.5664	.8241	.6873	1.4550	30
40	.5688	.8225	.6916	1.4460	20
50	.5712	.8208	.6959	1.4370	10
35° 0'	.5736	.8192	.7002	1.4281	55° 0'
10	.5760	.8175	.7046	1.4193	50
20	.5783	.8158	.7089	1.4106	40
30	.5807	.8141	.7133	1.4019	30
40	.5831	.8124	.7177	1.3934	20
50	.5854	.8107	.7221	1.3848	10
36° 0'	.5878	.8090	.7265	1.3764	54° 0'
10	.5901	.8073	.7310	1.3680	50
20	.5925	.8056	.7355	1.3597	40
30	.5948	.8039	.7400	1.3514	30
40	.5972	.8021	.7445	1.3432	20
50	.5995	.8004	.7490	1.3351	10
37° 0'	.6018	.7986	.7536	1.3270	53° 0'
10	.6041	.7969	.7581	1.3190	50
20	.6065	.7951	.7627	1.3111	40
30	.6088	.7934	.7673	1.3032	30
Angle	**Cos**	**Sin**	**Ctn**	**Tan**	**Angle**

Angle	Sin	Cos	Tan	Ctn	Angle
37°30'	0.6088	0.7934	0.7673	1.3032	52°30'
40	.6111	.7916	.7720	1.2954	20
50	.6134	.7898	.7766	1.2876	10
38° 0'	.6157	.7880	.7813	1.2799	52° 0'
10	.6180	.7862	.7860	1.2723	50
20	.6202	.7844	.7907	1.2647	40
30	.6225	.7826	.7954	1.2572	30
40	.6248	.7808	.8002	1.2497	20
50	.6271	.7790	.8050	1.2423	10
39° 0'	.6293	.7771	.8098	1.2349	51° 0'
10	.6316	.7753	.8146	1.2276	50
20	.6338	.7735	.8195	1.2203	40
30	.6361	.7716	.8243	1.2131	30
40	.6383	.7698	.8292	1.2059	20
50	.6406	.7679	.8342	1.1988	10
40° 0'	.6428	.7660	.8391	1.1918	50° 0'
10	.6450	.7642	.8441	1.1847	50
20	.6472	.7623	.8491	1.1778	40
30	.6494	.7604	.8541	1.1708	30
40	.6517	.7585	.8591	1.1640	20
50	.6539	.7566	.8642	1.1571	10
41° 0'	.6561	.7547	.8693	1.1504	49° 0'
10	.6583	.7528	.8744	1.1436	50
20	.6604	.7509	.8796	1.1369	40
30	.6626	.7490	.8847	1.1303	30
40	.6648	.7470	.8899	1.1237	20
50	.6670	.7451	.8952	1.1171	10
42° 0'	.6691	.7431	.9004	1.1106	48° 0'
10	.6713	.7412	.9057	1.1041	50
20	.6734	.7392	.9110	1.0977	40
30	.6756	.7373	.9163	1.0913	30
40	.6777	.7353	.9217	1.0850	20
50	.6799	.7333	.9271	1.0786	10
43° 0'	.6820	.7314	.9325	1.0724	47° 0'
10	.6841	.7294	.9380	1.0661	50
20	.6862	7274	.9435	1.0599	40
30	.6884	.7254	.9490	1.0538	30
40	.6905	.7234	.9545	1.0477	20
50	.6926	.7214	.9601	1.0416	10
44° 0'	.6947	.7193	.9657	1.0355	46° 0'
10	.6967	.7173	.9713	1.0295	50
20	.6988	.7153	.9770	1.0235	40
30	.7009	.7133	.9827	1.0176	30
40	.7030	.7112	.9884	1.0117	20
50	.7050	.7092	.9942	1.0058	10
45° 0'	.7071	.7071	1.0000	1.0000	45° 0'
Angle	**Cos**	**Sin**	**Ctn**	**Tan**	**Angle**

LOGARITHMS OF TRIGONOMETRIC FUNCTIONS

Angle	log Sin	log Cos	log Tan	log Ctn	Angle	Angle	log Sin	log Cos	log Tan	log Ctn	Angle
0° 0'	—	10.000	—	—	90° 0'	7°30'	9.1157	9.9963	9.1194	0.8806	82°30'
10	7.4637	10.000	7.4637	2.5363	50	40	9.1252	9.9961	9.1291	0.8709	20
20	7.7648	10.000	7.7648	2.2352	40	50	9.1345	9.9959	9.1385	0.8615	10
30	7.9408	10.000	7.9409	2.0591	30	8° 0'	9.1436	9.9958	9.1478	0.8522	82° 0'
40	8.0658	10.000	8.0658	1.9342	20	10	9.1525	9.9956	9.1569	0.8431	50
50	8.1627	10.000	8.1627	1.8373	10	20	9.1612	9.9954	9.1658	0.8342	40
1° 0'	8.2419	9.9999	8.2419	1.7581	89° 0'	30	9.1697	9.9952	9.1745	0.8255	30
10	8.3088	9.9999	8.3089	1.6911	50	40	9.1781	9.9950	9.1831	0.8169	20
20	8.3668	9.9999	8.3669	1.6331	40	50	9.1863	9.9948	9.1915	0.8085	10
30	8.4179	9.9999	8.4181	1.5819	30	9° 0'	9.1943	9.9946	9.1997	0.8003	81° 0'
40	8.4637	9.9998	8.4638	1.5362	20	10	9.2022	9.9944	9.2078	0.7922	50
50	8.5050	9.9998	8.5053	1.4947	10	20	9.2100	9.9942	9.2158	0.7842	40
2° 0'	8.5428	9.9997	8.5431	1.4569	88° 0'	30	9.2176	9.9940	9.2236	0.7764	30
10	8.5776	9.9997	8.5779	1.4221	50	40	9.2251	9.9938	9.2313	0.7687	20
20	8.6097	9.9996	8.6101	1.3899	40	50	9.2324	9.9936	9.2389	0.7611	10
30	8.6397	9.9996	8.6401	1.3599	30	10° 0'	9.2397	9.9934	9.2463	0.7537	80° 0'
40	8.6677	9.9995	8.6682	1.3318	20	10	9.2468	9.9931	9.2536	0.7464	50
50	8.6940	9.9995	8.6945	1.3055	10	20	9.2538	9.9929	9.2609	0.7391	40
3° 0'	8.7188	9.9994	8.7194	1.2806	87° 0'	30	9.2606	9.9927	9.2680	0.7320	30
10	8.7423	9.9993	8.7429	1.2571	50	40	9.2674	9.9924	9.2750	0.7250	20
20	8.7645	9.9993	8.7652	1.2348	40	50	9.2740	9.9922	9.2819	0.7181	10
30	8.7857	9.9992	8.7865	1.2135	30	11° 0'	9.2806	9.9919	9.2887	0.7113	79° 0'
40	8.8059	9.9991	8.8067	1.1933	20	10	9.2870	9.9917	9.2953	0.7047	50
50	8.8251	9.9990	8.8261	1.1739	10	20	9.2934	9.9914	9.3020	0.6980	40
4° 0'	8.8436	9.9989	8.8446	1.1554	86° 0'	30	9.2997	9.9912	9.3085	0.6915	30
10	8.8613	9.9989	8.8624	1.1376	50	40	9.3058	9.9909	9.3149	0.6851	20
20	8.8783	9.9988	8.8795	1.1205	40	50	9.3119	9.9907	9.3212	0.6788	10
30	8.8946	9.9987	8.8960	1.1040	30	12° 0'	9.3179	9.9904	9.3275	0.6725	78° 0'
40	8.9104	9.9986	8.9118	1.0882	20	10	9.3238	9.9901	9.3336	0.6664	50
50	8.9256	9.9985	8.9272	1.0728	10	20	9.3296	9.9899	9.3397	0.6603	40
5° 0'	8.9403	9.9983	8.9420	1.0580	85° 0'	30	9.3353	9.9896	9.3458	0.6542	30
10	8.9545	9.9982	8.9563	1.0437	50	40	9.3410	9.9893	9.3517	0.6483	20
20	8.9682	9.9981	8.9701	1.0299	40	50	9.3466	9.9890	9.3576	0.6424	10
30	8.9816	9.9980	8.9836	1.0164	30	13° 0'	9.3521	9.9887	9.3634	0.6366	77° 0'
40	8.9945	9.9979	8.9966	1.0034	20	10	9.3575	9.9884	9.3691	0.6309	50
50	9.0070	9.9977	9.0093	0.9907	10	20	9.3629	9.9881	9.3748	0.6252	40
6° 0'	9.0192	9.9976	9.0216	0.9784	84° 0'	30	9.3682	9.9878	9.3804	0.6196	30
10	9.0311	9.9975	9.0336	0.9664	50	40	9.3734	9.9875	9.3859	0.6141	20
20	9.0426	9.9973	9.0453	0.9547	40	50	9.3786	9.9872	9.3914	0.6086	10
30	9.0539	9.9972	9.0567	0.9433	30	14° 0'	9.3837	9.9869	9.3968	0.6032	76° 0'
40	9.0648	9.9971	9.0678	0.9322	20	10	9.3887	9.9866	9.4021	0.5979	50
50	9.0755	9.9969	9.0786	0.9214	10	20	9.3937	9.9863	9.4074	0.5926	40
7° 0'	9.0859	9.9968	9.0891	0.9109	83° 0'	30	9.3986	9.9859	9.4127	0.5873	30
10	9.0961	9.9966	9.0995	0.9005	50	40	9.4035	9.9856	9.4178	0.5822	20
20	9.1060	9.9964	9.1096	0.8904	40	50	9.4083	9.9853	9.4230	0.5770	10
30	9.1157	9.9963	9.1194	0.8806	30	15° 0'	9.4130	9.9849	9.4281	0.5719	75° 0'
Angle	log Cos	log Sin	log Ctn	log Tan	Angle	Angle	log Cos	log Sin	log Ctn	log Tan	Angle

LOGARITHMS OF TRIGONOMETRIC FUNCTIONS

Angle	log Sin	log Cos	log Tan	log Ctn	Angle	Angle	log Sin	log Cos	log Tan	log Ctn	Angle
15° 0'	9.4130	9.9849	9.4281	0.5719	75° 0'	22°30'	9.5828	9.9656	9.6172	0.3828	67°30'
10	9.4177	9.9846	9.4331	0.5669	50	40	9.5859	9.9651	9.6208	0.3792	20
20	9.4223	9.9843	9.4381	0.5619	40	50	9.5889	9.9646	9.6243	0.3757	10
30	9.4269	9.9839	9.4430	0.5570	30	23° 0'	9.5919	9.9640	9.6279	0.3721	67° 0'
40	9.4314	9.9836	9.4479	0.5521	20	10	9.5948	9.9635	9.6314	0.3686	50
50	9.4359	9.9832	9.4527	0.5473	10	20	9.5978	9.9629	9.6348	0.3652	40
16° 0'	9.4403	9.9828	9.4575	0.5425	74° 0'	30	9.6007	9.9624	9.6383	0.3617	30
10	9.4447	9.9825	9.4622	0.5378	50	40	9.6036	9.9618	9.6417	0.3583	20
20	9.4491	9.9821	9.4669	0.5331	40	50	9.6065	9.9613	9.6452	0.3548	10
30	9.4533	9.9817	9.4716	0.5284	30	24° 0'	9.6093	9.9607	9.6486	0.3514	66° 0'
40	9.4576	9.9814	9.4762	0.5238	20	10	9.6121	9.9602	9.6520	0.3480	50
50	9.4618	9.9810	9.4808	0.5192	10	20	9.6149	9.9596	9.6553	0.3447	40
17° 0'	9.4659	9.9806	9.4853	0.5147	73° 0'	30	9.6177	9.9590	9.6587	0.3413	30
10	9.4700	9.9802	9.4898	0.5102	50	40	9.6205	9.9584	9.6620	0.3380	20
20	9.4741	9.9798	9.4943	0.5057	40	50	0.6232	9.9570	9.6654	0.3346	10
30	9.4781	9.9794	9.4987	0.5013	30	25° 0'	9.6259	9.9573	9.6687	0.3313	65° 0'
40	9.4821	9.9790	9.5031	0.4969	20	10	9.6286	9.9567	9.6720	0.3280	50
50	9.4861	9.9786	9.5075	0.4925	10	20	9.6313	9.9561	9.6752	0.3248	40
18° 0'	9.4900	9.9782	9.5118	0.4882	72° 0'	30	9.6340	9.9555	9.6785	0.3215	30
10	9.4939	9.9778	9.5161	0.4839	50	40	9.6366	9.9549	9.6817	0.3183	20
20	9.4977	9.9774	9.5203	0.4797	40	50	9.6392	9.9543	9.6850	0.3150	10
30	9.5015	9.9770	9.5245	0.4755	30	26° 0'	9.6418	9.9537	9.6882	0.3118	64° 0'
40	9.5052	9.9765	9.5287	0.4713	20	10	9.6444	9.9530	9.6914	0.3086	50
50	9.5090	9.9761	9.5329	0.4671	10	20	9.6470	9.9524	9.6946	0.3054	40
19° 0'	9.5126	9.9757	9.5370	0.4630	71° 0'	30	9.6495	9.9518	9.6977	0.3023	30
10	9.5163	9.9752	9.5411	0.4589	50	40	9.6521	9.9512	9.7009	0.2991	20
20	9.5199	9.9748	9.5451	0.4549	40	50	9.6546	9.9505	9.7040	0.2960	10
30	9.5235	9.9743	9.5491	0.4509	30	27° 0'	9.6570	9.9499	9.7072	0.2928	63° 0'
40	9.5270	9.9739	9.5531	0.4469	20	10	9.6595	9.9492	9.7103	0.2897	50
50	9.5306	9.9734	9.5571	0.4429	10	20	9.6620	9.9486	9.7134	0.2866	40
20° 0'	9.5341	9.9730	9.5611	0.4389	70° 0'	30	9.6644	9.9479	9.7165	0.2835	30
10	9.5375	9.9725	9.5650	0.4350	50	40	9.6668	9.9473	9.7196	0.2804	20
20	9.5409	9.9721	9.5689	0.4311	40	50	9.6692	9.9466	9.7226	0.2774	10
30	9.5443	9.9716	9.5727	0.4273	30	28° 0'	9.6716	9.9459	9.7257	0.2743	62° 0'
40	9.5477	9.9711	9.5766	0.4234	20	10	9.6740	9.9453	9.7287	0.2713	50
50	9.5510	9.9706	9.5804	0.4196	10	20	9.6763	9.9446	9.7317	0.2683	40
21° 0'	9.5543	9.9702	9.5842	0.4158	69° 0'	30	9.6787	9.9439	9.7348	0.2652	30
10	9.5576	9.9697	9.5879	0.4121	50	40	9.6810	9.9432	9.7378	0.2622	20
20	9.5609	9.9692	9.5917	0.4083	40	50	3.6833	9.9425	9.7408	0.2592	10
30	9.5641	9.9687	9.5954	0.4046	30	29° 0'	9.6856	9.9418	9.7438	0.2562	61° 0'
40	9.5673	9.9682	9.5991	0.4009	20	10	9.6878	9.9411	9.7467	0.2533	50
50	9.5704	9.9677	9.6028	0.3972	10	20	3.6901	9.9404	9.7497	0.2503	40
22° 0'	9.5736	9.9672	9.6064	0.3936	68° 0'	30	9.6923	9.9397	9.7526	0.2474	30
10	9.5767	9.9667	9.6100	0.3900	50	40	9.6946	9.9390	9.7556	0.2444	20
20	9.5798	9.9661	9.6136	0.3864	40	50	9.6968	9.9383	9.7585	0.2415	10
30	9.5828	9.9656	9.6172	0.3828	30	30° 0'	9.6990	9.9375	9.7614	0.2386	60° 0'
Angle	log Cos	log Sin	log Ctn	log Tan	Angle	Angle	log Cos	log Sin	log Ctn	log Tan	Angle

LOGARITHMS OF TRIGONOMETRIC FUNCTIONS

Angle	log Sin	log Cos	log Tan	log Ctn	Angle
30° 0'	9.6990	9.9375	9.7614	0.2386	60° 0'
10	9.7012	9.9368	9.7644	0.2356	50
20	9.7033	9.9361	9.7673	0.2327	40
30	9.7055	9.9353	9.7701	0.2299	30
40	9.7076	9.9346	9.7730	0.2270	20
50	9.7097	9.9338	9.7759	0.2241	10
31° 0'	9.7118	9.9331	9.7788	0.2212	59° 0'
10	9.7139	9.9323	9.7816	0.2184	50
20	9.7160	9.9315	9.7845	0.2155	40
30	9.7181	9.9308	9.7873	0.2127	30
40	9.7201	9.9300	9.7902	0.2098	20
50	9.7222	9.9292	9.7930	0.2070	10
32° 0'	9.7242	9.9284	9.7958	0.2042	58° 0'
10	9.7262	9.9276	9.7986	0.2014	50
20	9.7282	9.9268	9.8014	0.1986	40
30	9.7302	9.9260	9.8042	0.1958	30
40	9.7322	9.9252	9.8070	0.1930	20
50	9.7342	9.9244	9.8097	0.1903	10
33° 0'	9.7361	9.9236	9.8125	0.1875	57° 0'
10	9.7380	9.9228	9.8153	0.1847	50
20	9.7400	9.9219	9.8180	0.1820	40
30	9.7419	9.9211	9.8208	0.1792	30
40	9.7438	9.9203	9.8235	0.1765	20
50	9.7457	9.9194	9.8263	0.1737	10
34° 0'	9.7476	9.9186	9.8290	0.1710	56° 0'
10	9.7494	9.9177	9.8317	0.1683	50
20	9.7513	9.9169	9.8344	0.1656	40
30	9.7531	9.9160	9.8371	0.1629	30
40	9.7550	9.9151	9.8398	0.1602	20
50	9.7568	9.9142	9.8425	0.1575	10
35° 0'	9.7586	9.9134	9.8452	0.1548	55° 0'
10	9.7604	9.9125	9.8479	0.1521	50
20	9.7622	9.9116	9.8506	0.1494	40
30	9.7640	9.9107	9.8533	0.1467	30
40	9.7657	9.9098	9.8559	0.1441	20
50	9.7675	9.9089	9.8586	0.1414	10
36° 0'	9.7692	9.9080	9.8613	0.1387	54° 0'
10	9.7710	9.9070	9.8639	0.1361	50
20	9.7727	9.9061	9.8666	0.1334	40
30	9.7744	9.9052	9.8692	0.1308	30
40	9.7761	9.9042	9.8718	0.1282	20
50	9.7778	9.9033	9.8745	0.1255	10
37° 0'	9.7795	9.9023	9.8771	0.1229	53° 0'
10	9.7811	9.9014	9.8797	0.1203	50
20	9.7828	9.9004	9.8824	0.1176	40
30	9.7844	9.8995	9.8850	0.1150	30
Angle	log Cos	log Sin	log Ctn	log Tan	Angle

Angle	log Sin	log Cos	log Tan	log Ctn	Angle
37°30'	9.7844	9.8995	9.8850	0.1150	52°30'
40	9.7861	9.8985	9.8876	0.1124	20
50	9.7877	9.8975	9.8902	0.1098	10
38° 0'	9.7893	9.8965	9.8928	0.1072	52° 0'
10	9.7910	9.8955	9.8954	0.1046	50
20	9.7926	9.8945	9.8980	0.1020	40
30	9.7941	9.8935	9.9006	0.0994	30
40	9.7957	9.8925	9.9032	0.0968	20
50	9.7973	9.8915	9.9058	0.0942	10
39° 0'	9.7989	9.8905	9.9084	0.0916	51° 0'
10	9.8004	9.8895	9.9110	0.0890	50
20	9.8020	9.8884	9.9135	0.0865	40
30	9.8035	9.8874	9.9161	0.0839	30
40	9.8050	9.8864	9.9187	0.0813	20
50	9.8066	9.8853	9.9212	0.0788	10
40° 0'	9.8081	9.8843	9.9238	0.0762	50° 0'
10	9.8096	9.8832	9.9264	0.0736	50
20	9.8111	9.8821	9.9289	0.0711	40
30	9.8125	9.8810	9.9315	0.0685	30
40	9.8140	9.8800	9.9341	0.0659	20
50	9.8155	9.8789	9.9366	0.0634	10
41° 0'	9.8169	9.8778	9.9392	0.0608	49° 0'
10	9.8184	9.8767	9.9417	0.0583	50
20	9.8198	9.8756	9.9443	0.0557	40
30	9.8213	9.8745	9.9468	0.0532	30
40	9.8227	9.8733	9.9494	0.0506	20
50	9.8241	9.8722	9.9519	0.0481	10
42° 0'	9.8255	9.8711	9.9544	0.0456	48° 0'
10	9.8269	9.8699	9.9570	0.0430	50
20	9.8283	9.8688	9.9595	0.0405	40
30	9.8297	9.8676	9.9621	0.0379	30
40	9.8311	9.8665	9.9646	0.0354	20
50	9.8324	9.8653	9.9671	0.0329	10
43° 0'	9.8338	9.8641	9.9697	0.0303	47° 0'
10	9.8351	9.8629	9.9722	0.0278	50
20	9.8365	9.8618	9.9747	0.0253	40
30	9.8378	9.8606	9.9772	0.0228	30
40	9.8391	9.8594	9.9798	0.0202	20
50	9.8405	9.8582	9.9823	0.0177	10
44° 0'	9.8418	9.8569	9.9848	0.0152	46° 0'
10	9.8431	9.8557	9.9874	0.0126	50]
20	9.8444	9.8545	9.9899	0.0101	40
30	9.8457	9.8532	9.9924	0.0076	30
40	9.8469	9.8520	9.9949	0.0051	20
50	9.8482	9.8507	9.9975	0.0025	10
45° 0'	9.8495	9.8495	0.0000	0.0000	45° 0'
Angle	log Cos	log Sin	log Ctn	log Tan	Angle

Index

Abel, 394
Abscissa, 111
Absolute inequalities, 250
Absolute value, 2, 478
Addition, algebraic, 2
  of fractions, 82, 86
  of like terms, 11
  of polynomials, 12
  of radicals, 194
  of signed numbers, 3
Addition-subtraction method, 121
Age problems, 32, 107
Algebra, structure of, 480
  sets and, 480
Algebraic expressions, 7, 10
Algebraic terms, 7
Analytic geometry, 419
Angles, 358
  cosine of, 360
  cotangent of, 361
  finding, 366, 372
  sine of, 360
  tangent of, 361
Antilogarithms, 335
Area of triangle, 422
Arithmetic mean(s), 301
Arithmetic progressions, 297, 318
  last term of, 299
  problems in, 305, 318
  terms of, 301
Arithmetic series, 303
  sum of, 303
Associative law, 478
Average deviation, 440
Axes, coordinate, 110
  ellipse, 268
  hyperbola, 271
Axioms, 24, 217
  of inequalities, 250, 252
Axis of parabola, 261
Axis of symmetry, 261

Base, of logarithm, 323
  of exponent, 323
Binomial(s), common factor, 49
  factoring, 62
  multiplying, 47
  products of, 45
  radicals, square root of, 204
  squaring, 46
Binomial theorem, 383
  applying, 386
  expanding, 393
  finding a term, 389
  numerical approximation, 393
  proof of, 385
Brackets, 16
Briggs, Henry, 330

Cancellation, 77
Cartesian set, 472
Cauchy, 207
Central tendency, 440
Chapter review, 21, 41, 72, 92, 108, 153, 171, 188, 211, 240, 258, 276, 294, 321, 356, 380, 395, 416, 442
Character of roots, 243
Characteristic of logarithms, 327
Check in equations, 97
Circle(s), 266
  equation of, 266, 421
  imaginary, 276
  point, 276
Clearing of fractions, 96
Closure, 478
Coefficient(s), 9
Coin problems, 34
Combination problems, 134
Combinations, 405
  equal, 407
  formulas, 406
  problems in, 410
Common difference, 297

Common factor, binomial, 49
  monomial, 47
Common fractions, 317
Common logarithms, 325
Common ratio, 308
Commutative law, 479
Complete factoring, 63
Complete quadratic equation, 215
Completing the square, 219, 231
Complex fractions, 89
Complex numbers, 206, 208
Compound interest, 347
Conditional equation, 23
Conditional inequalities, 250
Conic sections, 274
Conjugate radicals, 202
Consecutive integers, 31, 106
Constant term, 115
Coordinates, 111
Coordinate system, 110
Cosine(s), 360
Cotangent(s), 361
Cube root, 61
Cube(s), 44
  difference between, 61
  sum of, 61
Cumulative frequency curve, 438
  quartiles in, 438
Cumulative review, 41, 72, 93, 109, 154,
    172, 188, 211, 241, 258, 277, 296,
    322, 356, 381, 395, 417, 443

Data, experimental, 429
  ordering, 432
  straight line, 429
Degree of equation, 24, 214
Denominator, rationalizing, 201
Dependent linear equations, 121
Descartes, René, 207
Determinant(s)
  area of triangle by, 422
  diagonal of, 142
  elements of, 142
  evaluating, 143
  expanded, 143
  order, 142
    second, 143
    third, 148
  solving equations by, 146
  term of, 143
Deviation, 440
Difference, of cubes, 61
  of squares, 55
Digit problems, 132, 292

Dimbo, doings of, 13, 60, 127, 153,
    188, 205, 234, 289, 345, 374, 411
Direct variation, 164
Discriminant, 243
Dividend, 15
Division
  of fractions, 80
  by logarithms, 338, 341
  of monomials, 15, 19
  of polynomials, 19
  of radicals, 197, 200
  of signed numbers, 6
  by slide rule, 353
  synthetic, 65
  by zero, 24, 96
Divisor, 15
Domain, of relation, 475
  of variable, 467
Dürer, magic square, 107

Element(s), of a determinant, 142
  identity, 479
  inverse, 479
  of sets, 467
Elimination, by addition-subtraction, 121
  by substitution, 122
Ellipse, 268
  imaginary, 276
  point, 276
Equation(s), 23
  check in, 97
  conditional, 23
  from data, 429
  decimal, 25, 26
  degree of, 24, 214
  dependent, 121
  equivalent, 95
  exponential, 324, 345
  first degree, 23, 26, 49, 112
  forming, 248
  fractional, 95, 98
  inconsistent, 120
  of line, 423, 428
  linear, 115, 117, 279, 280, 282
  literal, 26, 49, 98, 126, 225
  member of, 23
  quadratic, 58, 214, 219, 224,
    225, 227, 260, 279, 282, 284
  in quadratic form, 239
  radical, 209, 238
  root of, 23, 222, 227, 243
  simultaneous, 119, 121, 126, 128
  in two variables, 472
  types of, 121
Euler, Leonard, 207, 394

Evaluating, algebraic expressions, 10
  formulas, 27
  power of i, 206
  radicals, 220
Examination, review 1, 457
  review 2, 462
Exchange problems, 128
Experimental data, 429
Exponent(s), 9
  base of, 323
  fractional, 180
  laws of, 174
  negative, 179
  zero, 179
Expressions, algebraic, 7
  evaluating, 10
  exponential, 181, 183
  mixed, 88
Extremes of proportion, 160

Factor, 9
  common binomial, 49
  common monomial, 47
Factorial notation, 388
Factoring, 47
  binomials, 62
  complete, 63
  difference between cubes, 61
  difference between squares, 55
  by grouping, 51
  solving quadratic equations by, 58
  sum of two cubes, 61
  trinomials, 52, 54
Factor theorem, 70
First-degree equations, 23, 26, 49, 112, 120
Flashback, 88, 106, 164, 187, 207, 274,
  306, 330, 366, 394
Focus, ellipse, 268
  hyperbola, 270
Formula, quadratic, 221
Formulas, 27
  evaluating, 27, 343
  geometric, 234, 344
  solving, 27, 344
Fourth proportional, 160
Fractional equations, 95, 99
  simultaneous, 124
Fractional exponent, 180
Fractions, adding, 82
  algebraic, 74
  complex, 89
  dividing, 80
  equivalent, 85
  fundamental principles of, 74
  multiplying, 79

Fractions — *continued*
  reduced to lowest terms, 77
  signs of, 75
  subtracting, 82
Frequency distribution, 434
Frequency polygon, 436
Function(s), quadratic, 227
  sets and, 476
  trigonometric, 359, 362, 366, 370, 489,
    492
  value, 68
Fundamental operations, 2
Fundamental principles, 397
  to combinations, 409
  to fractions, 74

Gauss, Karl Friedrich, 306
Geometric mean(s), 311
Geometric progressions, 297, 308, 314
  infinite, 317
  last term of, 309
  problems in, 318
Geometric series, 312
  infinite, 315, 317
  sum of, 312
Geometry problems, 232
Googol, 187
Googolplex, 187
Graph(s), of circle, 266, 274
  of ellipse, 268, 274
  first-degree equations, 112
  of functions, 477
  of hyperbola, 271, 274
  linear equations, 112, 115, 117, 118, 280
  of logarithmic function, 333
  parabola, 263, 266, 274
  quadratic function, 227
  of relations, 475–476
  of solution sets, 468
  solving for imaginary roots, 229
  solving for inequalities, 254
  in solving linear and quadratic
    equations, 282
  in solving problems, 150
  in solving a quadratic equation, 229,
    231
  in solving simultaneous linear equations,
    119
  in solving simultaneous quadratic
    equations, 283
Greek mathematicians, 274
Grouping, factoring by, 51, 57
  symbols of, 16
Grouping terms, 51
Groups, 479

Handwriting, importance of, vii
Horizontal axis, 110
Hyperbola, 270

i, powers of, 206
Identity, 23
Identity element, 479
Imaginary numbers, 206, 208
Imaginary unit, 205
Inconsistent equations, 120
Index of a radical, 190
Index of a root, 44
Inequalities, 242
    absolute, 250
    axioms of, 250, 252
    conditional, 250
    first-degree, 251
    second-degree, 252, 255
    solving by graphs, 254
    in two variables, 474
Infinite geometric series, 315
    line demonstration of, 316
    sum of, 315, 317
Integer problems, 106
Integers, consecutive, 31
Intercept form, 424
Intercepts, 114
Interpolation, 334, 370, 375
Intersection of sets, 470
Inverse element, 479
Inverse variation, 166, 168
Investment problems, 36, 135, 293
Irrational numbers, 200

Joint variation, 168
Just for fun, 4, 142, 198, 370

Lattice of points, 473
Law, associative, 478
    commutative, 479
    of exponents, 174
    of signs, 3, 4, 5, 6, 44
    of sines, 378
Lever problems, 39, 40
Like radicals, 194
Like terms, 10
Line, straight, 113
    distance between points, 420
    equation of, 113, 117, 424, 425
    slope of, 117, 424
Linear equations, 115, 121
    dependent, 121
    inconsistent, 120
    parameters of, 427
    quadratic and, 279
    slope of graph of, 117

Linear equations — *continued*
    slope-intercept form of, 117
    systems in three unknowns, 148
    writing, 428
Linear and quadratic equations
    solved graphically, 280
Literal equations, 49, 126, 225
Literal numbers, 1, 98
Locating points, 111, 472
Logarithm(s), base of, 323
    characteristic of, 327
    common, 325
    definition of, 324
    in evaluating formulas, 343
    finding powers by, 339–341
    finding products by, 336
    finding quotient by, 338, 341
    finding roots by, 339, 341
    invention of, 330
    meaning of, 323
    need of, 323
    tables of mantissa(s) of, 487
    of trigonometric functions, 375, 492
Logarithmic curve, 333
Logarithmic equations, 324, 345
Lowest common denominator, 83, 88

Magic square, 107
Mantissa(s) of logarithm, 327, 330
    table of, 487
Mathematical vocabulary, 211, 355, 442
Mean(s), arithmetic, 301
    geometric, 311
    of proportion, 160
Mean proportional, 160
Median, finding, 432
Member of equation, 23
Mixed expressions, 88
Mixture problems, 103
Monomial(s), common factor, 47
    in division, 15
    in multiplication, 14
    powers of, 43
    roots of, 43
Motion problems, 101, 235, 294
Müller, John, 366
Multiple-choice test 1, 445
    test 2, 449
    test 3, 453
Multiplication, of binomials, 47
    of fractions, 79
    law of signs, 5
    by logarithms, 327, 341
    magic square, 107
    of monomials, 14, 18

Multiplication — *continued*
  of polynomials, 18
  of radicals, 195, 199
  of signed numbers, 5
  by slide rule, 353

Napier, John, 330
Nature of roots, quadratic equation, 243
Negative exponent, 179
Negative number, 2
Newton, Isaac, 394
Number(s), addition of, 2
  complex, 206, 208
  cube of, 44
  division of, 6, 7
  imaginary, 200, 206, 208
  irrational, 200
  literal, 1, 98
  multiplication of, 5
  negative, 2
  ordered pairs of, 472
  positive, 2
  problems, 28, 131, 232, 235, 289, 293
  rational, 200
  real, 200
  representing, 28
  signed, 2
  standard notation, 185, 327
  standard position, 327
  subtraction of, 4
  used in algebra, 1
Numerical approximation, 393
Numerical coefficient, 9

Oblique triangles, solving, 377
Odds, 413
Ogive, 438
Order, of a determinant, 142
  of operations, 8
  of a radical, 190
Ordered pairs, 472
Ordering data, 432
Ordinate, 111
Origin, 110

Parabola, 260
Parameters, 426
Parentheses, 16
Pascal, 394
  triangle of, 388
Permutations, 400
  circular, 404
  and combination, 410
Point(s), locating, 111, 472
  plotting, 111, 472

Point circle, 276
Point ellipse, 276
Point-slope, equation of line, 424
Polynomial(s), addition of, 12
  in division, 19
  factoring, 49, 56
    by factor theorem, 70
  in multiplication, 18
  subtracting, 12
Powers, ascending, 18
  descending, 18
  of i, 206
  in law of exponents, 174
  by logarithms, 339
  of monomials, 43
  of numbers, table of, 486
  of unity, 180
Prime factor, 63
Principal diagonal, 142
Principal square root, 44
Probability, 412
  problems in, 415
Problems, age, 32, 107
  in arithmetic progression, 305
  coin, 34
  in combination, 134, 410
  in compound interest, 347
  consecutive integers, 31, 106
  digit, 132, 292
  exchange, 128
  in fractional equations, 99
  in geometric progressions, 318
  in geometry, 232
  graphs, solving by, 150
  integers, 31, 106
  investment, 36, 135, 293
  lever, 39
  mixture, 103
  motion, 101, 235, 294
  number, 28, 131, 232, 235, 289, 293
  in probability, 415
  in quadratics, 289
  ratio, 158
  stream, 138
  work, 105, 140, 237
Product(s), of two binomials, 45
  of roots of quadratic equations, 247
  special, 43
Progressions, arithmetic, 297, 318
  geometric, 297, 314
Proportion, extremes of, 160
  means of, 160
  with slide rule, 353
  terms of, 160
Pythagorean law, 359

Quadratic equation(s), complete, 215
  defined, 214
  from roots, 248
  incomplete, 215, 217
  roots
    character of, 243
    product of, 247
    sum of, 246
  solved by completing square, 219, 231
  solved by factoring, 58, 60, 215, 231
  solved by formula, 224, 231
  solved by graphs, 227, 231
  systems of linear and, 279, 282
  systems solved algebraically, 285
  systems solved graphically, 284
  in two variables, 260
Quadratic formula, 221
Quadratic function, graph of, 227
Quadrants, 110
Quartiles, finding, 433
  from ogive, 438
Quotient, 15

Radical equations, 208, 238
Radical(s), adding, 194
  combining, 195
  conjugate, 202
  dividing, 197, 200
  evaluating, 220
  index of, 44
  like, 194
  multiplying, 195, 199
  order, 190
  similar, 194
  simplifying, 191
  subtracting, 194
  symbol, 44
Radicand(s), 190
  integral, 193
  reducing, 191
Range of relation, 475
Ratio(s), defined, 157
  trigonometric, 359
Ratio problems, 158
  with repeating decimals, 170
Rational number, 200
Rational roots, 244
Rationalizing denominators, 201
Reducing fractions, 77
Relation(s), 475
Remainder theorem, 69
Repeating decimals, 170
Review, chapter, 21, 41, 72, 92, 108, 153,
    171, 188, 211, 240, 258, 276, 294,
    321, 356, 380, 385, 416, 442

Review — continued
  cumulative, 41, 72, 93, 109, 154, 172,
    188, 211, 241, 258, 277, 296, 322,
    356, 381
Review examination(s), no. 1, 457
  no. 2, 462
Review exercises, 256
Right triangle(s), 358
  solving, 364, 367, 373
    by logarithms, 376
Roots, cube, 44
  extraneous, 97
  of first-degree equation, 23
  forming equation from, 248
  found by logarithms, 339
  index of, 44
  of monomials, 43, 190
  nature of, 243
  product of, 247
  of quadratic equations, 243
  square, 44
  sum of, 246
Rule of Three, 164

Scientific notation, 185
Set(s), 467–481
  algebraic structure and, 480
  Cartesian, 472
  elements of, 467
  equations in two variables, 473
  functions, 476
  graphing, 468–477
  groups, 479
  indicating, 467
  inequalities in two variables, 474
  intersection of, 470
  ordered pairs, 472
  relations, 475
  solution, 468
  subsets, 468
  union of, 469
  universal, 467
  variables, 467
  Venn diagrams, 470
Sequences, 297
Series, arithmetic, 303
  geometric, 312
  infinite, 315
Sextant, 366
Signed numbers, 3, 4, 5, 6
Signs of fractions, 75
Similar figures, 162
Simplification, of fractions, 89
  of radicals, 191

Simultaneous linear equations, 119
  solved by addition-subtraction, 121
  solved by determinants, 145, 148
  solved by graphs, 119
  solved by substitution, 122
  in three unknowns, 128
Simultaneous literal equations, 126
Sines, 360
  law of, 378
Slide rule, 350
Slope, of a line, 116
  slope-intercept, 117
  point-slope, 424
Soh-cah-toa, 362
Solution set, 468
Solvemini, 394
Special products, 43
Square root(s), approximate, 482
  binomial radicals, 204
  complex numbers, 207
  of monomials, 44
  principal, 44
  by slide rule, 352
  table of, 482
Square(s), of binomials, 46
  completing the, 219, 231
  factoring difference between, 55
  factoring trinomial, 54, 219
  by slide rule, 352
  table of, 486
Standard notation, 185
Statistics, 428
Straight line, fitting data to, 429
Stream problems, 138
Student, advice to, vi
Study, suggestions for, ix
Subset, 468
Substitution method, 122
Subtraction, of fractions, 82, 86
  of like terms, 11
  of polynomials, 12
  of radicals, 194
  of signed numbers, 4
Subtrahend, 4
Sum of roots, 246
Symbols of grouping, 16
Symmetry, axis of, 261
Synthetic division, 65

Table, of approximate square roots, 482
  of logarithms of trigonometric functions, 492
  of mantissas of logarithms, 331, 487
  of powers and roots, 486

Table — *continued*
  of values of trigonometric functions, 364, 489
Tangents, 361
Terms, algebraic, 7
  of a determinant, 143
  of a fraction, 77
  of grouping, 51
  like, 10
  of a proportion, 160
Tests, 91
  multiple-choice, 445, 449, 453
Theorem, binomial, 383
  factor, 70
  remainder, 69
Third proportional, 160
Transposing, 24
Triangle(s), area by determinants, 422
  oblique, 377
  right, 359
  similar, 162
Trigonometric functions, 359, 362, 366, 370, 489, 492
Trigonometry, 358, 366
Trinomials, factoring, 52
Trinomial squares, 54, 219
Turning point, parabola, 261
Two-point form, 423

Union of sets, 469

Variability, 440
  measures of, 441
Variables, 113
  equations in two, 473
  inequalities in two, 474
  in quadratic equation, 260
  sets and, 467
Variation, direct, 164, 168
  inverse, 166, 168
  joint, 168
Venn diagrams, 470
Vertex, parabola, 260
Vertical axes, 111
Vieta, 394
Vocabulary, mathematical, 211, 355, 442

Words, mathematical vocabulary, 211, 355, 442
Work problems, 105, 140, 237

Zero, division by, 24, 96
Zero exponent, 179

ANSWERS

INTERMEDIATE *Algebra*

ENLARGED EDITION

SHUTE–KLINE–SHIRK–WILLSON

AMERICAN BOOK COMPANY   *New York*

Sc. P. 765432

Answers

Page 3. — 1. 35   2. 21   3. − 21   4. − 81   5. 0   6. 4   7. 60   8. − 72

Page 4. — 9. 9   10. − 100   11. − 1   12. − 6   13. 85   14. − 4   15. 6   16. − 48
17. 0   18. 30   19. − 31   20. 1   21. − 20   22. 1   23. − 9   24. − 8

Page 5. — 1. 11   2. 57   3. − 52   4. − 50   5. 57   6. − 4   7. 29   8. − 11   9. 34
10. 0   11. − 76   12. 10   13. − 10   14. − 22   15. 53   16. − 9   17. − 68   18. − 50
19. 118   20. − 40   21. 50   22. 36   23. 80   24. 5

Page 6. — 1. − 80   2. 54   3. − 42   4. 120   5. − 150   6. − 240   7. − 90   8. − 123
9. − 76   10. 440   11. 1200   12. − 225   13. − 32   14. 30   15. − 56   16. − 27
17. 1   18. − 5   19. − 250   20. − 132   21. 52   22. 0   23. $\frac{1}{8}$ 24. − 15

Page 7. — 1. − 4   2. − 2   3. 8   4. 9   5. 4   6. − 4   7. − 9   8. − 6   9. 1   10. 40
11. − 7   12. 4   13. − 5   14. 24   15. − 4   16. 3   17. − 36   18. 36   19. − 4
20. − 5   21. 19   22. − 1   23. 0   24. 12

Page 8. — 1. binomial   2. monomial   3. trinomial   4. monomial   5. binomial
6. trinomial   7. binomial   8. binomial   9. trinomial   10. binomial   11. monomial
12. trinomial

Page 9. — 1. 21   2. − 7   3. 0   4. 11   5. 8   6. − 39   7. − 2   8. − 19   9. 13
10. 4   11. − 3   12. 23   13. 2   14. − 14   15. − 3   16. 0   17. − 90   18. − 14

Page 10. — 1. 3, 3 x 2. 1, 2, 1
1. 13   2. − 7   3. 3   4. − 9   5. − 11   6. 0

Page 11. — 1. − a 2. 8 x 3. − b 4. − 8 y 5. − 2 a 6. x 7. − 4 x^2 8. − 4 x^2
9. 2 b^2 − 3 b 10. − 5 xy^2

Page 12 — 1. 8 a − 2 b − 2 c 2. 5 x − 3 y + 4 z 3. 19 x^2 + 4
4. 6 a^3 + 2 a^2b + 5 ab^2 − 2 b^3 5. 18 x^3 − 6 x^2 + 5 x 6. 9 a − b + 4 c 7. − 3 x^2 + 6 x + 3
8. − 13 x^3 + 24 x^2 + 5 x + 4   9. 3 a^3 + 9 a^2 − 2 a + 2   10. 5 x^3 − 2 x^2y + 4 xy^2 − 2 y^3

Page 13. — 1. 5 a − 2 b − 15 c 2. 2 x − 2 y + z 3. − x^2 + 2 x + 12
4. 2 x^3 + 7 x^2 + 7 x − 8   5. a^4 − 6 a^3 + a^2 − 9 a + 19   6. 15 a^3 − 20 a^2b − 25 ab^2 − 15 b^3
7. 8 a^3 − 7 a^2b + 5 ab^2 − 20 b^3 8. − 2 x^2 + 2 x + 24   9. − 2 y^2 + 7 y 10. − 6 x − 8 y + 16

Doings of Dimbo. − 3 x^2 is − 27, not + 27.   Correct answer is − 60.

Page 15. — 1. − 48 ab 2. 30 a^3 3. − 16 x^4 4. − 21 x^3y^3 5. 4 a^5 6. 30 a^2b^2
7. 18 a^3b^2 8. 27 m^6 9. − x^4

Page 16. — 1. x^2 2. − 2 a^2 3. − 4 y 4. 2 x^6 5. − x^4y^3 6. − 3 a^5b^{10} 7. − 3 a^2
8. − 3 x 9. 24 x^2 10. − 10 r^2t

Page 17. — 1. 16 a + 2 b 2. 5 m − 6   3. 6 x − 2   4. 2 x + 11 a + 4 b 5. 6 m + 7 n
6. 2 p + 2 q − 4   7. r + s 8. − 13 a − b − 6 c 9. 15 m − 2 n 10. − 2 a

11. $3x - (y - a) - 2b$ 12. $x^2 + (-3x + 2)$ 13. $+ (a^5 - a^4 + a^3) - (a^2 - a + 1)$
14. $a^2 - (b^2 - 2bc + c^2)$ 15. $+ (ax + ay) - (bx + by)$

Page 18. — 1. $5a - 5b + 5c$ 2. $-2x^3 + x^2 - x$ 3. $2a^3 - 2a^2 - 2a$
4. $5x^3 - 20x^2 + 10x$ 5. $-2ab + 2b^2 + 2b^3$ 6. $-x^2y - x^2y^2 + xy^2$ 7. $-8a + 4b - 12c$
8. $-20a^3 + 5a^2b^2$ 9. $-3y + 4y^2 - y^3$ 10. $3x^2y - x^2y^2 + 5xy^2$ 11. $-6a^2 - 4ab + 2b^2$
12. $a^4b - 2a^3b^2 + a^2b^3$ 13. $-4x - 9$ 14. $2a$ 15. $7x - 5$

Page 19. — 1. $6x^2 - 11x - 10$ 2. $20a^2 + 7ab - 6b^2$ 3. $x^3 - 5x^2 + 11x - 15$
4. $3y^4 - 14y^3 + 8y^2 + y - 4$ 5. $x^4 + x^3 - x^2 + x - 2$ 6. $3x^4 - 2x^3 - 13x^2 + 20x - 8$
7. $4x^2 - 23x + 28$ 8. $a^3 - a^2 + a + 3$ 9. $x^4 + 3x^3 - 7x^2 - 15x + 18$
10. $-y^4 - 2y^3 + 11y^2 - 2$ 11. $a^3 - b^3$ 12. $x^2 + 2xy + y^2 - z^2$

1. $2x + y$ 2. $5x^2 - 3$ 3. $8a^3 + a$ 4. $-8a + 5b - 7c$ 5. $5x^3 - 2$ 6. $3a^2 - 5a$
7. $-9y^4 - 11y^3 + 2y^2$ 8. $xy^2 - 9y$ 9. $-3m^2 + 9m - 11$ 10. $2b^2 - 7b + 3$
11. $-3x + 1 - 5x^2y$ 12. $-3x^4 + 4x^3 - x^2 + 1$

Page 21. — 1. $3x - 2$ 2. $2x + 3$ 3. $y^2 + y + 1$ 4. $2a^3 + 3a^2 - a - 1$
5. $3x^2 + xy - y^2$ 6. $2x^2 - 3x + 1$ 7. $a^2 + ab + 2b^2 - \dfrac{b^3}{a - b}$ 8. $25a^2 + 10a + 4$
9. $4x^2 - 2xy + y^2$ 10. $3a^2 + 5b^2 - \dfrac{2b^3}{a - 2b}$ 11. $x + y$ 12. $b + c$ 13. $K^2 + K$
14. $x + y + z$ 15. $-z + y + w$ 16. $a + b + c$ 17. $2m + 3n$ 18. $-8n + 10q + 6m$
19. $a^2 + 2a - 3$ 20. $a^2 + 3ab + b^2$
1. $2x^2$ 2. x^6 3. $2, 1, 3$ 4. 2 5. -2 6. $3 - 4x$

Page 22. — 7. 13 8. 1 9. $-15x^3$ 10. $-4xy^2$ 11. (a) $6x^3 - 10x^2$ (b) $-3x^2 + 2x$
12. $-a + 2b - 9c$ 13. $-a$ 14. $3x^3 + 2x^2 - 2x + 5$ 15. $x^2 - 5x + 6$
16. $3a^2 - 2ab - b^2$ 17. $x^3 + x^2y^2 + y^3$ 18. $2c^2 + 3cd + 4d^2$

Page 25. — 1. -9 2. $-\dfrac{1}{3}$ 3. 2 4. -4 5. 1 6. $-\dfrac{2}{3}$ 7. $\dfrac{1}{2}$ 8. 1 9. -12
10. $\dfrac{22}{7}$ 11. $-\dfrac{11}{2}$ 12. $\dfrac{15}{2}$

Page 26. — 1. 2 2. 6 3. -9 4. -2 5. 5 6. 8 7. 64 8. 1 9. 3 10. 900

1. $\dfrac{b}{m}$ 2. $\dfrac{4 + a - b}{2}$ 3. $\dfrac{3 - b + c}{p}$ 4. $\dfrac{2n - m}{3}$

Page 27. — 5. $\dfrac{a + 4c}{2b}$ 6. $\dfrac{4 - a}{2a}$ 7. $\dfrac{3b - 7}{6b}$ 8. $\dfrac{7m + 6}{2m}$ 9. $-\dfrac{12}{5}$ 10. 12

1. (a) $\dfrac{A}{w}$ (b) $\dfrac{A}{l}$ (c) 31 2. (a) $\dfrac{2A}{h}$ (b) $\dfrac{2A}{b}$ (c) 4 3. (a) $\dfrac{S - 360}{180}$ (b) 2
4. (a) $\dfrac{2A}{b + b'}$ (b) 8

Page 28. — 5. (a) $\dfrac{9C + 160}{5}$ (b) 68 6. (a) $\dfrac{2S}{t^2}$ (b) 32 7. (a) $\dfrac{2gE}{v^2}$ (b) $\dfrac{Wv^2}{2E}$ (c) $\dfrac{25}{2}$
8. (a) $\dfrac{Pw}{d^2l}$ (b) $\dfrac{rd^2l}{P}$ (c) 50

1. $2x$ 2. $x + 5$ 3. $x - b$ 4. $5x$ 5. $50 - l$

Page 29. — 6. $25 - s$ 7. $l - 100$ 8. $s + 5$ 9. $\$20,000 - x$ 10. $16 - d$ 11. $b + x$
12. $x - b$

1. $6x = 3x + 2$ 2. $11x + 7 = 4x + 65$ 3. $4 + 2x = 17$ 4. $7 + 16x = 31$
5. $32x - 17 = 12 + 15x$ 6. $64 = 18 + 2x$ 7. $72 = 4x - 3$ 8. $17 + 2x = 3x - 3$

Page 30. — 9. $50 - x = 2x - 2$ 10. $2x = 12 + 50$ 11. $7 + 4x = 31$ 12. $8x - 21 = 51$
13. $3x - 10 = 78$ 14. $4x = 5 + (8 - x)$ 15. $2x = (x + 28) - 12$ 16. $3x = 44 + (x + 8)$

Page 31. — 1. $46, 50$ 2. $60, 84$ 3. $40, 52$ 4. $24, 51$ 5. $33, 55$ 6. 25
7. $15, 21$ 8. $12, 15$

Page 32. — 1. 99, 100, 101   2. 36, 38, 40   3. 61, 63, 65   4. 27, 28, 29
5. 24, 26, 28   6. 14, 16, 18   7. 29, 31, 33   8. 8, 9, 10, 11, 12

Page 33. — (The following answers are given in the same order as the blank spaces appear in the given boxes.)
1. $x - 5$ $x + 9$ 2. $6x + 6$ $6x + 11$ 3. $x - 15$ $x - 10$ 4. $x - 2$ $x + 6$
   $x - 10$ $x + 4$ $x + 6$ $x + 11$ $3x - 15$ $3x - 10$ $22 - x$ $30 - x$
5. $3x - 1$ $3x + 2$
   $x + 4$ $x + 7$

Page 34. — 1. 10 yr., 40 yr.   2. Harriet 2 yr., Ruth 8 yr.   3. 3 yr., 23 yr.
4. 22 yr., 44 yr.   5. Amy 10 yr., Howard 25 yr.   6. George 12 yr., John 38 yr.
7. Stephen 12 yr., Olin 18 yr.   8. Martha 18 yr., Kate 42 yr.

Page 35. — (The following answers are given in the same order as the blank spaces appear in the given boxes.)
1. $5x$ 2. $4.50 - 0.25x$ 3. $80 - 35x$ 4. $0.10x$
   $150 - 10x$ $0.50x$ $60x$ $0.50x + 0.75$
                                  $25x$ $1.50x - 2.00$

Page 36. — 1. 3 dimes, 3 nickels, 6 quarters   2. 3 quarters, 7 dimes, 5 nickels
3. 1 half dollar, 6 dimes, 4 nickels   4. 2 quarters, 4 half dollars, 6 dimes
5. 14 nickels, 12 half dollars, 40 dimes   6. 16 dimes, 24 nickels 7. 7 dimes,
4 nickels, 5 quarters

Page 37. — 1. $.06x$ 2. $200 - .04x$ 3. $.05x$ 4. $.195x$ 5. $500x$ 6. $.0325x$
7. $400x$ 8. $.07x$, $.0325(25,000 - x)$
(The following answers are given in the same order as the blank spaces appear in the given boxes.)

1. $0.03x$ 2. $200 - 0.04x$ 3. $0.08x$
                                 $1500 - 0.03x$

Page 38. — 4. $0.035x$
                 $0.11x + 2750$
1. \$1500 at 3 %, \$3000 at 9 %   2. \$4000 at 3 %, \$3000 at 5 %   3. \$11,800 in industry, \$8200 in real estate

Page 39. — 4. \$10,000 at 1 %, \$20,000 at 3 %, \$20,000 at 5 %   5. \$5000 at $5\frac{1}{2}$ %, \$75,000 at $3\frac{1}{2}$ %   6. \$1800 at $7\frac{1}{4}$ %, \$2900 at $4\frac{1}{2}$ %   7. \$12,000 at $5\frac{1}{2}$ %, \$15,200 at 6 %, \$22,000 at $6\frac{1}{4}$ %   8. \$1000 at 6 %, \$3000 at 8 %, \$1500 at 4 %

Page 40. — 1. 12 ft.   2. 72 lb.   3. 175 lb.   4. $623\frac{1}{3}$ lb.   5. 60 lb. boy sits 4 ft. from fulcrum, 40 lb. boy sits 6 ft. from fulcrum   6. 1 ft.   7. 80 lb.

Page 41. — 1. 3 2. 1 3. $\frac{1}{2}$ 4. -1 5. $\dfrac{P}{4q}$ 6. $x = 15 + (12 - x)$ 7. $81 + x = 12 - x$
8. 8   9. 45, 3   10. Daughter is 8 yr., mother is 28 yr.   11. 80 lb.   12. 3 quarters, 6 nickels, 12 dimes   13. \$12,000 at $6\frac{1}{2}$ %, \$8000 at $3\frac{1}{2}$ %   14. 45, 47, 49
1. $2x^2 + 14x - 11$ 2. -68

Page 42. — 3. $3a^4b^2 - 18a^3b^3 + 6a^2b^4 - 12ab^5$ 4. $x - y$ 5. $-2a + b$ 6. $-\frac{1}{2}$
7. $-\dfrac{bc}{10}$ 8. -7 9. $x + 25 = 44 - 2x$ 10. $3x - 11$ 11. 1 quarter, 5 dimes, 9 nickels   12. \$7500 in bonds, \$15,000 in savings bank

Page 45. — 1. $16x^2$ 2. $9b^4$ 3. $36a^2$ 4. $-8y^3$ 5. $-8x^6y^3$ 6. $-32x^{15}$ 7. $16a^4b^8$
8. $-32c^{10}d^5$ 9. $\pm 10x$ 10. $-2b$ 11. $9r^2s^3$ 12. $3mn^3$ 13. $a - b$ 14. $-5x^4y^5$

Page 46. — 1. $9a^2 - 4b^2$ 2. $x^2 - 9y^2$ 3. $p^2 - q^2$ 4. $16r^2 - s^2$ 5. $x^2 - y^2$
6. $x^2 - 16$ 7. $4c^2d^2 - 9$ 8. $9\pi^2 - 1$ 9. $a^4 - b^2$ 10. $9a^4b^2 - 49$ 11. $\frac{1}{4}r^2s^4 - \frac{1}{9}$
12. $0.25c^4d^6 - 1$

1. $m^2 + 2mn + n^2$ 2. $a^2 - 2ab + b^2$ 3. $p^2 + 2pq + q^2$ 4. $r^2 + 2rs + s^2$
5. $c^2 - 2cd + d^2$ 6. $4a^2 + 4a + 1$ 7. $1 - 6b + 9b^2$ 8. $9x^2 + 6xy + y^2$
9. $4x^2 - 4xy + y^2$ 10. $a^2 - 4ab + 4b^2$ 11. $4m^2 - 12mn + 9n^2$ 12. $9p^2 + 12pq + 4q^2$

Page 47. — 1. $x^2 + 5x + 6$ 2. $y^2 - 7y + 6$ 3. $a^2 - a - 12$ 4. $4x^2 - 20x - 11$
5. $2x^2 + 5x - 25$ 6. $xa - xb + ya - yb$ 7. $35 + 2y - y^2$ 8. $2x^2 + 5x - 12$
9. $6ab - 4ay + 3bx - 2xy$ 10. $3x^2 + 5xy - 2y^2$ 11. $12x^2 + 20xy - 25y^2$
12. $25x^2 - 5xy - 6y^2$ 13. $63 - 10x - 8x^2$ 14. $a^4 - 3a^2c + 6a^2b - 18bc$
15. $a^2b^4 - ab^2 - 2$ 16. $x^3 + 3x^2 - 2x - 6$ 17. $12x^2 - 2x - 30$ 18. $60x^2 + 10xy - 350y^2$

Page 48. — 1. $a(x + y)$ 2. $x(a - b)$ 3. $m(n + p)$ 4. $r(s - t)$ 5. $2(a + b)$
6. $3(x + y - z)$ 7. $x(a - b + c)$ 8. $2a(m + n + p)$ 9. $4(1 + 2a + 3b)$
10. $5(5x - 2y + 1)$ 11. $3(3c + 2d - e)$ 12. $10(1 - 2r + 3s)$

1. $6(x - 2y)$ 2. $a(b + c)$ 3. $\pi(R^2 + r^2)$ 4. $5(2a - 5b + c)$ 5. $x(1 + y)$
6. $b(1 - ab)$

Page 49. — 7. $7(1 - 2x + x^3)$ 8. $2\pi r(h + r)$ 9. $4c^2d^2(2d + 5c)$
10. $13y^2(3y^2 - 5y - 1)$ 11. $xy(-x^2y + x - y^2)$ 12. $2ac(1 + 2a - 3c)$
13. $14c(c^2 - 3c + 4)$ 14. $3z(-2xy - 5yz - 4xz)$ 15. $2xy^2(3x - 6y - 2x^2)$
16. $a^2x^4y^2(a^3y^2 + x^3 + axy^4)$ 17. $5a^2b^2(4 - 2a + 3a^3b^2)$ 18. $3a(a - 3b + 6c - 2)$

1. $\dfrac{7a - b}{3}$ 2. $\dfrac{5a}{a + b}$ 3. $\dfrac{a^2}{a - b}$ 4. $\dfrac{a}{2a - b}$ 5. $\dfrac{b + a}{b - a}$ 6. $\dfrac{a}{1 - a}$ 7. $-\dfrac{2ab}{a - b}$ 8. $\dfrac{3a - b^2}{a - b}$
9. $\dfrac{c^2 - a}{c - 1}$ 10. $\dfrac{a + rl}{1 - r}$ 11. $\dfrac{a - l}{1 - n}$ 12. $\dfrac{ar^n - a}{a - r}$

Page 51. — 1. $(x + y)(2 - a)$ 2. $(a + 2b)(2x - y)$ 3. $(x^2 + y)(a + 1)$
4. $(y^2 + 3)(1 - x)$ 5. $(5x + 6)(2a - 3b)$ 6. $(a - b)(x - y)$ 7. $(y - 1)(2a + b)$
8. $(x + 1)(a + b + 1)$ 9. $(2a - 1)(3 - x - y)$ 10. $(x + 2)(a + b + c)$
11. $(2x^3 - 3)(a - 2b + 2)$ 12. $(x - y)(x + y - 1)$ 13. $(x + 1)(2a + 1)$
14. $(c + d)(ab - 1)$

Page 52. — 1. $(a + b)(y + x)$ 2. $(a - b)(y + x)$ 3. $(a - b)(x - y)$ 4. $(x - y)(2a - 3)$
5. $(4a - 3b)(x - y)$ 6. $(3x - 5y)(3x - 1)$ 7. $(a - b)(a - 1)$ 8. $(4a - 3b)(2x - 5y)$
9. $(2a - 3b)(3r + 2s)$ 10. $(5a - 2b)(3x - 7y)$ 11. $(2xy + a)(3b - 1)$
12. $(3y^2 - 1)(5x^2 + 1)$

Page 53. — 1. $(x + 2)(x + 1)$ 2. $(x - 3)(x - 1)$ 3. $(m + 1)(m + 8)$ 4. $(p - 3)(p - 4)$
5. $(r + 2)(r + 7)$ 6. $(x - 2y)(x - y)$ 7. $(3 - y)(2 - y)$ 8. $(5 - s)(3 - s)$
9. $(8 - t)(5 - t)$ 10. $(6 + y)(5 + y)$ 11. $(2 - y)(9 - y)$ 12. $(m - 6n)(m - n)$
13. $(x - 5)(x + 1)$ 14. $(y - 9)(y + 4)$ 15. $(m - 9)(m + 3)$ 16. $(x + 10y)(x - 2y)$
17. $(4y + x)(10y - x)$ 18. $(7p + q)(4p - q)$

1. $(x + 2)(x + 3)$ 2. $(x - 7)(x - 1)$ 3. $(y - 5)(y - 2)$ 4. $(a - 5b)(a - 4b)$
5. $(y - 3)(y + 2)$ 6. $(a - 8)(a + 3)$ 7. $(3m - 1)(2m - 1)$ 8. $(5p - 1)(2p + 1)$
9. $(2x + 1)(x + 2)$ 10. $(4a - 3)(a - 2)$ 11. $(3y + 7)(y - 2)$ 12. $(3z - 4)(z + 2)$

Page 54. — 13. $y(2y - 1)(y + 3)$ 14. $2(2y + 3)(y - 2)$ 15. $(1 - y)(1 - y)$
16. $(5b - 2)(b + 3)$ 17. $(8x - 5)(3x + 1)$ 18. $(5a - 4)(2a + 3)$ 19. $(5x + 1)(4x - 3)$
20. $(y - 6)(-y - 3)$ 21. $3y(5x - 1)(x + 3)$ 22. $4(s - 9)(s - 4)$ 23. $(4a - 1)(9a + 2)$
24. $y(2x + 9z)(x + 3z)$ 25. $(5 - 3a)(1 + 9a)$ 26. $(5a - 6b)(3a + 2b)$
27. $(x + y - 5)(x + y + 3)$ 28. $(3a + 3b - 1)(a + b - 2)$ 29. $(ya - 4)(ya - 5)$
30. $(3x^n + 1)(x^n + 4)$

1. $(a + b)^2$ 2. $(x - y)^2$ 3. $(c + d)^2$ 4. $(m - n)^2$ 5. $(a + 1)^2$ 6. $(b - 1)^2$ 7. $(x + 2)^2$
8. $(m + 3)^2$ 9. $(y - 2)^2$ 10. $(y - 3)^2$ 11. $(a + 4)^2$ 12. $(b - 4)^2$

Page 55. — 1. $(3x + 4)^2$ 2. $(2y - 1)^2$ 3. $(3a - 5b)^2$ 4. $9(2m + n)^2$ 5. $(5a - 2b)^2$
6. $(2b - 7c)^2$ 7. $(8x + 9y)^2$ 8. $(1 - 10t)^2$ 9. $(4x + 3y)^2$ 10. $(7x^2 - 4y)^2$
11. $(6r - 5t)^2$ 12. $(x + .2)^2$

Page 56. — 1. $(m - n)(m + n)$ 2. $(x - y)(x + y)$ 3. $(p - q)(p + q)$ 4. $(x - 5)(x + 5)$
5. $(m - 3)(m + 3)$ 6. $(3r - 4s)(3r + 4s)$ 7. $(2a - 3b)(2a + 3b)$
8. $(4x - 5y)(4x + 5y)$ 9. $(7a - 6b)(7a + 6b)$ 10. $(9x - 8y)(9x + 8y)$

1. $(a - 3bc)(a + 3bc)$ 2. $4(3x - 5yz)(3x + 5yz)$ 3. $(2 - abc)(2 + abc)$
4. $(10a - x^2)(10a + x^2)$ 5. $2(4a - 5b)(4a + 5b)$ 6. $(a^7 - 9)(a^7 + 9)$
7. $(9b^4 - 7c^4)(9b^4 + 7c^4)$ 8. $3(x - 4)(x + 4)$ 9. $(3a^2 - b^3)(3a^2 + b^3)$
10. $5(x - 2)(x + 2)(x^2 + 4)$ 11. $2x^2y(2x - y)(2x + y)$ 12. $3ab^2(3a - 2b)(3a + 2b)$
13. $(.7 - .2x)(.7 + .2x)$ 14. $(x^a - 8)(x^a + 8)$ 15. $(1.1x^3 - 1.3y^{2a})(1.1x^3 + 1.3y^{2a})$

Page 57. — 1. $(a + b - 2)(a + b + 2)$ 2. $(x - y - 3)(x - y + 3)$
3. $(2a - b - 5)(2a - b + 5)$ 4. $(a + 7 - 7b)(a + 7 + 7b)$ 5. $(m + n - 2a)(m + n + 2a)$
6. $(p + q - 8r)(p + q + 8r)$ 7. $(r - s - 9)(r - s + 9)$ 8. $(x + y - 10)(x + y + 10)$
9. $(2a - b - 11)(2a - b + 11)$ 10. $(a + 2b - 12)(a + 2b + 12)$
11. $(5 - a - b)(5 + a + b)$ 12. $(4 - x + y)(4 + x - y)$

1. $(3 - x - y)(3 + x + y)$ 2. $(a - b - x)(a - b + x)$ 3. $(2a - x + y)(2a + x - y)$
4. $(2a - b - c)(2a - b + c)$ 5. $(1 - a - b)(1 + a + b)$ 6. $(a - b + c)(a + b - c)$
7. $(m - n - r)(m - n + r)$ 8. $(2x - 3a - 2b)(2x + 3a + 2b)$
9. $(3a - 2b - x - y)(3a - 2b + x + y)$ 10. $(2x - y - a + 2b)(2x - y + a - 2b)$
11. $(x + 5 - 2a + 2b)(x + 5 + 2a - 2b)$ 12. $(15a + 3b - 15x + 10y)(15a + 3b + 15x - 10y)$

Page 58. — 1. $(x + 3 - y)(x + 3 + y)$ 2. $(a - 2 - b)(a - 2 + b)$
3. $(2x - y - 1)(2x - y + 1)$ 4. $(3a - 2x - 1)(3a + 2x + 1)$ 5. $(2x - y + 2)(2x + y - 2)$
6. $(a - b + c)(a + b - c)$ 7. $(5c - a + 5b)(5c + a - 5b)$ 8. $(x - y + 3)(x + y - 3)$
9. $(1 - x - 3y)(1 + x + 3y)$ 10. $(y^2 - x - 1)(y^2 + x - 1)$

Page 60. — 1. 5, 1   2. 6, −3   3. −4, 2   4. 8, 2   5. −7, 6   6. $\frac{5}{3}$, 2   7. $-\frac{1}{3}$, 2
8. $\frac{8}{7}$, $-\frac{1}{2}$ 9. $-\frac{5}{2}$, $\frac{5}{2}$ 10. 0, $\frac{7}{6}$ 11. $\frac{5}{2}$, 4   12. $\frac{5}{2}$, −8   13. $-\frac{3}{2}$, 6   14. $\frac{7}{3}$, −2   15. 0, $\frac{5}{4}$
16. 6, 4   17. $\frac{1}{3}$, −3   18. 12, 1   19. 3, −3   20. 0, 4

Doings of Dimbo. Dimbo failed to find the common factor $(x + y)$. Answer is $(x + y)(x - y - 1)$.

Page 62. — 1. $(x - y)(x^2 + xy + y^2)$ 2. $(x + y)(x^2 - xy + y^2)$ 3. $(2b - 1)(4b^2 + 2b + 1)$
4. $x^2(1 + 3c)(1 - 3c + 9c^2)$ 5. $(4m + 5n)(16m^2 - 20mn + 25n^2)$
6. $(3c - 2d)(9c^2 + 6cd + 4d^2)$ 7. $2(2a - 5b)(4a^2 + 10ab + 25b^2)$
8. $a(ax - y)(a^2x^2 + axy + y^2)$ 9. $(2b^2 + m^2)(4b^4 - 2b^2m^2 + m^4)$
10. $(.1y - z)(.01y^2 + .1yz + z^2)$ 11. $\left(\dfrac{2}{y} - n\right)\left(\dfrac{4}{y^2} + \dfrac{2n}{y} + n^2\right)$
12. $(a + b - c)([a + b]^2 + [a + b]c + c^2)$

Page 63. — 1. $(x + y)(x^4 - x^3y + x^2y^2 - xy^3 + y^4)$ 2. $(x - y)(x^4 + x^3y + x^2y^2 + xy^3 + y^4)$
3. $(a - 1)(a^4 + a^3 + a^2 + a + 1)$ 4. $(1 - y)(1 + y + y^2 + y^3 + y^4)$ 5. $(x + 1)(x^4 - x^3 + x^2 - x + 1)$
6. $(x - y)(x^6 + x^5y + x^4y^2 + x^3y^3 + x^2y^4 + xy^5 + y^6)$
7. $(m + n)(m^6 - m^5n + m^4n^2 - m^3n^3 + m^2n^4 - mn^5 + n^6)$ 8. $(a - 1)(a^6 + a^5 + a^4 + a^3 + a^2 + a + 1)$
9. $(a + 2)(a^4 - 2a^3 + 4a^2 - 8a + 16)$ 10. $(3x - 1)(81x^4 + 27x^3 + 9x^2 + 3x + 1)$
11. $2x(2x - 1)(16x^4 + 8x^3 + 4x^2 + 2x + 1)$ 12. $2xy(3y - 1)(81y^4 + 27y^3 + 9y^2 + 3y + 1)$

Page 64. — 1. $(a - 2b)(a + 2b)$ 2. $5a^2(a - 3)(a + 3)$ 3. $(2x + 1)(x + 3)$
4. $(y + 7)(y - 5)$ 5. $(2m + 3)^2$ 6. $7(p - 4q)(p + 4q)$ 7. $3b(3b + 2)(b - 5)$
8. $(x + y - 3)(x + y + 3)$ 9. $(a + b)(x - y)$ 10. $x(a + b - c)$ 11. $(x - 6y)^2$
12. $(m - 2n)(m^2 + 2mn + 4n^2)$ 13. $9(m + n)(m^2 - mn + n^2)$ 14. $(5r - p - 2q)(5r + p + 2q)$
15. $2y(3x - 5)^2$ 16. $(3a + 1)(9a^2 - 3a + 1)$ 17. $(a + b)(x - y)$ 18. $(x + 1 - y)(x + 1 + y)$
19. $49(2bc + d^3e^2)(2bc - d^3e^2)$ 20. $x(a - 1)(a + 1)$ 21. $x(y - 4)(y + 3)$ 22. $(x - y)(m - n)$
23. $(a + 3b)(x - 2y)$ 24. $13(a + b - 2c)(a + b + 2c)$ 25. $(a - b)(a^2 + ab + b^2 - 1)$
26. $(c - a + b)(c + a - b)$ 27. $\pi(r - s)(r^2 + rs + s^2)$ 28. $3xy(3x - 5y)(3x + 5y)$
29. $2(x + 4)^2$ 30. $6(a + 2)(a + 5)$ 31. $st(s - 2)(s + 1)$ 32. $(3x - y - 2)(3x - y + 2)$

Page 65. — 33. $9(2r + 2s - 1)(2r + 2s + 1)$ 34. $(8x + 5y)(x + 2y)$
35. $(x - y)(x + y)(a + b)$ 36. $(9 + y)(8 - y)$ 37. $3(2p + 3)(p - 2)$ 38. $x(x - 2)(x + 2)(x^2 + 4)$
39. $2a(2 - 15x)(2 + 15x)$ 40. $(a - 4)^2(a + 4)^2$ 41. $a(x + by)(x^2 - xby + b^2y^2)$
42. $2(x - 2)(x + 2)(x^2 - 5)$ 43. $(4a - 7)(3a + 2)$ 44. $a(a - x)(b + x)$
45. $3y^2(y - 5)(y + 5)(y - 1)(y + 1)$ 46. $(s - p)(r - q)$ 47. $15(m - 3r)(n + 2s)$

48. $(x + y)(x - y)(x^2 + xy + y^2)$ **49.** $(x - 2)(x - 1)(x + 1)$ **50.** $a(9 + x)(8 - 3x)$
51. $(a + c)(a + 2b - c)$ **52.** $(x - 2)(x + 2)(x + 1)$ **53.** $(x + y)(1 - x - y)(1 + x + y)$
54. $(x^2 - x + 2)(x + 2)(x - 1)$ **55.** $.4ax(1 - 5x)(1 - x)$ **56.** $2b(5 + 7y)^2$ **57.** $(12y + .5)^2$
58. $(x + y)(x^4 - x^3y + x^2y^2 - xy^3 + y^4)$ **59.** $10(x - 2)(x^4 + 2x^3 + 4x^2 + 8x + 16)$
60. $(5a + 5b - 2)^2$ **61.** $a(a + 1)^2(a + 2)$ **62.** $(x + y)(x - y - 1)$ **63.** $(x + 2a)(x - y)$
64. $2(8a - 9b)^2$ **65.** $2(2x - 1)(2x + 1)(x - 3)(x + 3)$ **66.** $(a + b)(a^2 - ab + b^2 - a + b)$
67. $a(a^n - 1)(a^n + 1)$ **68.** $(4y^b + 5)(y^b - 12)$ **69.** $(xy - 3)(27nxy + 4m)$ **70.** $(x^n + y^n)^2$
71. $(x - 2)(x - 3)(x + 2)$ **72.** $x(x + 2)(x - 1)^2$ **73.** $(a - 1)(2a + 3)(a + 3)$
74. $(9x - 11y - r - s)(9x - 11y + r + s)$ **75.** $(2a + 5b)(2a + 5b + 1)$ **76.** $a^x(a + 4)(a - 1)$

Page 67. — **1.** $x^2 - 3x + 2$ **2.** $x^2 - 5x + 6$ **3.** $x^2 + 5x + 6$ **4.** $x^3 - x^2 + 3x - 6$
5. $x^2 + x - 1 + \dfrac{5}{x - 1}$ **6.** $x^2 + 5x + 13 + \dfrac{19}{x - 2}$ **7.** $3x^3 + 4x^2 + 8x + 17 + \dfrac{39}{x - 2}$
8. $-3x^2 + 2x + \dfrac{1}{x + 3}$

Page 69. — **1.** 13   **2.** 6   **3.** 6   **4.** 0   **5.** 0   **6.** -4 **7.** 18   **8.** 12

Page 71. — **1.** $(x - 1)^3$ **2.** $(x - 1)(x^2 + 2x - 1)$ **3.** $(x - 2)(x^2 - 2x - 2)$
4. $(x - 2)(x^2 + x + 2)$ **5.** $(x + 1)(x - 2)(x + 2)$ **6.** $(x - 1)(x + 2)(x^2 + 1)$
7. $(x + 2)(x + 3)(x^2 + 1)$ **8.** $(x + 2)(2x^2 + x + 1)$ **9.** $(x + 1)(x^2 + 2x + 2)$
10. $(x + 2)(x^2 - x + 1)$ **11.** $(x - 1)^2(x + 1)$ **12.** $(x + 1)(3x + 2)(x - 2)$

1. 1, 2, 3   **2.** -1, 2, 4   **3.** 1, -2, -2 **4.** 1, 4, 6   **5.** 2, 2, 2   **6.** -1, 1, 2, 3
7. 1, -2, 2, 3   **8.** -1, -2, -3 **9.** -1, 3, 4   **10.** 0, 1, 3, 5

Page 72. — **1.** $-4a^2 + 6ab - 2ac$ **2.** $9x^2 - 25$ **3.** $4y^2 - 12y + 9$ **4.** $6a^2 + 13ab - 5b^2$
5. $6x^2 - 17xy + 12y^2$ **6.** $6ab + 14a - 3b - 7$ **7.** $3x(5x^2 - 21x + 4)$ **8.** $12a^2 + 36ab + 27b^2$
9. $9x^3y - xy^3$ **10.** $3a^2b - a^2b^2 + 6ab - 2ab^2$ **11.** $4x^2 + 7xy - 17y^2$ **12.** $-49y^2 - 42xy + 42y$
13. $-2ab$ **14.** $3(x - y)(a - b)$ **15.** $(x - y)(a - b)$ **16.** $(y - 6)(y - 4)$
17. $(a - b - 1)(a - b + 1)$ **18.** $5a(a - 2b)(a^2 + 2ab + 4b^2)$ **19.** $2(3x + 1)(9x^2 - 3x + 1)$
20. $(a - 1)(x - y)(x + y)$ **21.** $(a + b - c)(a + b + c)$ **22.** $3(y - 2)(y + 2)(y^2 - 5)$
23. $(-2x + 5)(x + 3)$ **24.** $x(3 - 2x)(3 + 2x)(2 - x)(2 + x)$ **25.** $(2a + 2b + 1)(a + b - 2)$
26. $(a - b)(x + 1)^2$ **27.** $(x + y)(a - 1)(a^2 + a + 1)$ **28.** $3(x - 1)(x^4 + x^3 + x^2 + x + 1)$
29. $(x - 1)(x + 4)(x - 3)$ **30.** $\dfrac{a + b}{a - b}$ **31.** $\dfrac{2mn}{m + n}$ **32.** $-\dfrac{3}{4}$, 7   **33.** -1 **34.** 6, 2
35. -1, 2, 3   **36.** 1   **37.** -16 **38.** 9

1. $a^2 - b^2$ **2.** -7 **3.** $x^3 + 4x^2 - 2x$

Page 73. — **4.** $x^2 + xy + y^2$ **5.** 2   **6.** $7x$ **7.** $-x^3 + 6x$ **8.** $\dfrac{4ab}{a + b}$ **9.** 2
10. $x(5x - 2)(2x + 3)$ **11.** $-9, 8$ **12.** 8 nickels, 13 dimes, 16 quarters

Page 76. — **1.** 5   **2.** $-m$ **3.** $6t$ **4.** $-c$ **5.** $c + d$ **6.** $(a - b)$ **7.** $3a - b - c$
8. (6) (a) (b)   **9.** $-\dfrac{2}{a}$ **10.** $\dfrac{3}{7}$ **11.** $\dfrac{8}{c}$ **12.** $\dfrac{x}{y}$ **13.** $-\dfrac{4}{a + b}$ **14.** $\dfrac{c}{(a)(b)}$ **15.** $\dfrac{x}{3 + y}$
16. $-\dfrac{1}{(x + 2)^2}$ **17.** $\dfrac{(a)(b)(c)(d)}{x + y}$ **18.** $\dfrac{7}{a - b} + \dfrac{c}{a - b}$ **19.** $\dfrac{3m}{b^2 - c^2} - \dfrac{m - n}{b^2 - c^2}$

Page 77. — **20.** $\dfrac{r}{y - x} - \dfrac{r + t}{y - x} - \dfrac{r - t}{y - x}$ **21.** $\dfrac{8}{r - s - t} + \dfrac{2x}{r - s - t} - \dfrac{3y}{r - s - t}$
22. $\dfrac{2a}{x - a} - \dfrac{3x}{x - a}$ **23.** $\dfrac{2}{a - b + c} - \dfrac{3}{a - b + c} + \dfrac{4}{a - b + c}$
24. $\dfrac{5}{(a - b)(a + b)} + \dfrac{8}{(a - b)(a + b)} + \dfrac{2}{(a - b)(a + b)}$ **25.** $\dfrac{-4}{(x - a)^2} - \dfrac{6}{(x - a)^2} + \dfrac{3}{(x - a)^2}$

Page 78. — **1.** $\dfrac{7}{3}$ **2.** $\dfrac{2d}{c^4}$ **3.** $\dfrac{yz^8}{3}$ **4.** m **5.** -4 **6.** $\dfrac{2b - 1}{2}$ **7.** 1   **8.** $\dfrac{3(3b + 5)}{1 - b}$
9. $\dfrac{a(y - 2)}{y^2 - 2y + 4}$ **10.** $\dfrac{2y - 5}{y - 5}$

Page 79. — 11. $-y(y^2 + x^2)$ 12. $\dfrac{a+b}{c}$ 13. $y-1$ 14. $\dfrac{x+3y}{3y-x}$ 15. $\dfrac{c-8d}{d-8c}$

16. $\dfrac{3}{3a-1}$ 17. $\dfrac{2a}{3b}$ 18. $3b-2$ 19. $\dfrac{a^t}{a^t-b^r}$ 20. $x+y+z$ 21. $\dfrac{x-y}{x^4-x^3y+x^2y^2-xy^3+y^4}$

22. $\dfrac{2+c-3d}{2-c-3d}$ 23. $\dfrac{d-c}{d^2+c^2}$ 24. $-\dfrac{4a+8b+1}{2a+4b+1}$

Page 81. — 1. $\dfrac{6b}{5c^2}$ 2. $\dfrac{tw^4}{rx^3}$ 3. $\dfrac{14d^3}{3b^2}$ 4. $\dfrac{y}{8x}$ 5. $\dfrac{5m}{3}$ 6. $\dfrac{x-2y}{7x+2y}$ 7. $\dfrac{b(a-3b)}{a(a+b)}$

8. $\dfrac{a(2b+1)}{10}$ 9. $\dfrac{2(1-x)}{9(x+2)}$ 10. $\dfrac{ab(a-b)}{2a+b}$ 11. $\dfrac{x}{x-y}$ 12. $\dfrac{7}{3x-1}$ 13. $\dfrac{r^2}{(r-4t)^2}$

14. $\dfrac{2m-n}{2m+n}$

Page 82. — 15. $\dfrac{a^2(a^2-25c^2)}{b^2(a^2-36c^2)}$ 16. $-\dfrac{2}{(x+3)(x+2)}$ 17. $\dfrac{ab}{6b-a}$ 18. $\dfrac{bc(c-a-b)}{a(b+c)}$

19. $\dfrac{(x-3)(2x-1)}{3}$ 20. $-\dfrac{1}{2}$ 21. $\dfrac{a^2}{c^2}$ 22. -3 23. $\dfrac{x+2}{2x}$ 24. 1 25. $\dfrac{m-p+n}{m+p-n}$

26. $\dfrac{x(4x+3)}{3x+4}$ 27. $\dfrac{x+2}{x-4}$ 28. $\dfrac{3(x-3)}{x(x+2)}$

Page 84. — 1. 18 2. 108 3. 676 4. rst 5. $12x^3y^5z^3$ 6. $3(y-3)(y+3)$
7. $xy^2(x+y)$ 8. $(x-y)^2(x+y)$ 9. $3(m+n)(m-n)$ 10. $(x-6)(x+4)$
11. $(x-4)(x+3)(x+5)$ 12. $(x-1)^2(x+1)^2$ 13. $(c-d)^4$
14. $(m+2)(m+3)(m-6)(m+1)$ 15. $(x-2)(x+2)(x-3)$

Page 85. — 1. $\dfrac{9x}{36},\ \dfrac{2y}{36},\ \dfrac{4z}{36}$ 2. $\dfrac{6b}{21ab},\ \dfrac{35a}{21ab},\ \dfrac{11}{21ab}$ 3. $\dfrac{4yz^2}{x^2y^2z^2},\ \dfrac{5xyz}{x^2y^2z^2},\ \dfrac{2x^2}{x^2y^2z^2}$

4. $\dfrac{a(a+4b)}{(a-2b)(a+4b)},\ \dfrac{b(a-2b)}{(a-2b)(a+4b)}$ 5. $\dfrac{5cd}{2(3c-d)},\ \dfrac{4cd}{2(3c-d)}$

6. $\dfrac{5(x+3)}{6(x-3)(x+3)},\ \dfrac{8(x-3)}{6(x-3)(x+3)}$ 7. $\dfrac{3x(x-1)}{(x-1)^3},\ \dfrac{2x^2(x-1)^2}{(x-1)^3},\ \dfrac{5x^3}{(x-1)^3}$

8. $\dfrac{a-1}{(2a-1)(2a+1)},\ \dfrac{6(2a-1)}{(2a-1)(2a+1)}$ 9. $\dfrac{7(a-2)}{(a+2)^2(a-2)},\ \dfrac{-5(a+2)}{(a+2)^2(a-2)}$

10. $\dfrac{(x-1)(x-5)}{(x+3)(x+4)(x-5)},\ \dfrac{(x+1)(x+4)}{(x+3)(x+4)(x-5)},\ \dfrac{(x+2)(x+3)}{(x+3)(x+4)(x-5)}$

11. $\dfrac{5cd(d+c)}{4(4d+c)(d-c)(d+c)},\ \dfrac{-2cd(4d+c)}{4(4d+c)(d-c)(d+c)}$ 12. $\dfrac{5(2x^2-1)}{5(x-2)(x^2+2x+4)},$

$\dfrac{5(x^2+2x+4)}{5(x-2)(x^2+2x+4)},\ \dfrac{2x(x-2)}{5(x-2)(x^2+2x+4)}$

Page 87. — 1. $\dfrac{19}{36}$ 2. $\dfrac{27c}{56}$ 3. $\dfrac{20a-18b+c}{48}$ 4. $\dfrac{20+2x+15y}{10}$ 5. $\dfrac{3bc+2c+1}{abc}$

6. $\dfrac{2b^3-4ab+a^3}{a^2b^2}$ 7. $\dfrac{5x+1}{12}$ 8. $\dfrac{x-3}{40}$ 9. $-\dfrac{2}{z}$ 10. $-\dfrac{6x+1}{20x}$ 11. $\dfrac{14-16y}{9y}$

12. $\dfrac{5a-b}{(a-b)(a+b)}$ 13. $\dfrac{d^2-2c^2}{cd(c+d)}$ 14. 3 15. -2 16. $\dfrac{4y-3x}{(y+x)(y-x)}$ 17. $\dfrac{25}{12(x-y)}$

18. $\dfrac{2a}{(a+2b)(a-2b)^2}$ 19. $\dfrac{3a-b}{a-b}$ 20. $\dfrac{4cd}{(d+c)(d-c)}$ 21. 0 22. $\dfrac{6}{b-a}$

23. $\dfrac{7x^2+7y^2}{(x+3y)(2x-y)}$ 24. $\dfrac{x^2-7}{2x+3}$ 25. $\dfrac{(x+y)^2}{x^2-xy+y^2}$ 26. $\dfrac{b-3a}{a-b}$ 27. $\dfrac{2n^2+5mn}{m(n-m)(n+m)}$

28. $\dfrac{3x-10}{(x-5)(x+4)}$ 29. $\dfrac{6y+7}{(y-2)(y-3)(y+2)}$ 30. $-\dfrac{4a+2}{(a+2)(a+3)(a+1)}$

31. $\dfrac{2\,b}{(3\,b-c)\,(b+c)}$ **32.** $\dfrac{x+2}{2\,(x^2+x+1)}$ **33.** 0   **34.** $\dfrac{7\,x+3\,y}{3\,(x+3\,y)\,(2\,x-3\,y)}$

35. $\dfrac{3\,x-5\,y+2\,z}{(x-y)\,(y-z)\,(x-z)}$

Page 89. — 1. $\dfrac{x-y}{x+y}$ **2.** $\dfrac{a}{a-b}$ **3.** $-\dfrac{1}{m}$ **4.** $-\dfrac{1}{c+b}$ **5.** $\dfrac{a-2}{a+3}$ **6.** $\dfrac{x+4y}{x-3y}$

7. $\dfrac{a}{a+1}$ **8.** $\dfrac{2\,x+1}{2\,x}$ **9.** $\dfrac{1-a}{1+a}$ **10.** $-\dfrac{x+y}{y}$ **11.** $\dfrac{(x-2\,y)\,(x-y)}{(x+y)\,(x+2\,y)}$ **12.** 1

Page 90. — 1. $\dfrac{xw}{y}$ **2.** $\dfrac{x-y}{x+y}$ **3.** $\dfrac{x-yw}{my+n}$ **4.** $\dfrac{4}{3}$ **5.** $\dfrac{xy}{2\,y+3\,x}$ **6.** $\dfrac{a}{2\,b}$ **7.** $-a$

8. $\dfrac{y}{y+5}$ **9.** $x\,(x-2)$ **10.** -2 **11.** $\dfrac{b-2}{2\,b}$ **12.** $\dfrac{4-x}{4+x}$ **13.** $\dfrac{2\,(x+2)}{x\,(x-2)}$ **14.** $-\dfrac{x^2}{x^2+4}$

15. $\dfrac{(a+b)\,(a-2\,b)}{a}$

Page 91. — 16. $\dfrac{4\,(3\,x+4\,y)}{3\,x\,(3\,x-4\,y)}$ **17.** $\dfrac{1}{x\,(3+2\,x)}$ **18.** $-\dfrac{3\,a+5\,b}{a}$ **19.** $\dfrac{5}{4}$ **20.** 1

21. $\dfrac{a+2\,b}{a-3\,b}$ **22.** $b-1$ **23.** $\dfrac{9}{8}$ **24.** $\dfrac{344}{39}$ **25.** $\dfrac{27}{7}$

1. true   **2.** false   **3.** false   **4.** false   **5.** true   **6.** false

Page 92. — 7. false   **8.** false   **9.** true   **10.** false   **11.** true   **12.** true   **13.** true
14. false   **15.** false   **16.** true   **17.** true   **18.** false   **19.** true   **20.** true   **21.** false
22. false

1. (a) $-\dfrac{a}{b}$ or $\dfrac{-a}{b}$ (b) $-\dfrac{2}{3}$ or $\dfrac{-2}{3}$ (c) $-\dfrac{a}{(x)\,(y)\,(z)}$ (d) $\dfrac{x}{(a)\,(b)\,(c)\,(d)\,(e)}$

(e) $-\dfrac{4}{a+b}$ or $\dfrac{-4}{a+b}$ (f) $\dfrac{4}{a+b+c}$ or $-\dfrac{4}{a+b+c}$ **2.** (a) $\dfrac{4y}{7w}$ (b) $-\dfrac{6\,(a-b)}{a\,(a+b)}$

(c) $\dfrac{(c-d)^2}{c^2+cd+d^2}$ (d) $\dfrac{5\,a+3}{2\,(a+2)}$ (e) $\dfrac{x-2}{x^2-1}$

Page 93. — 3. (a) $\dfrac{a\,(b-a)}{b}$ (b) $\dfrac{2-5\,x}{x-2}$ (c) $\dfrac{a^2\,(1-a)}{3\,(1+a)}$ (d) $\dfrac{x\,(1+2\,x+4\,x^2)}{2\,(1+2\,x^2)}$

4. (a) $-ab$ (b) -1 (c) $\dfrac{(m+1)^2}{(m-1)^2}$ (d) $\dfrac{a^4-4}{2\,a\,(a+2)\,(a^2-2\,a+2)}$ **5.** (a) $-\dfrac{3\,x}{20}$

(b) $\dfrac{c+2\,b+3\,a}{abc}$ (c) $-\dfrac{1}{72}$ (d) $\dfrac{1}{rs}$ (e) $\dfrac{2\,xy}{y^2-x^2}$ (f) $\dfrac{x+11}{(x-4)\,(x+2)\,(x+1)}$

(g) $\dfrac{4\,x^2-4}{(x-2)^2\,(x+2)}$ (h) $\dfrac{1}{2\,x-3}$ **6.** (a) -1 (b) $\dfrac{2\,(5\,b+4)}{b\,(4\,b-5)}$ **7.** (a) $\dfrac{2}{c+d}$ (b) $\dfrac{cd-2}{2\,d}$

(c) $\dfrac{x+3}{x+1}$ (d) $\dfrac{8}{3}$

1. 14   **2.** -5 **3.** $18\,x^3-6\,x^2-10\,x-2$ **4.** $4\,a^2+17\,a-15$

Page 94. — 5. 12   **6.** -3 **7.** (a) $6\,x^2+x-12$ (b) $a^2x^2-b^2$ (c) $2\,m^3-4\,m^2n+2\,mn^2$
(d) $-6\,x^3y+9\,x^2y^2-3\,xy^3$ **8.** (a) $(2\,x-7\,y)\,(2\,x+7\,y)$ (b) $(3\,a-4)\,(2\,a-3)$
(c) $(x-2)\,(x+2)\,(x-1)\,(x+1)$ (d) $2\,a\,(x-a)^2$ (e) $(m-n)\,(x-y)$

(f) $(2\,x+1-2\,y)\,(2\,x+1+2\,y)$ (g) $\dfrac{2\,mn+n}{m+n}$ **10.** $\dfrac{1}{2}$, 2   **11.** Mary is 16 yr.,

Mother is 38 yr.   **12.** \$3000   **13.** $\dfrac{4\,x+y}{(x-y)^2}$ **14.** $\dfrac{2\,b+ab}{a-b}$ **15.** -3

Page 97. —1. 4   **2.** $-\frac{1}{2}$ **3.** 7   **4.** -5 **5.** 6   **6.** -3 **7.** -8 **8.** $\frac{14}{3}$ **9.** 3   **10.** -6 **11.** $\frac{1}{2}$ **12.** $-\frac{3}{5}$ **13.** $\frac{11}{4}$ **14.** 12   **15.** $-2, 1$ **16.** $-\frac{2}{5}, \frac{3}{2}$ **17.** 6   **18.** $\frac{19}{12}$ **19.** $\frac{1}{2}$ **20.** -2

Page 98. —21. $\frac{2}{5}, -1$ **22.** no solution   **23.** 1   **24.** 3   **25.** $\frac{3}{2}$ **26.** $-\frac{1}{3}$ **27.** $6, -6$ **28.** $-\frac{5}{4}$ **29.** 4   **30.** no solution   **31.** -6 **32.** 1   **33.** $-3, 2$

Page 99. —1. $\frac{p-n}{m}$ **2.** $\frac{a}{b}$ **3.** ab **4.** $\frac{m}{bt}$ **5.** $5t$ **6.** $\frac{5c}{2b}$ **7.** $\frac{ad}{b}$ **8.** $\frac{ad}{5}$ **9.** $\frac{a}{3a+2}$ **10.** $-3b$ **11.** $a-c$ **12.** $b+2c$ **13.** $\frac{3a}{2}$ **14.** $-2c$ **15.** $2m-n$ **16.** $\frac{1}{3a}$ **17.** $\frac{p-2b}{2}$ **18.** $\frac{A-2a^2}{4a}$ **19.** $\frac{T-2\pi r}{2\pi r}$ **20.** $\frac{A}{1+RT}$ **21.** $\frac{2K}{c}$ **22.** $\frac{mv^2}{f}$ **23.** $\frac{5F-160}{9}$ **24.** $\frac{E-TR}{T}$ **25.** $\frac{2S}{a+l}$ **26.** $\frac{Rs}{s-R}$ **27.** $\frac{sR}{2\pi rE}$ **28.** $\frac{S-a}{S}$

1. $n+5, \dfrac{n}{n+5}$ **2.** $\dfrac{x+3}{x+2}$ **3.** $\dfrac{11+x}{15+x}, \dfrac{11+x}{15+x} = \dfrac{2}{3}$

Page 100. —4. $\frac{1}{3}$ **5.** $\frac{1}{x}$ **6.** $\frac{7}{5}$ **7.** $\frac{n-1}{n}$ **8.** Bruce, $(b-6)$ darts; Ed, $(c+6)$ darts   **9.** $\dfrac{x}{2}, \dfrac{x}{3}$ **10.** $x+\dfrac{1}{x}$ **11.** $3+\dfrac{x}{2}$ **12.** $\dfrac{x+c}{3}, \dfrac{5}{7}(y-c)$

1. 36   **2.** 24   **3.** 5   **4.** $\frac{2}{3}, 3$ **5.** 6, 10   **6.** $\frac{5}{13}$ **7.** 30   **8.** 21   **9.** John has \$15, Bill has \$20.

Page 101. — 10. \$360

1. 40 mph   **2.** $\dfrac{160}{x}$ mph   **3.** 186 mi.   **4.** xm mi.   **5.** 650 mi.   **6.** $x+y$ mi., $2x+2y$ mi.   **7.** $x-1, 40x, 35(x-1), 40x+35(x-1)$

Page 102. — 8. $(5+y)$ mph, $\dfrac{10}{5+y}$ hr., $(5-y)$ mph, $\dfrac{m}{5-y}$

1. 12:30 P.M.   **2.** 45 min.

Page 103. — 3. 2 mph   **4.** 6 mi.   **5.** Mr. Jones' rate was 39 mph; Mr. Smith's, 52 mph.   **6.** 144 mi.   **7.** Rate of northbound train, 30 mph; rate of westbound train, 40 mph.

1. 2 qt.   **2.** $.10x$ qt.   **3.** $(x-8)$ qt.   **4.** $2(x-3)$ ct.   **5.** $(15-0.25x)$ lb.   **6.** $40(100-x)$ ct.   **7.** $[.30x+.25(20-x)]$ oz.   **8.** $[60x+100(120-x)]$ ct.

Page 104. — 1. creams, 32 lb.; nuts, 48 lb.   **2.** medium-sized eggs, 33 doz.; large-sized eggs, 45 doz.   **3.** 354 adult tickets, 216 children's tickets   **4.** 8 airmail stamps, 33 3¢ stamps, 46 2¢ stamps   **5.** 15 oz.   **6.** $7\frac{1}{2}$ qt.

Page 105. — 1. $\frac{1}{3}$ **2.** $\frac{1}{x}$ **3.** $\dfrac{2}{x-3}$ **4.** $\dfrac{1}{y}, \dfrac{3}{y}$ **5.** $\dfrac{5x}{12}$ **6.** $\dfrac{2x-3}{x(x-3)}, \dfrac{5(2x-3)}{x(x-3)}$

1. $3\frac{3}{7}$ hr.   **2.** $2\frac{2}{9}$ hr.

Page 106. — 3. $7\frac{1}{2}$ da.   **4.** $3\frac{3}{7}$ hr.   **5.** 15 da.   **6.** $4\frac{2}{5}$ hr.

1. 11, 12   **2.** 29, 31   **3.** 12, 13   **4.** 11, 13, 15; $-3, -1, 1$ **5.** 8, 10, 12   **6.** 3, 4, 5

Page 107. — 1. Joan is 15 yr., Peggy is 12 yr.

Page 108. — 2. 5 yr. and 3 yr. 3. 20 yr. 4. 12 yr. 5. 21 yr.

1. 10 2. $\frac{1}{2}$ 3. $2(a-b)$ 4. $\dfrac{9C+160}{5}$ 5. 4 6. 4 mi. per sec
7. 10 oz. of 48% acid, 30 oz. of 24% acid 8. Mrs. Black, 6 hr.; daughter, 12 hr.
9. 6, 8, 10, 12 10. 15 yr.

Page 109. — 1. $x^3 - 4x^2 + 1$ 2. 1 3. $x^2 + x + 4 + \dfrac{9}{x-3}$ 4. $2x+5$ 5. -2
6. $a^2b(a+2b)(a-b)$ 7. $(m+n)(3m+n)$ 8. $(9x^2 + 16y^4)(3x+4y^2)(3x-4y^2)$
9. $(c-a-3d)(c+a-d)$ 10. $(5x+1)(x-5)$ 11. $(4x+3)(3x-2)$
12. $2(2b-1)(4b^2+2b+1)$ 13. $a(x^b - y^b)(x^b + y^b)$ 14. $(5a-3)(5a+3)(a^2+1)$
15. $(x-1)(x+2)^2$ 16. $\dfrac{2a}{9b^2}$ 17. $\dfrac{c+d}{cd}$ 18. -1 19. 30 20. 900 mi.

Page 111. — 1. $(2, 2)$ 2. $(-2, -2)$ 3. $(0, 4)$ 4. $(4, 0)$ 5. $(-2, 5)$ 6. $(1, -3)$
7. $(-4, 1)$ 8. $(0, -2)$ 9. $(-1, 0)$

Page 112. — 10. (a) second (b) fourth (c) third (d) first 11. (a) x (b) y
(c) y (d) x 12. (a) -7 (b) -6 (c) $1\frac{1}{2}$ (d) .5 13. (a) -3 (b) 2 (c) $2\frac{1}{2}$ (d) -5
14. (a) 0 (b) 6 (c) 3 (d) 3 15. (a) 4 (b) 5 (c) 0 (d) 2.5 16. (a) y axis
(b) x axis (c) origin 17. (a) first (b) third (c) second (d) fourth

Nos. 1–9 require graphs.

Page 115. — Nos. 1–15 require graphs.

Page 116. — Nos. 16–20 require graphs.

Page 118. — 1. $y = \frac{1}{5}x - 2$; slope is $\frac{1}{5}$; y intercept is -2. 2. $y = -2x - 8$;
slope is -2; y intercept is -8. 3. $y = -\frac{7}{3}x + 2$; slope is $-\frac{7}{3}$; y intercept is 2.
4. $y = -8x + 20$; slope is -8; y intercept is 20 5. $y = -\frac{5}{4}x - 2$; slope is $-\frac{5}{4}$;
y intercept is -2. 6. $y = -\frac{3}{4}x + 3$; slope is $-\frac{3}{4}$; y intercept is 3.
7. $y = -6x + 4$; slope is -6; y intercept is 4. 8. $y = -2x - 5$; slope is -2;
y intercept is -5. 9. $y = -\frac{3}{8}x + 2$; slope is $-\frac{3}{8}$; y intercept is 2.
10. $x - y = -1$ 11. $x + y = -1$ 12. $4x - 2y = -1$ 13. $x + 3y = 18$ 14. $y = 4$
15. $x - 2y = 0$ 16. $2x - 10y = -3$ 17. $2x + 8y = 3$ 18. $2x - 8y = -1$

Nos. 1–8 require graphs.

Page 119. — 9. $y = -3x + 5$ 10. $y = \frac{5}{2}x + 4$ 11. $y = -\frac{1}{7}x + 1$ 12. $y = -\frac{4}{3}x + 5$

Page 120. — 1. $x = 4$, $y = 4$ 2. $x = 5$, $y = -2$ 3. $x = 2$, $y = 3$ 4. $x = -11$, $y = -4$
5. $x = 0$, $y = 5$ 6. $x = 2$, $y = -1$ 7. $x = -1$, $y = 6$ 8. $x = 2$, $y = 4$ 9. $x = 1$, $y = 1$

Page 121. — 1. inconsistent 2. simultaneous 3. dependent 4. simultaneous
5. simultaneous 6. dependent 7. inconsistent 8. inconsistent 9. simultaneous

Page 123. — 1. $x = 3$, $y = 6$ 2. $x = 2$, $y = -1$ 3. $x = 2$, $y = 3$ 4. $x = 5$, $y = 3$
5. $x = 6$, $y = 7$ 6. $x = 0$, $y = -3$ 7. $x = 3$, $y = 2$ 8. $x = 7$, $y = 10$ 9. $x = 4$, $y = -2$
10. $x = -0.1$, $y = -0.2$ 11. $x = -\frac{1}{2}$, $y = -\frac{1}{3}$ 12. $x = -3$, $y = 0.4$
13. $x = -6$, $y = -5$ 14. $x = 11$, $y = 7$ 15. $x = 15$, $y = -8$

Page 125. — 1. $r = \frac{1}{3}$, $s = \frac{1}{5}$ 2. $x = \frac{1}{4}$, $y = \frac{1}{3}$ 3. $m = \frac{1}{9}$, $n = -\frac{1}{4}$ 4. $x = 5$, $y = 1$

5. $r = 2$, $s = -3$ 6. $x = -1$, $y = -3$ 7. $x = -2$, $y = 4$ 8. $m = \frac{1}{2}$, $n = \frac{1}{4}$

Page 126. — 1. $x = \dfrac{r + s}{2}$, $y = \dfrac{r - s}{2}$ 2. $x = \dfrac{m + n}{4}$, $y = \dfrac{m - n}{2}$

3. $x = \dfrac{2}{p + q}$, $y = \dfrac{4}{p - q}$ 4. $x = \dfrac{1}{a + b}$, $y = \dfrac{2}{a - b}$ 5. $x = -\dfrac{s}{2}$, $y = 2s$

6. $x = \dfrac{1}{2m}$, $y = \dfrac{1}{3m}$ 7. $x = 2a$, $y = \dfrac{a}{3}$ 8. $x = \dfrac{s^2 + r^2}{s + r}$, $y = \dfrac{s - r}{r + s}$

9. $x = m + n$, $y = m - n$ 10. $x = p + q$, $y = pq$ 11. $x = a + b$, $y = -\dfrac{a}{b}$

12. $x = rs$, $y = \dfrac{r}{s}$ 13. $x = a^2 - b^2$, $y = a^2 + b^2$ 14. $x = m + n$, $y = m - n$

Page 127. — Doings of Dimbo. $x = 7$, $y = 1$

Page 128. — 1. $x = 6$, $y = 3$, $z = 2$ 2. $x = 5$, $y = 2$, $z = 1$ 3. $x = 1$, $y = 3$, $z = 5$
4. $x = 1$, $y = 2$, $z = 3$ 5. $x = -5$, $y = 15$, $z = 0$ 6. $x = 2$, $y = 3$, $z = 5$
7. $x = 0$, $y = -12$, $z = -17$ 8. $x = 7$, $y = 11$, $z = 1$

1. 85 ¢, 50 ¢

Page 129. — 2. $(8 + x)$ dollars, $(12 - x)$ dollars   3. $(y + 5)$ cards, $(x - 5)$ cards
4. $(d - 2)$ books, $(j + 2)$ books   5. $(2000 + d)$ dollars, $(5000 - d)$ dollars
6. $(e + 5000)$ dollars, $(s - 5000)$ dollars

Page 130. — 1. Husband owned 40 shares, wife 30 shares.   2. Bill had $1.00; Walt, $2.00.   3. Wood's share, $12,000; Storey's share, $8,000
4. Beck had $20,000; Rawlings, $70,000.   5. 1st period, 24 students; 2nd period, 28 students   6. 90 boys on tennis squad, 65 boys on handball squad

Page 131. — 7. Kennel owner owned 14 puppies; dealer, 16 puppies.

1. 1st no., 3; 2nd no., 1   2. 1st no., 3; 2nd no., 4   3. $\frac{1}{2}$, $\frac{1}{3}$ 4. $\frac{9}{8}$ 5. $\frac{3}{26}$ 6. $\frac{2}{7}$

Page 132. — 7. $\frac{2}{5}$ 8. $\frac{5}{12}$ 9. 1st no., -1; 2nd no., 2; 3rd no., 5
10. 1st no., 17; 2nd no., 9; 3rd no., 13

1. 2, 9, 4   2. 587   3. 11   4. $10t + u$, $t + u$, $10u + t$

Page 133. — 1. 37   2. 49   3. 85   4. 45   5. 84   6. 94

Page 134. — 7. 38   8. 432

Page 135. — 1. tea, $1.20 per lb.; coffee, $0.94 per lb.   2. hamburgers, 27¢ each; milk, 12¢ per bottle   3. peppermints, $0.66 per lb.; fruits, $1.10 per lb.
4. reserved seat, $1.10; unreserved seat, $0.60   5. mechanic, $2.10 per hr.; assistant, $1.25 per hr.   6. "x" liquid, 13 oz. per measure; "y" liquid, 17 oz. per measure

1. $\frac{3}{100}$ 2. $\frac{5}{200}$ 3. $\frac{9}{200}$ 4. $\frac{4}{100}d$ 5. $\frac{7}{100}s$ 6. $\frac{9}{100}b$

Page 136. — 7. $\frac{8}{100}r$ 8. $\frac{3}{100}x + \frac{9}{200}y$

Page 137. — 1. real estate, $20,000; insurance policy, $12,000   2. $8,000 in bonds, $12,000 in stocks   3. $20,000 in stock A, $24,000 in stock B

Page 138. — 4. $1,000 in soft drinks, $500 in candy bars   5. bank, $360; bonds, $600

Page 139. — **1.** crew's rate in still water, 14 mph; rate of stream, 2 mph **2.** man's rate in still water, 4 mph; rate of stream, 1 mph **3.** rate of plane in still air 250 mph; rate of wind, 20 mph **4.** rate of plane in still air, 280 mph; rate of tail wind, 20 mph; rate of head wind, 40 mph **5.** original speed of boat, 7 mph; rate of stream, 1 mph

Page 141. — **1.** Earl, 2 hr.; Gary, 3 hr. **2.** Jane, 12 hr.; mother, 4 hr. **3.** 1st pipe, 240 min.; 2nd pipe, 80 min. **4.** 1st machine, $3\frac{15}{31}$ hr.; 2nd machine, $7\frac{5}{7}$ hr. **5.** 1st pipe, 3 hr.; 2nd pipe, 12 hr.

Page 142. — **6.** 1st pipe, 4 hr.; 2nd pipe, 6 hr.; 3rd pipe, 12 hr. **7.** 1st pipe, $2\frac{1}{2}$ hr.; 2nd pipe, $1\frac{2}{3}$ hr.; 3rd pipe, 2 hr.

Just for Fun. Pipe opened $\frac{1}{2}$ hr.

Page 144. — **1.** 40 **2.** 10 **3.** 105 **4.** $\frac{7}{16}$ **5.** $-\frac{2}{27}$ **6.** $\frac{69}{8}$ **7.** $-\frac{9}{5}$ **8.** -0.56 **9.** -11.94 **10.** $-\frac{13}{14}$ **11.** $\frac{25}{14}$ **12.** $-\frac{9}{8}$ **13.** 12 **14.** $-\frac{8}{3}$ **15.** 0 **16.** $\dfrac{c_1 b_2 - c_2 b_1}{a_1 b_2 - a_2 b_1}$ **17.** $\dfrac{a_1 c_2 - a_2 c_1}{a_1 b_2 - a_2 b_1}$ **18.** 0.4

Page 145. — (One answer is given for ex. 19–26. There are others.)

19. $\begin{vmatrix} a & d \\ c & b \end{vmatrix}$ **20.** $\begin{vmatrix} 6 & \frac{1}{4} \\ 12 & 8 \end{vmatrix}$ **21.** $\begin{vmatrix} 0.2 & 0.4 \\ 0.6 & 0.3 \end{vmatrix}$ **22.** $\begin{vmatrix} 17 & 1 \\ 13 & 1 \end{vmatrix}$ **23.** $\begin{vmatrix} 22 & 1 \\ -15 & 1 \end{vmatrix}$

24. $\begin{vmatrix} r & v \\ -t & s \end{vmatrix}$ **25.** $\begin{vmatrix} 4 & 2 \\ 3 & 4 \end{vmatrix}$ **26.** $\begin{vmatrix} 4 & 6 \\ 2 & 3 \end{vmatrix}$

Page 147. — **1.** $x = -1, y = 1$ **2.** $m = \frac{1}{2}, n = 0$ **3.** $x = 6, y = 5$ **4.** $x = \frac{11}{7}, y = \frac{2}{7}$ **5.** $p = \frac{1}{2}; q = \frac{1}{3}$ **6.** $v = 2, w = 0$ **7.** $r = 2, s = 3$ **8.** $x = 2, y = 4$ **9.** $x = \frac{4}{23}, y = \frac{3}{23}$ **10.** $x = 6, y = 6$ **11.** $m = 5, n = 7$ **12.** $r = \frac{1}{2}, s = \frac{1}{3}$ **13.** $p = \frac{2}{5}, q = -\frac{1}{7}$ **14.** $x = \frac{1}{3}, y = \frac{3}{4}$ **15.** $x = \frac{1}{56}, y = \frac{10}{7}$

Page 148. — **1.** 8 **2.** 28 **3.** 0 **4.** 0 **5.** 0 **6.** 24

Page 150. — **1.** $x = 1, y = 1, z = -1$ **2.** $x = 3, y = 2, z = 1$ **3.** $x = 1, y = 0, z = -1$ **4.** $x = \frac{1}{2}, y = -1, z = \frac{1}{3}$ **5.** $x = 1, y = -1, z = -2$ **6.** $x = 1, y = -\frac{1}{2}, z = -2$ **7.** $x = 1, y = 2, z = 3$ **8.** $x = 60, y = 60, z = 20$ **9.** $x = 1, y = 2, z = -\frac{1}{2}$ **10.** $x = -\frac{2}{3}, y = -\frac{1}{4}, z = 12$

Page 152. — **1.** (a) 60 mi. (b) 30 mi. (c) 15 mi. **2.** (a) 34 mi. (b) 22 mi. (c) 13 mi. **3.** 6:12 P.M. **4.** 8:00 P.M., 1 hr. 48 min. **5.** 7:30 P.M., 225 mi. **6.** 10:54 (app.) A.M. **7.** 5:36 A.M.

Page 153. — **Doings of Dimbo.** Dimbo used wrong signs of determinants.

1. (a) inconsistent (b) simultaneous (c) dependent **2.** b

Page 154. — **3.** x axis **4.** slope, 3; y intercept, $-\frac{7}{2}$ **5.** $2x + 3y = 12$ **6.** $x = 4, y = 3$ **7.** $x = 1, y = 2$ **8.** $r = 6, s = -\frac{5}{2}$ **9.** $m = 3, n = -\frac{1}{2}$ **10.** $x = 4, y = -\frac{1}{3}$ **11.** $x = a + b, y = 1$ **12.** $x = \frac{1}{2}, y = -\frac{1}{3}$ **13.** plane, 120 mph;

wind, 20 mph   **14.** mechanic, 40 hr.; assistant, 60 hr.   **15.** $32,000 in real estate, $28,000 in stocks

Page 155. — **16.** $4\frac{1}{2}$ ¢ per mi. by train; $2\frac{3}{4}$ ¢ per mi. by bus   **17.** 2.78   **18.** 0.88

19. One of several determinants is $\begin{vmatrix} 6 & 2 \\ 3 & 3 \end{vmatrix}$ **20.** 13   **21.** $x = \frac{96}{17}$, $y = \frac{60}{17}$ **22.** $-\frac{35}{88}$

1. $4 - 3a - 2a^2$ **2.** $3(3r + 2s)(2r - s)$ **3.** $(a^2 + b^2)(x - y)$ **4.** $\dfrac{2 - t - 2t^2}{t^2 - 1}$ **5.** 5

6. $\dfrac{2a + x}{a + 2x}$ **7.** $\dfrac{2A - rm + cr}{c}$ **8.** 2

Page 156. — **9.** $y = -3x + 5$ **10.** $x = 0$, $y = 2b$ **11.** $x = 5$, $y = 6$ **12.** 6 qt.

Page 157. — **1.** $\frac{3}{4}$ **2.** $\dfrac{2a}{3b}$ **3.** $7m^4 : 4n^6$ **4.** $27 : 28$ **5.** $2 : 3$

Page 158. — **6.** $\dfrac{1}{p^2 + pq + q^2}$ **7.** $-\dfrac{9a + 1}{9}$ **8.** $y(x - y) : (x^2 - xy + y^2)$ **9.** $7 : 2$
10. $38 : 33$ **11.** $\pi : 1$ **12.** $4 : 1$

Page 159. — **1.** 12, 27   **2.** $2\frac{2}{3}$ in.   **3.** for halls and stairway, 2835 sq. ft. of marble; for floors, 16,065 sq. ft. of rubberized blocks   **4.** meat dep't., 20,000 sq. ft.; fruit dep't., 15,000 sq. ft.; grocery dep't., 40,000 sq. ft.; supply dep't. 10,000 sq. ft. **5.** $\dfrac{11}{3}$, $\dfrac{77}{9}$ **6.** $18.20, $15.60   **7.** 60 cc.   **8.** 30, 36   **9.** Walter is 20 yr.; Byron, 64 yr.   **10.** Bob is 9 yr.; Morgan, 18 yr.   **11.** Goeffry is 40 yr.; Rowland, 12 yr. **12.** $8 : 1$

Page 160. — **1.** 6   **2.** 4   **3.** 3   **4.** a **5.** 15   **6.** $6b$ **7.** 40   **8.** $\dfrac{1}{a}$ **9.** $\dfrac{2a}{b}$ **10.** 0

Page 161. — **1.** 3   **2.** 5   **3.** $\dfrac{10}{3}$ **4.** $\dfrac{3}{10}$ **5.** 24   **6.** $6.00   **7.** 33   **8.** ±.25   **9.** 3 **10.** 4   **11.** 9   **12.** 20

Page 162. — **1.** 2.5 in., 6 in.   **2.** $21\frac{1}{3}$ in.   **3.** 486 sq. in.

Page 163. — **4.** 24π cu. in.   **5.** (a) 10 in.   (b) $\frac{1}{6}$ ft.   (c) 0.125 yd.   **6.** 6 in. **7.** $17\frac{1}{2}$ in.   **8.** $14\frac{2}{17}$ in.   **9.** 24 sq. in.

Page 165. — **1.** 3   **2.** $\dfrac{5}{4}$ **3.** $\dfrac{11}{60}$ **4.** $\dfrac{3}{16}$ **5.** $86.80   **6.** 320 ft./sec.   **7.** $1.35 **8.** 400 ft.   **9.** 9 lb.

Page 166. — **10.** $16\frac{1}{3}$ gal. per min.   **11.** 12 gal.   **12.** $1\frac{3}{4}$ mi.

Page 167. — **1.** 12   **2.** 55   **3.** $\dfrac{1}{32}$ **4.** $\dfrac{5}{36}$ **5.** $\dfrac{9}{64}$ **6.** 16 hr.   **7.** approx. 1580 lb. **8.** 25 rpm

Page 168. — **9.** $33\frac{1}{3}$ lb.   **10.** $\sqrt{50}$ or approx. 7 ft.   **11.** generator pulley, 4800 rpm; for pulley, 7200 rpm

Page 169. — **1.** 8   **2.** 15   **3.** $\dfrac{27}{4}$ **4.** $\dfrac{5}{28}$ **5.** 0.54 sq. in.   **6.** $13\frac{1}{2}$ in.   **7.** 900 cc. **8.** 8 lb./sq. in.

Page 170. — 9. 12 hr. 10. 4

1. $\frac{2}{9}$ 2. $\frac{2}{3}$ 3. $\frac{8}{9}$ 4. $\frac{4}{3}$ 5. $\frac{23}{9}$ 6. $\frac{28}{33}$ 7. $\frac{38}{11}$ 8. $\frac{413}{99}$ 9. $\frac{77}{333}$ 10. $\frac{169}{999}$

Page 171. — 1. $\frac{20}{1}$ 2. $\frac{11}{3}$ 3. Byron, \$520; Mabel, \$480 4. 1st no., 4; 2nd no., 14
5. 3 6. 0.4 7. Father is 52 yr.; son is 20 yr. 8. (*a*) directly (*b*) inversely
(*c*) jointly as y and z (*d*) directly as x and inversely as z 9. $\triangle ABC$, $31\frac{1}{4}$ sq. in.;
$BCED$, $11\frac{1}{4}$ sq. in. 10. $\frac{82}{33}$ 11. 600 lb. 12. 80 g.

Page 172. — 1. $4 - 3a - 2a^2$ 2. 30 3. $(2r - 3s)(r + 5s)$
4. $(2c - 3d - 4)(2c - 3d + 4)$ 5. $\dfrac{1 + 3a - 2a^2}{2(a^2 - 1)}$ 6. 2 7. $-(x + y)$ 8. $x = -2,\ y = \frac{5}{2}$
9. $\dfrac{2s - 2an}{n(n - 1)}$ 10. $.02d$ 11. $\dfrac{3k}{c}$ 12. $\dfrac{n - d}{n}$ 14. 1st boy, 6 hr.; 2nd boy, 4 hr.
15. \$16,000 in store, \$30,000 in bonds

Page 173. — 16. food, \$2250; shelter, \$675; clothing, \$450; miscellaneous needs,
\$225 17. 8 18. $\frac{500}{243}$ 19. $x = \frac{68}{57},\ y = \frac{70}{57}$

Page 178. — 1. x^6 2. y^7 3. a^{14} 4. x^{3a} 5. x^{b+c} 6. y^8 7. x^{r+s} 8. y^{4m}
9. y^{2+n} 10. y^{2a+b} 11. x^4 12. x^4 13. x^2 14. x^4 15. x^{2a} 16. y^2 17. y^{3a}
18. x^{m-n} 19. y^{2n-4} 20. y^{r-s}

1. x^{2n} 2. x^{6n} 3. y^{8a} 4. x^{5r} 5. x^{3r+2} 6. x^{a+1} 7. x 8. x^n 9. x^5 10. x^2
11. x^6 12. x^{15} 13. x^{7n} 14. $x^{a(n+1)}$ 15. $-x^6$ 16. x^2 17. x^3 18. x^3 19. x^{5a}
20. $x^3 y$ 21. $x^2 y^8$ 22. $a^6 b^9 c^3$ 23. $a^{16} b^4 c^{20}$ 24. $x^{3a} y^{3b} c3$ 25. $-x^5 y^5 z^{10}$ 26. $\dfrac{x^6}{y^3}$
27. $\dfrac{x^{ay}}{y^{by}}$ 28. $\dfrac{r^{14p}}{s^{6p}}$ 29. $\dfrac{x^{4nk}}{y^{6mk}}$

Page 182. — 1. 1 2. 1 3. 1 4. 5 5. 1 6. 1 7. 1 8. 8 9. 9 10. $\frac{3}{2}$ 11. 7
12. 5 13. 2 14. $\frac{1}{2}$ 15. 9 16. -2 17. $\frac{1}{4}$ 18. $\frac{1}{125}$

1. 9 2. $\frac{27}{8}$ 3. $\frac{3}{2}$ 4. 32 5. 9 6. 2 7. 125 8. 72 9. 1.2 10. .1 11. .5
12. .3 13. $\sqrt[5]{x^3}$ 14. $\sqrt{a^5}$ 15. $\sqrt[6]{x^5}$ 16. $\sqrt[3]{y^2}$ 17. $\sqrt{a}$ 18. $\sqrt[4]{x^5}$ 19. $\sqrt{b^3}$ 20. $\sqrt[3]{s}$
21. $x^{\frac{1}{2}}$ 22. $y^{\frac{1}{3}}$ 23. $x^{\frac{3}{2}}$ 24. $x^{\frac{3}{5}}$ 25. $x^{\frac{2}{3}}$ 26. $y^{\frac{5}{3}}$ 27. $a^{\frac{5}{2}}$ 28. $x^{\frac{7}{4}}$ 29. $\dfrac{1}{x^2}$
30. $\dfrac{1}{y^3}$ 31. x^2 32. $x^{\frac{2}{3}}$ 33. $\dfrac{1}{m^{\frac{1}{2}}}$ 34. n^3 35. $y^{\frac{1}{2}}$ 36. $\dfrac{y^2}{x^2}$

Page 184. — 1. 8 2. 1 3. 1 4. $\frac{9}{4}$ 5. 250 6. 8 7. $\frac{2}{3}$ 8. $\frac{1715}{64}$ 9. $\frac{4}{3}$ 10. $\frac{197}{27}$
11. $\dfrac{b}{x^5}$ 12. $\dfrac{y^2}{x^3}$ 13. $x^2 y^2$ 14. $\dfrac{a^2}{b^3 c}$ 15. $\dfrac{c^2}{a^2 b^2}$ 16. $-\dfrac{3}{x}$ 17. $\dfrac{2xy}{3}$ 18. $\dfrac{a^3 b}{c^2}$ 19. $-2xy^2$

Page 185. — 20. $\dfrac{1}{x^3}$ 21. $\dfrac{z}{x^3 y}$ 22. $-\dfrac{b}{5a^5}$ 23. $\dfrac{2x}{y}$ 24. $\dfrac{1}{x + y}$ 25. x^6 26. $\dfrac{b - a}{ab}$
27. $\dfrac{y + x}{xy}$ 28. $\dfrac{x^2 + y^2}{xy}$ 29. $\dfrac{2}{xy}$ 30. $-\dfrac{1}{3x}$ 31. x 32. $x^{\frac{5}{4}}$ 33. x^2 34. y 35. a

36. $b^{\frac{1}{3}}$ 37. $a^{\frac{26}{5}}$ 38. $a^{\frac{15}{4}}$ 39. $a^{\frac{11}{6}}$ 40. 1 41. 1 42. x^3 43. $\frac{1}{x}$ 44. x 45. x^8

46. 1 47. $x-y$ 48. $\frac{x^4-2x^2+1}{x^2}$ 49. $x^{4a}+x^{2a}$ 50. $\frac{y^2-x^2}{x^2y^2}$ 51. $\frac{y^{2a}-x^{2a}}{x^{2a}y^{2a}}$

52. $\frac{y^2+x^2}{y^2}$ 53. $\frac{1}{b^3+a^3}$ 54. $\frac{b+a}{ab}$ 55. $\frac{1}{m}+1$ 56. $x^{\frac{1}{2}}+y^{\frac{1}{2}}$ 57. $x^{\frac{2}{3}}+x^{\frac{1}{3}}y^{\frac{1}{3}}+y^{\frac{2}{3}}$

58. $6a-5a^{\frac{3}{4}}+9a^{\frac{1}{2}}-10a^{\frac{1}{4}}$ 59. $a^{\frac{1}{2}}-b^{\frac{1}{2}}$ 60. $\dfrac{4}{a^{\frac{5}{3}}b^{\frac{2}{9}}}$ 61. $a^2b^4c^{\frac{4}{3}}$ 62. $\dfrac{bc^{\frac{2}{5}}}{a^2}$

63. $\dfrac{y^6z^{\frac{3}{4}}}{x^{\frac{3}{5}}}$ 64. $xy^2s^2z^{2s}$ 65. $\dfrac{x^{\frac{1}{2}}y^6}{z^3}$ 66. $\dfrac{a}{b^2c^5}$ 67. $-\dfrac{a^4b^3}{c^5}$ 68. $\dfrac{8b^{\frac{15}{2}}}{27a^{12}}$ 69. $\dfrac{a^{10}}{bc^{12}}$

70. $\dfrac{2a^4z}{3x^2}$ 71. $\dfrac{4y^6z^2}{x^4a^{\frac{1}{2}}}$ 72. $\dfrac{t}{as}$

Page 187.— 1. 2.56×10^9 2. 3.015×10^{10} 3. 9.7×10^{12} 4. 8.08×10^{-8}
5. 9.1×10^{-10} 6. 1.1×10^{-13} 7. 1.101×10^{12} 8. 8.003×10^{12} 9. 1.09×10^{-10}
10. 2×10^{-9} 11. 350,000,000 12. .000000201 13. 26,900,000,000
14. 370,000,000,000 15. .00000105 16. .00000091

Page 188.—Doings of Dimbo. $\dfrac{1}{ab^4c^{\frac{3}{2}}}$

1. $\sqrt[5]{y^3}$ 2. $x^{\frac{7}{3}}$ 3. 48 4. $-\frac{5}{4}$ 5. $-12a^2bc^2$ 6. $\dfrac{x^2}{y}$ 7. (a) 3.71×10^{11}

(b) 7.9×10^{-7} 8. $\dfrac{25}{a^2}$ 9. $x+1$ 10. $2a^{\frac{2}{3}}-a^{\frac{1}{3}}+2$

1. $\dfrac{1}{x+y}-2\left(\dfrac{1}{x}+\dfrac{1}{y}\right)$

Page 189.— 2. 30 3. $\dfrac{x+4}{2}$ 4. $\frac{64}{3}$ 5. $(x^a-y^{-2b})(x^a+y^{-2b})$ 6. Slope is 3;

y intercept is 7. 7. 8 8. $x=3,\ y=1$ 9. $\dfrac{ab}{a+b}$ 10. $(x-2)(x-3)(2x-1)$

11. $11\frac{3}{7}$ pt. 12. $15\frac{2}{3}$

Page 191.— 1. $2\sqrt2$ 2. 15 3. $3\sqrt2$ 4. $5\sqrt2$ 5. $5\sqrt3$ 6. $6\sqrt{10}$ 7. $6\sqrt2$
8. $7\sqrt3$ 9. 2 10. $2\sqrt2$ 11. $3\sqrt[3]{2}$ 12. $3\sqrt[3]{3}$ 13. $10\sqrt[3]{5}$ 14. $6x^2$ 15. $12a\sqrt x$
16. $10ax^2\sqrt2$ 17. $50b\sqrt{2a}$ 18. $2x\sqrt[3]{2}$ 19. $2x\sqrt[3]{4x}$ 20. $3a\sqrt[3]{b}$ 21. $6x\sqrt[3]{2x}$
22. $30x^3\sqrt[3]{2x^2}$ 23. $14axy\sqrt{2y}$ 24. $4\sqrt2$ 25. 2 26. $\sqrt[4]{2}$ 27. $\frac{1}{2}$

Page 192.— 28. $6x^2\sqrt[4]{2}$ 29. $2a\sqrt[6]{b}$ 30. $-6ab\sqrt{2ab}$ 31. $-6x\sqrt[3]{2}$ 32. $-3xy\sqrt[3]{y^2}$
33. $a+b$ 34. $x(2x+3a)\sqrt x$ 35. $(x+y)\sqrt{x-y}$ 36. $(x-y)\sqrt{(x^2+xy+y^2)(x+y)}$

1. $\sqrt2$ 2. $\sqrt7$ 3. $\sqrt3$ 4. $\sqrt[3]{4}$ 5. $\sqrt5$ 6. 2 7. $\sqrt{5a}$ 8. $\sqrt{5x}$ 9. $y\sqrt{6x}$ 10. $2\sqrt[3]{s^2}$
11. $9x$ 12. $5x^2\sqrt x$ 13. $3y^2\sqrt y$ 14. $4a^2\sqrt{10a}$ 15. $6a$ 16. x^2y^3 17. a^n 18. $2y^2$

Page 193.— 1. $\frac{1}{3}\sqrt3$ 2. $\frac{1}{5}\sqrt{10}$ 3. $\frac{1}{7}\sqrt{21}$

Page 194. — **4.** $\frac{2}{5}\sqrt{10}$ **5.** $3\sqrt{6x}$ **6.** $2\sqrt{5x}$ **7.** $\frac{1}{3}\sqrt[3]{3}$ **8.** $\frac{1}{2}\sqrt[3]{20}$ **9.** $\frac{1}{5}\sqrt[3]{75}$
10. $\frac{1}{2}\sqrt[4]{2}$ **11.** $2\sqrt[3]{5x}$ **12.** $5\sqrt[4]{6x}$ **13.** $\frac{1}{10}\sqrt{15}$ **14.** $\frac{1}{3}\sqrt{3}$ **15.** $\frac{2}{3}\sqrt[3]{6}$ **16.** $\frac{x}{6}\sqrt{3}$
17. $\frac{x}{3}\sqrt[3]{3}$ **18.** $\frac{6}{5}\sqrt{5x}$ **19.** $\frac{1}{3y}\sqrt{15xy}$ **20.** $\frac{5x}{4}\sqrt{2y}$ **21.** $\frac{4x^2}{3a^2b}\sqrt[3]{ay^2}$ **22.** $\frac{2xy}{ab}\sqrt[4]{xy^2ab}$
23. $\frac{x^2}{y}\sqrt[n]{y}$ **24.** $\frac{y^3}{x}\sqrt[n]{x^2}$

Page 195. — **1.** $8\sqrt{3}$ **2.** $\sqrt{2}$ **3.** $5\sqrt{a}$ **4.** $\sqrt{x}+3\sqrt{y}$ **5.** $3\sqrt{ab}$ **6.** $11\sqrt{5}-5\sqrt{3}$
7. $2\sqrt{x}+3\sqrt{y}$ **8.** $11\sqrt{3}+\sqrt{x}$ **9.** $2\sqrt{a}+\sqrt{b}+\sqrt{c}$ **10.** $7\sqrt{a}-2\sqrt{b}$

1. $3\sqrt{2}$ **2.** $4\sqrt{3}$ **3.** $4\sqrt{5}$ **4.** $2\sqrt{x}$ **5.** $8\sqrt[3]{2}$ **6.** $4\sqrt[3]{4}$ **7.** $\frac{32}{3}\sqrt[3]{3}$ **8.** 0 **9.** $-6\sqrt{5}$
10. $\frac{47}{4}\sqrt{10}$ **11.** $10\sqrt{2}$ **12.** $8\sqrt{2}-2\sqrt{5}$ **13.** $\sqrt{3x}+3\sqrt[3]{3x}-3\sqrt{5x}+3\sqrt[3]{2x}$ **14.** 0
15. $6\sqrt[5]{2}$ **16.** $3\sqrt[4]{2}$

Page 196. — **1.** $\sqrt{6}$ **2.** $3\sqrt{2}$ **3.** $2\sqrt{3}$ **4.** 18 **5.** 4 **6.** 3 **7.** 40 **8.** 5 **9.** $3x$
10. $9\sqrt{7}$ **11.** 48 **12.** $30x\sqrt{2}$ **13.** $x-2$ **14.** $16(x-1)$ **15.** $75a\sqrt{3a}$ **16.** $\sqrt{a^2-b^2}$
17. $5a$ **18.** 2 **19.** $3\sqrt[4]{2}$ **20.** $2(x-y)$ **21.** -1 **22.** 2 **23.** $14-4\sqrt{6}$ **24.** $47-6\sqrt{10}$
25. $55-12\sqrt{21}$ **26.** $21-7\sqrt{15}$ **27.** 23 **28.** $19+8\sqrt{3}$ **29.** $37-12\sqrt{7}$ **30.** $x-5$
31. $1-2\sqrt{x}+x$ **32.** $49-14\sqrt{x}+x$ **33.** $x-4\sqrt{x+1}+5$ **34.** $8-6\sqrt{2x-1}+2x$
35. $2x+2\sqrt{x^2-x-2}-1$ **36.** $x-12\sqrt{x-5}+31$ **37.** $5x-1+2\sqrt{6x^2-3x}$
38. $5x+5-2\sqrt{5x+4}$

Page 198. — **1.** 2 **2.** 2 **3.** 5 **4.** $3\sqrt{3}$ **5.** 2 **6.** $2a$ **7.** 3 **8.** 2 **9.** 2 **10.** 9
11. $7\sqrt{3}$ **12.** 15 **13.** $3\sqrt{2}$ **14.** $\frac{3}{4}\sqrt[3]{2}$ **15.** $\frac{2}{9}\sqrt[3]{9}$ **16.** $\frac{2}{5}$ **17.** $\frac{3}{10}\sqrt[5]{4}$ **18.** $5x$
19. $8x$ **20.** $3x^2y$

Page 199. — **1.** $\sqrt[6]{108}$ **2.** $\sqrt[12]{648}$ **3.** $\sqrt[6]{500}$ **4.** $\sqrt[6]{12,500}$ **5.** $\sqrt[6]{32}$ **6.** $\sqrt[10]{128}$
7. $\sqrt[6]{200}$ **8.** $\sqrt[6]{18}$ **9.** $\sqrt[6]{48}$ **10.** $\sqrt[10]{2187}$ **11.** $\sqrt[12]{a^5}$ **12.** $a\sqrt[12]{a^5}$

Page 200. — **1.** $\sqrt[12]{54}$ **2.** $\sqrt[6]{32}$ **3.** $\sqrt[6]{2}$ **4.** $\sqrt[6]{24}$ **5.** $\sqrt[6]{5}$ **6.** $\sqrt[12]{2}$ **7.** $\sqrt[4]{2}$ **8.** $\sqrt[6]{3}$
9. $\frac{2}{3}\sqrt[6]{648}$ **10.** $\frac{1}{2}\sqrt[6]{72}$ **11.** $\sqrt[6]{x}$ **12.** $\sqrt[4]{a^3}$

Page 201. — **1.** rational   **2.** rational   **3.** irrational   **4.** imaginary   **5.** rational
6. rational   **7.** irrational   **8.** imaginary   **9.** imaginary   **10.** rational   **11.** rational
12. imaginary   **13.** irrational   **14.** imaginary   **15.** rational   **16.** irrational

Page 202. — **1.** $\frac{\sqrt{10}}{2}$ **2.** $\frac{5\sqrt{3}}{3}$ **3.** $4\sqrt{2}$ **4.** $3\sqrt{7}$ **5.** $7\sqrt{5}$ **6.** $\frac{\sqrt{6}}{3}$ **7.** $\frac{\sqrt{21}}{3}$
8. $\frac{\sqrt{66}}{6}$ **9.** $\frac{2\sqrt{15}}{5}$ **10.** $\sqrt{30}$ **11.** $\frac{5\sqrt{2}}{2}$ **12.** $\frac{3\sqrt{35}}{10}$ **13.** $\sqrt{30}$ **14.** $\frac{\sqrt[3]{15}}{3}$ **15.** $\frac{\sqrt[3]{12}}{2}$
16. $2\sqrt[3]{3}$ **17.** $5\sqrt[3]{2}$ **18.** $\frac{5\sqrt[3]{5}}{3}$ **19.** $\frac{3\sqrt[3]{100}}{10}$ **20.** $\frac{5\sqrt[4]{18}}{3}$

Page 203. — **1.** $3+\sqrt{5}$ **2.** $\sqrt{15}-\sqrt{10}$ **3.** $\frac{14(5-2\sqrt{3})}{13}$ **4.** $5-2\sqrt{6}$ **5.** $\frac{4-\sqrt{2}}{7}$
6. $\frac{\sqrt{30}+3\sqrt{2}}{2}$ **7.** $2\sqrt{6}-5$ **8.** $4+\sqrt{15}$ **9.** $17+4\sqrt{15}$

Page 204. — 10. $\dfrac{a^2 + b^2x + 2\,ab\sqrt{x}}{a^2 - b^2x}$　　　**11.** $-60 - 13\sqrt{21}$　　　**12.** $-\dfrac{12 + 5\sqrt{35}}{17}$

13. $\dfrac{3\,a + 4\,b + 8\sqrt{ab}}{a - 4\,b}$　　**14.** $\dfrac{a^2 + a\sqrt{a-1} + a\sqrt{a+1} + \sqrt{a^2-1}}{a^2 - a + 1}$　　**15.** $\dfrac{x + 5 - 4\sqrt{x+1}}{x - 3}$

16. $\dfrac{a^2 - \sqrt{a^4 - b^4}}{b^2}$

Page 205. — 1. $\pm(\sqrt{6} - \sqrt{5})$　**2.** $\pm(2 + \sqrt{2})$　**3.** $\pm(3 - 2\sqrt{2})$　**4.** $\pm(\sqrt{5} + \sqrt{2})$
5. $\pm(\sqrt{7} - 1)$　**6.** $\pm(\sqrt{5} + 5)$　**7.** $\pm(3 - \sqrt{3})$　**8.** $\pm(\sqrt{6} + 2\sqrt{3})$　**9.** $\pm(2 + \sqrt{3})$
10. $\pm(3 + \sqrt{5})$　**11.** $\pm(\sqrt{6} + 2\sqrt{2})$　**12.** $\pm(\sqrt{5a+b} + \sqrt{5a-b})$

Doings of Dimbo. $2\sqrt{3} - 3$

Page 206. — 1. $-i$　**2.** $-2i$　**3.** i　**4.** $-i$　**5.** $2i$　**6.** $-i-1$　**7.** $2 + 2i$　**8.** -4
9. $-i$　**10.** 0

Page 208. — 1. $-\sqrt{10}$　**2.** -5　**3.** $-4\sqrt{3}$　**4.** -10　**5.** 18　**6.** $-10\sqrt{6}$　**7.** $-5\sqrt{15}$
8. -9　**9.** -18　**10.** -20　**11.** $12\,i$　**12.** $i\sqrt{2}$　**13.** $19\,i\sqrt{3}$　**14.** $7 + 6\,i\sqrt{2}$　**15.** $21 - 20\,i$
16. $-5 + 2\sqrt{6}$　　**17.** 5　　**18.** -29　**19.** $40 + 6\,i\sqrt{3}$　　**20.** $\dfrac{6\,a^2 - b}{9\,a^2 + b} + \dfrac{5\,a\sqrt{b}}{9\,a^2 + b}\,i$
21. $\dfrac{2\sqrt{3} - 6}{15} + \dfrac{\sqrt{3} + 12}{15}\,i$　　**22.** 1　　**23.** $\dfrac{10}{17} - \dfrac{11}{17}\,i$　　**24.** $-\dfrac{1}{2} + i$　　**25.** $\pm(3 + i)$
26. $\pm(1 - 2\,i)$　**27.** $\pm(2 - i)$　**28.** $\pm(3 + 2\,i)$　**29.** $\pm(4 - 3\,i)$　**30.** $\pm(5 - 4\,i)$

Page 209. — 1. 9　**2.** 6　**3.** 25　**4.** no solution　**5.** 6　**6.** 6　**7.** 3　**8.** 5　**9.** $-\dfrac{1}{3}$
10. 13

Page 210. — 11. no solution　**12.** no solution　**13.** $-\dfrac{4}{3}$　**14.** -8　**15.** $\dfrac{9}{2}$　**16.** $\dfrac{6}{5}$
17. 4　**18.** 4　**19.** 9　**20.** 16

1. no solution　**2.** 16　**3.** 7　**4.** no solution　**5.** 5　**6.** no solution

Page 211. — 7. 6　**8.** 3　**9.** no solution　**10.** no solution　**11.** 4　**12.** -2

1. $\sqrt[3]{3}$　**2.** $5\sqrt{10}$　**3.** $\sqrt{5}$　**4.** $2x\sqrt{x}$　**5.** $\dfrac{1}{7}\sqrt{21}$　**6.** $2\sqrt{5\,x}$

Page 212. — 7. $\sqrt{-4},\ \sqrt{-\dfrac{6}{7}}$　**8.** $-2\dfrac{1}{2},\ 0.689$　**9.** $\dfrac{3\sqrt{2}}{2}$　**10.** $2\sqrt[3]{2} - \dfrac{1}{4}\sqrt{2}$　**11.** -11
12. $18 + 11\sqrt{6}$　　**13.** $4x + 2 - 2\sqrt{3\,x^2 + 6\,x}$　　**14.** $\dfrac{5}{3}\sqrt{5}$　　**15.** $2x$　　**16.** $2 - \sqrt{6}$
17. $\pm(3 + \sqrt{2})$　**18.** $\sqrt[6]{288}$　**19.** $\dfrac{1}{2}\sqrt[10]{512}$　**20.** 6　**21.** $\dfrac{1}{4}$　**22.** 81　**23.** $-2\sqrt{15}$　**24.** $26 + 7\,i$
25. $\dfrac{8}{61} - \dfrac{27}{61}\,i$　**26.** $\pm(4 + 2\,i)$

1. $c = 65 + 6\,k$　**2.** $y = 3\,x + 4$

Page 213. — 3. 26　**4.** $(a - b)(m - 1)(m + 1)$　**5.** -5　**6.** $-\dfrac{b}{a + 3\,b}$　**7.** $57 - 12\sqrt{15}$
8. 8　**9.** $2 + 5\,i$　**10.** $\sqrt{6} - 1$　**11.** $x = a + 1,\ y = a - 1$　**12.** increases from -3 to 0
13. 10 in.　**14.** \$14,000　**15.** 19

Page 216. — 1. $0, -5$ 2. $0, \frac{2}{3}$ 3. $4, -4$ 4. $\frac{5}{2}, -\frac{5}{2}$ 5. $0, 5$ 6. $-3, 2$ 7. $5, 1$ 8. $-6, -2$ 9. $7, -6$ 10. $\frac{3}{2}, -4$ 11. $-\frac{5}{3}, 2$ 12. $\frac{2}{5}, \frac{5}{2}$ 13. $-\frac{5}{6}, 4$ 14. $6, -5$ 15. $-9, 6$ 16. $-6, -1$

Page 217. — 17. $-\frac{1}{2}, 5$ 18. $-8, 4$ 19. $\frac{1}{3}, 3$ 20. $-15, 3$ 21. $5, -3$ 22. $0, 1$ 23. $\frac{9}{2}, 5$ 24. $\frac{5}{2}, 3$

Page 218. — 1. ± 7 2. ± 6 3. ± 10 4. $\pm \frac{5}{2}$ 5. $\pm \frac{4}{3}$ 6. $\pm \frac{13}{5}$ 7. $\pm \frac{12}{7}$ 8. $\pm \sqrt{5}$ 9. $\pm 2\sqrt{2}$ 10. $\pm \frac{5}{\sqrt{3}}$ 11. ± 3 12. ± 2 13. $\pm \frac{2\sqrt{7}}{5}$ 14. $\pm \frac{8\sqrt{3}}{9}$ 15. $\pm \frac{\sqrt{30}}{2}$ 16. $4, -2$ 17. $13, -3$ 18. $7, -3$ 19. $5, -13$ 20. $12, 0$ 21. $3 \pm \sqrt{10}$ 22. $\frac{3 \pm 2\sqrt{2}}{2}$ 23. $\frac{-1 \pm 2\sqrt{3}}{3}$ 24. $\frac{3 \pm \sqrt{6}}{5}$ 25. $2, -1$ 26. $\frac{-1 \pm \sqrt{15}}{2}$ 27. ± 6 28. ± 5 29. ± 17 30. $\pm 3\sqrt{2}$ 31. $\pm i\sqrt{6}$ 32. $\pm \frac{7}{3}$

Page 219. — 1. 25 2. 81 3. 1 4. $\frac{25}{4}$ 5. $\frac{81}{4}$ 6. $\frac{25}{4}$ 7. $\frac{1}{25}$ 8. $\frac{4}{49}$ 9. $\frac{1}{16}$ 10. $\frac{1}{9}$ 11. $\frac{b^2}{4}$ 12. $\frac{b^2}{4a^2}$

Page 221. — 1. $\frac{-3 \pm \sqrt{17}}{2}$ 2. $\frac{-5 \pm \sqrt{37}}{2}$ 3. $6, -5$ 4. $3 \pm \sqrt{5}$ 5. $2 \pm \sqrt{6}$ 6. $-4 \pm 2\sqrt{3}$ 7. $\frac{-3 \pm \sqrt{11}}{2}$ 8. $4, -\frac{1}{3}$ 9. $\frac{2 \pm \sqrt{7}}{3}$ 10. $\frac{3 \pm \sqrt{3}}{2}$ 11. $\frac{1}{2}, -\frac{2}{3}$ 12. $\frac{3 \pm \sqrt{33}}{2}$ 13. $2.62, 0.38$ 14. $2.79, -1.79$ 15. $.41, -7.41$ 16. $7.32, .68$ 17. $.85, -2.35$ 18. $1.39, .36$ 19. $.93, -3.59$ 20. $-.29, -1.71$ 21. $3.69, -.36$ 22. $1.31, -.31$ 23. $.58, -2.58$ 24. $7.74, .26$

Page 223. — 1. $a = 2, b = 3, c = 4$ 2. $a = 4, b = 2, c = -3$ 3. $a = 3, b = -5, c = 2$ 4. $a = 7, b = -6, c = -5$ 5. $a = 1, b = 10, c = -8$ 6. $a = 6, b = -4, c = -1$ 7. $a = 3, b = 9, c = -16$ 8. $a = 2, b = -3, c = 12$ 9. $a = 3, b = 0, c = -14$ 10. $a = m, b = -2m, e = 4$ 11. $a = a - b, b = c, c = -d$ 12. $a = 2p, b = -(p + q), e = -r$ 13. $a = -1, b = +(2a + b), c = -5$ 14. $a = 1 + b, b = -a, c = -p$ 15. $a = 1 - m, b = 1 + n, c = p$ 16. $a = p + q, b = -1, c = q$

Page 225. — 1. $\frac{3 \pm \sqrt{41}}{4}$ 2. $\frac{-3 \pm \sqrt{6}}{3}$ 3. $2 \pm \sqrt{2}$ 4. $\frac{1 \pm \sqrt{61}}{10}$ 5. $\frac{5}{2}, -\frac{3}{2}$ 6. $-1 \pm i$ 7. $\frac{1}{3}, -2$ 8. $\frac{3}{2}, \frac{1}{2}$ 9. $\frac{3 \pm \sqrt{105}}{12}$ 10. $\frac{3 \pm i}{2}$ 11. $\frac{-5 \pm \sqrt{19}}{2}$ 12. $\frac{-3 \pm \sqrt{13}}{6}$ 13. $17, 2$ 14. $\frac{5}{2}, \frac{1}{2}$ 15. $\frac{1 \pm \sqrt{7}}{6}$ 16. $\frac{6}{5}, 0$ 17. $\frac{1 \pm \sqrt{97}}{8}$ 18. $2 \pm 3i$ 19. $\frac{5 \pm \sqrt{10}}{3}$ 20. $\frac{-3 \pm \sqrt{3}}{2}$ 21. $\frac{7}{8}, 0$ 22. $\frac{4 \pm \sqrt{14}}{2}$ 23. $\frac{2 \pm i\sqrt{5}}{2}$ 24. $\pm \frac{2\sqrt{3}}{3}$ 25. $\frac{3}{2}, \frac{2}{3}$ 26. $\frac{2 \pm \sqrt{34}}{10}$ 27. $\frac{3 \pm \sqrt{39}}{2}$ 28. $\frac{1 \pm \sqrt{11}}{4}$ 29. $\frac{1 \pm \sqrt{17}}{3}$

Page 226. — 1. $a, -a$ 2. $0, \frac{b}{a}$ 3. $a, -a$ 4. $3a, -3a$ 5. $\frac{1}{a}, -\frac{1}{a}$ 6. $-2a, a$ 7. $3b, -2b$ 8. $-5b, 3b$ 9. $\frac{a}{2}, 3a$ 10. $\frac{b}{3}, \frac{b}{2}$ 11. $\frac{2b}{a}, \frac{b}{a}$ 12. $\pm(a - b)$ 13. $\pm(a + b)$

14. $2a + b$, $2a - b$ 15. $b + a$, $b - a$ 16. $a - 4$, $a - 1$ 17. a, b

18. $\dfrac{4b + a \pm \sqrt{16b^2 + 8ba + a^2 + 16}}{4}$ 19. $\dfrac{a - b \pm \sqrt{a^2 - 2ab + 5b^2}}{2}$ 20. $\dfrac{a \pm \sqrt{5a^2 - 4b^2}}{2}$

Page 230. — 1. 5, −1 2. 2, −2 3. 0, −2 4. 3.6, −1.6 5. −1, −5 6. 2, 2
7. 5, 5 8. −0.5, 1.5 9. 0.3, −1.8 10. −1.5, 3 11. 0.5, −1.9 12. −1.5 ± 0.9i
13. −0.5 ± 1.3i 14. 1.5 ± 1.7i 15. −0.3 ± 1.2i 16. 0.3 ± 0.5i

Page 231. — 1. 5, −4 2. −7, −3 3. $\dfrac{3}{2}$, −2 4. $3a$, −$3a$ 5. 0, −$\dfrac{5}{2}$ 6. 4 ± 3$\sqrt{2}$

7. $\dfrac{3 \pm \sqrt{7}}{2}$ 8. $\dfrac{a}{2}$, $3a$ 9. $\dfrac{1 \pm i\sqrt{3}}{2}$ 10. $\dfrac{6 \pm \sqrt{21}}{3}$ 11. 10 ± 3$\sqrt{10}$ 12. −$\dfrac{1}{5}$, $\dfrac{1}{3}$

13. $\dfrac{5 \pm \sqrt{5}}{4}$ 14. $\dfrac{5}{2}$, −$\dfrac{2}{3}$ 15. $\dfrac{-5 \pm \sqrt{109}}{6}$ 16. −$\dfrac{2}{3}$, −$\dfrac{1}{2}$ 17. $\dfrac{4 \pm \sqrt{6}}{5}$ 18. $\dfrac{2 \pm i\sqrt{5}}{3}$

19. $\dfrac{3}{4}$, −$\dfrac{2}{3}$ 20. −$\dfrac{1}{5}$, $\dfrac{2}{7}$ 21. 6, −4 22. −$\dfrac{1}{4}$, −8 23. 3, −3 24. 0, −$\dfrac{7}{2}$ 25. 4, −2

26. −1 ± $i\sqrt{7}$ 27. 8, −6 28. −$\dfrac{3}{2}$, 3 29. 0, 7 30. −2 ± 2$i\sqrt{11}$ 31. −5, 7

Page 232. — 32. $\dfrac{-5 \pm 5i\sqrt{7}}{2}$ 33. −a, $2b$ 34. $\dfrac{a}{2}$, $\dfrac{a}{2}$ 35. ±$(b - a)$

1. 9, −2 2. $\dfrac{7}{2}$, −3 3. 12, 14; −14, −12 4. 9, 11; −11, −9 5. $\dfrac{2}{3}$, $\dfrac{3}{2}$ 6. −$\dfrac{2}{5}$, $\dfrac{5}{2}$

7. $\dfrac{1}{2}$, 6

Page 233. — 1. 8 ft. × 15 ft.   2. altitude, 8 ft.; base, 12 ft.
3. 9 ft. and 14 ft.; 1 ft. and 6 ft.   4. 8 ft.   5. 9 in. × 12 in.   6. 15 in. × 20 in.
7. 160 ft.

Page 234. — 8. 12 in., 3 in.

Doings of Dimbo. $x = 8$, −1

1. going 48 mph, returning 60 mph

Page 235. — 2. going 6 mph, returning 4 mph 3. 1st man 45 mph, 2nd man 55 mph
4. 50 mph 5. 300 mph

Page 236. — 1. smaller farm 70 A., larger farm 80 A.   2. 50   3. 25
4. 1st wire 20 ft., 2nd wire 60 ft. 5. 100 6. 10 doz.

Page 237. — 1. man 6 da., son 12 da. 2. faster machine 3 hr., slower machine 5 hr.
3. 8 da. 4. Allen 3 hr., Bob 4 hr., Carl 6 hr. 5. 12 hr.

Page 238. — 1. 5, −5 2. −$\dfrac{3}{5}$, $\dfrac{3}{2}$ 3. −$\dfrac{5}{2}$, 5 4. 4, 12 5. 2 6. 6 7. −5 8. 5
9. 25 10. 1 11. −4 12. 12 13. 2, −1 14. −4 15. 5, 1 16. 23 17. −1 18. 0
19. $\dfrac{27}{4}$ 20. 5

Page 239. — 21. $\dfrac{9}{5}$ 22. 10 23. $\dfrac{1}{19}$, $\dfrac{1}{3}$ 24. 3

Page 240. — 1. ± 2, ± 1 2. ± 3, ± 2 3. 25, 1 4. 4 5. 16 6. −8, 1 7. −2, 1
8. −$\dfrac{1}{4}$, $\dfrac{1}{2}$ 9. 27, 1 10. −$\dfrac{8}{27}$, 8 11. $\dfrac{1}{8}$, 8 12. $\dfrac{27}{8}$, 1 13. 7 14. $\dfrac{13}{2}$, 6 15. 5
16. 5, −1, 0, 4

1. (a) ± 6 (b) 0, $\dfrac{9}{2}$ (c) −$\dfrac{3}{2}$, 5 (d) $\dfrac{7 \pm \sqrt{109}}{2}$ (e) $\dfrac{-7 \pm \sqrt{97}}{2}$ (f) 3, −2   2. (a) $\dfrac{a}{2}$, 2b

(b) $a + b$, $a - b$ 3. −1.2, 3.2 4. −1 ± i 5. $\dfrac{2}{3}$ 6. 512, −1 7. 4, 2 8. $\dfrac{-b \pm \sqrt{b^2 - 4ac}}{2a}$

Page 241. — **9.** 1st rate 60 mph, 2nd rate 50 mph
10. larger faucet 10 hr., smaller faucet 15 hr.

1. $a(x+3)(x-1)$ **2.** $x=-3,\ y=5$ **3.** 2   **4.** 8   **5.** $\dfrac{2x+2}{x^2-9}$ **6.** $6\sqrt{6}$ **7.** $\dfrac{b^2c^{12}}{a^4}$

8 -41 **9.** $\dfrac{2A-hy}{h}$ **10.** \$7500 at 4%, \$9000 at 5%   **11.** 14 in., 48 in.
12. 1st boy 48 mph, 2nd boy 45 mph

Page 246. — **1.** real, unequal, irrational   **2.** imaginary   **3.** real, unequal, rational
4. real, equal, rational   **5.** real, equal, rational   **6.** imaginary   **7.** real, unequal, rational
8. real, unequal, irrational   **9.** real, unequal, irrational   **10.** real, unequal, rational
11. real, equal, rational   **12.** real, unequal, rational   **13.** imaginary
14. real, unequal, irrational   **15.** real, unequal, rational   **16.** real, unequal, rational
17. imaginary   **18.** imaginary   **19.** real, unequal, rational   **20.** real, unequal, rational
21. real, unequal, rational   **22.** ± 5 **23.** 4   **24.** $-10,\ 2$ **25.** $4,\ -\dfrac{4}{3}$ **26.** $-\dfrac{7}{4},\ 2$
27. 1, 9   **28.** $-\dfrac{5}{3},\ 5$ **29.** 6, 2   **30.** $-9,\ -1$ **31.** -2 **32.** $\dfrac{16}{3}$ **33.** $3,\ -\dfrac{17}{9}$

Page 248. — **1.** $s=-\dfrac{3}{2},\ p=2$ **2.** $s=\dfrac{4}{5},\ p=\dfrac{1}{5}$ **3.** $s=-\dfrac{4}{3},\ p=-\dfrac{3}{2}$ **4.** $s=0,\ p=\dfrac{2}{9}$
5. $s=\dfrac{5}{8},\ p=0$ **6.** $s=5,\ p=\dfrac{10}{7}$ **7.** $s=\dfrac{7}{3},\ p=-2$ **8.** $s=2,\ p=\dfrac{11}{2}$ **9.** $s=-\dfrac{3}{2},\ p=-6$
10. $s=2,\ p=\dfrac{1}{5}$ **11.** $s=3,\ p=\dfrac{2}{3}$ **12.** $s=-\dfrac{6}{5},\ p=\dfrac{4}{3}$ **13.** $s=\dfrac{3b}{2a},\ p=\dfrac{p}{2a}$
14. $s=\dfrac{n}{m^2},\ p=-\dfrac{p}{m^2}$ **15.** $s=\dfrac{1}{a+b},\ p=\dfrac{5}{a+b}$ **16.** $s=\dfrac{1}{r-1},\ p=\dfrac{p+q}{r-1}$ **17.** $-\dfrac{1}{2},\ 2$
18. $3,\ -2$ **19.** ± 4 **20.** $0,\ 6$

Page 249. — **1.** $x^2-6x+8=0$ **2.** $x^2-x-20=0$ **3.** $x^2-x-56=0$
4. $x^2+13x+36=0$ **5.** $2x^2-7x+3=0$ **6.** $4x^2+7x-2=0$ **7.** $6x^2-7x+2=0$
8. $16x^2-8x-3=0$ **9.** $x^2-5x=0$ **10.** $x^2-81=0$ **11.** $2x^2+x=0$
12. $10x^2+9x-9=0$ **13.** $x^2+2ax-3a^2=0$ **14.** $4x^2-8bx+3b^2=0$
15. $x^2-2ax+a^2-b^2=0$ **16.** $x^2-2ax-2bx-3a^2+10ab-3b^2=0$
17. $x^2-2=0$ **18.** $x^2-6x+7=0$

Page 250. — **19.** $4x^2-8x+1=0$ **20.** $4x^2+4x-19=0$ **21.** $x^2-4x+5=0$
22. $x^2+6x+13=0$ **23.** $4x^2-4ax+a^2-b=0$ **24.** $x^2-2ax+a^2+b^2=0$
25. $9x^2-12x+7=0$ **26.** $16x^2-16x+49=0$

Page 252. — **1.** 1, 3   **2.** 3, 2, 3   **3.** 2, 4   **4.** 2, 3   **5.** 3, 1, 3   **6.** 2, 4

1. $x>5$ **2.** $x<-2$ **3.** $x<5$ **4.** $x<3$ **5.** $x<4$ **6.** $x<-2$ **7.** $x<0$ **8.** $x>1$
9. $x>\dfrac{7}{3}$ **10.** $x>-6$ **11.** $x>-\dfrac{12}{5}$ **12.** $x<11$

Page 254. — **1.** $6>x>-2$ **2.** $3>x>-5$ **3.** $5>x>-4$ **4.** $x<1,\ x>3$
5. $x<-3,\ x>-2$ **6.** $2>x>-7$ **7.** $x<-4,\ x>\dfrac{5}{2}$ **8.** $\dfrac{5}{2}>x>\dfrac{3}{2}$ **9.** $\dfrac{1}{2}>x>-1$
10. $\dfrac{1}{2}>x>-\dfrac{2}{5}$ **11.** $x<-\dfrac{3}{2},\ x>-\dfrac{1}{3}$ **12.** $\dfrac{5}{2}>x>-\dfrac{7}{3}$

Page 255. — **1.** (a) $x<-3,\ x>-1$ (b) $-1>x>-3$ (c) $-1, 3$ **2.** $x>4,\ x<0.5$
3. $-3.3<x<-0.2$ (approx.)   **4.** All values of x satisfy the inequality.   **5.** no value of x
6. $x=4$

Page 256. — **1.** $m<-5,\ m>5$ **2.** $m<-10,\ m>2$ **3.** $5>m>-\dfrac{5}{3}$
4. $m<-2,\ m>-2$ **5.** $m>4$ **6.** $2>m>-\dfrac{7}{4}$ **7.** $6>m>2$ **8.** $3>m>-\dfrac{17}{9}$

1. (a) imaginary (b) -7 (c) real (d) rational   2. (a) real (b) equal (c) rational (d) 0 (e) real   3. (a) ± 8 (b) 1 (c) 4 (d) 16   4. $k \gtreqless 4$

Page 257. — 5. $k > \frac{81}{4}$ 6. $\frac{27}{2}$ 7. $x^2 + 3x + 8 = 0$ 8. (a) No, when a, b, and c are real, $b^2 - 4ac$ cannot be the even root of a negative number.   (b) Yes, the discriminant will be negative when $4ac > b^2$.

9. -1 a root -2 the constant term

$-\frac{3}{5}$ the sum of the roots   3   a numerical coefficient

$-\frac{2}{5}$ the product of the roots   5   another numerical coefficient

$\frac{2}{5}$ another root   49   the discriminant

10. 8   11. $\frac{1}{9}$ 12. $x^2 + 2x - 15 = 0$ 13. -2 14. no   15. no   16. yes   17. $\frac{1}{2}$

Page 258. — 1. (a) real, unequal, irrational (b) imaginary (c) real, equal, rational (d) real, unequal, rational   2. (a) $x^2 + 2x - 15 = 0$ (b) $6x^2 - ax - 2a^2 = 0$ (c) $x^2 - 6x - 11 = 0$ (d) $16x^2 - 16x + 5 = 0$ 3. (a) $s = \frac{3}{2}$, $p = 2$ (b) $s = 0$, $p = -\frac{16}{3}$ (c) $s = 2$, $p = 0$ (d) $s = q$, $p = -r$ 4. 5, 3   5. $x > -3$ 6. $2 > x > -5$ 7. -11, 5 8. (a) $m > \frac{16}{3}$ (b) $m < \frac{16}{3}$ 9. ± 18 10. $k > 36$

1. $18x^3 - 33x^2 - 30x$ 2. $3\sqrt{7}$ 3. $0, -\dfrac{b}{2a}$ 4. $\pm \frac{1}{2}\sqrt{100 - x^2}$ 5. $(m - 3n + 1)(m + 3n - 1)$ 6. $\frac{4}{3}$ 7. three positive integers: 1, 2, 3   8. $\pm \frac{1}{2}, \pm 3$ 9. $\pm 2\sqrt{2}$

Page 259. — 10. $x = \frac{11}{159}$, $y = -\frac{11}{85}$ 11. $m^2 \geqq -8p$ 12. $3a^{\frac{1}{2}}b^6$ 13. 1 14. First number is 7, second number is 26.   15. $x = 1, y = -3, z = 5$ 16. $-1.5 \pm 1.3i$ **Page 262.** — 1. (a) $x = 2$ (b) $x = -\frac{3}{2}$ (c) $x = 0$ (d) $x = \frac{5}{2}$ (e) $x = 0$ 2. c, e

Page 263. — 3. c, d   4. (a) 9 (b) -7 (c) 16 (d) -4 (e) -18 (f) -1 5. (0, 0), (1, 0) 6. (0, 0), (2, 0)   7. (0, 0), $(-1, 0)$ 8. (0, 0), $(-5, 0)$ 9. (0, 0), (2, 0)   10. (0, 0), (4, 0) 11. (0, 0), $(-5, 0)$ 12. (0, 0), $(-2, 0)$ 13. (0, 0)   14. (1, 0)   15. (3, 0)   16. $(-2, 0)$ 17. $(-5, 0)$ 18. $\left(\frac{1}{2}, 0\right)$ 19. $\left(\frac{4}{3}, 0\right)$ 20. $\left(-\frac{4}{5}, 0\right)$ 21. (1, 0)   22. $(-1, 0)$ 23. $\left(\frac{3}{2}, 0\right)$ 24. $\left(-\frac{6}{5}, 0\right)$

Page 264. — 1. vertex $(1, -6)$ 2. vertex $(0, 0)$ 3. vertex $(2, -1)$ 4. vertex $(0, -4)$

5. vertex $(4, 0)$ 6. vertex $\left(\frac{3}{2}, -\frac{29}{4}\right)$ 7. vertex $(-9, -6)$ 8. vertex $\left(-\frac{5}{2}, -\frac{25}{4}\right)$ 9. vertex $\left(-\frac{1}{2}, \frac{25}{4}\right)$ 10. vertex $\left(-\frac{3}{2}, \frac{41}{4}\right)$ 11. vertex $\left(\frac{1}{6}, -\frac{49}{12}\right)$ 12. vertex $\left(\frac{15}{2}, \frac{25}{4}\right)$ 13. vertex $\left(\frac{3}{2}, -\frac{5}{4}\right)$ 14. vertex $\left(-\frac{1}{4}, \frac{23}{24}\right)$

Page 265. — 1. (0, 0), (0, 1)   2. (0, 0), (0, 3)   3. (0, 0), (0, -1)   4. (0, 0), (0, -4) 5. (0, 0), (0, 3)   6. (0, 0), (0, 4)   7. (0, 0), (0, -2)   8. (0, 0), (0, -3)   9. (0, 0)

10. (0, 1)   11. (0, 4)   12. (0, -3)   13. (0, -7)   14. $\left(0, \frac{1}{3}\right)$ 15. $\left(0, \frac{3}{4}\right)$ 16. $\left(0, -\frac{5}{6}\right)$ 17. (0, 2)   18. (0, 6)   19. $\left(0, \frac{5}{3}\right)$ 20. $\left(0, -\frac{2}{7}\right)$

Page 266.—1. coordinates of vertex $\left(\frac{3}{4}, \frac{1}{2}\right)$ **2.** vertex (1, 3)   **3.** vertex (0,0)
4. vertex (0, 2)   **5.** vertex $\left(\frac{15}{4}, \frac{3}{2}\right)$ **6.** vertex (−6, 0)   **7.** vertex $\left(-\frac{9}{4}, -\frac{3}{2}\right)$
8. vertex $\left(\frac{25}{4}, -\frac{1}{2}\right)$ **9.** vertex (−6, −9)   **10.** vertex $\left(-\frac{5}{4}, \frac{3}{2}\right)$ **11.** vertex $\left(-\frac{49}{12}, \frac{1}{6}\right)$
12. vertex $\left(\frac{23}{24}, -\frac{1}{4}\right)$

Pages 267–268.—The graph of each equation of ex. 1–12 is a circle whose center is the origin. The radii of the respective circles are:

1. 10   **2.** 6   **3.** 8   **4.** $\frac{5}{2}$ **5.** $5\sqrt{2}$ **6.** $2\sqrt{5}$ **7.** $\frac{9}{2}$ **8.** $\frac{14}{3}$ **9.** $\frac{7\sqrt{2}}{2}$ **10.** $\frac{2\sqrt{15}}{3}$
11. $2\sqrt{10}$ **12.** $\frac{\sqrt{70}}{2}$

Pages 269–270.—The graph of each equation of ex. 1–9 is an ellipse whose center is the origin. The points of intersection of the coordinate axes and the respective ellipses are:
1. (6, 0), (−6, 0), (0, 3), (0, −3)   **2.** (5, 0), (−5, 0), (0, 2), (0, −2)
3. (4, 0), (−4, 0), (0, 3), (0, −3)   **4.** (5, 0), (−5, 0), (0, 4), (0, −4)
5. (3, 0), (−3, 0), (0, 5), (0, −5)   **6.** (10, 0), (−10, 0), (0, 3.16), (0, −3.16)
7. (5, 0), (−5, 0), (3.64, 0), (−3.64, 0)   **8.** (3, 0), (−3, 0), (0, 2.44), (0, −2.44)
9. (3.16, 0), (−3.16, 0), (0, 4), (0, −4)

Page 272.—The graph of each equation of ex. 1–9 is a hyperbola whose center is the origin and whose axes are the coordinate axes. The coordinates of their respective vertices are:
1. (2, 0), (−2, 0)   **2.** (4, 0), (−4, 0)   **3.** (5, 0), (−5, 0)   **4.** (4.24, 0), (−4.24, 0)
5. (6, 0), (−6, 0)   **6.** (3, 0), (−3, 0)   **7.** (0, 3), (0, −3)   **8.** (0, 3), (0, −3)
9. (2, 0), (−2, 0)

Page 273.—The graph of each equation of ex. 1–9 is a hyperbola whose branches are in the following quadrants: **1.** 1st and 3rd   **2.** 1st and 3rd   **3.** 2nd and 4th
4. 1st and 3rd   **5.** 2nd and 4th   **6.** 1st and 3rd   **7.** 1st and 3rd   **8.** 1st and 3rd
9. 2nd and 4th

Page 274.—1. circle   **2.** straight line   **3.** hyperbola   **4.** hyperbola   **5.** parabola
6. parabola   **7.** ellipse   **8.** ellipse   **9.** hyperbola   **10.** hyperbola   **11.** parabola
12. hyperbola   **13.** circle   **14.** parabola   **15.** ellipse   **16.** hyperbola   **17.** straight line
18. parabola   **19.** hyperbola   **20.** circle   **21.** ellipse   **22.** hyperbola   **23.** parabola
24. parabola   **25.** straight line   **26.** y axis   **27.** x axis   **28.** y axis   **29.** x axis
30. 1st and 3rd   **31.** 2nd and 4th   **32.** all   **33.** all

Page 276.—1. (3, −2)

Page 277.—2. $x^2 + y^2 = 25$ **3.** See page 270.   **4.** yes   **5.** d **6.** yes
7. point at origin   **8.** x axis and y axis   **9.** two straight lines whose respective equations are $2x = 3y$ and $2x = -3y$ **10.** $x = 3$ **11.** y axis or $x = 0$ **12.** x axis or $y = 0$
13. $y = 3$ **14.** circle, center is origin, radius = 4   **15.** hyperbola with branches in 1st and 3rd quadrants   **16.** parabola, axis of symmetry the x axis, coordinates of vertex (0, 0)   **17.** hyperbola with center at origin, axes the coordinate axes, coordinates of respective vertices (−3, 0) and (3, 0)   **18.** ellipse, center at origin, coordinates of respective points of intersection of ellipse and axes are (−4, 0), (0, 2.4), (4, 0), (0, −2.4)   **19.** parabola, axis of symmetry $y = -1$, coordinates of vertex (−5, −1)

1. $(x - 6y - 3z)(x + 3z)$ **2.** $2\sqrt{2}$ **3.** 3 ft.   **4.** 3   **5.** $x = 5$, $y = -2$, $z = -3$
6. (a) 5, −3   (b) −3 < k < 5

Page 278.—7. $s = \frac{3}{2}$, $p = -2$, roots are real, irrational, unequal   8. 1.59, -1.26

9. $9x^2 - 12x + 7 = 0$ 10. $(-4, 1)$ 11. (a) ellipse (b) hyperbola   12. 48 mph

Page 281. — 1. $x = -5 \quad x = 12$ 2. $x = -3 \quad x = 2$ 3. $x = -1 \quad x = 4$
$\quad\quad y = -12 \quad y = 5$ $\quad y = -4 \quad y = 6$ $\quad y = -3 \quad y = 2$

4. $x = -4 \quad x = 5$ 5. $x = 2.6 \quad x = -4.4$ 6. $x = 2.5$ 7. $x = -6 \quad x = 8$
$y = 0 \quad y = -3$ $\quad y = -4.4 \quad y = 3.5$ $\quad y = 2.5$ $\quad y = 8 \quad y = -6$

8. $x = -3 \quad x = 1$ 9. $x = -2.25 \quad x = 2.25$ 10. no solution   11. $x = 3$
$y = 4 \quad y = -4$ $\quad y = -5 \quad y = 5$ $\quad\quad y = -3$

12. no solution

Page 282. — 1. $x = 8 \quad x = -6$ 2. $x = -4 \quad x = 6$ 3. $x = -3 \quad x = 1$
$\quad\quad y = -6 \quad y = 8$ $\quad y = -3 \quad y = 2$ $\quad y = 4 \quad y = -4$

4. $x = 5 \quad x = -5$ 5. $x = -4$ 6. $x = 6 \quad x = 0$ 7. $x = 3 \quad x = -2$
$y = \frac{9}{4} \quad y = -\frac{9}{4}$ $\quad y = 3$ $\quad y = 4 \quad y = -2$ $\quad y = -3 \quad y = -8$

8. $x = 3 \quad x = -3$ 9. $x = i \quad x = -i$ 10. $x = \frac{9}{14} \quad x = \frac{3}{2}$ 11. $x = -\frac{5}{3} \quad x = 5$

$y = 2 \quad y = -2$ $\quad y = 2i \quad y = -2i$ $\quad y = -\frac{13}{7} \quad y = -1$ $\quad y = -\frac{11}{3} \quad y = 3$

12. $x = -10 \quad x = 3$ 13. $x = 0 \quad x = -2$ 14. $x = -5 + 2i \quad x = -5 - 2i$

$y = -15 \quad y = -2$ $\quad y = -2 \quad y = 0$ $\quad y = \dfrac{5 + 8i}{3} \quad y = \dfrac{5 - 8i}{3}$

15. $x = \frac{39}{29} \quad x = 3$ 16. $x = 4 \quad x = 1$ 17. $x = -\frac{1}{4} \quad x = 2$

$y = -\frac{86}{29} \quad y = 2$ $\quad y = 2 \quad y = -1$ $\quad y = -\frac{35}{24} \quad y = -\frac{1}{3}$

Page 284. — 1. $x = -4 \quad x = -3 \quad x = 3 \quad x = 4$ 2. no solution
$\quad\quad y = -3 \quad y = -4 \quad y = 4 \quad y = 3$

3. $x = -4 \quad x = -1 \quad x = 2$ 4. $x = -3 \quad x = 0 \quad x = 3$
$y = -2 \quad y = -8 \quad y = 4$ $\quad y = 4 \quad y = -5 \quad y = 4$

5. $x = -3 \quad x = -3 \quad x = 3 \quad x = 3$ 6. $x = -5 \quad x = 5$ 7. $x = 0 \quad x = 0$
$y = 2 \quad y = -2 \quad y = 2 \quad y = -2$ $\quad y = -4 \quad y = 4$ $\quad y = 5 \quad y = -5$

8. $x = -2.7 \quad x = -2.2 \quad x = 2.7 \quad x = -2.2$ 9. $x = -4$ 10. no solution
$y = 3.7 \quad y = -3 \quad y = 3.7 \quad y = -3$ $\quad y = 1$

11. $x = -3.7 \quad x = -3.7 \quad x = 4.7 \quad x = 4.7$ 12. $x = 4.5 \quad x = 3.5$ 13. no solution
$y = 3.4 \quad y = -3.4 \quad y = 1.8 \quad y = -1.8$ $\quad y = 5.9 \quad y = 2.5$

14. $x = -2 \quad x = 2$
$y = 0 \quad y = 0$

Page 286. — 1. $x = 5 \quad x = -5 \quad x = 5 \quad x = -5$ 2. $x = 1 \quad x = 1 \quad x = -1 \quad x = -1$
$\quad\quad y = 2 \quad y = 2 \quad y = -2 \quad y = -2$ $\quad y = 4 \quad y = -4 \quad y = 4 \quad y = -4$

3. $x = 3 \quad x = 3 \quad x = -3 \quad x = -3$ 4. $x = 1 \quad x = -1 \quad x = 2 \quad x = -2$
$y = \frac{1}{2} \quad y = -\frac{1}{2} \quad y = \frac{1}{2} \quad y = -\frac{1}{2}$ $\quad y = -2 \quad y = -2 \quad y = 1 \quad y = 1$

5. $x = -3 \quad x = -3 \quad x = 4 \quad x = 4$ 6. $x = 0 \quad x = 0$
$y = 4 \quad y = -4 \quad y = 3 \quad y = -3$ $\quad y = 6 \quad y = -6$

7. $x = 3 \quad x = 3 \quad x = -3 \quad x = -3$ 8. $x = 5 \quad x = 5 \quad x = 4$
$y = \sqrt{3} \quad y = -\sqrt{3} \quad y = \sqrt{3} \quad y = -\sqrt{3}$ $\quad y = 3 \quad y = -3 \quad y = 0$

9. $x = \sqrt{2} \quad x = \sqrt{2} \quad x = -\sqrt{2} \quad x = -\sqrt{2}$ 10. $x = \frac{2}{3} \quad x = \frac{2}{3} \quad x = -\frac{2}{3} \quad x = -\frac{2}{3}$
$y = \frac{3}{2} \quad y = -\frac{3}{2} \quad y = \frac{3}{2} \quad y = -\frac{3}{2}$ $\quad y = \frac{3}{2} \quad y = -\frac{3}{2} \quad y = \frac{3}{2} \quad y = -\frac{3}{2}$

11. $x = \frac{1}{3} \quad x = \frac{1}{3} \quad x = -\frac{1}{3} \quad x = -\frac{1}{3}$ 12. $x = 6 \quad x = 6 \quad x = -2 \quad x = -2$
$y = 4 \quad y = -4 \quad y = 4 \quad y = -4$ $\quad y = \sqrt{19} \quad y = -\sqrt{19} \quad y = \sqrt{3} \quad y = -\sqrt{3}$

13. $x = 12 \quad x = -12 \quad x = 5 \quad x = -5$ 14. $x = \frac{7}{2} \quad x = \frac{7}{2} \quad x = -\frac{7}{2} \quad x = -\frac{7}{2}$
$y = -5 \quad y = -5 \quad y = 12 \quad y = 12$ $\quad y = \frac{7}{3} \quad y = -\frac{7}{3} \quad y = \frac{7}{3} \quad y = -\frac{7}{3}$

15. $x = \frac{5}{2}$ $x = -\frac{5}{2}$ **16.** $x = -\frac{50}{3}$ $x = -\frac{50}{3}$ $x = 6$ $x = 6$

$y = 0$ $y = 0$ $y = \frac{40}{3}i$ $y = -\frac{40}{3}i$ $y = 8$ $y = -8$

17. $x = 3\sqrt{2}$ $x = 3\sqrt{2}$ $x = -3\sqrt{2}$ $x = -3\sqrt{2}$ **18.** $x = 1$ $x = -1$ $x = i\sqrt{2}$ $x = -i\sqrt{2}$

$y = 2\sqrt{3}$ $y = -2\sqrt{3}$ $y = 2\sqrt{3}$ $y = -2\sqrt{3}$ $y = 2$ $y = 2$ $y = 1$ $y = 1$

19. $x = i$ $x = i$ $x = -i$ $x = -i$ **20.** $x = 2$ $x = 2$

$y = 2i$ $y = -2i$ $y = 2i$ $y = -2i$ $y = 3$ $y = -3$

Page 288. — 1. $x = 4$ $x = -4$ $x = 2$ $x = -2$ **2.** $x = 5$ $x = -5$ $x = 12$ $x = -12$

$y = 2$ $y = -2$ $y = 4$ $y = -4$ $y = 12$ $y = -12$ $y = 5$ $y = -5$

3. $x = 6$ $x = -6$ $x = 1$ $x = -1$ **4.** $x = 9$ $x = -2$

$y = 1$ $y = -1$ $y = 6$ $y = -6$ $y = -\frac{2}{3}$ $y = 3$

5. $x = \frac{3}{2}\sqrt{2}$ $x = -\frac{3}{2}\sqrt{2}$ $x = 4$ $x = -4$ **6.** $x = -3i$ $x = 3i$ $x = 5$ $x = -5$

$y = -4\sqrt{2}$ $y = 4\sqrt{2}$ $y = -3$ $y = 3$ $y = 5i$ $y = -5i$ $y = 3$ $y = -3$

7. $x = -11$ $x = 7$ **8.** $x = \frac{90}{7}$ $x = -4$ **9.** $x = \frac{1}{6}$ $x = -5$

$y = -8$ $y = 10$ $y = \frac{35}{3}$ $y = -8$ $y = -27$ $y = 4$

10. $x = -3$ $x = -8$ **11.** $x = -\frac{1}{3}$ $x = \frac{1}{2}$ **12.** $x = \frac{27}{5}$ $x = 3$

$y = 10$ $y = 5$ $y = -\frac{11}{3}$ $y = -2$ $y = -\frac{28}{5}$ $y = -2$

13. $x = -1$ $x = 1$ **14.** $x = -\frac{16}{27}$ $x = -5$ **15.** $x = \frac{1}{3}$ $x = -\frac{1}{3}$ $x = \frac{2}{3}$ $x = -\frac{2}{3}$

$y = -\frac{3}{2}$ $y = -1$ $y = \frac{9}{32}$ $y = 4$ $y = -\frac{2}{3}$ $y = \frac{2}{3}$ $y = -\frac{1}{3}$ $y = \frac{1}{3}$

16. $x = 2$ $x = -2$ $x = 6$ $x = -6$

$y = 3$ $y = -3$ $y = 1$ $y = -1$

Page 289. — Doings of Dimbo. Dimbo failed to plot second branch to get as a solution $x = -3$, $y = -2$.

Page 291. — 1. 9 and 6 or -9 and -6 **2.** 23 and -11 or 11 and 7   **3.** 5 and 9
4. 7 and 10 or 4 and 1   **5.** 10 in. by 8 in.   **6.** 10 ft., 16 ft.   **7.** 6 ft. square for each of the three alike, 10 ft. square for the fourth, or 8 ft. square for each of the three alike, 4 ft. square for the fourth

Page 292. — 8. larger square 21 yd. or 27 yd., smaller square 18 yd. or 6 yd.
9. 20 in. by 12 in.   **10.** 40 ft. and 50 ft.   **11.** $x = 12$ **12.** 8 units   **13.** 16   **14.** 32
15. 29 or 92   **16.** 73

Page 293. — 17. 36   **18.** 20 cameras, $15 profit per camera   **19.** 40 sets at $350 per set   **20.** 4 poles   **21.** 4 bales   **22.** 60 balls at $16 each   **23.** $4500 at 5 %

Page 294. — 24. 8 yr., rate 4 %   **25.** $6000 at $3\frac{1}{2}$ %   **26.** $1000   **27.** $-\frac{4}{3}$, 8

28. $\frac{11}{2}$, 10   **29.** 6, -6 **30.** 240 mi.   **31.** 2400 mi.   **32.** 800 mi., 400 mph   **33.** 2 mph

1. $x = -6$ $x = 3.6$ **2.** $x = -6$ $x = 3$

$y = 0$ $y = 4.8$ $y = -1$ $y = 2$

Page 295. — 3. no solution   **4.** $x = 1.1$ $x = 7.9$ **5.** $x = -4$ $x = 2$

$y = -7.9$ $y = -1.1$ $y = 1$ $y = -3$

6. $x = 0$ $x = 4$ **7.** $x = -8$ $x = -6$ $x = 6$ $x = 8$

$y = -3$ $y = 5$ $y = 6$ $y = 8$ $y = -8$ $y = -6$

8. $x = -4$ $x = -4$ $x = 4$ $x = 4$ **9.** $x = 3$ $x = 3$ **10.** no solution

$y = 3$ $y = -3$ $y = 3$ $y = -3$ $y = 1$ $y = -1$

11. $x = 2$ $x = -2$ **12.** $x = -4$ $x = 8$ **13.** $x = 0$ $x = 3$

$y = 3$ $y = -3$ $y = 2$ $y = -1$ $y = -4$ $y = 5$

14. $x = 0$ $x = 3$ **15.** $x = 2$ $x = 2$ $x = -2$ $x = -2$

$y = 2$ $y = -1$ $y = 3$ $y = -3$ $y = 3$ $y = -3$

16. $x = 2$ $x = -2$ $x = \sqrt{3}$ $x = -\sqrt{3}$ **17.** $x = 0$ $x = 0$ $x = -4$ $x = -4$
$y = -3$ $y = 3$ $y = -2\sqrt{3}$ $y = 2\sqrt{3}$ $y = i\sqrt{3}$ $y = -i\sqrt{3}$ $y = \sqrt{5}$ $y = -\sqrt{5}$

18. $x = \sqrt{6}$ $x = -\sqrt{6}$ $x = 2\sqrt{2}$ $x = -2\sqrt{2}$
$y = \frac{2}{3}\sqrt{6}$ $y = -\frac{2}{3}\sqrt{6}$ $y = \sqrt{2}$ $y = -\sqrt{2}$

19. $x = -5\sqrt{2}$ $x = -5\sqrt{2}$ $x = -3$ $x = 3$
$y = \frac{3}{2}\sqrt{2}$ $y = -\frac{3}{2}\sqrt{2}$ $y = 5$ $y = -5$

20. 500 sq. ft.   **21.** 48   **22.** 16 girls   **23.** $p = \pm\sqrt{1 - 2m}$ **24.** 12 mi. at 4 mph

Page 296. — **1.** $2a$ **2.** 3, 2   **3.** -23 **4.** $2(2x - 1)(4x^2 + 2x + 1)$ **5.** -1
6. $\dfrac{a^2 + p^2}{a^2 - p^2}$ **7.** $\dfrac{64}{9}$ **8.** 250   **9.** $x = \dfrac{k^2 + 9}{9}$ **10.** $m = -6$, $p = 7$ **11.** (3, 0)
12. (a) ellipse, x intercept ± 3, y intercept $\pm\sqrt{3}$ (b) parabola, x intercept 2, no y intercept   **13.** 8 ft. by 5 ft.   **14.** 13

Page 298. — **1.** yes; 10   **2.** no   **3.** yes; -3 **4.** yes; 99   **5.** yes; $1\frac{1}{2}$ **6.** no
7. yes; -5.1 **8.** no   **9.** no   **10.** yes; $\dfrac{1}{\sqrt{3}}$

1. yes; $-2\frac{5}{16}$ **2.** yes; $\dfrac{2\sqrt{3}}{3}$ **3.** yes; $\frac{1}{2}$ **4.** yes; $6\frac{2}{3}$ **5.** yes; $-5\frac{5}{9}$ **6.** no   **7.** no
8. no   **9.** yes; 1   **10.** no   **11.** common difference $5a$, 2nd term $-2a$, 5th term $13a$

Page 299. — **12.** $-2a + b, -a + b, b, 2a + b$ **13.** $\frac{3}{2}\sqrt{2}$ **14.** 0

Page 300. — **1.** 23   **2.** 43   **3.** 9   **4.** 184   **5.** $11\frac{1}{2}$ **6.** $\dfrac{37}{5}$ **7.** $13\sqrt{a}$ **8.** $b - 22c$
9. $\dfrac{55(c - d)}{3}$ **10.** $\dfrac{\sqrt{b} - n}{b}$ **11.** 49   **12.** -3 **13.** 21   **14.** $\frac{1}{3}$ **15.** -5 **16.** 10
17. $d = \dfrac{s - r}{2}, r, \dfrac{r + s}{2}, s$ **18.** $\frac{5}{3}$

Page 301. — **1.** 1, 4, 7   **2.** -7 **3.** 2   **4.** $a = -\frac{2}{5}$, $d = -\frac{3}{5}$ **5.** 0.6, 1, 1.4   **6.** -12.3
7. $\dfrac{7}{9}, \dfrac{19}{18}, \dfrac{4}{3}$, etc.

Page 303. — **1.** 2, 6, 10, 14   **2.** 0.65   **3.** $-9, -3, 3, 9, 15$ **4.** $\dfrac{\sqrt{x}}{2}$
5. $-\dfrac{5}{6}, -\dfrac{1}{2}, -\dfrac{1}{6}, \dfrac{1}{6}, \dfrac{1}{2}, \dfrac{5}{6}$ **6.** $\dfrac{7}{12}, \dfrac{1}{6}, -\dfrac{1}{4}, -\dfrac{2}{3}, -\dfrac{13}{12}$ **7.** 56   **8.** 38
9. $a + \dfrac{b}{2}, a + b, a + \dfrac{3b}{2}, a + 2b, a + \dfrac{5b}{2}$ **10.** $\dfrac{x - y}{3}, \dfrac{2x - y}{3}, \dfrac{3x - y}{3}, \dfrac{4x - y}{3}, \dfrac{5x - y}{3}$
11. p **12.** $\dfrac{a^2 + b^2}{a^2 - b^2}$

Page 304. — **1.** 990   **2.** -12 **3.** 315   **4.** 7

Page 305. — **5.** 2500   **6.** 1300   **7.** 12   **8.** 0.2   **9.** $-\frac{1}{3}$ **10.** $\dfrac{11}{3}$

Page 306. — **1.** 37, 46, 55   **2.** $-17, -15, -13, -11$ **3.** 4, 6, 8   **4.** 0.24, 0.48, 0.72, 0.96

Page 307. — **5.** $x = 3$; 6, 18, 30   **6.** $x = -3$; $-15, -3, 9$ **7.** She lost $167.95.
8. $-15, -11, -7, -3$ or 3, 7, 11, 15   **9.** $942, $924, 20 yr., $3780
10. $460, $4.58, 30 mo., $9.30   **11.** -1, 4; 3, 8   **12.** 550 ft.

Page 308. — 1. yes; 2   2. yes; $\frac{1}{3}$ 3. no   4. no   5. yes; x 6. yes; $\frac{1}{2}$ 7. yes; bc
8. yes; $\frac{1}{2}$ 9. no   10. yes; -3

1. yes; 5   2. yes; $\sqrt{3}$ 3. no   4. yes; $\sqrt{a}$ 5. yes; 0.01   6. no   7. yes; $\frac{\sqrt{a}}{\sqrt{b}}$
8. no   9. yes; $\frac{\sqrt{y}}{\sqrt{x}}$ 10. yes; $\frac{1}{\sqrt{c}-\sqrt{d}}$ 11. $-1, \frac{1}{2}, -\frac{1}{16}$

Page 309. — 12. $\frac{1}{2}\sqrt{7}, \frac{1}{2}\sqrt{14}, \sqrt{14}, 2\sqrt{7}$ 13. ± 1 14. $r=0.2; -1.5, -0.06$

Page 310. — 1. 512   2. 192   3. -1458 4. $\frac{1}{256}$ 5. -768 6. 81   7. $\frac{1}{64\,a^7}$
8. $-\frac{x^7}{2187}$ 9. $\pm 2\,x$ 10. $\frac{1}{5}$ 11. 6   12. $\pm 729\ pm^6n^{12}$

Page 311. — 13. $r=\pm\sqrt{2\,x}$; 6th term $\pm 4\,x^3\sqrt{6}$ 14. $r=\frac{1}{2}$, $a=4$; $r=2$, $a=\frac{1}{2}$
15. $r=\frac{1}{2}$, $a=48$

Page 312. — 1. 2, 4, 8, 16   2. 3, ± 6, 12, ± 24, 48   3. 1, 3, 9, 27, 81, 243
4. $-\frac{1}{21}, -\frac{1}{63}, -\frac{1}{189}$ or $\frac{1}{21}, -\frac{1}{63}, \frac{1}{189}$ 5. 0.01, ± 0.05, 0.25, ± 1.25, 6.25
6. $\pm\frac{9\,x^2}{8}$ 7. $\pm 3\,a$ 8. $\pm\frac{3\,a}{2}$ 9. $\pm\sqrt{mn}$ 10. $\sqrt[3]{\frac{p}{q}}$

Page 314. — 1. 2912   2. 2550   3. 2805   4. $\frac{2186}{2187}$ 5. -7812 6. -129
7. $\frac{40}{9}\sqrt{3}$ 8. $\frac{525}{256}$ 9. $\frac{31}{16}\sqrt{2}$ 10. 2

Page 315. — 1. $-\frac{2}{5}$, 5   2. $\pm\frac{1}{2}$ 3. 10   4. 10   5. $-\frac{2}{3}$, 10

Page 317. — 1. 12   2. 6   3. $\frac{32}{3}$ 4. $\frac{15}{2}$ 5. 27   6. -1 7. $\frac{1}{9}$ 8. $\frac{5}{4}\sqrt{5}$ 9. $-\frac{16}{7}$
10. $\frac{2}{3}$ 11. 32   12. $\frac{1}{6}$ 13. 2, 1, $\frac{1}{2}, \cdots$; 6, -3, $\frac{3}{2}, \cdots$ 14. $\frac{9}{2}$, 3, 2, $\cdots$; 9, 3, 1, $\cdots$
15. 18, $\frac{9}{2}$, $\frac{9}{8}, \cdots$ 16. 6, 3, $\frac{3}{2}, \cdots$

Page 318. — 1. $\frac{1}{3}$ 2. $\frac{5}{9}$ 3. $\frac{8}{9}$ 4. $\frac{8}{33}$ 5. $\frac{32}{99}$ 6. $\frac{16}{33}$ 7. $\frac{41}{333}$ 8. $\frac{908}{999}$ 9. $\frac{431}{990}$
10. $1\frac{2}{9}$ 11. $3\frac{64}{99}$ 12. $6\frac{328}{2475}$
1. \$843.15

Page 319. — 2. 2; 12, 6, 3   3. 220, 176, 132; 20, 16, 12   4. 4, 6, 10   5. 768
6. 16, 4, 1,   7. 20, 10, 5   8. -5, 1, 7, 49; 9, 1, -7, 49   9. 36 in.

Page 320. — 10. 48π sq. in.   11. 5:00 P.M.   12. \$25.31   13. $\frac{1}{64}$ 14. $\frac{7}{8}$ 15. 480 ft.

Page 321. — 16. \$1,562.50   17. $\frac{64}{729}$
1. 7   2. 13   3. 2500   4. 520   5. $\pm 10\,xy^2$ 6. $-10, -8.5, -7, -5.5, -4$
7. $-1, -4, -16, -64, -256, -1024$ 8. 1.2   9. 18, 12, 8, $\cdots$ 10. 9, 10.5, 12, 13.5, 15
11. 0.6, 1, 1.4   12. $x=15$; 18, 12, 8   13. $\frac{26}{33}$ 14. -2, 2, 6   15. 20, 5

Page 322. — 16. $\frac{2187}{125}$ cm., 240 cm.

1. $m = \frac{2}{3}$, $b = -5$ 2. $y^2 - 3y - 18$ 3. $(x + 1)(x^2 + x + 1)$ 4. $2\sqrt{7} + 4\sqrt{6} - 6\sqrt{5}$
5. $x = 3$, $y = -7$ 6. real, unequal, irrational   7. $9x^2 - 12x + 1 = 0$ 8. 5, 1   9. 2
10. 6 qt.   11. 1   12. $\frac{1}{96}$ 13. 36, 12, 4   14. 11.9 yr.   15. -1, 2.5

Page 324. — 1. $\log_{10} 1000 = 3$ 2. $\log_2 32 = 5$ 3. $\log_3 27 = 3$ 4. $\log_{10} 100,000 = 5$
5. $\log_n m = r$ 6. $\log_r t = 5$ 7. $\log_8 2 = \frac{1}{3}$ 8. $\log_{81} 3 = \frac{1}{4}$ 9. $\log_{1000} 100 = \frac{2}{3}$
10. $\log_2 \frac{1}{16} = -4$ 11. $\log_2 128 = 7$ 12. $\log_a 1 = 0$ 13. $\log_b 1 = 0$ 14. $\log_{10} 0.001 = -3$
15. $\log_{10} 0.1 = -1$ 16. $100 = 10^2$ 17. $16 = 2^4$ 18. $1 = b^0$ 19. $27 = 3^3$ 20. $32 = 4^{\frac{5}{2}}$
21. $100,000 = 10^5$ 22. $b = b^1$ 23. $\frac{1}{5} = 25^{-\frac{1}{2}}$ 24. $4 = 8^{\frac{2}{3}}$ 25. $256 = 4^4$ 26. $N = a^c$
27. $0.01 = 10^{-2}$

Page 325. — 1. 2   2. 3   3. 1000   4. 25   5. ± 2 6. 2   7. 0   8. 10   9. 1   10. 1
11. 16   12. 1   13. ± 5 14. 5   15. 3   16. -1 17. ± 10 18. ± 3 19. -2 20. 9   21. 9

Page 329. — 1. 0   2. 2   3. 2   4. -1 5. 1   6. 3   7. -2 8. 0   9. 1   10. 0   11. 1
12. 4   13. -4 14. 2   15. -1 16. 0

1. 9.63   2. 23.8   3. 7100   4. 6.154   5. 0.35   6. 0.00762

Page 330. — 7. 101.3   8. 7.0   9. 0.023   10. 70.   11. 30,000   12. 134.2   13. 0.1342
14. 6500   15. 0.0065   16. 1.07

Page 332. — 1. 0.8149   2. 0.2648   3. 0.6794   4. 1.4871   5. 2.6990   6. 0.9031
7. 2.5391   8. 1.8751   9. 4.7324   10. 0.6902   11. $9.7505 - 10$ 12. $8.7973 - 10$
13. $7.4409 - 10$ 14. 1.9063   15. $9.3802 - 10$ 16. 0.4969   17. $6.7160 - 10$
18. $8.3010 - 10$ 19. 3   20. 0.4786

Page 334. — 1. 3.6651   2. 3.6276   3. 3.6510   4. 1.6560   5. 0.7524   6. 2.8503
7. 0.9371   8. $9.9424 - 10$ 9. $8.8473 - 10$ 10. $7.0149 - 10$ 11. 0.3359   12. 4.9409
13. $9.3306 - 10$ 14. 0.4221   15. 0.7915   16. 5.9761   17. $8.7553 - 10$ 18. 2.9543
19. 3.4208   20. $9.8860 - 10$ 21. 0.0204   22. 3.0107   23. $9.5228 - 10$ 24. $9.2217 - 10$

Page 335. — 1. 5.52   2. 89.8   3. 135   4. 21.7   5. 0.0479   6. 300   7. 80,000
8. 0.00182   9. 3.88   10. 0.9   11. 447.5   12. 86.22

Page 336. — 13. 5.565   14. 21.14   15. 2.199   16. 8346   17. 63,159   18. 0.01945
19. .7127   20. 5505   21. 0.001082   22. 26.67   23. 0.7523   24. 507.4   25. 401,091
26. 0.02382   27. 12.95   28. 7088   29. 5.577   30. 373.8

Page 337. — 1. 80.6   2. 5.52   3. 720.5   4. 1579   5. 1193   6. 2448   7. 996.3
8. -40.44 9. 2354   10. 224.2   11. -866.2 12. 3.264   13. 18.94   14. 3.335
15. 39.85   16. 0.8268   17. 473.1   18. 605.6   19. 948   20. 25.81

Page 338. — 1. 24.7   2. 2.388   3. 31.68   4. 314.5   5. 66.43   6. 31.64   7. 0.361
8. 0.02835   9. 0.03156   10. 0.6099   11. 0.02321   12. 8.788   13. 214.1   14. 5.476
15. 0.004685   16. 40.0   17. 0.03768

Page 340. — 1. 841   2. 753.3   3. 2227   4. 0.1756   5. 97.18   6. 0.01977
7. 19,750   8. 1.479   9. $-23,270$ 10. 1.219   11. 0.5074   12. 1.218   13. 2.9   14. 220
15. 5.51   16. 1.445   17. 80.32   18. -3.559 19. 1.458   20. 0.52   21. 0.8335
22. 0.8278   23. 0.469   24. 0.433

Page 341. — 1. $\log K = \log r + \log s$ 2. $\log V = \log l + \log w + \log h$
3. $\log C = \log 2 + \log \pi + \log r$ 4. $\log I = \log P + \log R + \log T$
5. $\log r = \log d - \log t$ 6. $\log A = \log b + \log h - \log 2$ 7. $\log A = 2 \log s$
8. $\log S = \log 2 + \log \pi + \log r + \log h$ 9. $\log A = \log \pi + 2 \log r$

10. $\log S = \log 4 + \log \pi + 2 \log r$ **11.** $\log F = \log C + \log x - \log D$

12. $\log S = \log k + \log w + \log d - \log l$ **13.** $\log N = \log a + \frac{1}{2} \log b$

14. $\log a = \log x - (\log b + \log y)$ **15.** $\log S = \log g + 2 \log t - \log 2$

16. $\log a = \log \pi + 2 \log r + \log E - \log 180$ **17.** $\log R = 3 \log y + \frac{1}{2} \log x$

18. $\log t = \frac{1}{2}(\log 2 + \log S - \log g)$ **19.** $\log N = \frac{1}{3}(\log a + \log b - \log c)$

20. $\log c = 4 \log A - \frac{1}{3} \log w$

Page 342. — **1.** 26.9   **2.** 3.542   **3.** 1.134   **4.** 0.235   **5.** 2255   **6.** 4.007   **7.** 15.22

Page 343. — **8.** 28.2   **9.** 0.5336   **10.** 6.72   **11.** 830   **12.** 501.2   **13.** −37.57
14. 0.759   **15.** 7.07   **16.** 485.3   **17.** 5.456   **18.** 14.87   **19.** 2.438   **20.** 524.2

Page 344. — **1.** 227.6 sq. in.   **2.** 13.3 in.   **3.** 5.04 in.   **4.** 29.1 in.   **5.** 254.4 sq. in.
6. 680 ft.   **7.** 5%   **8.** 0.7 sec.   **9.** 659.3 cu. in.

Page 345. — **10.** 149.8 sq. in.

Doings of Dimbo. Dimbo should not have subtracted. $p = -54.35$

Page 346. — **1.** 7   **2.** 2   **3.** 4   **4.** −3   **5.** 2.09   **6.** 3.73   **7.** −4.25   **8.** 3.55
9. 1.07   **10.** 1.58   **11.** 1.87   **12.** 0.52   **13.** 1.19   **14.** 5.34   **15.** 2.74   **16.** 32   **17.** 5
18. 10   **19.** 2   **20.** 6   **21.** 4

Page 349. — **1.** $822.80   **2.** $1173   **3.** $2014   **4.** $2600   **5.** $1633   **6.** $1172
7. $1865   **8.** $2456   **9.** $3143   **10.** 9 yr.   **11.** 7 yr.   **12.** $126.80   **13.** $2463
14. $3902   **15.** $2309   **16.** $1589.63 or $1590 approx.   **17.** 11.9 yr. or approx. 12 yr.
18. $12,980

Pages 354-355. — Check results on slide rule with numerical computation by the student.

Page 356. — **1.** 4   **2.** 4   **3.** 2   **4.** 0.6020   **5.** 0.9542   **6.** 0.7781   **7.** 0.1761
8. 17.78   **9.** 37.47   **10.** 2.466   **11.** 0.7026   **12.** 0.6827   **13.** 1.323   **14.** 2.70
15. $3871   **16.** $3365   **17.** 5289 cu. ft.   **18.** 2

1. $-15\,b$ **2.** $x = 3, y = 2$

Page 357. — **3.** (a) $(7x - 2)(2x - 7)$ (b) $(a + \frac{2}{3}b)(a^2 - \frac{2}{3}ab + \frac{4}{9}b^2)$

(c) $(6a + b)(2a - b)$ **4.** $\frac{2b}{(a-b)(b-c)}$ **5.** $\frac{5-x}{x}$ **6.** -2 **7.** $\frac{3+5i}{2}$ **8.** $\pm(3+4i)$

9. 2   **10.** $\frac{-2 \pm \sqrt{10}}{3}$ **11.** no solution   **12.** $x^2 + 3 = 0$ **13.** $x = -\frac{1}{3}, y = -\frac{17}{3}$;

$x = 2, y = -1$ **14.** (a) hyperbola   (b) ellipse   (c) parobola   **15.** $-\frac{1}{2}$

16. $4(x - 3) = 8 + 2(x + 5)$ **17.** $12(y - x) = 850$ **18.** $\frac{xy}{5}$ mi.

19. base 8 in., altitude 5 in.   **20.** $\frac{7}{10}$

Page 362. — **1.** (a) $\sin A = \frac{1}{\sqrt{10}}$, $\cos A = \frac{3}{\sqrt{10}}$, $\tan A = \frac{1}{3}$, $\operatorname{ctn} A = 3$ (b) $70°$

2. (a) $\sin D = \frac{1}{\sqrt{2}}$, $\cos D = \frac{1}{\sqrt{2}}$, $\tan D = 1$, $\operatorname{ctn} D = 1$ (b) $\sin E = \frac{1}{\sqrt{2}}$, $\cos E = \frac{1}{\sqrt{2}}$,
$\tan E = 1$, $\operatorname{ctn} E = 1$

Page 363. — **2.** (c) equal (d) $45°$, $45°$ **3.** (a) $\sin x = \dfrac{r}{t}$, $\cos x = \dfrac{s}{t}$, $\tan x = \dfrac{r}{s}$, $\operatorname{ctn} x = \dfrac{s}{r}$ (b) $\sin y = \dfrac{s}{t}$, $\cos y = \dfrac{r}{t}$, $\tan y = \dfrac{s}{r}$, $\operatorname{ctn} y = \dfrac{r}{s}$ (c) $90°$ (d) $180°$ **4.** (a) $\sin \angle 1 = \dfrac{m}{n}$, $\cos \angle 1 = \dfrac{p}{n}$, $\tan \angle 1 = \dfrac{m}{p}$, $\operatorname{ctn} \angle 1 = \dfrac{p}{m}$ (b) $\sin \angle 2 = \dfrac{p}{n}$, $\cos \angle 2 = \dfrac{m}{n}$, $\tan \angle 2 = \dfrac{p}{m}$, $\operatorname{ctn} \angle 2 = \dfrac{m}{p}$, (c) $90°$

1. (a) $\sin A = \dfrac{8}{17}$, $\cos A = \dfrac{15}{17}$, $\tan A = \dfrac{8}{15}$, $\operatorname{ctn} A = \dfrac{15}{8}$ (b) $\sin B = \dfrac{15}{17}$, $\cos B = \dfrac{8}{17}$, $\tan B = \dfrac{15}{8}$, $\operatorname{ctn} B = \dfrac{8}{15}$ **2.** f = 10. $\sin D = \dfrac{4}{5}$, $\cos D = \dfrac{3}{5}$, $\tan D = \dfrac{4}{3}$, $\operatorname{ctn} D = \dfrac{3}{4}$ **3.** 180 ft. **4.** 1, $\sqrt{3}$, $\sin 30° = \dfrac{1}{2}$, $\cos 30° = \dfrac{\sqrt{3}}{2}$, $\tan 30° = \dfrac{1}{\sqrt{3}}$, $\operatorname{ctn} 30° = \sqrt{3}$

Page 364. — **5.** $\angle A = 60°$, $\angle ABC = 60°$, $\angle ABD = 30°$, $\angle CBD = 30°$, $\angle ADB = 90°$, $\angle CDB = 90°$, $AC = 2$ in., $AD = 1$ in., $BD = \sqrt{3}$ in., $\cos 60° = \dfrac{1}{2}$, $\tan 60° = \sqrt{3}$, $\sin 60° = \dfrac{\sqrt{3}}{2}$, $\operatorname{ctn} 60° = \dfrac{1}{\sqrt{3}}$

Page 366. — **1.** .2278 **2.** .0116 **3.** .9171 **4.** .9159 **5.** 1.0000 **6.** 1.7090 **7.** .9681 **8.** 1.2876 **9.** 10.385 **10.** .0349 **11.** .5735 **12.** .5000 **13.** .7050 **14.** .4006 **15.** .0987 **16.** $23°10'$ **17.** $86°20'$ **18.** $30°$ **19.** $76°40'$ **20.** $22°$ **21.** $3°30'$ **22.** $35°50'$ **23.** $58°30'$ **24.** $65°50'$ **25.** $38°10'$ **26.** $49°20'$ **27.** $45°10'$ **28.** $45°$ **29.** $71°10'$ **30.** $45°$

Page 368. — **1.** (a) 53.24 (b) $57°50'$

Page 369. — **2.** (a) 65.478 (b) $42°30'$ **3.** (a) $61°40'$ (b) 1000 **4.** (a) $13°50'$ (b) $76°10'$ **5.** (a) $65°10'$ (b) $24°50'$ **6.** $a = 167.1$, $b = 109.9$, $\angle B = 33°20'$ **7.** 28.8 ft. **8.** 925.53 ft. **9.** 43.38 ft. **10.** 40 ft.

Page 371. — **1.** .4449 **2.** .9439 **3.** 1.0325 **4.** .1086 **5.** .9812 **6.** .4813 **7.** .7024 **8.** 1.2776 **9.** .3969 **10.** 2.2028 **11.** .8653 **12.** .4139 **13.** 1.0799 **14.** .1739 **15.** 3.3438

Page 373. — **1.** $38°45'$ **2.** $54°3'$ **3.** $46°15'$ **4.** $18°47'$ **5.** $27°25'$ **6.** $32°37'$ **7.** $66°43'$ **8.** $74°59'$ **9.** $57°47'$ **10.** $45°48'$ **11.** $9°34'$ **12.** $15°13'$ **13.** $12°26'$ **14.** $28°15'$ **15.** $47°37'$

Page 374. — **1.** 742.9 **2.** 858 **3.** 114.1 **4.** $36°52'$ **5.** $19°28'$ **6.** 478 ft. approx. **7.** 144 ft. approx. **8.** 20.2 mi.

Doings of Dimbo. Dimbo should have subtracted 6 from 8465.

Page 376. — **1.** 9.5477−10 **2.** 0.1255 **3.** 0.1098 **4.** 9.5126−10 **5.** 9.6587−10 **6.** 9.9473−10 **7.** 9.9598−10 **8.** 9.9071−10 **9.** 0.4102 **10.** 0.1513 **11.** $7°30'$ **12.** $82°30'$ **13.** $41°20'$ **14.** $89°30'$ **15.** $45°40'$ **16.** $18°33'$ **17.** $87°16'$ **18.** $20°22'$ **19.** $61°57'$ **20.** $39°38'$

Page 377. — **1.** $a = 16.82$, $b = 17.82$, $B = 46°40'$ **2.** $b = 26.82$, $c = 29.63$ $B = 64°50'$ **3.** $a = 55.17$, $c = 63.29$, $B = 29°20'$ **4.** $a = 5.431$, $b = 3,958$, $A = 53°55'$ **5.** $c = 72.92$, $A = 40°33'$, $B = 49°27'$ **6.** $a = 634.7$, $A = 61°30'$, $B = 28°30'$ **7.** $b = 1421$, $c = 1752$, $A = 35°48'$ **8.** $a = 0.3734$, $c = 0.8404$, $A = 26°23'$ **9.** 183 ft. **10.** 2080 ft. **11.** 142 ft. **12.** base angles $43°20'$, vertex angle $93°20'$ **13.** 12.63 sq. in. **14.** 444.1 sq. in. **15.** 155 ft.

Page 379. — **1.** $B = 71°28'$; $C = 58°32'$; $c = 473.1$ **2.** $A = 67°30'$; $a = 3.648$, $c = 3.801$

Page 380. — 3. $A = 51° 46'$, $B = 60° 34'$, $b = 66.2$ **4.** $C = 47° 38'$, $b = 63.07$, $c = 57.03$ **5.** $C = 56° 17'$, $A = 61° 18'$, $a = 5368$ **6.** $C = 68°$, $a = 419.1$, $b = 358.8$ **7.** 685.5 ft.   **8.** 157.3 ft.

1. $51° 18'$ **2.** (a) 1.1599   (b) 0.8764   (c) 0.4411   **3.** (a) $48° 2'$ (b) $59° 12'$ (c) $25° 33'$ **4.** (a) 9.7833–10   (b) 0.0448   (c) 0.4533   **5.** (a) $24° 45'$ (b) $29° 26'$ (c) $47° 53'$ **6.** 135.4   **7.** 67.29   **8.** 1078

Page 381. — 9. 555.3   **10.** $51° 20'$ **11.** 357.5 ft.   **12.** 8.7 in.   **13.** $B = 36° 24'$, **14.** 144.2 ft.

1. 6   **2.** $2x^2 - 4x + 5 - \dfrac{2}{x+2}$ **3.** $\dfrac{1}{3}$ **4.** \$5000   **5.** $(m - r + 2t)(m + r - 2t)$

6. $(1 - a)(2b + c)$ **7.** $\dfrac{x(x^2 + 4)}{2(1 - 2x)}$ **8.** -2 **9.** (a) addition–subtraction, substitution, determinants, graphs   (b) $x = -1$, $y = 2$ **10.** $\dfrac{1}{2}\sqrt{3}$ **11.** 9

Page 382. — 12. $\dfrac{1}{3}$ **13.** (a) real, equal, rational   (b) imaginary   (c) real, unequal, irrational   **14.** $0.69, -2.19$ **15.** 3, 2   **16.** 10 in., 26 in.

Page 385. — 1. $x^3 + 3x^2y + 3xy^2 + y^3$ **2.** $m^4 + 4m^3n + 6m^2n^2 + 4mn^3 + n^4$
3. $a^5 + 5a^4b + 10a^3b^2 + 10a^2b^3 + 5ab^4 + b^5$ **4.** $x^4 - 4x^3y + 6x^2y^2 - 4xy^3 + y^4$
5. $a^5 - 5a^4b + 10a^3b^2 - 10a^2b^3 + 5ab^4 - b^5$
6. $x^7 + 7x^6y + 21x^5y^2 + 35x^4y^3 + 35x^3y^4 + 21x^2y^5 + 7xy^6 + y^7$
7. $x^6 - 6x^5y + 15x^4y^2 - 20x^3y^3 + 15x^2y^4 - 6xy^5 + y^6$
8. $a^7 - 7a^6b + 21a^5b^2 - 35a^4b^3 + 35a^3b^4 - 21a^2b^5 + 7ab^6 - b^7$
9. $x^{12} + 12x^{11}a + 66x^{10}a^2 + 220x^9a^3 + \cdots$
10. $m^{16} + 16m^{15}p + 120m^{14}p^2 + 560m^{13}p^3 + \cdots$
11. $m^{10} - 10m^9n + 45m^8n^2 - 120m^7n^3 + \cdots$
12. $a^{20} - 20a^{19}b + 190a^{18}b^2 - 1140a^{17}b^3 + \cdots$

Page 386. — 1. $a^5 + \dfrac{5}{2}a^4b + \dfrac{5}{2}a^3b^2 + \dfrac{5}{4}a^2b^3 + \dfrac{5}{16}ab^4 + \dfrac{1}{32}b^5$
2. $16x^4 + 32x^3y + 24x^2y^2 + 8xy^3 + y^4$ **3.** $a^5 + 10a^4b + 40a^3b^2 + 80a^2b^3 + 80ab^4 + 32b^5$
4. $\dfrac{x^4}{16} - \dfrac{x^3y}{2} + \dfrac{3x^2y^2}{2} - 2xy^3 + y^4$ **5.** $y^5 + \dfrac{5y^4z}{3} + \dfrac{10y^3z^2}{9} + \dfrac{10y^2z^3}{27} + \dfrac{5yz^4}{81} + \dfrac{z^5}{243}$
6. $\dfrac{x^4}{16} - \dfrac{x^3y}{6} + \dfrac{x^2y^2}{6} - \dfrac{2xy^3}{27} + \dfrac{y^4}{81}$ **7.** $32x^5 - 80x^4y + 80x^3y^2 - 40x^2y^3 + 10xy^4 - y^5$
8. $16a^4 - 96a^3b + 216a^2b^2 - 216ab^3 + 81b^4$ **9.** $256x^4 - 128x^3y + 24x^2y^2 - 2xy^3 + \dfrac{1}{16}y^4$
10. $32m^5 - \dfrac{80m^4n}{3} + \dfrac{80m^3n^2}{9} - \dfrac{40m^2n^3}{27} + \dfrac{10mn^4}{81} + \dfrac{n^5}{243}$ **11.** $\dfrac{a^{12}}{4096} - \dfrac{3a^{11}b}{128} + \dfrac{33a^{10}b^2}{32} - \cdots$
12. $x^{15} - 10x^{14}y + \dfrac{140x^{13}y^2}{3} - \cdots$ **13.** $\dfrac{x^{10}}{1024} - \dfrac{5x^9y}{128} + \dfrac{45x^8y^2}{64} - \dfrac{15x^7y^3}{2} + \cdots$
14. $a^{12} + 4a^{11}b + \dfrac{22a^{10}b^2}{3} + \dfrac{220a^9b^3}{27} + \cdots$

Page 387. — 1. $x^2 + 4x^{\frac{3}{2}}y + 6xy^2 + 4x^{\frac{1}{2}}y^3 + y^4$

2. $x^5 - 5x^4y^{\frac{1}{3}} + 10x^3y^{\frac{2}{3}} - 10x^2y + 5xy^{\frac{4}{3}} - y^{\frac{5}{3}}$ **3.** $a^{\frac{8}{3}} + 4a^2b^{\frac{1}{2}} + 6a^{\frac{4}{3}}b + 4a^{\frac{2}{3}}b^{\frac{3}{2}} + b^2$
4. $x^{12} - 6x^{10}y + 15x^8y^2 - 20x^6y^3 + 15x^4y^4 - 6x^2y^5 + y^6$

5. $x^{15} + 5x^{12}y^{\frac{1}{2}} + 10x^9y + 10x^6y^{\frac{3}{2}} + 5x^3y^2 + y^{\frac{5}{2}}$

6. $16a^{\frac{4}{3}} - 96ab^2 + 216a^{\frac{2}{3}}b^4 - 216a^{\frac{1}{3}}b^6 + 81b^8$ **7.** $a^{18} + 12a^{\frac{33}{2}}b^{\frac{2}{3}} + 66a^{15}b^{\frac{4}{3}} + \cdots$

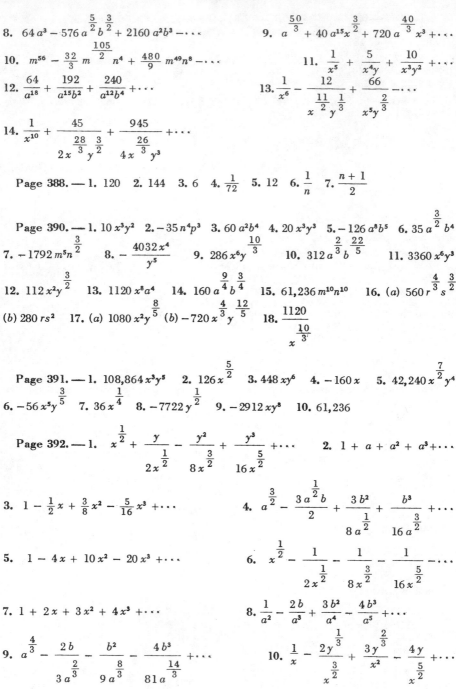

8. $64\,a^3 - 576\,a^{\frac{5}{2}}b^{\frac{3}{2}} + 2160\,a^2b^3 - \cdots$

9. $a^{\frac{50}{3}} + 40\,a^{15}x^{\frac{3}{2}} + 720\,a^{\frac{40}{3}}x^3 + \cdots$

10. $m^{56} - \frac{32}{3}\,m^{\frac{105}{2}}n^4 + \frac{480}{9}\,m^{49}n^8 - \cdots$

11. $\frac{1}{x^5} + \frac{5}{x^4y} + \frac{10}{x^3y^2} + \cdots$

12. $\frac{64}{a^{18}} + \frac{192}{a^{15}b^2} + \frac{240}{a^{12}b^4} + \cdots$

13. $\frac{1}{x^6} - \frac{12}{x^{\frac{11}{2}}y^{\frac{1}{3}}} + \frac{66}{x^5y^{\frac{2}{3}}} - \cdots$

14. $\frac{1}{x^{10}} + \frac{45}{2x^{\frac{28}{3}}y^{\frac{3}{2}}} + \frac{945}{4x^{\frac{26}{3}}y^3} + \cdots$

Page 388. — **1.** 120 **2.** 144 **3.** 6 **4.** $\frac{1}{72}$ **5.** 12 **6.** $\frac{1}{n}$ **7.** $\frac{n+1}{2}$

Page 390. — **1.** $10\,x^3y^2$ **2.** $-35\,n^4p^3$ **3.** $60\,a^2b^4$ **4.** $20\,x^3y^3$ **5.** $-126\,a^8b^5$ **6.** $35\,a^{\frac{3}{2}}b^4$

7. $-1792\,m^5n^{\frac{3}{2}}$ **8.** $-\frac{4032\,x^4}{y^5}$ **9.** $286\,x^6y^{\frac{10}{3}}$ **10.** $312\,a^{\frac{2}{3}}b^{\frac{22}{5}}$ **11.** $3360\,x^6y^3$

12. $112\,x^2y^{\frac{3}{2}}$ **13.** $1120\,x^8a^4$ **14.** $160\,a^{\frac{9}{4}}b^{\frac{3}{4}}$ **15.** $61{,}236\,m^{10}n^{10}$ **16.** (a) $560\,r^{\frac{4}{3}}s^{\frac{3}{2}}$

(b) $280\,rs^2$ **17.** (a) $1080\,x^2y^{\frac{8}{5}}$ (b) $-720\,x^{\frac{4}{3}}y^{\frac{12}{5}}$ **18.** $\frac{1120}{x^{\frac{10}{3}}}$

Page 391. — **1.** $108{,}864\,x^3y^5$ **2.** $126\,x^{\frac{5}{2}}$ **3.** $448\,xy^6$ **4.** $-160\,x$ **5.** $42{,}240\,x^{\frac{7}{2}}y^4$

6. $-56\,x^5y^{\frac{3}{5}}$ **7.** $36\,x^{\frac{1}{4}}$ **8.** $-7722\,y^{\frac{1}{2}}$ **9.** $-2912\,xy^8$ **10.** $61{,}236$

Page 392. — **1.** $x^{\frac{1}{2}} + \frac{y}{2x^{\frac{1}{2}}} - \frac{y^2}{8x^{\frac{3}{2}}} + \frac{y^3}{16x^{\frac{5}{2}}} + \cdots$ **2.** $1 + a + a^2 + a^3 + \cdots$

3. $1 - \frac{1}{2}x + \frac{3}{8}x^2 - \frac{5}{16}x^3 + \cdots$ **4.** $a^{\frac{3}{2}} - \frac{3a^{\frac{1}{2}}b}{2} + \frac{3b^2}{8a^{\frac{1}{2}}} + \frac{b^3}{16a^{\frac{3}{2}}} + \cdots$

5. $1 - 4x + 10x^2 - 20x^3 + \cdots$ **6.** $x^{\frac{1}{2}} - \frac{1}{2x^{\frac{1}{2}}} - \frac{1}{8x^{\frac{3}{2}}} - \frac{1}{16x^{\frac{5}{2}}} - \cdots$

7. $1 + 2x + 3x^2 + 4x^3 + \cdots$ **8.** $\frac{1}{a^2} - \frac{2b}{a^3} + \frac{3b^2}{a^4} - \frac{4b^3}{a^5} + \cdots$

9. $a^{\frac{4}{3}} - \frac{2b}{3a^{\frac{2}{3}}} - \frac{b^2}{9a^{\frac{8}{3}}} - \frac{4b^3}{81a^{\frac{14}{3}}} + \cdots$ **10.** $\frac{1}{x} - \frac{2y^{\frac{1}{3}}}{x^{\frac{3}{2}}} + \frac{3y^{\frac{2}{3}}}{x^2} - \frac{4y}{x^{\frac{5}{2}}} + \cdots$

11. $\dfrac{1}{x^{\frac{3}{2}}} + \dfrac{3\,y}{x^2} + \dfrac{6\,y^2}{x^{\frac{5}{2}}} + \dfrac{10\,y^3}{x^3} + \cdots$

12. $x^{\frac{1}{6}} + \dfrac{y^{\frac{1}{2}}}{2x^{\frac{1}{6}}} - \dfrac{y}{8x^{\frac{1}{2}}} + \dfrac{y^{\frac{3}{2}}}{16x^{\frac{5}{6}}} - \cdots$

Page 393. — 13. $\dfrac{7\,x^5}{8}$ **14.** $\dfrac{28}{r^9}$ **15.** $\dfrac{81\,b^4}{32\,a^5}$ **16.** $\dfrac{1309\,a^{18}}{81}$

Page 394. — 1. 2.1   **2.** 5.1   **3.** 2.0   **4.** 2.0   **5.** 5.8   **6.** 2.0   **7.** 1.06   **8.** 1.10
9. 0.97   **10.** 83.18   **11.** 132.55   **12.** 0.90   **13.** 1.157625   **14.** 1.1040808032
15. 1.0510100501   **16.** 1.16985856   **17.** 1.12550881   **18.** 1.076890625   **19.** 0.1
20. 0.2   **21.** 0.3   **22.** 0.0

Page 395. — 1. $x^5 - 5\,x^4y + 10\,x^3y^2 - 10\,x^2y^3 + 5\,xy^4 - y^5$

2. $16\,a^4 + 32\,a^3b + 24\,a^2b^2 + 8\,ab^3 + b^4$ **3.** $m^5 - \dfrac{5\,m^4n}{2} + \dfrac{5\,m^3n^2}{2} - \dfrac{5\,m^2n^3}{4} + \dfrac{5\,mn^4}{16} - \dfrac{n^5}{32}$

4. $\dfrac{x^{12}}{531{,}441} - \dfrac{8\,x^{11}y}{59{,}049} + \dfrac{88\,x^{10}y^2}{19{,}683} - \dfrac{1760\,x^9y^3}{19{,}683} + \cdots$

5. $x^5 + 20\,x^{\frac{9}{2}}y^{\frac{2}{3}} + 180\,x^4y^{\frac{4}{3}} + 960\,x^{\frac{7}{2}}y^2 + \cdots$

6. $\dfrac{2048}{x^{11}} + \dfrac{11{,}264}{x^{10}y} + \dfrac{28{,}160}{x^9y^2} + \dfrac{42{,}240}{x^8y^3} + \dfrac{42{,}240}{x^7y^4} + \cdots$ **7.** (a) 42 (b) $\dfrac{3}{2}$ (c) 126 (d) $2n$

8. $-448\,a^3b^{\frac{5}{2}}$ **9.** $\dfrac{143\,m^6n^{10}}{512}$ **10.** $\dfrac{1120\,y^{\frac{8}{3}}}{x^2}$ **11.** $30{,}618\,x^3$ **12.** $\dfrac{1}{x} - \dfrac{y}{x^2} + \dfrac{y^2}{x^3} - \dfrac{y^3}{x^4} + \dfrac{y^4}{x^5} + \cdots$
13. 1.04060401   **14.** 3.0

1. $(3x - 4)(8x + 9)$ **2.** $3\,a$ **3.** $x = 2,\ y = -4$ **4.** $3:4$ **5.** $2x^{\frac{2}{3}} + 3x^{\frac{1}{3}}y^{\frac{1}{3}} + 2y^{\frac{2}{3}}$
6. $15 - 4\sqrt{15}$

Page 396. — 7. (a) parabola (b) straight line (c) straight line (d) circle (e) hyperbola
(f) ellipse   **8.** $x = 4,\ y = 3;\ x = 4,\ y = -3;\ x = -3,\ y = 4;\ x = -3,\ y = -4$ **9.** 0.58
10. 24   **11.** $-144\,xy^{\frac{7}{3}}$ **12.** $56°19'$ **13.** $-1, \sqrt{3}, -\sqrt{3}$ **14.** 3 mph   **15.** $y = \dfrac{1}{3}$ **16.** 0.7, 3.7

Page 399. — 1. 30   **2.** 12   **3.** 20   **4.** 16   **5.** 120   **6.** 72   **7.** 36   **8.** 80

Page 400. — 1. 720   **2.** 12   **3.** (a) 20 (b) 8   **4.** 120   **5.** 960   **6.** (a) 6 (b) 27
7. (a) 60 (b) 48 (c) 42   **8.** 676,000

Page 401. — 1. 120   **2.** 720   **3.** 120   **4.** (a) 720 (b) 24   **5.** 5040   **6.** 720
7. 120   **8.** 6

Page 402. — 1. 120   **2.** 5040   **3.** 210   **4.** 60   **5.** 60   **6.** 504   **7.** 840   **8.** (a) 120
(b) 24   **9.** (a) 720 (b) 360   **10.** (a) 360 (b) 60

Page 404. — 1. (a) 2520   (b) 5040   (c) 30   (d) 180   **2.** (a) 6720 (b) 50,400
(c) 831,600 (d) 3870   **3.** 10   **4.** 210   **5.** 1260

Page 405. — 1. 24   **2.** 120   **3.** 720   **4.** 5040   **5.** 144

Page 407. — 1. 792   **2.** 495   **3.** 56   **4.** 126   **5.** 462   **6.** 715   **7.** 56   **8.** 126
9. 28   **10.** 15

Page 408. — 1. 780   **2.** 19,600   **3.** 45   **4.** 25   **5.** 4 or 12   **6.** $n = 15;\ 105$
7. $r = 5;\ 10$

Page 409. — 1. 309,672   **2.** 168   **3.** 200   **4.** 5880   **5.** 180   **6.** 2475

Page 410 — 1. 432   **2.** 54   **3.** 1344   **4.** 1152   **5.** 480   **6.** 49

Page 411—7. 432   8. 2880   9. $n = 5$ 10. 360   11. $n = 7$ 12. 3360   13. $n = 5$
14. 9 even integers

Doings of Dimbo. If Dimbo takes 3 socks, 2 will be alike.

Page 413.—1. $\frac{1}{2}$ 2. $\frac{1}{6}$ 3. $\frac{1}{1}$ (certainty)   4. 0 (impossible)   5. $\frac{2}{7}$ 6. $\frac{1}{8}$ 7. $\frac{1}{5}$
8. $\frac{1}{7}$ 9. $\frac{1}{2}$ 10. $\frac{9}{10}$

Page 414.—1. $\frac{2}{5}$ 2. $\frac{3}{5}$ 3. $\frac{2}{3}$ 4. $\frac{3}{2}$ 5. $\frac{3}{2}$ 6. $\frac{2}{3}$ 7. $\frac{3}{2}$ 8. $\frac{3}{5}$ 9. $\frac{5}{6}$ 10. $\frac{5}{11}$

Page 415.—1. $\frac{1}{2}$ 2. $\frac{3}{7}$ 3. $\frac{1}{30}$

Page 416.—4. $\frac{4}{91}$ 5. $\frac{12}{65}$ 6. $\frac{5}{2}$ 7. $\frac{1}{5}$ 8. $\frac{2}{25}$ 9. $\frac{1}{270,725}$ 10. $(a)\frac{1}{3}$ $(b)\frac{5}{18}$
$(c)\frac{6}{5}$ 11. $\frac{4}{{}_{52}C_{13}}$

1. (a) 720 (b) 56 (c) 120 (d) 120   2. 360   3. 40,320   4. 120   5. 990   6. 630,630
7. 40,320   8. 3168

Page 417.—9. 144,000   10. 27,720   11. 120   12. $n = 5$ 13. 24   14. 72
15. $n = 5$ 16. 18   17. in decimal system 900, in duodecimal system 1584, difference 684   18. 1,596,000   19. $\frac{1}{2}$ 20. $(a)\frac{1}{7}$ $(b)\frac{6}{1}$ 21. $(a)\frac{3}{7}$ $(b)\frac{7}{3}$ 22. $\frac{1}{5525}$

1. $0, -\frac{5}{2}$ 2. $k = 0$ 3. x 4. 16 terms

Page 418.—5. 12   6. –9, 3   7. $\frac{3}{2}$ 8. ±6   9. $a = 2, c = 3$ 10. $x = -1$
11. $10°\ 29'$ 12. 224.6 days   13. $x = 3$ 14. $x = -1$ $x = 3$ 15. 48 head of cattle
                                                     $y = 5$ $y = -3$
16. 9 ft.   17. $B = 61°\ 26', C = 53°\ 14', c = 44.96$

Page 420.—1. 5   2. 17   3. $3\sqrt{2}$ 4. $\sqrt{29}$ 5. $2\sqrt{13}$ 6. $5a$ 7. $4, 6, 2\sqrt{13}$

Page 421.—Nos. 8–10 are proofs.

Page 422.—1. $x^2 + 6x + y^2 + 10y - 2 = 0$ 2. $4x^2 - 48x + 4y^2 + 4y + 105 = 0$
3. $36x^2 - 36mx + 9m^2 + 36y^2 + 24ny + 4n^2 - 36r^2 = 0$ 4. center $(-7, 8)$, radius 10.
5. center $(12, -10)$, radius $\sqrt{249}$

Page 423.—1. $13\frac{1}{2}$ 2. 8   3. 15   4. 9   5. 43   6. $19\frac{1}{2}$ 7. 9   8. 36   9. 288
10. 81

Page 425.—1. $7x - 6y = -53$ 2. $3x - 2y = 9$ 3. $x - y = 1$ 4. $x - y = 15$

Page 426.—5. $4x + 5y = 11$ 6. $2x - y = -10$ 7. $x - 2y = 7$ 8. $5x + y = 45$
9. $5x - 3y = 27$ 10. $(-5, -2)$ 11. $2x + y = 6$ 12. $5x + y = 5$ 13. $10x - 6y = 15$
14. $12x + 33y = -88$ 15. $(-9, -4)$

Page 428.—1. $7x - 6y = -53$ 2. $3x - 2y = 9$ 3. $x - y = 1$ 4. $x - y = 15$
5. $2x - y = -10$ 6. $x - 2y = 7$ 7. $5x + y = 45$ 8. $5x - 3y = 27$ 9. $2x - y = -7$
10. $x + 4y = -20$ 11. $x - 2y = 7$ 12. $y = -8$ 13. $m = 3, b = -8$ 14. $m = -2,$
$b = -\frac{2}{3}$ 15. $m = \frac{7}{6}, b = \frac{2}{3}$ 16. $m = -\frac{9}{5}, b = \frac{8}{5}$ 17. –3   18. $3x - 2y = 6$
19. $3x + 2y = -4$

Page 431.—1. $2R = S$ 2. $P = Q + 7$ 3. $4x = 5y + 20$

Page 433.—1. median = \$79.10, Q_1 = \$65, Q_3 = \$87.45   2. median = 74, Q_1 = 66,
$Q_3 = 81$ 3. median = 68.5, Q_1 = 65, Q_3 = 71.5

Page 435. — 1. Sizes f   2. Scores f   **Page 436.** — 3. Height   f

Sizes	f
$12\frac{1}{2}$	1
12	3
$11\frac{1}{2}$	4
11	4
$10\frac{1}{2}$	5
10	7
$9\frac{1}{2}$	6
9	4
$8\frac{1}{2}$	4
8	3
$7\frac{1}{2}$	3
7	2
$6\frac{1}{2}$	1
6	1

Scores	f
96–99	1
92–95	2
88–91	4
84–87	5
80–83	6
76–79	6
72–75	8
68–71	6
64–67	5
60–63	3
56–59	1
52–55	2

Height	f
76–77.5	1
74–75.5	3
72–73.5	4
70–71.5	4
68–69.5	6
66–67.5	6
64–65.5	5
62–63.5	3
60–61.5	3

Page 437. — Nos. 1–3 require drawings.

Page 439. — 1. median $= 9\frac{1}{2}$, $Q_1 = 8\frac{1}{4}$, $Q_3 = 10\frac{1}{2}$ 2. median $= 74.8$, $Q_1 = 67.2$, $Q_3 = 83.5$

Page 440. — 3. median $= 73.2$, $Q_1 = 65.9$, $Q_3 = 81.5$

Page 441. — 1. \$75 approx.   2. 2.2 yr.   3. 3.1 min. approx.

Page 442. — 1. $5\sqrt{5}$ 2. $5x - 7y = -27$ 3. $x + 2y = -1$ 4. $3x - 2y = 6$
5. x intercept is 3, y intercept is -2.   6. proof   7. $22\frac{1}{2}$

Page 443. — 8. ordered data   9. 29   10. frequency distribution   11. 22
12. frequency polygon   13. ogive   14. 3.25   15. 3.8

1. $5(2a + 3b + 4)(2a + 3b - 4)$ 2. $\dfrac{4(2x + 3y)}{x - y}$ 3. $x = -1$, $y = 1$ 4. $\dfrac{16}{3}$ 5. $\dfrac{9\,x^3 y^2}{z}$

6. $3.8, -0.8$ 7. $\dfrac{-q \pm \sqrt{q^2 - 4pr}}{2p}$ 8. $-\dfrac{1}{2}$ 9. 9.993   10. $76° 26'$

Page 444. — 11. $16{,}016\, x^2 y^{\frac{10}{3}}$ 12. $\dfrac{1}{21}$ 13. 0   14. median $= 26.5$ in.

Page 445. — 1. d   2. a   3. b

Page 446. — 4. c   5. b   6. c   7. b   8. d   9. d   10. d   11. c   12. a   13. c
14. e   15. b

Page 447. — 16. d   17. e   18. e   19. b   20. c   21. d   22. c   23. c   24. d
25. b   26. d   27. a

Page 448. — 28. b   29. c   30. a   31. d   32. c   33. d   34. a   35. d   36. b
37. d

Page 449. — 38. d   39. c   40. b

1. c   2. a   3. b   4. d   5. c   6. b   7. c

Page 450. — 8. e   9. e   10. b   11. e   12. c   13. b   14. b   15. c   16. b
17. d

Page 451.—18. d   19. b   20. c   21. b   22. e   23. e   24. b   25. d   26. c   27. b   28. b

Page 452.—29. c   30. b   31. d   32. e   33. c   34. c   35. b   36. c   37. a   38. c

Page 453.—39. e   40. d

1. d   2. b   3. d   4. a   5. a

Page 454.—6. e   7. b   8. d   9. e   10. b   11. b   12. e   13. c   14. c   15. a   16. c   17. e   18. c   19. a

Page 455.—20. e   21. a   22. d   23. b   24. a   25. e   26. c   27. e   28. b   29. e

Page 456.—30. d   31. d   32. a   33. d   34. d   35. d   36. c   37. a   38. b

Page 457.—39. d   40. a

1. a   2. d   3. b   4. b   5. d   6. a

Page 458.—7. a   8. b   9. d   10. b   11. a   12. c   13. d   14. d   15. e   16. d   17. c

Page 459.—18. c   19. b   20. c   21. e   22. d   23. d   24. d   25. b

Page 460.—26. a   27. e   28. d   29. d   30. b   31. b   32. a

Page 461.—33. c   34. d   35. a   36. d   37. e   38. b

Page 462.—39. e   40. e

1. b   2. a   3. e   4. d   5. b   6. a

Page 463.—7. a   8. c   9. c   10. e   11. a   12. c   13. b   14. d   15. b   16. d

Page 464.—17. a   18. c   19. b   20. d   21. c   22. a   23. b   24. b   25. d   26. e   27. a

Page 465.—28. b   29. e   30. e   31. d   32. b

Page 466.—33. b   34. a   35. d   36. b   37. d   38. c   39. a   40. c

Page 469.—1. $S = \{$Alice, Anita$\}$ 2. $S = \{3, 4, 5\}$ 3. $x = 2, -4; S = \{2, -4\}$

4. $S = \{2, 3, 5, 7\}$ 5. (a) $x = 4$

(b) $x > 0$

(c) $x < -3, x > 3$

(d) $x \leqq 3$

Page 471.—1. (a) $A \cup B = \{1, 2, 3, 4, 5, 6, 7\}$ (b) $A \cap B = \{4, 5\}$ 2. Yes   3. (a) $A \cup B = \{1, 2, 3, 4, 5, 6, 7, 8, 9\}$ (b) $A \cap B = \phi$ (null set or empty set; no elements)

Page 472.—4. $x > 5$ and $x < 10$

$A \cap B$

$A \cup B$

5.   (a) $A \cup B$ (b) $A \cap B$ (c) $(A \cap B) \cup C$ (d) $(A \cup B) \cup C$

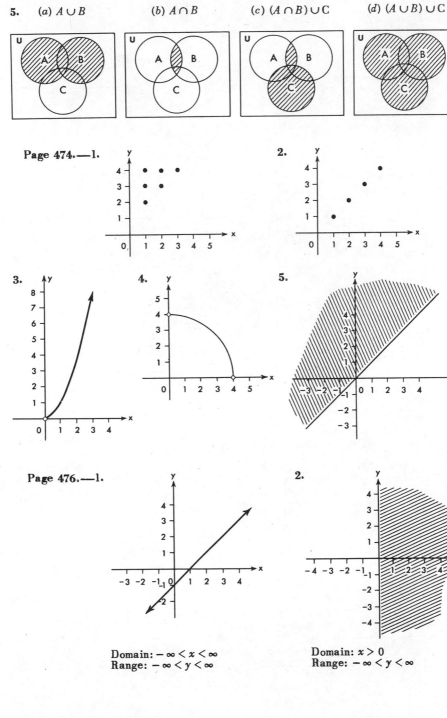

Page 474.—1.

2.

3.

4.

5.

Page 476.—1.

2.

Domain: $-\infty < x < \infty$
Range: $-\infty < y < \infty$

Domain: $x > 0$
Range: $-\infty < y < \infty$

3.

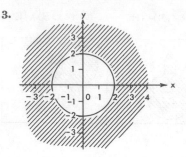

Domain: $-\infty < x < \infty$
Range: $-\infty < y < \infty$

4.

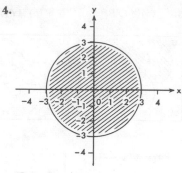

Domain: $-3 < x < 3$
Range: $-3 < y < 3$

5.

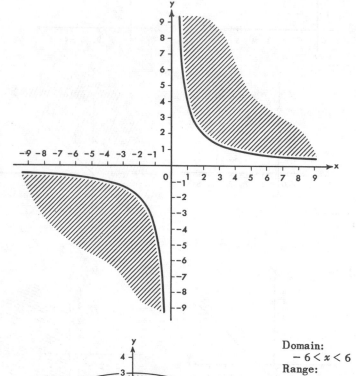

Domain:
    $x < 0,\ x > 0$
Range:
    $y < 0,\ y > 0$

6.

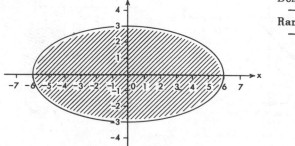

Domain:
    $-6 < x < 6$
Range:
    $-3 < y < 3$

Page 478.—1. (a) Function (b) Relation (c) Relation (d) Function (e) Relation
(f) Function

2. (a) $x = |y|$

A relation;
not a function.

(b) $|y| = |x|$

A relation;
not a function.

(c) $y > |x|$

A relation;
not a function.

(d) $|x| + |y| = 1$

A relation;
not a function.

(e) $|y| - |x| = 1$

A relation;
not a function.

(f) $|x| + |y| < 1$

A relation;
not a function.

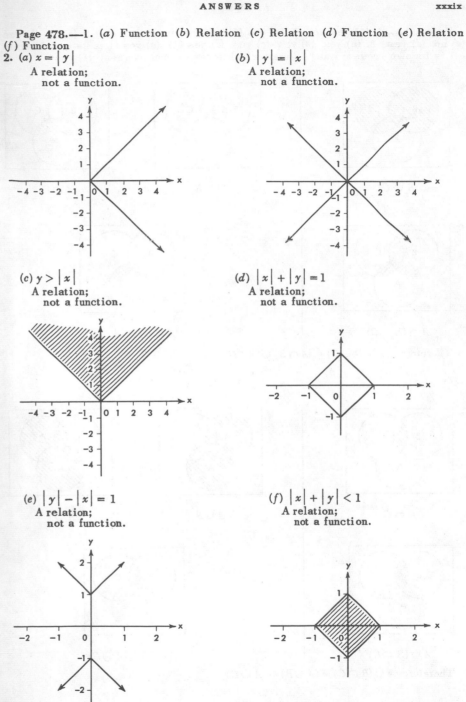

Page 481.—1. (a) yes (b) no (c) yes (0) (d) yes (its negative)   2. (a) no (b) yes
(c) no (d) yes   3. (a) yes (b) yes (c) yes (d) yes (1) (e) yes (1 is its own inverse;
− 1 is its own inverse; *i* and − *i* are each their respective inverses) (f) yes

4.

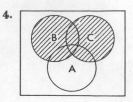
$B \cup C$

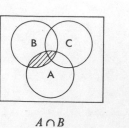
$A \cap B$

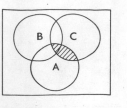
$A \cap C$

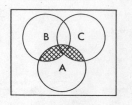
$A \cap (B \cup C)$

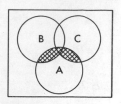
$(A \cap B) \cup (A \cap C)$

Therefore, $A \cap (B \cup C) = (A \cap B) \cup (A \cap C)$

5.

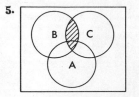
$B \cap C$

$A \cup B$

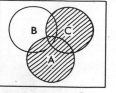
$A \cup C$

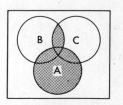
$A \cup (B \cap C)$

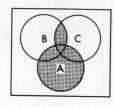
$(A \cup B) \cap (A \cup C)$

Therefore $A \cup (B \cap C) = (A \cup B) \cap (A \cup C)$

Page 481.—1. (a) yes (b) no (c) yes (0) (d) yes (its negative) 2. (a) no (b) yes (c) no (d) yes 3. (a) yes (b) yes (c) yes (d) yes (1) (e) yes (1 is its own inverse; — 1 is its own inverse; i and $— i$ are each their respective inverses) (f) yes

4.

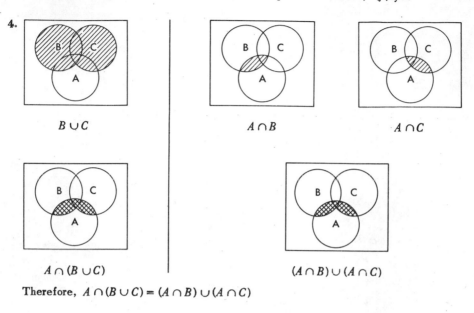

$B \cup C$

$A \cap B$

$A \cap C$

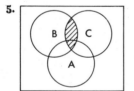

$A \cap (B \cup C)$

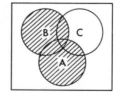

$(A \cap B) \cup (A \cap C)$

Therefore, $A \cap (B \cup C) = (A \cap B) \cup (A \cap C)$

5.

$B \cap C$

$A \cup B$

$A \cup C$

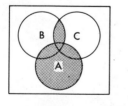

$A \cup (B \cap C)$

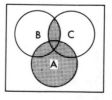

$(A \cup B) \cap (A \cup C)$

Therefore $A \cup (B \cap C) = (A \cup B) \cap (A \cup C)$

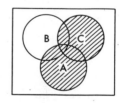

Page 478.—1. (a) Function (b) Relation (c) Relation (d) Function (e) Relation
(f) Function
2. (a) $x = |y|$

    A relation;
      not a function.

(b) $|y| = |x|$

    A relation;
      not a function.

(c) $y > |x|$

    A relation;
      not a function.

(d) $|x| + |y| = 1$

    A relation;
      not a function.

(e) $|y| - |x| = 1$

    A relation;
      not a function.

(f) $|x| + |y| < 1$

    A relation;
      not a function.

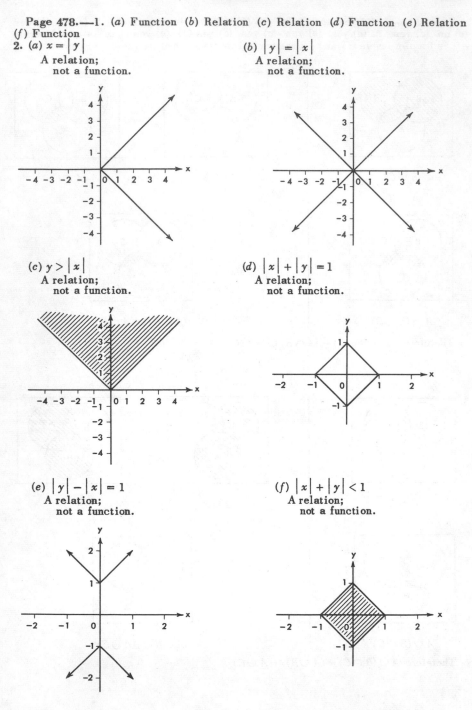